SPECIAL SERVICES
SOLANO COMMUNITY COLLEGE
SUISUN VALLEY ROAD
P.O. BOX 246
SUISUN CITY, CA. 94585

Learning Disabilities Center
Solano Community College
4000 Suisun Valley Road
Suisun City, CA 94585

Short Stories for
Teaching Literature

and Developing
Comprehension

Best
Short Stories

Raymond
Harris

Jamestown Publishers
Providence, Rhode Island

Short Stories for Teaching Literature
and Developing Comprehension

# Best
# Short Stories

Catalog No. 792
Catalog No. 792H, Hardcover Edition


Copyright © 1980
Jamestown Publishers, Inc.

Cover Design by Stephen R. Anthony
Illustrations by Mari-Ann Süvari Burgoyne

Printed in the United States




DO  82 83 84 85 86 8 7 6 5 4 3 2


ISBN 0-89061-209-9
ISBN 0-89061-318-4 Hardcover Edition

# Contents

# Acknowledgments

Acknowledgment is gratefully made to the following publishers for permission to reprint the works of the many authors appearing in this book.

"The Garden Party". Copyright©1922 by Alfred A. Knopf, Inc. and renewed 1950 by J. Middleton Murray. Reprinted from *The Short Stories of Katherine Mansfield,* by Katherine Mansfield, by permission of Albert A. Knopf, Inc.

"Tell Me How Long the Train's Been Gone". Copyright© 1967 by James Baldwin. Adapted from *Tell Me How Long the Train's Been Gone* by James Baldwin and used by permission of the publisher, The Dial Press.

"My Oedipus Complex". Copyright© 1950 by Frank O'Connor. Reprinted from *The Stories of Frank O'Connor,* by Frank O'Connor, by permission of Alfred A. Knopf, Inc.

"The Jilting of Granny Weatherall". Copyright© 1930, 1958 by Katherine Anne Porter. Reprinted from her volume *Flowering Judas and Other Stories* by permission of Harcourt Brace Jovanovich, Inc.

"The Wall". Copyright ©1945 and renewed 1973 by Random House, Inc. Reprinted from *The Bedside Book of Famous French Stories,* by Jean-Paul Sartre, translated by Maria Jolas, edited by Belle Becker and Robert N. Linscott, by permission of Random House, Inc.

"The Christian Roommates". Copyright© 1964 by John Updike. Reprinted from *The Music School,* by John Updike, by permission of Alfred A. Knopf, Inc. First appeared in *The New Yorker.*

Many of the literary lessons, introductions and exercises reflect the creative talent and astute critical perception of Christine Powers. The author gratefully acknowledges her role as colleague and coadjutor in the creation of this work.

R.H.

# Introduction
# to the Teacher

For a short-story lover to call a personal list of favorites BEST is as dangerous as it is immodest; it calls forth the cold disdain and frigid criticism of all
other short-story lovers, all of whom have their own ideas of what is best.
Nevertheless, we have consciously and without apology called our collection BEST SHORT STORIES, feeling that few who appreciate the form can fault
us for the quality of the selections. While there are certainly hundreds of
stories that are as good, there are none better.

There are four Nobel Laureates among the authors: Faulkner, Steinbeck,
Sartre and Singer. Katherine Mansfield and Katherine Anne Porter are
represented by the two stories often considered their best, and Shirley
Jackson is represented by her masterpiece, "The Lottery."

Hawthorne, Poe and Twain represent the classic Americans, while
Updike, Baldwin, Asimov and Capote represent the modern Americans.
Jean-Paul Sartre represents the best of the modern continental European
tradition, and Frank O'Connor represents the magical storytelling of the
Irish. And finally, there is Woody Allen, in a class by himself, with one of
the funniest prize-winning stories you may ever hope to read.

Because each story provides its own insight into the pleasures of reading,
students will find them entrancing and you will find them a joy to teach.

The three major objectives of the text are:

- To teach the short story form and to demonstrate how to read first-rate
  literature with awareness of various levels of meaning.
- To introduce and promote basic understanding of literary elements:
  setting; point of view; conflict; characterization; theme; tone and
  mood; symbolism; figurative language and dialogue.
- To teach and enhance reading comprehension skills in twelve principal areas.

The following teaching elements accompany each short story:

**An Introduction** that begins each unit prepares students to read with greater understanding by resolving in advance any problems that may exist with the situation, characters or language in the story to come. And the information provided here about the author's life and techniques helps readers appreciate each storyteller more. It is important that students read the introductions because they will enhance the students' understanding of both the stories and the lessons.

**A Literary Lesson** in each unit provides basic information about one element of literature illustrated by the story that follows. The first lesson deals with the short story as a genre and prepares the students for the other units. Four lessons deal with special types of short stories: science fiction, humor, satire and folklore. Nine lessons deal with literary elements such as setting and point of view. And the final lesson deals with the meaning of a short story through a step-by-step analysis of "The Lottery." Taken together, these lessons form a good basis for understanding literary forms and content; they may be used profitably as an introduction to literature.

**The Tasks.** Each lesson uses at least four passages from the story to illustrate the topic under discussion. Following the lesson, students are assigned four "tasks" to guide them as they read the story. These tasks help readers find four more examples of the literary elements discussed in the lesson. Exercises after the story check to see how well readers have accomplished the tasks.

**Lesson-Related Exercises.** Following each reading selection there are practice exercises in which students can use what they have learned about the particular literary element or type of short story discussed in the lesson. Passages designated in the "tasks" are excerpted in the practice exercises, and students are asked to answer questions based on these sample passages.

**Skill-Oriented Comprehension Questions,** keyed directly to twelve specific reading and reasoning skills, follow each story. All twenty-five questions are labeled according to skill. Question types are distributed throughout the units to give students ample practice in each skill. The following key to the skills is provided at the end of each comprehension section for quick reference:

---

Comprehension Skills: a — isolating details; b — recalling specific facts; c — retaining concepts; d — organizing facts; e — understanding the main idea; f — drawing a conclusion; g — making a judgment; h — making an inference; i — recognizing tone; j — understanding characters; k — appreciation of literary forms; l — understanding vocabulary.

---

These twelve question types reflect those aspects of comprehension that we believe can be adequately sampled. We hasten to acknowledge that true comprehension can not be conveniently separated into twelve independent activities—we all know that more than one skill is used in answering any one question. We have, therefore, labeled each question according to what we believe is the major or dominant skill used in arriving at the correct answer.

We also realize that certain question types overlap; however, we have held to certain distinctions to stimulate the reader to greater subtlety of thought. Fine distinctions between making a judgment and drawing a conclusion do exist, as well as distinctions between making an inference and drawing a conclusion.

Here is a detailed description of the skills measured by the twelve types of comprehension questions:

**Isolating Details.** This skill calls upon the reader to detach or separate an individual part from among other parts.

**Recalling Specific Facts.** This asks the reader to bring back from memory a precise event or circumstance.

**Retaining a Concept.** This skill tests the reader's ability to keep in mind and recall a generalization or idea formed by mentally combining characteristics and details.

**Organizing Facts.** This asks the reader to form stated, interdependent or coordinated events or circumstances into a whole.

**Understanding the Main Idea.** This requires the reader to perceive clearly the writer's primary intention as interpreted in the light of important details.

**Drawing a Conclusion.** This requires the reader to arrive at the one decision justified by the stated evidence.

**Making a Judgment.** This requires the reader to arrive at a sound decision (not necessarily the only one) based on the stated evidence.

**Making an Inference.** This asks the reader to arrive at a deduction based on assumed premises.

**Recognizing Tone.** This measures the reader's ability to appreciate those qualities of style that reveal an author's attitude or point of view, and to identify the atmosphere in which the characters exist and events take place.

**Understanding Characters.** This requires that the reader appreciate the aggregate of features and traits that form an individual nature of some person.

**Appreciation of Literary Forms.** This requires the reader to distinguish among the various types of writing and figures of speech.

**Knowledge of Word Meanings.** Vocabulary has not been treated as a separate entity, but has been included with comprehension—where it belongs. Thus each word is presented contextually.


**The Comprehension Skills graph** at the end of the book allows students to make a visual record of the kinds of questions that they miss among the twelve specific skills. If a pattern emerges showing that they frequently miss one kind of question, they may need remedial action in this skill area. (Jamestown's *Comprehension Skills Series* is an ideal tool to use for remedial comprehension. Separate booklets for each of the comprehension skills are available at both intermediate and advanced levels of performance.)

**The Comprehension Scores graph** also provided allows students to record their overall progress through the reading selections. An answer key for self-correction can be found after the last unit.

**Discussion Guides.** Each unit contains ten discussion questions which deal with three aspects of literary criticism: analysis of the literary element or genre discussed in the lesson, interpretation of meanings and implications inherent in the selection and analysis of the author's technique.

**The Writing Exercise.** The writing assignment is designed to give the student first-hand experience with the literary technique or genre discussed in the lesson. Since reading and writing improvement go hand-in-hand, the reading selections broaden students' knowledge of writing techniques. In turn, the writing exercises can deepen the students' understanding and appreciation of the writing styles found in their reading.

*Best Short Stories* is a companion text to *Best-Selling Chapters*. Together, the two books create an effective program for teaching literature and developing comprehension.

# Introduction
# to the Student

The stories you are about to read are among the finest in the world, written by some of the world's best storytellers. If you enjoy good stories—and who doesn't?—you will surely enjoy reading these. But, in addition to enjoying the stories, you also will be asked to think of storytelling as the art that it is.

Like other arts—such as music, painting, sculpture and architecture—storytelling has definable forms and content that you can see, feel, think about and discuss. In music, for example, you can identify the beat or tempo that distinguishes a waltz from a march, rock from jazz, and blues from swing, even though the various forms are similar in some ways. Horns, strings and drums can all be manipulated to give the music different characters that, in turn, can inspire different moods and feelings in a listener. Then you can discuss what the composer and arranger have done to make the piece of music better, worse or just different from others you have heard. You can say why you enjoyed it or why you didn't.

When you read a story, you know almost at once whether it is a mystery, science fiction, adventure, romance or another type. Sometimes you know it is a romantic mystery or mysterious science fiction. But each story can be identified by its content and given a label. And each story has a form given to it by its own characteristics—such as the plot, the kind of people you meet, the tone and mood or the setting. As you read you will be asked to think about all the elements that make each story what it is, and about how those story elements make you feel as you read.

Each unit in the text contains a story and a lesson that discusses one special aspect of the art of storytelling. By the time you have finished the book, you will have a good basic knowledge of all the major elements that make up a well-written and enjoyable tale. Exercises that are part of each unit will show you how much you have learned and how well you have understood the stories.

# TIPS FOR USING THE TEXT

**1. The Introduction.** Each unit begins with an introduction. Be sure to read the introduction carefully. It provides the background you need to understand the story and the lesson.

**2. The Lesson.** Read each lesson carefully and thoughtfully. Pay close attention to the sample passages from the story that are included in the lesson. These illustrate the story element under discussion. At the end of the lesson you are asked to watch for other passages in the story that further illustrate the story element you have just learned about. These directions are in a box headed "As you read the story:" Copy these directions on a piece of paper and watch for the passages as you read. You will be asked questions about these other passages when you finish your reading.

**3. The Story.** Read carefully, but also read for enjoyment. Watch for elements discussed in the lesson—plot, setting, characterization and so on. And be sure to find and note the passages you have been asked to watch for.

**4. The Comprehension Questions.** The twenty-five multiple-choice questions that follow the story test for specific reading and reasoning skills. Each question is labeled with a letter in parentheses; the letter indicates the skill that the question tests such as (a) isolating details and (b) recalling specific facts. The key for the labels is located at the end of the comprehension questions for each unit.

To complete this section, answer the twenty-five multiple-choice questions without referring to the story. When you have finished, turn to the answer key and correct your answers. Next, turn to the graphs at the end of the book, and follow the directions given there for recording your progress throughout the text.

**5. The Practice Exercises.** The four exercises in this section will help you see how well you have spotted the literary techniques discussed in the lesson. Each exercise consists of a passage from the story, followed by two questions. The passages are the ones you were asked to watch for. Complete this section by answering all questions and then correcting your answers using the key after the last unit.

**6. The Discussion Guides.** Try to discuss these questions with others. If your class situation does not provide time for discussion, or if you are working alone, think about these questions carefully before going on.

**7. The Writing Exercise.** Each writing exercise relates to what you have read in the lesson and in the reading selection. You can often improve your writing by trying to imitate good writers. To whatever extent you can, try to imitate the author of the story as you write.

Unit 1
**The Short Story**

# The Garden
Party

Katherine Mansfield

# Introduction

We have chosen a story by Katherine Mansfield to start our book of short stories because she was so good at her craft. When she describes a character, you can see the person at once. When she describes a setting, you are instantly there. When she tells you how someone feels, you recognize the feeling immediately, understand it, and make it your own. This is a great advantage for a short-story writer because so much must be done in so little space. "The Garden Party" is one of Mansfield's best stories and is often considered a perfect example of the technique of short-story writing.

Laura Sheridan is the young teen-age daughter of a successful upper-middle-class family living in New Zealand. In the course of one day she is destined to learn a great deal about the meaning of social difference and class distinction in British society in the early part of the twentieth century. In the process she will also learn a great deal about herself and her own feelings.

"The Garden Party" is a story about human feelings, human nature, and the real barriers of feeling that exist between people who are rich and those who are poor. Like most young girls, Laura knows only people from her own limited world, which in this case is a rich and comfortable one. When Laura's mother gives her an opportunity to direct a group of workmen on a small project, Laura is struck by how nice and how entirely human working-class people can be. It's hard to know what she thought about workmen before, though we are told, later in the story, that as a child she had been warned about walking through their neighborhood.

The day of the party is a very happy one for Laura—an absolutely perfect day, in fact—until it is marred by news that a young carter (wagon driver) from the neighborhood has been killed in an accident. His horse had shied at a traction engine (tractor) and he was thrown from his wagon. Laura reacts dramatically. The garden party must be stopped! How can they all be happy when a poor man from the neighborhood is lying dead and his wife can hear the band playing and them having a good time? But cooler heads prevail. "People like that don't expect sacrifices from us," her mother tells her.

A new hat and a successful afternoon make things considerably better for Laura. But afterwards she is sent to the dead man's home with a basket of party leftovers. Now she must truly evaluate her feelings about rich people and poor people, her world and the shabby world she will become involved in. There is a lot to think about, not just for Laura, but for the reader as well. After all, we have our social and class differences, too. Most of us are sheltered and rarely meet people from outside our own world. How well do we mix with others who are different from us? How do times of great emotion change our feelings toward one another?

Katherine Mansfield was especially good when she was dealing with feelings and emotions. Unfortunately, she has not left us much of her work. She died of tuberculosis in 1923 when she was only thirty-four and just beginning to receive the recognition she deserved. Katherine Mansfield is a pen name. Her real name was Kathleen Mansfield Beauchamp Murry. The daughter of a well-to-do banker-industrialist, she was born in New Zealand in 1888 and spent her childhood there, in the village of Karori, near Wellington. She was a brilliant and sensitive woman and an unusually keen observer of the world around her. Mansfield characters have been called uncannily real. Her stories often have a poetic quality about them— carefully worked out in every detail, compact and filled with intense feeling. If you enjoy "The Garden Party," and it is hard not to, you will surely want to go on to read her somewhat longer works *Prelude* and *At the Bay,* based on her childhood in New Zealand. Like all Mansfield stories, you will find them a most worthwhile, entertaining and memorable experience.

# The Short Story

When you stop to think about it, stories are as much a part of our lives as eating and sleeping. We live with stories from the time our toes are tweaked to the beat of "This little piggy went to market..." until we are finally laid to rest with a parable, a story from the Bible, and an obituary—a little narrative account of the life we led. In between are stories parents tell, stories on television and in the movies, stories in newspapers and magazines, family stories, gossipy stories from friends. And, of course, there are all the stories in the books we read.

Stories told around campfires are as old as human language itself, and written stories have been with us at least since the time of the ancient Egyptians, six thousand years ago. People love stories, always have and always will. They are one of the most important methods of human communication.

Stories in book form come in a variety of sizes—short, medium, long, extra-short and extra-long. Novels are the long ones, ranging anywhere from 150 pages to huge thousand-page volumes, while medium length stories, 75 to 150 pages or so, are called novelettes or novellas. The stories we will deal with are short, some having as few as eight pages, some having as many as forty pages. But most are around ten pages or so, and typically named for their size—short stories.

Short stories resemble their larger cousins, the novels, in many ways, but there are also some important differences. The most obvious difference is that an author has more room to move around in a novel simply because it is so much longer than a short story. There are usually a number of different situations presented in a novel and two or more parallel stories, or plot lines, which are related and finally brought together at the end. There are many characters who are developed at some length, and many ideas or themes are dealt with.

A short story, on the other hand, most often tells of one situation or a single experience. There is one story, one plot line. Usually, a short story encompasses a relatively short period of time. And even in stories that tell of events occurring over a number of years, time is compressed and events are carefully chosen to illustrate a single continuing situation. Only one or two principal characters are used in short stories and few supporting characters. Finally, all the situations, characters, settings and other story elements contribute to the development of only one overriding theme.

While it is impossible to provide one definition that applies to all short stories, it will probably be worthwhile to keep the following description in mind that applies to most of them.

> A short story is an account of a single incident or experience that reflects upon human nature, human feelings and the human condition. In length it is about as long as a single chapter in a novel, so that setting, situation, character, conflict, climax, resolution, and other story elements must all be compressed into a very small space.

**1. Establishing Setting and Situation.** As a master of the short story form, Katherine Mansfield could compress more meaning and feeling into a single sentence than most authors can manage in a dozen paragraphs. Her paragraphs accomplish what chapters do for others. Her short story "The Garden Party" is the length of only a short chapter in a novel, yet she crowds into it volumes about the feelings of a teen-age girl as she becomes aware of social differences among people.

Notice how, in a single opening paragraph, you come to know where you are, what the dominant feeling of the moment is, and what is going to happen. You are plunged at once into the experience.

> And after all the weather was ideal. They could not have had a more perfect day for a garden-party if they had ordered it. Windless, warm, the sky without a cloud. Only the blue was veiled with a haze of light gold, as it is sometimes in early summer. The gardener had been up since dawn, mowing the lawns and sweeping them, until the grass and the dark flat rosettes where the daisy plants had been seemed to shine. As for the roses, you could not help feeling they understood that roses are the only flowers that impress people at garden-parties; the only flowers that everybody is certain of knowing. Hundreds, yes, literally hundreds, had come out in a single night; the green bushes bowed down as though they had been visited by archangels.

Everything is perfect. There are broad lawns, a beautiful garden and a gardener, so we are obviously in a situation where life is at least upper middle class. And upper-middle-class life at this moment seems heavenly. There is a golden haze over everything, and the rose bushes are so gloriously laden that it seems they must have been visited by angels during the night. In this idyllic setting there is to be a garden party.

**2. Introducing the Main Character.** In a few more paragraphs we meet Laura, the main character of the story and the only character we will really be concerned with. She is a teen-ager who is having her first encounter with responsibility and with people from a world beyond her own. Her mother has asked her to direct the men who have come to put up the marquee, a large open-sided tent often used to protect the food and guests at outdoor parties.

Away Laura flew, still holding her piece of bread-and-butter. It's so delicious to have an excuse for eating out of doors, and besides, she loved having to arrange things; she always felt she could do it so much better than anybody else.

Four men in their shirt-sleeves stood grouped together on the garden path. They carried staves covered with rolls of canvas, and they had big tool bags slung on their backs. They looked impressive. Laura wished now that she had not got the bread-and-butter, but there was nowhere to put it, and she couldn't possibly throw it away. She blushed and tried to look severe and even a little bit short-sighted as she came up to them.

"Good morning," she said, copying her mother's voice. But that sounded so fearfully affected that she was ashamed, and stammered like a little girl, "Oh—er—have you come—is it about the marquee?"

In this short space we come to know Laura intimately. She is a young lady but has enough little girl left in her so that she is not comfortable in either role. She has the volatile feelings of a child, the emerging feelings of an adult for the world and people about her, and she doesn't know what to do with them. Apparently this is her first person-to-person independent encounter with working-class people. (Remember, this is a social setting which existed in the early part of our century.)

**3. Building the Conflict.** As young people will, Laura makes snap judgments and easy decisions based entirely on her feelings at the moment. Having been impressed by the easy-going manners of the workmen, she decides she is a socially enlightened person. In a few paragraphs, the author prepares Laura, and the readers, for the human dilemma which will be the whole point of the story.

Oh, how extraordinarily nice workmen were, she thought. Why couldn't she have workmen for friends rather than the silly boys she danced with...? She would get on much better with men like these.

It's all the fault, she decided... of these absurd class distinctions. Well, for her part, she didn't feel them. Not a bit, not an atom.... Just to prove how happy she was, just to show the tall fellow how at home she felt, and how she despised stupid conventions, Laura took a big bite of her bread-and-butter.... She felt just like a work-girl.

This is a master stroke of short-story writing. It is, all at once, humorous, appealing, and full of insight into the nature of a young girl and the working of her mind. Laura is woman enough to realize she has experienced an important lesson in human relationships, but the child in her fails to understand exactly what it is she has learned. She reacts like a little girl, taking a big bite of bread-and-butter which somehow makes her feel very democratic and "just like a working girl." If the story went no further than this, we could be satisfied that we have shared a real experience and some important feelings with Laura.

For several pages things build toward a perfect day until echoes from a more sordid world intrude upon Laura's happiness with herself. A poor workingman has been killed, and in her new feeling of social enlightenment Laura wants to stop the garden party. Now two opposite states of human condition are set in glaring contrast by the author, and Laura finds it's not as easy as she thought to bring two extremes of society together. There's more to it than taking a big bite of bread and butter.

> "But we can't possibly have a garden party with a man dead just outside the front gate." [Laura said]
> That really was extravagant, for the little cottages were in a lane to themselves at the very bottom of a steep rise that led up to the house. A broad road ran between. True, they were far too near. They were the greatest possible eyesore, and they had no right to be in that neighborhood at all.

What a change from how nice working people are! This is not Laura now but the author injecting the realities of a social attitude. Those dirty little houses don't belong in a "nice" neighborhood. And in a little bit we see the feeling about lower-class people that has been bred into Laura and her family.

> When the Sheridans were little they were forbidden to set foot there because of the revolting language and of what they might catch. But since they were grown up, Laura and Laurie on their prowls sometimes walked through. It was disgusting and sordid. They came out with a shudder. But still one must go everywhere; one must see everything. So through they went.

We are just about halfway through the story now. The author has set up one side of Laura's experience and has prepared us for the other side. Seen person-to-person, working-class people are awfully nice sometimes. But the world they live in is revolting, disgusting and sordid to people from Laura's world. Is this a familiar attitude in our own society? Does this situation apply to your own world? Is this a situation you can understand because you have heard of it or experienced it before?

**4. Building toward a Climax and a Resolution.** As stories go, we have covered a lot of ground in a short space of time. The garden party goes on in spite of the workingman's death. Finally, with a delightful day behind her, Laura's new-found social maturity is put to a test. She is delegated to take a basket of party leftovers to the family of the dead man. At this point the author abruptly changes the mood of the story, and we hurtle toward the climax of the situation and the climax of our experience. Notice how different things are from the heavenly setting of the garden party.

It was just growing dusky as Laura shut their garden gates. A big dog ran by like a shadow. The road gleamed white, and down below in the hollow the little cottages were in deep shade. How quiet it seemed after the afternoon. Here she was going down the hill to somewhere where a man lay dead, and she couldn't realize it. Why couldn't she? She stopped a minute. And it seemed to her that kisses, voices, tinkling spoons, laughter, the smell of crushed grass were somehow inside her. She had no room for anything else. How strange! She looked up at the pale sky, and all she thought was, "Yes, it was the most successful garden party."

There is no golden haze over everything now. It is dusky. There are shadows, and the little cottages where Laura will find the dead man are in deep shade. In this one paragraph the author takes Laura from her comfortable world and thrusts her into another that is less beautiful. Then notice how easily the author explains that Laura is really not able to tear herself free from the world she belongs to: "... it seemed to her that kisses, voices, tinkling spoons, laughter, the smell of crushed grass were somehow inside her. She had no room for anything else."

The climax will come shortly as Laura arrives at the poor cottage of the dead man and meets his family, but we can't spoil the story for you by telling you how things work out. The ending may seem a bit inconclusive, but as you finish reading ask yourself if Katherine Mansfield hasn't resolved Laura's dilemma after all. Is this a complete story despite its short length? And do you feel that you have learned something about human nature and the human condition from Laura's experience, in a rather short space of time?

If you can answer "yes" to all these questions, you will be able to say you have just read a good short story.

---

**As you read the story:**

- Notice how Laura's attitude toward working-class people changes as she talks to the workmen who have come to erect the marquee.

- Notice the impression of Laura's world that is created by her description of the sounds, the air and the light inside her house.

- Compare your impression of Laura's world to your impression of the cottage where the workman lay dead.

- Think carefully about Laura's thoughts and words as she looks at the dead man.

# The Garden Party
## Katherine Mansfield

And after all the weather was ideal. They could not have had a more perfect day for a garden-party if they had ordered it. Windless, warm, the sky without a cloud. Only the blue was veiled with a haze of light gold, as it is sometimes in early summer. The gardener had been up since dawn, mowing the lawns and sweeping them, until the grass and the dark flat rosettes where the daisy plants had been seemed to shine. As for the roses, you could not help feeling they understood that roses are the only flowers that impress people at garden-parties; the only flowers that everybody is certain of knowing. Hundreds, yes, literally hundreds, had come out in a single night; the green bushes bowed down as though they had been visited by archangels.

Breakfast was not yet over before the man came to put up the marquee.

"Where do you want the marquee put, mother?"

"My dear child, it's no use asking me. I'm determined to leave everything to you children this year. Forget I am your mother. Treat me as an honored guest."

But Meg could not possibly go and supervise the men. She had washed her hair before breakfast, and she sat drinking her coffee in a green turban, with a dark wet curl stamped on each cheek. Jose, the butterfly, always came down in a silk petticoat and a kimono jacket.

"You'll have to go, Laura; you're the artistic one."

Away Laura flew, still holding her piece of bread and butter. It's so delicious to have an excuse for eating out of doors, and besides, she loved having to arrange things; she always felt she could do it so much better than anybody else.

Four men in their shirt-sleeves stood grouped together on the garden path. They carried staves covered with rolls of canvas, and they had big toolbags slung on their backs. They looked impressive. Laura wished now that she had not got the bread and butter, but there was nowhere to put it, and she couldn't possibly throw it away. She blushed and tried to look severe and even a little bit shortsighted as she came up to them.

"Good morning," she said, copying her mother's voice. But that sounded so fearfully affected that she was ashamed, and stammered like a little girl, "Oh—er—have you come—is it about the marquee?"

"That's right, miss," said the tallest of the men, a lanky freckled fellow, and he shifted his toolbag, knocked back his straw hat and smiled down at her. "That's about it."

His smile was so easy, so friendly that Laura recovered. What nice eyes he had, small, but such a dark blue! And now she looked at the others, they were smiling too. "Cheer up, we won't bite," their smile seemed to say. How very nice workmen were! And what a beautiful morning! She mustn't mention the morning; she must be businesslike. The marquee.

"Well, what about the lily lawn? Would that do?"

And she pointed to the lily lawn with the hand that didn't hold the bread and butter. They turned, they stared in the direction. A little fat chap thrust out his underlip, and the tall fellow frowned.

"I don't fancy it," said he. "Not conspicuous enough. You see, with a thing like a marquee," and he turned to Laura in his easy way, "you want to put it somewhere where it'll give you a bang slap in the eye, if you follow me."

Laura's upbringing made her wonder for a moment whether it was quite respectful of a workman to talk to her of bang slap in the eye. But she did quite follow him.

"A corner of the tennis court," she suggested. "But the band's going to be in one corner."

"H'm, going to have a band, are you?" said another of the workmen. He was pale. He had a haggard look as his dark eyes scanned the tennis court. What was he thinking?

"Only a very small band," said Laura gently. Perhaps he wouldn't mind so much if the band was quite small. But the tall fellow interrupted.

"Look here, miss, that's the place. Against those trees. Over there. That'll do fine."

Against the karakas. Then the karaka trees would be hidden. And they were so lovely, with their broad, gleaming leaves, and their clusters of yellow fruit. They were like trees you imagined growing on a desert island, proud, solitary, lifting their leaves and fruits to the sun in a kind of silent splendour. Must they be hidden by a marquee?

They must. Already the men had shouldered their staves and were making for the place. Only the tall fellow was left. He bent down, pinched a sprig of lavender, put his thumb and forefinger to his nose and snuffed up the smell. When Laura saw that gesture she forgot all about the karakas in her wonder at him caring for things like that—caring for the smell of lavender. How many men that she knew would have done such a thing? Oh, how extraordinarily nice workmen were, she thought. Why couldn't she have workmen for friends rather than the silly boys she danced with and who came to Sunday night supper? She would get on much better with men like these.

It's all the fault, she decided, as the tall fellow drew something on the back of an envelope, something that was to be looped up or left to hang, of these absurd class distinctions. Well, for her part, she didn't feel them. Not a bit, not an atom.... And now there came the chock-chock of wooden hammers. Someone whistled, someone sang out, "Are you right there, matey?" "Matey!" The friendliness of it, the—the. Just to prove how happy she was, just to show the tall fellow how at home she felt, and how she despised stupid conventions, Laura took a big bite of her bread and butter as she stared at the little drawing. She felt just like a workgirl.

"Laura, Laura, where are you? Telephone, Laura!" a voice cried from the house.

"Coming!" Away she skimmered, over the lawn, up the path, up the steps, across the veranda, and into the porch. In the hall her father and Laurie were brushing their hats ready to go to the office.

"I say, Laura," said Laurie very fast, "you might just give a squiz at my coat before this afternoon. See if it wants pressing."

"I will," said she. Suddenly she couldn't stop herself. She ran at Laurie and gave him a small, quick squeeze. "Oh, I do love parties, don't you?" gasped Laura.

"Ra-ther," said Laurie's warm, boyish voice, and he squeezed his sister too, and gave her a gentle push. "Dash off to the telephone, old girl."

The telephone. "Yes, yes; oh yes. Kitty? Good morning, dear. Come to lunch? Do, dear. Delighted of course. It will only be a very scratch meal— just the sandwich crusts and broken meringue shells and what's left over. Yes, isn't it a perfect morning? Your white? Oh, I certainly should. One moment—hold the line. Mother's calling." And Laura sat back. "What, mother? Can't hear."

Mrs. Sheridan's voice floated down the stairs. "Tell her to wear that sweet hat she had on last Sunday."

"Mother says you're to wear that *sweet* hat you had on last Sunday. Good. One o'clock. Bye-bye."

Laura put back the receiver, flung her arms over her head, took a deep breath, stretched and let them fall. "Huh," she sighed, and the moment after the sigh she sat up quickly. She was still, listening. All the doors in the house seemed to be open. The house was alive with soft, quick steps and running voices. The green baize door that led to the kitchen regions swung open and shut with a muffled thud. And now there came a long, chuckling absurd sound. It was the heavy piano being moved on its stiff castors. But the air! If you stopped to notice, was the air always like this? Little faint winds were playing chase, in at the tops of the windows, out at the doors. And there were two tiny spots of sun, one on the inkpot, one on a silver photograph frame, playing too. Darling little spots. Especially the one on the inkpot lid. It was quite warm. A warm little silver star. She could have kissed it.

The front door bell pealed, and there sounded the rustle of Sadie's print skirt on the stairs. A man's voice murmured; Sadie answered, careless, "I'm sure I don't know. Wait. I'll ask Mrs. Sheridan."

"What is it, Sadie?" Laura came into the hall.

"It's the florist, Miss Laura."

It was indeed. There, just inside the door, stood a wide, shallow tray full of pots of pink lilies. No other kind. Nothing but lilies—canna lilies, big pink flowers, wide open, radiant, almost frighteningly alive on bright crimson stems.

"O-oh, Sadie!" said Laura, and the sound was like a little moan. She crouched down as if to warm herself at that blaze of lilies; she felt they were in her fingers, on her lips, growing in her breast.

"It's some mistake," she said faintly. "Nobody ever ordered so many. Sadie, go and find mother."

But at that moment Mrs. Sheridan joined them.

"It's quite right," she said calmly. "Yes, I ordered them. Aren't they lovely?" She pressed Laura's arm. "I was passing the shop yesterday, and I saw them in the window. And I suddenly thought for once in my life I shall have enough canna lilies. The garden party will be a good excuse."

"But I thought you said you didn't mean to interfere," said Laura. Sadie had gone. The florist's man was still outside at his van. She put her arm around her mother's neck and gently, very gently, she bit her mother's ear.

"My darling child, you wouldn't like a logical mother, would you?" Don't do that. Here's the man."

He carried more lilies still, another whole tray.

"Bank them up, just inside the door, on both sides of the porch, please," said Mrs. Sheridan. "Don't you agree, Laura?"

"Oh, I *do* mother."

In the drawing room Meg, Jose and good little Hans had at last succeeded in moving the piano.

"Now, if we put this chesterfield against the wall and move everything out of the room except the chairs, don't you think?"

"Quite."

"Hans, move these tables into the smoking room, and bring a sweeper to take these marks off the carpet and—one moment, Hans—" Jose loved giving orders to the servants, and they loved obeying her. She always made them feel they were taking part in some drama. "Tell mother and Miss Laura to come here at once."

"Very good, Miss Jose."

She turned to Meg. "I want to hear what the piano sounds like, just in case I'm asked to sing this afternoon. Let's try over 'This Life is Weary.' "

*Pom!* Ta-ta-ta *Tee*-ta! The piano burst out so passionately that Jose's face changed. She clasped her hands. She looked mournfully and enigmatically at her mother and Laura as they came in.

> This Life is *Wee*-ary,
> A Tear—a Sigh.
> A Love that *Chan*-ges,
>   This Life is *Wee*-ary,
> A Tear—a Sigh.
> A Love that *Chan*-ges,
> And then.   Good-bye!

But at the word "Good-bye," and although the piano sounded more desperate than ever, her face broke into a brilliant, dreadfully unsympathetic smile.

"Aren't I in good voice, mummy?" she beamed.

> This Life is *Wee*-ary,
> Hope comes to Die.
> A Dream—a *Wa*-kening.

But now Sadie interrupted them. "What is it, Sadie?"

"If you please, m'm, cook says have you got the flags for the sandwiches?"

"The flags for the sandwiches, Sadie?" echoed Mrs. Sheridan dreamily. And the children knew by her face that she hadn't got them. "Let me see." And she said to Sadie firmly, "Tell cook I'll let her have them in ten minutes."

Sadie went.

"Now, Laura," said her mother quickly. "Come with me into the smoking room. I've got the names somewhere on the back of an envelope. You'll have to write them out for me. Meg, go upstairs this minute and take that wet thing off your head. Jose, run and finish dressing this instant. Do you hear me, children, or shall I have to tell your father when he comes home tonight? And—and, Jose, pacify cook if you do go into the kitchen, will you? I'm terrified of her this morning."

The envelope was found at last behind the dining room clock, though how it had got there Mrs. Sheridan could not imagine.

"One of you children must have stolen it out of my bag, because I remember vividly—cream cheese and lemon curd. Have you done that?"

"Yes."

"Egg and—" Mrs. Sheridan held the envelope away from her. "It looks like mice. It can't be mice, can it?"

"Olive, pet," said Laura, looking over her shoulder.

"Yes, of course, olive. What a horrible combination it sounds. Egg and olive."

They were finished at last, and Laura took them off to the kitchen. She found Jose there pacifying the cook, who did not look at all terrifying.

"I have never seen such exquisite sandwiches," said Jose's rapturous voice. "How many kinds did you say there were, cook? Fifteen?"

"Fifteen, Miss Jose."

"Well, cook, I congratulate you."

Cook swept up crusts with the long sandwich knife, and smiled broadly.

"Godber's has come," announced Sadie, issuing out of the pantry. She had seen the man pass the window.

That meant the cream puffs had come. Godber's were famous for their cream puffs. Nobody ever thought of making them at home.

"Bring them in and put them on the table, my girl," ordered cook.

Sadie brought them in and went back to the door. Of course Laura and Jose were far too grown-up to really care about such things. All the same, they couldn't help agreeing that the puffs looked very attractive. Very. Cook began arranging them, shaking off the extra icing sugar.

"Don't they carry one back to all one's parties?" said Laura.

"I suppose they do," said practical Jose, who never liked to be carried back. "They look beautifully light and feathery, I must say."

"Have one each, my dears," said cook in her comfortable voice. "Yer ma won't know."

Oh, impossible. Fancy cream puffs so soon after breakfast. The very idea made one shudder. All the same, two minutes later Jose and Laura were licking their fingers with that absorbed inward look that only comes from whipped cream.

"Let's go into the garden, out by the back way," suggested Laura. "I want to see how the men are getting on with the marquee. They're such awfully nice men."

But the back door was blocked by cook, Sadie, Godber's man and Hans. Something had happened.

"Tuk-tuk-tuk," clucked cook like an agitated hen. Sadie had her hand clapped to her cheek as though she had toothache. Hans's face was screwed up in the effort to understand. Only Godber's man seemed to be enjoying himself; it was his story.

"What's the matter? What's happened?"

"There's been a horrible accident," said cook. "A man has been killed."

"A man killed! Where? How? When?"

But Godber's man wasn't going to have his story snatched from under his very nose.

"Know those little cottages just below here, miss?" Know them? Of course, she knew them. "Well, there's a young chap living there, name of Scott, a carter. His horse shied at a traction engine, corner of Hawke Street this morning, and he was thrown out on the back of his head. Killed."

"Dead!" Laura stared at Godber's man.

"Dead when they picked him up," said Godber's man with relish. "They were taking the body home as I come up here." And he said to the cook, "He's left a wife and five little ones."

"Jose, come here." Laura caught hold of her sister's sleeve and dragged her through the kitchen to the other side of the green baize door. There she paused and leaned against it. "Jose!" she said, horrified, "however are we going to stop everything?"

"Stop everything, Laura!" cried Jose in astonishment. "What do you mean?"

"Stop the garden party, of course." Why did Jose pretend?

But Jose was still more amazed. "Stop the garden party? My dear Laura, don't be so absurd. Of course we can't do anything of the kind. Nobody expects us to. Don't be so extravagant."

"But we can't possibly have a garden party with a man dead just outside the front gate."

That really was extravagant, for the little cottages were in a lane to themselves at the very bottom of a steep rise that led up to the house. A broad road ran between. True, they were far too near. They were the greatest possible eyesore, and they had no right to be in that neighborhood at all. They were little mean dwellings painted a chocolate brown. In the garden patches there was nothing but cabbage stalks, sick hens and tomato cans. The very smoke coming out of their chimneys was poverty stricken. Little rags and shreds of smoke, so unlike the great silvery plumes that uncurled from the Sheridans' chimneys. Washerwomen lived in the lane and sweeps and a cobbler, and a man whose house front was studded all over with minute birdcages. Children swarmed. When the Sheridans were little they were forbidden to set foot there because of the revolting language and of what they might catch. But since they were grown up, Laura and Laurie on their prowls sometimes walked through. It was disgusting and sordid. They came out with a shudder. But still one must go everywhere; one must see everything. So through they went.

"And just think of what the band would sound like to that poor woman," said Laura.

"Oh, Laura!" Jose began to be seriously annoyed. "If you're going to stop a band playing every time someone has an accident, you'll lead a very strenuous life. I'm every bit as sorry about it as you. I feel just as sympathetic." Her eyes hardened. She looked at her sister just as she used to when they were little and fighting together. "You won't bring a drunken workman back to life by being sentimental," she said softly.

"Drunk! Who said he was drunk?" Laura turned furiously on Jose. She said, just as they had used to say on those occasions, "I'm going straight up to tell mother."

"Do dear," cooed Jose.

"Mother, can I come into your room?" Laura turned the big glass doorknob.

"Of course, child. Why, what's the matter? What's given you such a color?" And Mrs. Sheridan turned round from her dressing table. She was trying on a new hat.

"Mother, a man's been killed." began Laura.

"*Not* in the garden?" interrupted her mother.

"No, no!"

"Oh, what a fright you gave me!" Mrs. Sheridan sighed with relief, and took off the big hat and held it on her knees.

"But listen, mother," said Laura. Breathless, half choking, she told the dreadful story. "Of course, we can't have our party, can we?" she pleaded. "The band and everybody arriving. They'd hear us, mother; they're nearly neighbors!"

To Laura's astonishment her mother behaved just like Jose; it was harder to bear because she seemed amused. She refused to take Laura seriously.

"But, my dear child, use your common sense. It's only by accident we've heard of it. If someone had died there normally—and I can't understand how they keep alive in those poky little holes—we should still be having our party, shouldn't we?"

Laura had to say "yes" to that, but she felt it was all wrong. She sat down on her mother's sofa and pinched the cushion frill.

"Mother, isn't it really terribly heartless of us?" she asked.

"Darling!" Mrs. Sheridan got up and came over to her, carrying the hat. Before Laura could stop her she had popped it on. "My child!" said her mother, "the hat is yours. It's made for you. It's much too young for me. I have never seen you look such a picture. Look at yourself!" And she held up her hand mirror.

"But mother," Laura began again. She couldn't look at herself; she turned aside.

This time Mrs. Sheridan lost patience just as Jose had done.

"You are being very absurd, Laura," she said coldly. "People like that don't expect sacrifices from us. And it's not very sympathetic to spoil everybody's enjoyment as you're doing now."

"I don't understand," said Laura, and she walked quickly out of the room into her own bedroom. There, quite by chance, the first thing she saw was this charming girl in the mirror, in her black hat trimmed with gold daisies, and a long black velvet ribbon. Never had she imagined she could look like that. Is mother right? she thought. And now she hoped her mother was right. Am I being extravagant? Perhaps it was extravagant. Just for a moment she had another glimpse of that poor woman and those little children, and the body being carried into the house. But it all seemed blurred, unreal, like a picture in the newspaper. I'll remember it again after the party's over, she decided. And somehow that seemed quite the best plan....

Lunch was over by half-past one. By half-past two they were all ready for the fray. The green-coated band had arrived and was established in a corner of the tennis court.

"My dear!" trilled Kitty Maitland, "aren't they too like frogs for words? You ought to have arranged them round the pond with the conductor in the middle on a leaf."

Laurie arrived and hailed them on his way to dress. At the sight of him Laura remembered the accident again. She wanted to tell him. If Laurie agreed with the others, then it was bound to be all right. And she followed him into the hall.

"Laurie!"

"Hallo!" He was halfway upstairs, but when he turned round and saw Laura he suddenly puffed out his cheeks and goggled his eyes at her. "My word, Laura; you do look stunning," said Laurie. "What an absolutely topping hat!"

Laura said faintly "Is it?" and smiled up at Laurie, and didn't tell him after all.

Soon after that people began coming in streams. The band struck up; the hired waiters ran from the house to the marquee. Wherever you looked there were couples strolling, bending to the flowers, greeting, moving on over the lawn. They were like bright birds that had alighted in the Sheridan's garden for this one afternoon, on their way to—where? Ah, what happiness it is to be with people who all are happy, to press hands, press cheeks, smile into eyes.

"Darling Laura, how well you look!"

"What a becoming hat, child!"

"Laura, you look quite Spanish. I've never seen you look so striking."

And Laura, glowing, answered softly, "Have you had tea? Won't you have an ice? The passion-fruit ices really are rather special." She ran to her father and begged him. "Daddy darling, can't the band have something to drink?"

And the perfect afternoon slowly ripened, slowly faded, slowly its petals closed.

"Never a more delightful garden party..." "The greatest success..." "Quite the most..."

Laura helped her mother with the good-byes. They stood side by side in the porch till it was all over.

"All over, all over, thank heaven," said Mrs. Sheridan. "Round up the others, Laura. Let's go and have some fresh coffee. I'm exhausted. Yes, it's been very successful. But oh, these parties, these parties! Why will you children insist on giving parties!" And they all of them sat down in the deserted marquee.

"Have a sandwich, daddy dear. I wrote the flag."

"Thanks." Mr. Sheridan took a bite and the sandwich was gone. He took another. "I suppose you din't hear of a beastly accident that happened today?" he said.

"My dear," said Mrs. Sheridan, holding up her hand, "we did. It nearly ruined the party. Laura insisted we should put it off."

"Oh, mother!" Laura didn't want to be teased about it.

"It was a horrible affair all the same," said Mr. Sheridan. "The chap was married too. Lived just below in the lane, and leaves a wife and half a dozen kiddies, so they say."

An awkward little silence fell. Mrs. Sheridan fidgeted with her cup. Really, it was very tactless of father...

Suddenly she looked up. There on the table were all those sandwiches, cakes, puffs, all uneaten, all going to be wasted. She had one of her brilliant ideas.

"I know," she said. "Let's make up a basket. Let's send that poor creature some of this perfectly good food. At any rate, it will be the greatest treat for the children. Don't you agree? And she's sure to have neighbors calling in and so on. What a point to have it all ready prepared. Laura!" She jumped up. "Get me the big basket out of the stairs cupboard."

"But, mother, do you really think it's a good idea?" said Laura.

Again, how curious, she seemed to be different from them all. To take scraps from their party. Would the poor woman really like that?

"Of course! What's the matter with you today? An hour or two ago you were insisting on us being sympathetic, and now—"

"Oh, well! Laura ran for the basket. It was filled, it was heaped by her mother.

"Take it yourself, darling." said she. "Run down just as you are. No, wait, take the arum lilies too. People of that class are so impressed by arum lilies."

"The stems will ruin her lace frock," said practical Jose.

So they would. Just in time. "Only the basket, then. And, Laura!"—her mother followed her out of the marquee— "don't on any account"

"What, mother?"

No, better not put such ideas into the child's head!" "Nothing! Run along."

It was just growing dusky as Laura shut their garden gates. A big dog ran by like a shadow. The road gleamed white, and down below in the hollow the little cottages were in deep shade. How quiet it seemed after the afternoon. Here she was going down the hill to somewhere where a man lay dead, and she couldn't realize it. Why couldn't she? She stopped a minute. And it seemed to her that kisses, voices, tinkling spoons, laughter, the smell of crushed grass were somehow inside her. She had no room for anything else. How strange! She looked up at the pale sky, and all she thought was, "Yes, it was the most successful party."

Now the broad road was crossed. The lane began, smoky and dark. Women in shawls and men's tweed caps hurried by. Men hung over the palings; the children played in the doorways. A low hum came from the mean little cottages. In some of them there was a flicker of light, and a shadow, crab-like moved across the window. Laura bent her head and hurried on. She wished now she had put on a coat. How her frock shone! And the big hat with the velvet streamer—if only it was another hat! Were the people looking at her? They must be. It was a mistake to have come; she knew all along it was a mistake. Should she go back even now?

No, too late. This was the house. It must be. A dark knot of people stood outside. Beside the gate an old, old woman with a crutch sat in a chair, watching. She had her feet on a newspaper. The voices stopped as Laura drew near. The group parted. It was as though she was expected, as though they had known she was coming here.

Laura was terribly nervous. Tossing the velvet ribbon over her shoulder, she said to a woman standing by, "Is this Mrs. Scott's house?" and the woman, smiling queerly, said, "It is, my lass."

Oh, to be away from this! She actually said, "Help me, God," as she walked up the tiny path and knocked. To be away from those staring eyes, or to be covered up in anything, one of those women's shawls even. I'll just leave the basket and go, she decided. I shan't even wait for it to be emptied.

Then the door opened. A little woman in black showed in the gloom.

Laura said, "Are you Mrs. Scott?" But to her horror the woman answered, "Walk in please, miss," and she was shut in the passage.

"No," said Laura, "I don't want to come in. I only want to leave this basket. Mother sent—"

The little woman in the gloomy passage seemed not to have heard her. "Step this way, please, miss," she said in an oily voice, and Laura followed her.

She found herself in a wretched little low kitchen, lighted by a smoky lamp. There was a woman sitting before the fire.

"Em," said the little creature who had let her in. "Em! It's a young lady." She turned to Laura. She said meaningly, "I'm 'er sister, Miss. You'll excuse 'er, won't you?"

"Oh, but of course!" said Laura. "Please, please don't disturb her. I—I only want to leave—"

But at that moment the woman at the fire turned round. Her face, puffed up, red, with swollen eyes and swollen lips, looked terrible. She seemed as though she couldn't understand why Laura was there. What did it mean? Why was this stranger standing in the kitchen with a basket? What was it all about? And the poor face puckered up again.

"All right, my dear," said the other. "I'll thank the young lady."

And again she began, "You'll excuse her, miss, I'm sure," and her face, swollen too, tried an oily smile.

Laura only wanted to get out, to get away. She was back in the passage. The door opened. She walked straight through into the bedroom, where the dead man was lying.

"You'd like a look at 'im, wouldn't you?" said Em's sister, and she brushed past Laura over to the bed. "Don't be afraid, my lass,—" and now her voice sounded fond and sly, and fondly she drew down the sheet—" 'e looks a picture. There's nothing to show. Come along, my dear."

Laura came.

There lay a young man, fast asleep—sleeping so soundly, so deeply, that he was far, far away from them both. Oh, so remote, so peaceful. He was dreaming. Never wake him up again. His head was sunk in the pillow, his eyes were closed; they were blind under the closed eyelids. He was given up to his dream. What did garden parties and baskets and lace frocks matter to him? He was far from all those things. He was wonderful, beautiful. While they were laughing and while the band was playing, this marvel had come to the lane. Happy . . . happy . . . . All is well, said that sleeping face. This is just as it should be. I am content.

But all the same you had to cry, and she couldn't go out of the room without saying something to him. Laura gave a loud childish sob.

"Forgive my hat," she said.

And this time she didn't wait for Em's sister. She found her way out of the door, down the path, past all those dark people. At the corner of the lane she met Laurie.

He stepped out of the shadow. "Is that you, Laura?"

"Yes."

"Mother was getting anxious. Was it all right?"

"Yes, quite. Oh, Laurie!" She took his arm, she pressed up against him.

"I say, you're not crying, are you?" asked her brother.

Laura shook her head. She was.

Laurie put his arm round her shoulder. "Don't cry," he said in his warm, loving voice. "Was it awful?"

"No," sobbed Laura. "It was simply marvelous. But, Laurie—" She stopped, she looked at her brother. "Isn't life," she stammered, "isn't life—" But what life was she couldn't explain. No matter. He quite understood.

"*Isn't* it, darling?" said Laurie.

# Unit 1

## The Garden Party

- **Comprehension Questions**
- **The Short Story**
- **Discussion Guides**
- **Writing Exercise**

# COMPREHENSION QUESTIONS

For each of the following statements and questions, select the option containing the most complete or most accurate answer.

1. Roses, it seems, are the best flowers to have at a garden party because
(a) they're the
   - ☐ a. easiest to grow and display.
   - ☐ b. most beautiful and abundant.
   - ☐ c. most fragrant.
   - ☐ d. only flowers that everyone recognizes.

2. Which of the following choices best defines *affected* as used in, " 'Good
(l) morning,' she said, copying her mother's voice. But that sounded so fearfully *affected* that she was ashamed. . ."?
   - ☐ a. Emotional          ☐ c. Cold
   - ☐ b. Artificial          ☐ d. Girlish

3. It would seem that Laura
(h) ☐ a. is very pleased with her lifestyle.
   - ☐ b. is uncomfortable living the way she does.
   - ☐ c. would change her way of living if she could.
   - ☐ d. is embarrassed by all the beauty around her.

4. When one of the workmen says, " . . . going to have a band, are you?"
(f) Laura replies, gently, "Only a very small band." The reader may conclude from Laura's answer that she
   - ☐ a. looks down on workmen.
   - ☐ b. wishes it were a bigger band.
   - ☐ c. feels a bit guilty about her wealth.
   - ☐ d. is amused by the workman.

5. As Laura talks to the workmen, she begins to feel that the invisible
(c) barriers that separated the social classes in her society were
   - ☐ a. unfortunate but necessary.
   - ☐ b. right and just.
   - ☐ c. ordained by God.
   - ☐ d. absurd and silly.

6. Laura's newly formed ideas about the working class are
(g) □ a. realistic.            □ c. prejudiced.
    □ b. naive.               □ d. cynical.


7. If you had to pin a political label on Laura at this point in her life,
(g) you would probably call her
    □ a. a communist.
    □ b. conservative and reactionary.
    □ c. reasonably democratic.
    □ d. a revolutionary.


8. For the Sheridans and their guests at the garden party, life is
(e) □ a. gracious and pleasant.
    □ b. full of cares and worry.
    □ c. boring and humdrum.
    □ d. meaningless.


9. There's an abrupt change in mood in this story that occurs when
(d) □ a. Jose sits down at the piano and sings.
    □ b. the florist delivers the flowers.
    □ c. Laura directs the men putting up the marquee.
    □ d. news comes that a workingman was killed.


10. When Laura hears that a workman from a nearby cottage has been
(b) killed, she wants to
    □ a. stop the party.
    □ b. send over the canna lilies.
    □ c. invite his widow to their garden party.
    □ d. wear black at the garden party.


11. The attitude of the tradesman who reports the fatal accident shows
(f) that some people
    □ a. enjoy an accident.
    □ b. don't want to hear about accidents.
    □ c. are blood-thirsty.
    □ d. dislike someone who brings bad news.


12. Which of the following choices best defines the word *mean* as used
(l) in, "They were little *mean* dwellings painted a chocolate brown."?
    □ a. Scantily furnished        □ c. Crude and cheerless
    □ b. Rude and impolite         □ d. Cozy and inviting

13. When Laura tells Jose and her mother that the party must be stopped,
(i) they express
   □ a. amusement and annoyance.
   □ b. sympathy and concern.
   □ c. shock and horror.
   □ d. respect and admiration.

14. At this point in her life, Laura Sheridan might be charactized as
(j) □ a. silly and scatterbrained.
   □ b. sensitive and compassionate.
   □ c. selfish and inconsiderate.
   □ d. strong and independent.

15. What does Laura wear to the party that makes her look quite stunning?
(a) □ a. A long white dress.       □ c. A black hat
    □ b. Sheer silk stockings      □ d. Black patent-leather shoes

16. The attitude of the servants toward the Sheridan family might best
(c) be described as
    □ a. suspicious.               □ c. democratic and familiar.
    □ b. hostile and grudging.     □ d. respectful but affectionate.

17. Onomatopoeia is a figure of speech in which words mimic sounds.
(k) "Ribit," for example, mimics the noise of a frog. Which of the following
    quotations from the story is *not* an example of onomatopoeia?
    □ a. *Pom*! Ta-ta-ta *Tee*-ta! The piano burst out. . . .
    □ b. And now there came a long, chuckling, absurd sound.
    □ c. The chock-chock of wooden hammers
    □ d. 'Tuk-tuk-tuk,' clucked cook like an agitated hen.

18. "And the perfect afternoon slowly ripened, slowly faded, slowly its
(k) petals closed." This metaphor describes the afternoon by comparing
    it with
    □ a. the evening.              □ c. a flower.
    □ b. a piece of fruit.         □ d. an ideal.

19. A reader gets the impression that, when it comes to unpleasant realities
(h) such as poverty and death, upper-class people would
    □ a. like to correct injustices as much as possible.
    □ b. like to share the sorrows of their less-fortunate neighbors.
    □ c. like to hear all the ugly details.
    □ d. just as soon pretend they didn't exist.

20. After the garden party, Laura goes to the home of the dead workman
(a) with
    ☐ a. some arum lilies.
    ☐ b. money.
    ☐ c. some second-hand clothes.
    ☐ d. a basket of party left-overs.


21. Throughout her visit to the dead man's family, Laura feels
(i) ☐ a. nervous and embarrassed.
    ☐ b. superior and condescending.
    ☐ c. sympathetic and motherly.
    ☐ d. sad and grief-stricken.


22. The expression on the dead man's face is
(b) ☐ a. pained.           ☐ c. sorrowful.
    ☐ b. peaceful.        ☐ d. blank.


23. The one person in the Sheridan household who seems to understand
(f) Laura the best is
    ☐ a. her mother.      ☐ c. her brother, Laurie.
    ☐ b. her sister, Jose.   ☐ d. the maid, Sadie.


24. If Laura grows up to be like her mother and sisters, chances are she
(j) will become
    ☐ a. less sure of herself.
    ☐ b. less sensitive and compassionate.
    ☐ c. less aware of social status.
    ☐ d. less pleased with her way of life.


25. After reading this story, one would have to conclude that rich people
(e) and poor people
    ☐ a. have a lot in common.
    ☐ b. lead much the same kinds of lives.
    ☐ c. envy each other.
    ☐ d. are separated in many ways.

---

Comprehension Skills: a — isolating details; b — recalling specific facts; c — retaining concepts; d — organizing facts; e — understanding the main idea; f — drawing a conclusion; g — making a judgment; h — making an inference; i — recognizing tone; j — understanding characters; k — appreciation of literary forms; l — understanding vocabulary.

# THE SHORT STORY

## Practice Exercise A

Already the men had shouldered their staves and were making for the place. Only the tall fellow was left. He bent down, pinched a sprig of lavender, put his thumb and fore-finger to his nose and snuffed up the smell. When Laura saw that gesture she forgot all about the karakas in her wonder at him caring for things like that—caring for the smell of lavender.

1. The gesture of the man is used by the author to show that like everyone else, workingmen
   ☐ a. often destroy things like flowers.
   ☐ b. can appreciate delicate things.
   ☐ c. try to impress girls with flowers.
   ☐ d. dislike class distinctions.

2. The paragraph expresses an idea about workmen that is new to Laura and important to the point of the story. Underline the sentence that expresses the idea. Circle the one word, which is repeated twice, that expresses a human emotion shared by Laura and the workman.

## Practice Exercise B

The house was alive with soft, quick steps and running voices. The green baize door that led to the kitchen regions swung open and shut with a muffled thud. And now there came a long, chuckling absurd sound. It was the heavy piano being moved on its stiff castors. But the air! If you stopped to notice, was the air always like this? Little faint winds were playing chase, in at the tops of the windows, out at the doors. And there were two tiny spots of sun, one on the inkpot, one on a silver photograph frame, playing too. Darling little spots. Especially the one on the inkpot lid. It was quite warm. A warm little silver star. She could have kissed it.

1. With this description the author tells you that Laura's world is
   ☐ a. busy and noisy.
   ☐ b. drafty and over-furnished.
   ☐ c. funny and absurd.
   ☐ d. warm and alive.

2. Authors use *personification* to make inanimate objects seem human and alive. Underline at least two expressions in the paragraph that are examples of personification.

## Practice Exercise C

The little woman in the gloomy passage seemed not to have heard her. "Step this way, please, miss," she said in an oily voice, and Laura followed her.

She found herself in a wretched little low kitchen, lighted by a smoky lamp. There was a woman sitting before the fire.

"Em," said the little creature who had let her in. "Em! It's a young lady." She turned to Laura. She said meaningly, "I'm 'er sister, Miss. You'll excuse 'er, won't you?"

1. Compare this passage with the passage in Exercise B. They express several exactly opposite feelings. One set of opposites expressed by the two passages is
   - ☐ a. dry versus oily.
   - ☐ b. quiet versus noisy.
   - ☐ c. bright versus dark.
   - ☐ d. hot versus cold.

2. Authors often choose adjectives with long vowel sounds to convey unpleasant or mysterious feelings — words such as *eerie, creepy, greasy, moaning, groaning,* and so on. Find and circle at least two such adjectives in this passage. (Try reading the passage from Exercise B, aloud and with expression. Then read this one. Notice how different they sound.)

## Practice Exercise D

What did garden parties and baskets and lace frocks matter to him? He was far from all those things. He was wonderful, beautiful. While they were laughing and while the band was playing, this marvel had come to the lane. Happy... happy.... All is well, said that sleeping face. This is just as it should be. I am content.

1. Two opposite sides of Laura are seen here that we have seen many times throughout the story. She is both
   - ☐ a. mature and childlike.
   - ☐ b. silly and serious.
   - ☐ c. rich and poor.
   - ☐ d. thoughtless and considerate.

2. One line in this passage is most typical of Katherine Mansfield. It is a very short line that expresses all of Laura's confused conflicts and feelings. It is funny and rather sad at the same time, and almost acts as an exclamation point for the meaning of the story. Find the line and circle it.

# DISCUSSION GUIDES

## Analyzing the Short Story

1. In a short story space counts. Only the most important details are included. Why, then, does Katherine Mansfield give ten lines to a rather silly song: "This life is Wee-ary. . . ."? (Hint: Compare song with the last paragraph of the story.)

2. True to short-story form, there is only one main character in the story—Laura. But the brief appearances of other people must serve a purpose, too. What do each of these people do for the story?

    | Mrs. Sheridan | the tall workman | the cook |
    |---|---|---|
    | Jose | Laurie | the dead man |

3. The story is called "The Garden Party," but the party itself is the shortest episode in the story. Why?

## Interpreting the Story

4. We are never told exactly how old Laura Sheridan is. How old do you think she is? Find passages in the story that support your opinion.

5. Mrs. Sheridan and Jose think Laura is being "extravagant" when she wants to stop the garden party. Who is right, Laura or Jose and Mrs. Sheridan? What would you have done under similar circumstances?

6. An American historian reported the following incident. At the end of the last century a mine owner was told that his miners (poor immigrant laborers) were suffering under horrible working conditions. Said the mine owner, "People like that don't suffer. Why, they can't even speak English!" Can you find this attitude in the story? How does this attitude still exist in the world today?

7. Will Laura grow up to be just like her mother, or will she be different? Explain your opinion using quotations from the story if possible.

## Analyzing the Author's Technique

8. To show that the girls are young, somewhere between girlhood and womanhood, Katherine Mansfield has them, at times, acting like little girls, and, at other times, acting rather grown-up. Find several examples of each action to show how this has been done.

9. The author makes quite a point about Laura's hat on two occasions. Once when she is making a fuss about stopping the party because a man has been killed; once when she is looking at the dead man. How does Katherine Mansfield use the hat to emphasize the meaning of the story?

10. It has been said that Katherine Mansfield's writing is sometimes like poetry. Find at least two paragraphs that sound poetic to you. Try rewriting the paragraphs in the form of a poem without changing any of the words. (Remember, lines in poetry do not have to rhyme.)

## WRITING EXERCISE

Here are seven typical Katherine Mansfield sentences taken from the story. You are told what feeling each expresses. In each case a similar sentence follows with parts omitted. Use your imagination to fill in the blanks and make your own Mansfield-type sentences. It is your own ideas that are wanted. There are no "correct" answers.

1. The green bushes bowed down as though they had been visited by archangels. (Feeling: Something is extremely beautiful and awe-inspiring.)

   The pine trees reached toward the sky as if they _____

   _____

2. "Cheer up, we won't bite," their smile seemed to say. (Feeling: Friendly, unspoken communication.)

   _____ , their kindly eyes beckoned.

3. "Only a very small band," said Laura gently. Perhaps he wouldn't mind so much if the band was quite small. (Feeling: Self-conscious and apologetic because you are better off than someone else.)

   "Only a _____ , "he said to the

   hungry-looking man. Perhaps he wouldn't_____ if the _____

   _____ was not very big.

4. Away she skimmered over the lawn. (Feeling: Lively, carefree, youthful activity.)

   _____he _____ down the road.

5. She crouched down as if to warm herself at that blaze of lilies. (Feeling: Enjoyment of something beautiful.)

He_____as if to _____
in the laughing brook.

6. Jose and Laura were licking their fingers with that absorbed inward look that only comes from whipped cream. (Feeling: Absolute childlike interest in something.)

Mike and Peter had their faces screwed in a knot with that _____

_____ that only comes from _____

_____ .

7. It seemed to her that kisses, voices, tinkling spoons, laughter, the smell of crushed grass were somehow inside her. (Feeling: A pleasant feeling or experience that you recognize has become an important part of your life.)

After the dance it seemed that _____

_____

would always be a part of me.

# Tell Me How Long the Train's Been Gone

## James Baldwin

# Introduction

"Tell Me How Long the Train's Been Gone" is about a small boy named Leo Proudhammer who lives in Harlem with his parents and his older brother, Caleb. Leo is ten, and just learning what it means to grow up Black in a white society.

Leo has not had much contact with whites. Racial boundaries in New York City are rigidly defined, as Leo discovers riding the subways one Saturday evening. When he first gets on, the passengers are mostly Black. Beyond a certain point, however, the Black people abruptly disappear and the car fills with whites. Close up like this, white people are an alien species whom Leo regards with a mixture of fear and fascination. But even from a distance, they dominate his life and that of his family in subtle ways that Leo is only beginning to understand.

Leo's father, who is from Barbados, is a proud man who tells his sons that they are the descendants of Black kings. But in Harlem, Mr. Proudhammer drinks too much and grovels before the white landlord. Leo's mother cajoles the storekeepers into accepting partial payment for the weekly groceries, but she pays dearly in both inflated prices and lost dignity. And Leo's brother, Caleb, shows signs of the same bitterness that has driven their father to drink.

"Are white people—*people*?" Leo asks his brother. "People like us?" But this is one question Leo must answer for himself. So, like clues to a mystery, Leo is collecting facts, pushing them around in his head, and looking for the answer to a question that is becoming more and more central to his life.

Like Leo Proudhammer, James Baldwin grew up in Harlem. Looking back on his childhood Baldwin once said, "We can dismiss it with the restrained observation that I certainly would not consider living it again." The oldest of nine children, he grew up holding a baby with one hand and a book with the other, and began plotting novels at about the time he learned to read.

Baldwin's first real experience with racism occurred when he was eighteen and working in a defense plant in New Jersey during World War II. "I knew about the South, of course, and about how Southerners treated Negroes and how they expected them to behave," recalls Baldwin, "but it had never entered my mind that anyone would look at me and expect *me* to behave that way." At countless lunch counters, bars, and bowling alleys he was told, "We don't serve Negroes here," or he was simply ignored. It was during this period that he first contracted "that dread chronic disease, the unfailing symptom of which is a kind of blind fever, a pounding in the skull and fire in the bowels." The disease, of course, is hatred. And hatred had consumed his father.

Baldwin was never close to his father, a preacher. Like little Leo's father in the story, Baldwin's father was a proud man "who lived and died in an intolerable bitterness of spirit." After his father's death, Baldwin came to realize that bitterness was folly, and that hatred never failed to destroy the one who hated.

About his writing Baldwin said recently: "You write in order to change the world, knowing perfectly well that you probably can't, but also knowing that literature is indispensable to the world. In some way, your aspirations and concern for a single man in fact do begin to change the world. The world changes according to the way people see it, and if you alter, even by a millimeter, the way a person looks or people look at reality, then you can change [the world]."

# Setting

Many readers dismiss setting as just another word for scenery—a quaint New England village, the Golden Gate Bridge, or a picture postcard view of the Grand Canyon—something an author throws in to distract the reader in case the plot lags. That view of setting is like calling Beethoven's Fifth Symphony "background music"! Setting, however, plays a more active role in a story than you might think.

Setting contributes important information to a story: it tells the geographical location, the physical surroundings and the historical period in which the story is set. An author uses a variety of devices to give this information—devices like sights, sounds, and smells, actual historical events, styles of architecture and clothing and modes of transportation. All these details help orient the reader in a particular time and place.

But what is not so obvious to a casual reader is the extent to which setting influences other elements of a story. Far from playing a passive role in storytelling, setting makes a number of important contributions: it suggests action; it helps make a story believable; it expresses the theme and it helps create the atmosphere that the reader is made to experience.

"Tell Me How Long the Train's Been Gone" is about a small boy growing up in Harlem, and this setting, as you will see, pervades the entire story.

**1. Setting Suggests Action.** Conceivably, just about anything can happen just about anywhere. The fact is, however, that every setting has a certain potential for action that we recognize almost without realizing it. When, for instance, we peer down a dark, dingy alley and think, "This is a great place for a murder," or admire a sunny, gracious home and wonder, "How could anyone be unhappy here?" we are voicing certain expectations suggested by the setting. Looking at it from another angle, when a tragic death mars a joyous wedding party, we are stunned because tragedy is the last thing we expect in a joyous setting.

Authors are well aware of this, and they choose settings that help them tell their story. If they are successful, the reader will come away with the feeling that this particular setting practically invites the chain of events that follows.

There is a good example of this in Baldwin's story. Harlem, a Black community in New York City, is almost synonomous with the term "urban ghetto." In the following passage the narrator of the story, a small boy named Leo Proudhammer, describes the apartment his family lived in. What possibilities does this setting suggest to you—that is, what kinds of actions might you expect will follow?

> For days on end, in the wintertime, we huddled around the gas stove in the kitchen, because the landlord gave us no heat. When windows were broken, the landlord took his time about fixing them; the wind made the cardboard we stuffed in the windows rattle all night long; and when snow came, the weight of the snow forced the cardboard inward and onto the floor. Whenever the apartment received a fresh coat of paint, we bought the paint and did the painting ourselves; we killed the rats. A great chunk of the kitchen ceiling fell one winter, narrowly missing our mother.

Notice how every detail of this setting is cold, cheerless and uninviting. The lack of heat in the winter, the broken windows that go unreplaced, the snow spilling into the apartment, the rats and the falling chunks of ceiling, all suggest that here, life is a struggle. The enemy, as far as Leo can see, is the landlord. In a larger sense, however, the landlord represents society, and in Harlem, society is the white community which owns the buildings and stores and polices the streets. A reader can't help thinking that anyone who lives in a place like this is going to resent a society that allows such conditions to exist. Given this setting, then, conflict with society seems inevitable. And, as it turns out, this is precisely what the story is all about.

**2. Setting Helps Make a Story Believable.** Another contribution of setting is to help make the story more believable. A setting that strikes the reader as true-to-life tends, in turn, to make the whole story ring true.

One way an author creates a believable setting is by using lots of details— details describing a place, like the tenement apartment we just looked at, and details describing people. People dress differently and behave differently in, say, a church, from the way they do at a party. You are also likely to meet a different class of people depending on where you are. Thus, details about people can be as revealing as details about places.

In the following passage, Baldwin describes the people in a subway car to create this setting from "Tell Me How Long the Train's Been Gone." What details does he focus on to make this setting, and the whole story, seem believable?

> For a time, during these expeditions, I simply sat and watched the people. Lots of people would be dressed up, for this was Saturday night. The women's hair would be all curled and straightened, and the lipstick on their full lips looked purple and

make-believe against the dark skins of their faces. They wore very fancy capes or coats, in wonderful colors, and long dresses, and sometimes they had jewels in their hair, and sometimes they wore flowers on their dresses. They were almost as beautiful as movie stars. And so the men with them seemed to think.

The hair of the men was slick and wavy, brushed up into pompadours; or they wore very sharp hats, brim flicked down dangerously over one eye, with perhaps one flower in the lapel of their many-colored suits. They laughed and talked with their girls, but quietly, for there were white people in the car. The white people would scarcely ever be dressed up and did not speak to each other at all—only read their papers and stared at the advertisements. But they fascinated me more than the colored people did, because I knew nothing at all about them and could not imagine what they were like.

The author describes the passengers on this subway car in some detail because here, the people *are* the setting. A subway car is going to look the same no matter what part of the city it is passing through. But the passengers who ride on it are more distinctive.

In this scene, most of the passengers are Black, which suggests that this part of the subway line passes through predominantly Black neighborhoods. The way the passengers are dressed and the way they act are also part of the setting. The women are all dressed up, with jewels in their hair and flowers pinned to their long dresses. To a small boy, they look almost as dazzling as movie stars. Their escorts are also decked out for Saturday night, with a flower in the lapel of their colorful suits and hat brims tilted at a rakish angle.

In sharp contrast are the few white passengers in the car. Somber and remote, their very presence has a subduing effect on the festive mood of the Black party-goers. From the point of view of a small boy who is still awed by fancy clothes and white strangers, this is just a subway ride on a Saturday night. But the reader can see beyond his limited viewpoint and sense the undercurrent of racial tension in the car.

A detailed setting like this has the impact of a photograph, and, like a photograph, we accept it as a representation of the real world. One false note, however—like the white passengers chatting with the Blacks for no apparent reason—and the reader would be instantly suspicious of anything this narrator has to say. But because every detail in this setting rings true, we are willing to believe in Leo Proudhammer and, by extension, in the whole story.

**3. Setting Expresses the Theme.** A successful setting emphasizes the theme of a story by providing the most appropriate surroundings for expressing a particular theme. One of the best examples of this is the Mississippi River in *Huckleberry Finn*. An important theme in this story is Huck's escape from society. Huck makes his escape down the river on a raft. Thus the setting—the Mississippi River—becomes the vehicle for the theme.

A major theme in the story you are about to read concerns racial prejudice in America. It's hard to think of a better setting for the development of this theme than Harlem, where the evidence of racism and its effect on people's lives are everywhere. But for the sake of contrast, the author provides a number of other settings like the following one. Here is the same subway car we just looked at, only now it's in a different part of town. How does this setting express the theme of the story?

> Underground, I received my first apprehension of New York neighborhoods and, underground, first felt what may be called a civic terror. I very soon realized that after the train had passed a certain point, going uptown or downtown, all the colored people disappeared. The first time I realized this, I panicked and got lost. I rushed off the train, terrified of what these white people might do to me, with no colored person around to protect me—even to scold me, even to beat me; at least, their touch was familiar, and I knew that they did not, after all, intend to kill me—and got on another train only because I saw a black man on it. But almost everyone else was white.

This setting gives the author the opportunity to make two important points which help develop the theme of racial prejudice. First, the moving subway car graphically illustrates the segregation of Blacks and whites in New York City. Along one stretch of the line, most of the passengers are Black. One stop later, almost all the Blacks have disappeared and the passengers are mostly white. It's as if the train crossed an invisible dividing line between the Black community and the white community.

The second point this setting helps make is the consequences of segregation. Because Blacks live in one part of the city and whites in another, they grow up afraid of each other. To Leo, white people are an alien species who might suddenly turn on him and even kill him.

The implication is hard to miss: racial prejudice springs from ignorance, and ignorance breeds fear, mistrust and hostility. A subway car provides an ideal setting to express this theme.

**4. Setting Creates Atmosphere.** A good story draws the reader into its own special world by creating a certain atmosphere, or feeling, that it passes along to the reader. A story about war, for example, may convey feelings of shock and horror, and a story of the old West might have an atmosphere of adventure and excitement. The setting is an important contribution to the atmosphere of many stories.

Where you are has a lot to do with the way you feel. You're more likely to feel peaceful strolling by the ocean than you are walking on a busy city street. Story settings affect readers in the same way. A war story set in a town that has been devastated by bombs is going to contribute to the reader's feelings of shock and horror. And the open range of the old West, with its associations of freedom, self-reliance and the unknown, is a natural setting for an adventure story.

Every setting carries certain associations which an author counts on to help establish the atmosphere. The feelings that you get from reading "Tell Me How Long the Train's Been Gone" are due in large part to its settings, like the condemned house in the paragraph below. What feelings do you associate with this setting?

So I stepped out on my stoop again and stood there for a long time, wondering what to do. Then I thought of a condemned house, around the corner from us. We played there sometimes, though it was very dangerous and we were not supposed to. What possessed me to go there now, I don't know, except that I could not think of another dry place in the whole world. I started running east, down our block. I turned two corners and came to the house, with its black window sockets. The house was completely dark. I had forgotten how afraid I was of the dark, but the rain was drenching me. I ran down the cellar steps and clambered into the house through one of the broken windows. I squatted there in a still, dry dread, not daring to look into the house but staring outward. I was holding my breath. I heard an endless scurrying in the darkness, a perpetual busyness, and I thought of rats, of their teeth and ferocity and fearful size, and I began to cry again.

This is the kind of setting that sends a shudder through the reader. The drenching rain that drives Leo to seek shelter in the condemned house casts a dreary pall over the scene. The house itself, with its black window sockets, its broken windows, and the rats scurrying in the darkness calls to mind a decaying corpse. The atmosphere of this setting is gloomy and vaguely sinister; its effect on both Leo and the reader is bleak and depressing.

In "Tell Me How Long the Train's Been Gone," setting does more than just provide a location for the action; it actually unifies the whole story. As you read, notice how the setting dominates almost every scene. When you finish, you will probably conclude that, in this story, the setting is actually a participant in the action.

As you read the story:

- Look for contrasts the author draws between Barbados and Harlem. What theme does this contrast suggest?

- Look for the details that make the Proudhammer's tenement a believable setting.

- Be aware of the party setting as it appears to Leo.

- Look for the devices the author uses to communicate the party atmosphere to the reader.

# Tell Me How Long
# the Train's Been Gone
## James Baldwin

My brother, Caleb, was seventeen when I was ten. We were very good friends. In fact, he was my best friend and, for a very long time, my only friend.

I do not mean to say that he was always nice to me. I got on his nerves a lot, and he resented having to take me around with him and be responsible for me when there were so many other things he wanted to be doing. Therefore, his hand was often up against the side of my head, and my tears caused him to be punished many times. But I knew, somehow, anyway, that when he was being punished for my tears, he was not being punished for anything he had done to me; he was being punished because that was the way we lived; and his punishment, oddly, helped unite us. More oddly still, even as his great hand caused my head to stammer and dropped a flame-colored curtain before my eyes, I understood that he was not striking *me*. His hand leaped out because he could not help it, and I received the blow because I was there. And it happened, sometimes, before I could even catch my breath to howl, that the hand that had struck me grabbed me and held me, and it was difficult indeed to know which of us was weeping. He was striking, striking out, striking out; the hand asked me to forgive him. I felt his bewilderment through the membrane of my own. I also felt that he was trying to teach me something. And I had, God knows, no other teachers.

For our father—how shall I describe our father?—was a ruined Barbados peasant, exiled in a Harlem which he loathed, where he never saw the sun or sky he remembered, where life took place neither indoors nor without, and where there was no joy. By which I mean no joy that he remembered. Had he been able to bring with him any of the joy he had felt on that far-off island, then the air of the sea and the impulse to dancing would sometimes have transfigured our dreadful rooms. Our lives might have been very different.

But no, he brought with him from Barbados only black rum and blacker pride and magic incantations, which neither healed nor saved.

He did not understand the people among whom he found himself; they had no coherence, no stature and no pride. He came from a race which had been flourishing at the very dawn of the world—a race greater and nobler than Rome or Judea, mightier than Egypt—he came from a race of kings, kings who had never been taken in battle, kings who had never been slaves. He spoke to us of tribes and empires, battles, victories and monarchs of whom we had never heard—they were not mentioned in our textbooks—and invested us with glories in which we felt more awkward than in the secondhand shoes we wore. In the stifling room of his pretensions and expectations, we stumbled wretchedly about, stubbing our toes, as it were, on rubies, scraping our shins on golden caskets, bringing down, with a childish cry, the splendid purple tapestry on which, in pounding gold and scarlet, our destinies and our inheritance were figured. It could scarcely have been otherwise, since a child's major attention has to be concentrated on how to fit into a world which, with every passing hour, reveals itself as merciless.

If our father was of royal blood and we were royal children, our father was certainly the only person in the world who knew it. The landlord did not know it; our father never mentioned royal blood to *him*. When we were late with our rent, which was often, the landlord threatened, in terms no commoner had ever used before a king, to put us in the streets. He complained that our shiftlessness, which he did not hesitate to consider an attribute of the race, had forced him, an old man with a weak heart, to climb all these stairs to plead with us to give him the money we owed him. And this was the last time; he wanted to make sure we understood that this was the last time.

Our father was younger than the landlord, leaner, stronger and bigger. With one blow, he could have brought the landlord to his knees. And we knew how much he hated the man. For days on end, in the wintertime, we huddled around the gas stove in the kitchen, because the landlord gave us no heat. When windows were broken, the landlord took his time about fixing them; the wind made the cardboard we stuffed in the windows rattle all night long; and when snow came, the weight of the snow forced the cardboard inward and onto the floor. Whenever the apartment received a fresh coat of paint, we bought the paint and did the painting ourselves; we killed the rats. A great chunk of the kitchen ceiling fell one winter, narrowly missing our mother.

We all hated the landlord with a perfectly exquisite hatred, and we would have been happy to see our proud father kill him. We would have been glad to help. But our father did nothing of the sort. He stood before the landlord, looking unutterably weary. He made excuses. He apologized. He swore that it would never happen again. (We knew that it *would* happen again.) He begged for time. The landlord would finally go down the stairs, letting us and all the neighbors know how good-hearted he was, and our father would walk into the kitchen and pour himself a glass of rum.

But we knew that our father would never have allowed any black man to speak to him as the landlord did, as policemen did, as storekeepers and welfare workers and pawnbrokers did. No, not for a moment. He would have thrown him out of the house. He would certainly have made a black man know that he was not the descendant of slaves! He had made them know it so often that he had almost no friends among them, and if we had followed his impossible lead, we would have had no friends, either. It was scarcely worthwhile being the descendant of kings if the kings were black and no one had ever heard of them.

And it was because of our father, perhaps, that Caleb and I clung to each other, in spite of the great difference in our ages; or, in another way, it may have been precisely the difference in our ages that made the clinging possible. I don't know. It is really not the kind of thing anyone can ever know. I think it may be easier to love the really helpless younger brother, because he cannot enter into competition with one on one's own ground, or on any ground at all, and can never question one's role or jeopardize one's authority. In my own case, certainly, it did not occur to me to compete with Caleb, and I could not have questioned his role or his authority, because I needed both. He was my touchstone, my model and my only guide.

Anyway, our father, dreaming bitterly of Barbados, despised and mocked by his neighbors and all but ignored by his sons, held down his unspeakable factory job, spread his black gospel in bars on the weekends, and drank his rum. I do not know if he loved our mother. I think he did.

They had had five children—only Caleb and I, the first and the last, were left. We were both dark, like our father; but two of the three dead girls had been fair, like our mother.

She came from New Orleans. Her hair was not like ours. It was black, but softer and finer. The color of her skin reminded me of the color of bananas. Her skin was as bright as that, and contained that kind of promise, and she had tiny freckles around her nose and a small black mole just above her upper lip. It was the mole, I don't know why, which made her beautiful. Without it, her face might have been merely sweet, merely pretty. But the mole was funny. It had the effect of making one realize that our mother liked funny things, liked to laugh. The mole made one look at her eyes—large, extraordinary dark eyes, eyes which seemed always to be amused by something, eyes which looked straight out, seeming to see everything, seeming to be afraid of nothing. She was a soft, round, plump woman. She liked nice clothes and dangling jewelry, which she mostly didn't have, and she liked to cook for large numbers of people, and she loved our father.

She knew him—knew him through and through. I am not being coy or colloquial but bluntly and sadly matter-of-fact when I say that I will now never know what she saw in him. What she saw was certainly not for many eyes; what she saw got him through his working week and his Sunday rest; what she saw saved him. She saw that he was a man. For her, perhaps, he was a great man. I think, though, that, for our mother, any man was great who aspired to become a man: this meant that our father was very rare and precious. I used to wonder how she took it, how she bore it—his rages, his tears, his cowardice.

On Saturday nights, he was almost always evil, drunk and maudlin. He came home from work in the early afternoon and gave our mother some money. It was never enough, of course, but he always kept enough to go out and get drunk. She never protested, at least not as far as I know. Then she would go out shopping. I would usually go with her, for Caleb would almost always be out somewhere, and our mother didn't like the idea of leaving me alone in the house. And this was probably, after all, the best possible arrangement. People who disliked our father were sure (for that very reason) to like our mother; and people who felt that Caleb was growing to be too much like his father could feel that I, after all, might turn out like my mother. Besides, it is not, as a general rule, easy to hate a small child. One runs the risk of looking ridiculous, especially if the child is with his mother.

And especially if that mother is Mrs. Proudhammer. Mrs. Proudhammer knew very well what people thought of Mr. Proudhammer. She knew, too, exactly how much she owed in each store she entered, how much she was going to be able to pay, and what she had to buy. She entered with a smile, ready.

"Evening. Let me have some of them red beans there."

"Evening. You know, you folks been running up quite a little bill here."

"I'm going to give you something on it right now. I need some cornmeal and flour and some rice."

"You know, I got my bills to meet, too, Mrs. Proudhammer."

"Didn't I just tell you I was going to pay? I want some cornflakes too, and some milk." Such merchandise as she could reach, she had already placed on the counter.

"When do you think you're going to be able to pay this bill? All of it, I mean."

"You know I'm going to pay it just as soon as I can. How much does it all come to? Give me that end you got there of that chocolate cake." The chocolate cake was for Caleb and me. "Well, now you put this against the bill." Imperiously, as though it were the most natural thing in the world, she put two or three dollars on the counter.

"You lucky I'm softhearted, Mrs. Proudhammer."

"Things sure don't cost this much downtown—you think I don't know it? Here." And she paid him for what she had bought. "Thank you. You been mighty kind."

And we left the store. I often felt that in order to help her, I should have filled my pockets with merchandise while she was talking. But I never did, not only because the store was often crowded or because I was afraid of being caught by the storekeeper, but because I was afraid of humiliating her. When I began to steal, not very much later, I stole in stores that were not in our neighborhood, where we were not known.

When we had to do "heavy" shopping, we went marketing under the bridge at Park Avenue—Caleb, our mother and I; and sometimes, but rarely, our father came with us. The most usual reason for heavy shopping was that some relatives of our mother's, or old friends of both our mother's and our father's, were coming to visit. We were certainly not going to let them go away hungry—not even if it meant, as it often did, spending more than we had. In spite of what I have been suggesting about our father's temperament, and no matter how difficult he may sometimes have been with us, he was much too proud to offend any guest of his; on the contrary, his impulse was to make them feel that his home was theirs; and besides, he was lonely, lonely for his past, lonely for those faces which had borne witness to that past. Therefore, he would sometimes pretend that our mother did not know how to shop, and our father would come with us, under the bridge, in order to teach her.

There he would be, then, uncharacteristically, in shirt-sleeves, which made him look rather boyish; and as our mother showed no desire to take shopping lessons from him, he turned his attention to Caleb and me. He would pick up a fish, opening the gills and holding it close to his nose. "You see that? That fish looks fresh, don't it? Well, that fish ain't as fresh as I am, and I *been* out of the water. They done doctored that fish. Come on." And we would walk away, a little embarrassed but, on the whole, rather pleased that our father was so smart.

Meantime, our mother was getting the marketing done. She was very happy on days like this, because our father was happy. He was happy, odd as his expression of it may sound, to be out with his wife and his two sons. If we had been on the island that had been witness to his birth, instead of the unspeakable island of Manhattan, he felt that it would not have been so hard for us all to trust and love each other. He sensed, and I think he was right, that on that other, never to be recovered island, his sons would have looked on him very differently, and he would have looked very differently on his sons. Life would have been hard there, too; we would have fought there, too, and more or less blindly suffered and more or less blindly died. But we would not have been (or so it was to seem to all of us forever) so wickedly menaced by the mere fact of our relationship, would not have been so frightened of entering into the central, most beautiful and valuable facts of our lives. We would have been laughing and cursing and tussling in the water, instead of stammering under the bridge; we would have known less about vanished African kingdoms and more about each other. Or, not at all impossibly, more about both.

If it was summer, we bought a watermelon, which either Caleb or our father carried home, fighting with each other for this privilege. They looked very like each other on those days—both big, both black, both laughing.

Caleb always looked absolutely helpless when he laughed. He laughed with all his body, perhaps touching his shoulder against yours, or putting his head on your chest for a moment, and then careening off you, halfway across the room or down the block. I will always hear his laughter. He was always happy on such days, too. If our father needed his son, Caleb certainly needed his father. Such days, however, were rare—one of the reasons, probably, that I remember them now.

Eventually, we all climbed the stairs into that hovel which, at such moments, was our castle. One very nearly felt the drawbridge rising behind us as our father locked the door.

The bathtub could not yet be filled with cold water and the melon placed in the tub, because this was Saturday, and, come evening, we all had to bathe. The melon was covered with a blanket and placed on the fire escape. Then we unloaded what we had bought, rather impressed by our opulence, though our father was always, by this time, appalled by the money we had spent. I was always sadly aware that there would be nothing left of all this once tomorrow had come and gone and that most of it, after all, was not for us, but for others.

Our mother was calculating the pennies she would need all week—carfare for our father and for Caleb, who went to a high school out of our neighborhood; money for the life insurance; money for milk for me at school; money for light and gas; money put away, if possible, toward the rent. She knew just about what our father had left in *his* pockets and was counting on him to give me the money I would shortly be demanding to go to the movies. Caleb had a part-time job after school and already had his movie money. Anyway, unless he was in a very good mood or needed me for something, he would not be anxious to go to the movies with me.

Our mother never insisted that Caleb tell her where he was going, nor did she question him as to how he spent the money he made. She was afraid of hearing him lie, and she did not want to risk forcing him to lie. She was operating on the assumption that he was sensible and had been raised to be honorable and that he, now more than ever, needed his privacy.

But she was very firm with him, nevertheless. "I do not want to see you rolling in here at three in the morning, Caleb. I want you here in time to eat, and you know you got to take your bath."

"Yes, indeed, ma'am. Why can't I take my bath in the morning?"

"Don't you start being funny. You know you ain't going to get up in time to take no bath in the morning."

"Don't nobody want you messing around in that bathroom all morning long, man," said our father. "You just git back in the house like your ma's telling you."

"Besides," I said, "you never wash out the tub."

Caleb looked at me in mock surprise and from a great height, allowing his chin and his lids simultaneously to drop and swiveling his head away from me.

"I see," he said, "that everyone in this family is ganging up on me. All right, Leo. I was planning to take you to the show with me, but now I've changed my mind."

"I'm sorry," I said quickly. "I take it back."

"You take *what* back?"

"What I said—about you not washing out the tub."

"Ain't no need to take it back," our father said stubbornly. "It's true. A man don't take back nothing that's true."

"So *you* say," Caleb said, with a hint of a sneer. But before anyone could possibly react to this, he picked me up, scowling into my face, which he held just above his own. "You take it back?"

"Leo ain't going to take it back," our father said.

Now I was in trouble. Caleb watched me, a small grin on his face. "You take it back?"

"Stop teasing that child, and put him down," our mother said. "The trouble ain't that Caleb don't wash out the tub—he just don't wash it out very clean."

"I never knew him to wash it out," our father said, "unless I was standing behind him."

"Well, ain't neither one of you much good around the house," our mother said.

Caleb laughed and set me down. "You didn't take it back," he said.

I said nothing.

"I guess I'm just going to have to go on without you."

Still, I said nothing.

"You going to have that child to crying in a minute," our mother said. "If you going to take him go on and take him. Don't do him like that."

Caleb laughed again. "I'm going to take him. The way he got them eyes all ready to water, I'd better take him somewhere." We walked toward the door. "But you got to make up *your* mind," he said to me, "to say what *you* think is right."

I grabbed Caleb's hand, the signal for the descent of the drawbridge. Our mother watched us cheerfully as we walked out; our father watched us balefully. Yet there was a certain humor in his face, too, and a kind of pride.

"Dig you later," Caleb said, and the door closed behind us.

The hall was dark, smelling of cooking, of stale wine, of rotting garbage. We dropped down the stairs, Caleb going two at a time, pausing at each landing, briefly, to glance back up at me. I dropped down behind him as fast as I could. When I reached the street level, Caleb was already on the stoop, joking with some of his friends, who were standing in the doorway—who seemed always to be in the doorway.

I didn't like Caleb's friends, because I was afraid of them. I knew the only reason they didn't try to make life hell for me, the way they made life hell for a lot of the other kids, was because they were afraid of Caleb. I went through the door, passing between my brother and his friends, down to the sidewalk, feeling, as they looked briefly at me and then continued joking with Caleb, what they felt—that here was Caleb's round-eyed, frail and useless sissy of a little brother. They pitied Caleb for having to take me out. On the other hand, they also wanted to go to the show, but didn't have the money. Therefore, in silence, I could crow over them even as they despised me. But this was always a terribly risky, touch-and-go business, for Caleb might, at any moment, change his mind and drive me away.

I always stood, those Saturday afternoons, in fear and trembling, holding on to the small shield of my bravado, while waiting for Caleb to come down the steps of the stoop, away from his friends, to me. I braced myself, always, for the moment when he would turn to me, saying, "Okay, kid. You run along. I'll see you later."

This meant that I would have to go to the movies by myself and hang around in front of the box office, waiting for some grown-up to take me in. I could not go back upstairs, for this would be informing my mother and father that Caleb had gone off somewhere after promising to take me to the movies.

Neither could I simply hang around, playing with the kids on the block. For one thing, my demeanor, as I came out of the house, very clearly indicated that I had better things to do than play with *them;* for another, they were not terribly anxious to play with *me;* and, finally, my remaining on the block would have had exactly the same effect as my going upstairs.

To remain on the block after Caleb's dismissal was to put myself at the mercy of the block and to put Caleb at the mercy of our parents.

So I prepared myself, those Saturdays, to respond with a cool "Okay. See you later," and then to turn indifferently away, and walk. This was surely the most terrible moment. The moment I turned away, I was committed, I was trapped, and I then had miles to walk, so it seemed to me, before I would be out of sight, before the block ended and I could turn onto the avenue. I wanted to run out of that block, but I never did. I never looked back. I forced myself to walk very slowly, looking neither right nor left, striving to seem at once distracted and offhand; concentrating on the cracks in the sidewalk and stumbling over them; trying to whistle, feeling every muscle in my body, feeling that all the block was watching me, and feeling, which was odd, that I deserved it.

And then I reached the avenue, and turned, still not looking back, and was released from those eyes at least; but now I faced other eyes, eyes coming toward me. These eyes were the eyes of children stronger than me, who would steal my movie money; these eyes were the eyes of white cops, whom I feared, whom I hated with a literally murderous hatred; these eyes were the eyes of old folks, who might wonder what I was doing on this avenue by myself.

And then I got to the show. Sometimes someone would take me in right away, and sometimes I would have to stand there and wait, watching the faces coming to the box office. And this was not easy, since I didn't, after all, want everyone in the neighborhood to know I was loitering outside the movie house waiting for someone to take me in. If it came to our father's attention, he would kill both Caleb and me.

Eventually, I would see a face which looked susceptible. I would rush up to him—it was usually a man, for men were less likely to be disapproving—and whisper, "Take me in," and give him my dime. Sometimes the man simply took the dime and disappeared inside; sometimes he gave my dime back to me and took me in anyway. Sometimes I ended up wandering around the streets—but I couldn't wander into a strange neighborhood, because I would be beaten up if I did—until I figured the show was out. It was dangerous to get home too early, and, of course, it was practically lethal to arrive too late. If all went well, I could cover for Caleb, saying that I had left him with some boys on the stoop. Then, if *he* came in too late, it could not be considered my fault.

But if wandering around this way was not without its dangers, neither was it without its discoveries and delights. I discovered subways. I discovered, that is, that I could ride on subways by myself and, furthermore, that I could usually ride for nothing. Sometimes, when I ducked under the turnstile, I was caught, and sometimes great black ladies seized on me as a pretext for long, very loud, ineffably moral lectures about wayward children breaking their parents' hearts. Sometimes, doing everything in my power not to attract their attention, I endeavored to look as though I were in the charge of a respectable-looking man or woman, entering the subway in their shadow and sitting very still beside them. It was best to try to sit *between* two such people, for each would automatically assume that I was with the other. There I would sit, then, in a precarious anonymity, watching the people, listening to the roar, watching the lights of stations flash by. It seemed to me that nothing was faster than a subway train, and I loved the speed, because the speed was dangerous.

For a time, during these expeditions, I simply sat and watched the people. Lots of people would be dressed up, for this was Saturday night. The women's hair would be all curled and straightened, and the lipstick on their full lips looked purple and make-believe against the dark skins of their faces. They wore very fancy capes or coats, in wonderful colors, and long dresses, and sometimes they had jewels in their hair, and sometimes they wore flowers on their dresses. They were almost as beautiful as movie stars. And so the men with them seemed to think.

The hair of the men was slick and wavy, brushed up into pompadours; or they wore very sharp hats, brim flicked down dangerously over one eye, with perhaps one flower in the lapel of their many-colored suits. They laughed and talked with their girls, but quietly, for there were white people in the car. The white people would scarcely ever be dressed up and did not speak to each other at all—only read their papers and stared at the advertisements. But they fascinated me more than the colored people did, because I knew nothing at all about them and could not imagine what they were like.

Underground, I received my first apprehension of New York neighborhoods and, underground, first felt what may be called a civic terror. I very soon realized that after the train had passed a certain point, going uptown or downtown, all the colored people disappeared. The first time I realized this, I panicked and got lost. I rushed off the train, terrified of what these white people might do to me, with no colored person around to protect me—even to scold me, even to beat me; at least, their touch was familiar, and I knew that they did not, after all, intend to kill me—and got on another train only because I saw a black man on it. But almost everyone else was white.

The train did not stop at any of the stops I remembered. I became more and more frightened, frightened of getting off the train and frightened of staying on it, frightened of saying anything to the man and frightened that he would get off the train before I could say anything to him. He was my salvation, and he stood there in the unapproachable and frightening form that salvation so often takes. At each stop, I watched him with despair.

To make matters worse, I suddenly realized that I had to pee. Once I realized it, this need became a torment; the horror of wetting my pants in front of all these people made the torment greater. Finally, I tugged at the man's sleeve. He looked down at me with a gruff, amused concern; then, reacting, no doubt to the desperation in my face, he bent closer.

I asked him if there was a bathroom on the train.

He laughed. "No," he said, "but there's a bathroom in the station." He looked at me again. "Where're you going?"

I told him that I was going home.

"And where's home?"

I told him.

This time he did not laugh. "Do you know where you are?" he said.

I shook my head. At that moment, the train came into a station, and after several hours, it rolled to a stop. The doors opened, and the man led me to the bathroom. I ran in, and hurried, because I was afraid he would disappear. But I was glad he had not come in with me.

When I came out, he stood waiting for me. "Now," he said, "you in Brooklyn. You ever hear of Brooklyn? What you doing out here by yourself?"

"I got lost," I said.

"I *know* you got lost. What I want to know is how *come* you got lost? Where's your mama? Where's your daddy?"

I almost said that I didn't have any, because I liked his face and his voice and was half hoping to hear him say that *he* didn't have any little boy and would just as soon take a chance on me. But I told him that my mama and daddy were at home.

"And do they know where *you* are?"

I said, "No." There was a pause.

"Well, I know they going to make your tail hot when they see you." He took my hand. "Come on."

And he led me along the platform and then down some steps and along a narrow passage and then up some steps onto the opposite platform. I was very impressed by this maneuver; in order to accomplish the same purpose, I had always left the subway station and gone up into the street. Now that the emergency was over, I was in no great hurry to leave my savior. I asked him if he had a little boy.

"Yes," he said, "and if *you* was my little boy, I'd paddle your behind so you couldn't sit down for a week."

I asked him how old was his little boy, what was his name and if his little boy was at home.

"He *better* be at home!" He looked at me and laughed. "His name is Jonathan. He ain't but five years old." His gaze refocused, sharpened. "How old are you?"

I told him that I was ten, going on eleven.

"You a pretty bad little fellow," he said then.

I tried to look repentant, but I would not have dreamed of denying it.

"Now, look here," he said, "this here's the uptown side. Can you read, or don't you never go to school?" I assured him that I could read. "Now, to get where you going, you got to change trains." He told me where. "Here, I'll write it down for you." He found some paper in his pockets but no pencil. We heard the train coming. He looked about him in helpless annoyance, looked at his watch, looked at me. "It's all right. I'll tell the conductor."

But the conductor, standing between two cars, had rather a mean pink face.

My savior looked at him dubiously. "He *might* be all right. But we better not take no chances." He pushed me ahead of him into the train. "You know you right lucky that I got a little boy? If I didn't, I swear I'd just let you go on and *be* lost. You don't know the kind of trouble you going to get me in at home. My wife ain't *never* going to believe *this* story."

I told him to give me his name and address and I would write a letter to his wife and to his little boy, too.

This caused him to laugh harder than ever. "You only say that because you know I ain't got no pencil. You are one *hell* of a shrewd little boy."

I told him that then maybe we should get off the train and that I would go back home with him.

This made him grave. "What does your father do?"

This question made me uneasy. I stared at him for a long time before I answered. "He works in a—" I could not pronounce the word—"he has a job."

He nodded. "I see. Is he home now?"

I really did not know, and I said I did not know.

"And what does your mother do?"

"She stays home."

Again he nodded. "You got any brothers or sisters?"

I told him no.

"I see. What's your name?"

"Leo."

"Leo what?"

"Leo Proudhammer."

He saw something in my face. "What do you want to be when you grow up, Leo?"

"I want to be—" and I had never said this before—"I want to be a—a movie actor. I want to be a—actor."

"You pretty skinny for that," he said.

"That's all right," I told him. "Caleb's going to teach me to swim. That's how you get big."

"Who's Caleb?"

I opened my mouth, I started to speak. I checked myself as the train roared into a station. He glanced out the window, but did not move. "He swims," I said.

"Oh," he said after a very long pause, during which the doors slammed and the train began to move. "Is he a good swimmer?"

I said that Caleb was the best swimmer in the world.

"Okay," my savior said, "okay," and put his hand on my head again and smiled at me.

I asked him what his name was.

"Charles," he said, "Charles Williams. But you better call me *Uncle* Charles, you little devil, because you have certainly ruined my Saturday night." The train came into a station. "Here's where we change," he said.

We got out of the train and crossed the platform and waited.

"Now," he said, "this train stops exactly where you going. Tell me where you going."

I stared at him.

"I want you," he said, "to tell me exactly where you *going*. I can't be fooling with you all night."

I told him.

"You sure that's right?"

I told him I was sure.

"I got a very good memory," he said. "Give me your address. Just say it, I'll remember it."

So I said it, staring into his face as the train came roaring in.

"If you don't go straight home," he said, "I'm going to come see your daddy, and when we find you, you'll be mighty sorry." He pushed me into the train and put one shoulder against the door. "Go on, now," he said, loud enough for all the car to hear. "Your mama'll meet you at the station where I told you to get off." He repeated my subway stop, pushed the angry door with his shoulder, and then said gently, "Sit down, Leo." He remained in the door until I sat down. "So long, Leo," he said then, and stepped backward out. The doors closed. He grinned at me and waved, and the train began to move.

I waved back. Then he was gone, the station was gone, and I was on my way back home.

I never saw that man again, but I made up stories about him, I dreamed about him, I even wrote a letter to him and his wife and his little boy, but I never mailed it.

I never told Caleb anything about my solitary expeditions. I don't know why. I think that he might have liked to know about them. I suppose, finally, at bottom, I said nothing because my expeditions belonged to me.

Another time, it was raining, and it was still too early for me to go home. I felt very, very low that day. It was one of the times that my tongue and my body refused to obey me, and I had not been able to work up the courage to ask anyone to take me in to the show. The ticket taker was watching me, or so I thought, with a hostile suspicion. Actually, it's very unlikely he was thinking at all, and certainly not of me. But I walked away from the show, because I could no longer bear his eyes, or anybody's eyes.

I walked the long block east from the movie house. The street was empty, black and glittering. The water soaked through my coat at the shoulders, and water dripped down my neck from my cap. I began to be afraid. I could not stay out in the rain, because then my father and mother would know I had been wandering the streets. I would get a beating, and, though Caleb was too old to get a beating, he and my father would have a terrible fight, and Caleb would blame it all on me and would not speak to me for days.

I began to hate Caleb. I wondered where he was. I started in the direction of our house, only because I did not know what else to do. Perhaps Caleb would be waiting for me on the stoop.

The avenue, too, was very long and silent. Somehow, it seemed old, like a picture in a book. It stretched straight before me, endless, and the streetlights did not so much illuminate it as prove how dark it was. The rain was falling harder. Cars sloshed by, sending up sheets of water. From the bars, I heard music, faintly, and many voices. Straight ahead of me a woman walked, very fast, head down, carrying a shopping bag. I reached my corner and crossed the wide avenue. There was no one on my stoop.

Now I was not even certain what time it was; but I knew it wasn't time yet for the show to be over. I walked into my hallway and wrung out my cap. I was sorry that I had not made someone take me in to the show, because now I did not know what to do. I *could* go upstairs and say that we had not liked the movie and had left early and that Caleb was with some boys on the stoop. But this would sound strange, and Caleb, who would not know what story I had told, would, therefore, be greatly handicapped when he came home.

I could not stay because my father might not be in my hallway, at home and might come in. I could not go into the hallway of another building, because if any of the kids who lived in the building found me, they would have the right to beat me up. I could not go back out into the rain. I stood next to the big, cold radiator, and I began to cry. But crying wasn't going to do me any good, either, especially as there was no one to hear me.

So I stepped out on my stoop again and stood there for a long time, wondering what to do. Then I thought of a condemned house, around the corner from us. We played there sometimes, though it was very dangerous and we were not supposed to. What possessed me to go there now, I don't know, except that I could not think of another dry place in the whole world. I started running east, down our block. I turned two corners and came to the house, with its black window sockets. The house was completely dark. I had forgotten how afraid I was of the dark, but the rain was drenching me. I ran down the cellar steps and clambered into the house through one of the broken windows. I squatted there in a still, dry dread, not daring to look into the house but staring outward. I was holding my breath. I heard an endless scurrying in the darkness, a perpetual busyness, and I thought of rats, of their teeth and ferocity and fearful size, and I began to cry again.

I don't know how long I squatted there this way or what was in my mind. I listened to the rain and the rats. Then I was aware of another sound—I had been hearing it for a while without realizing it. This was a moaning sound, a sighing sound, a sound of strangling, which mingled with the sound of the rain and with a muttering, cursing human voice. The sounds came from the door that led to the backyard.

I wanted to stand, but I crouched lower; wanted to run, but could not move. Sometimes the sounds seemed to come closer, and I knew that this meant my death; sometimes they diminished or ceased altogether, and then I knew that my assailant was looking for me. I looked toward the backyard door, and I seemed to see, silhouetted against the driving rain, a figure, half bent, moaning, leaning against the wall, in indescribable torment; then there seemed to be two figures, sighing and grappling, moving so quickly that it was impossible to tell which was which, two creatures, each in a dreadful, absolute, silent single-mindedness attempting to strangle the other!

I watched, crouching low. A very powerful and curious excitement mingled itself with my terror and made the terror greater. I could not move. I did not dare move. The figures were quieter now. It seemed to me that one of them was a woman, and she seemed to be crying, pleading for her life. But her sobbing was answered only by a growling sound. The muttered, joyous curses began again; the murderous ferocity began again, more bitterly than ever. The sobbing began to rise in pitch, like a song.

Then, everything was still, all movement ceased. Then I heard only the rain and the scurrying of the rats. It was over; one of them, or both of them, lay stretched out, dead or dying in this filthy place. It happened in Harlem every Saturday night. I could not catch my breath to scream. Then I heard a laugh, a low, happy, wicked laugh, and the figure turned in my direction and seemed to start toward me.

Then I screamed and stood up straight, bumping my head on the window frame and losing my cap, and scrambled up the cellar steps. I ran head down, like a bull, away from that house and out of that block. I ran up the steps of my stoop and bumped into Caleb.

"Where the hell have you been? Hey! What's the matter with you?"

I had jumped up on him, almost knocking him down, trembling and sobbing.

"You're *soaked.* Leo, what's the matter? Where's your cap."

But I could not say anything. I held him around the neck with all my might, and I could not stop shaking.

"Come on, Leo," Caleb said, in a different tone, "tell me what's the matter." He pried my arms loose and held me away from him, so that he could look into my face. "Oh, little Leo. Little Leo. What's the matter, baby?" He looked as though he were about to cry himself, and this made me cry harder than ever. He took out his handkerchief and wiped my face and made me blow my nose. My sobs began to lessen, but I could not stop trembling. He thought that I was trembling from cold, and he rubbed his hands roughly up and down my back and rubbed my hands between his. "What's the matter?"

I did not know how to tell him.

"Somebody try to beat you up?"

I shook my head. "No."

"What movie did you see?"

"I didn't go. I couldn't find nobody to take me in."

"And you just been wandering around in the rain all night?"

"Yes."

He sat down on the hallway steps. "Oh, Leo." Then, "You mad at me?"

I said, "No. I was scared."

He nodded. "I reckon you were, man." He wiped my face again. "You ready to go upstairs? It's getting late."

"Okay."

"How'd you lose your cap?"

"I went in a hallway to wring it out—and—I put it on the radiator, and I heard some people coming—and—I ran away, and I forgot it."

"We'll say you forgot it in the movies."

"Okay."

We started up the stairs.

"Leo," he said, "I'm sorry about tonight. I'm really sorry. I won't let it happen again. You believe me?"

"Sure. I believe you." I smiled up at him.

He squatted down. "Give us a kiss."

I kissed him.

"Okay. Climb up. I'll give you a ride. Hold on, now."

He carried me piggyback up the stairs.

Thereafter, we evolved a system, which did not, in fact, work too badly.

When things went wrong and he could not be found, I was to leave a message for him at a certain store on the avenue. This store had a bad reputation—more than candy and hot dogs and soda pop were sold there; Caleb himself had told me this and told me not to hang out there. But he said he would see to it that they treated me all right.

I went in the store one Saturday night, and one of the boys who was always there, a boy about Caleb's age, looked up and smiled and said, "You looking for your brother? Come on, I'll take you to him."

This was not the agreed-on formula. I was to be *taken* to Caleb only in cases of real emergency, which wasn't the case this time. I was there because the show was over a little earlier than usual, and since it was only about a quarter past eleven, I figured I had about half an hour to wait for Caleb.

When the boy made his invitation, I assumed it was because of some prearrangement with the owner of the store, a very dour, silent black man, who looked at me from behind his counter and said nothing.

I said, "Okay," and the boy, whose name was Arthur, said, "Come on, Sonny. I'm going to take you to a party." He took my hand and led me across the avenue and into a long, dark block.

We walked the length of the block in silence, crossed another avenue and went into a big house in the middle of the block. We were in a big vestibule, with four locked apartment doors staring away from each other. It was not really clean, but it was fairly clean. We climbed three flights of stairs. Arthur knocked on the door, a very funny knock, not loud. After a moment, I heard a scraping sound, then the sound of a chain rattling and a bolt being pulled back. The door opened.

A lady, very black and rather fat, wearing a blue dress, held the door for us. She said, "Come on in. Now, what you doing here with this child?"

"Had to do it. It's all right. It's Caleb's brother."

We started down a long, dark hall, with closed rooms on either side of it, toward the living room. One of the rooms was the kitchen. A smell of barbecue made me realize that I was hungry. The living room was really two living rooms. The far one looked out on the street. There were six or seven people in the room, women and men. They looked exactly like the men and women who frightened me when I saw them standing on the corners, laughing and joking in front of the bars. But they did not seem frightening here. A record player was going, not very loud. They had drinks in their hands, and there were half-empty plates of food around the room. Caleb was sitting on the sofa, with his arm around a girl in a yellow dress.

"Here's your little brother," said the fat black lady in blue.

Arthur said to Caleb, "It was just better for him not to have to wait there tonight."

Caleb smiled at me. I was tremendously relieved that he was not angry. I was delighted by this party, even though it made me shy. "Come on over here," Caleb said. I went to the sofa. "This is my kid brother. His name is Leo. Leo, this is Dolores. Say hello to Dolores."

Dolores smiled at me—I thought she was very pretty—and said, "I'm very happy to meet you, Leo. How've you been?"

"Just fine," I said.

"Don't you want to know how *she's* been?" Caleb grinned.

"No," said the fat black lady, and laughed. "I'm sure he don't want to know that. I bet he's hungry. You been stuffing yourself all night, Caleb. Let me give him a little bit of my barbecue and a glass of ginger ale." She already was beginning to propel me out of the room.

I looked at Caleb. Caleb said, "Just remember we ain't got all night. Leo, this is Miss Mildred. She cooked everything, and she's a might good friend of mine. What do you say to Miss Mildred, Leo?"

"Dig Caleb being the big brother," Arthur muttered, and laughed.

"Thank you, Miss Mildred," I said.

"Come on in the kitchen," she said, "and let me try to put some flesh on them bones." She walked me into the kitchen. "Now, you sit right over there," she said. "Won't take me but a minute to warm this up." She sat me at the kitchen table and gave me a napkin and poured the ginger ale. "What grade you in at school, Leo?" I told her. "You must be a right smart boy, then," she said, with a pleased smile. "Do you like school, Leo?"

I told her what I liked best was Spanish and history and English composition.

This caused her to look more pleased than ever. "What do you want to be when you grow up?"

Somehow, I could not tell her what I had told the man, my friend, on the train. I said I wasn't sure, that maybe I would be a schoolteacher.

"That's just what I wanted to be," she said proudly, "and I studied right hard for it, too, and I believe I would have made it, but then I had to go and get myself mixed up with some no-count nigger. I didn't have no sense. I didn't have no better sense but to marry him. Can you beat that?" And she laughed and set my plate in front of me. "Go on, now, eat. Foolish me. Now, your brother," she said suddenly, "he's a right fine boy. He wants to make something of himself. He's got ambition. That's what I like— *ambition*. Don't you let him be foolish. Like me. You like my barbecue?"

"Yes, ma'am," I said. 'It's good."

"Let me give you some more ginger ale," she said, and poured it.

I was beginning to be full. But I didn't want to go, although I knew that, now, it was really beginning to be late. While Miss Mildred talked and moved about the kitchen, I listened to the voices coming from the other room, the voices and the music. They were playing a kind of purple, lazy dance music, a music that was already in my bones, along with the wilder music from which the purple music sprang. The voices were not like the music, though they corroborated it. I listened to a girl's voice, gravelly and low, indignant and full of laughter. The room was full of laughter. It exploded, at intervals, and rolled through the living room and hammered at the walls of the kitchen.

Every once in a while, I heard Caleb, booming like a trumpet, drowning out the music. I wondered how often Caleb came here and how he had met these people, who were so different, at least as it seemed to me, from any of the people who ever came to our house.

Then Caleb's hand was on my neck. Dolores stood in the doorway, smiling. "You stuffed yourself enough, little brother?" Caleb said. "Because we got to get out of here now."

We walked slowly down the hall, Miss Mildred, Dolores and Caleb and me. We reached the door, which had a metal pole built into it in such a way as to prevent its being opened from the outside, and a heavy piece of chain around the top of the three locks.

Miss Mildred began, patiently, to open the door. "Leo," she said, "don't you be no stranger. You make your brother bring you back to see me, you hear?" She got the pole out of the way and then undid the chain. To Caleb, she said, "Bring him by some afternoon. I ain't got nothing to do. I'll be glad to look after him." The last lock yielded, and Miss Mildred opened the door. We were facing the bright hall lights: no, the building was not very clean. "Good night, Leo," Miss Mildred said, and then she said good night to Dolores and Caleb. She closed the door.

I heard the scraping sound again, and we walked down the stairs.

"She's nice," I said.

Caleb said, yawning, "Yeah, she's a very nice lady." Then he said, "Now, I don't want you telling nobody at home about this, you hear?" I swore I wouldn't tell. "It's our secret," Caleb said.

It was colder in the streets than it had been before.

Caleb took Dolores' arm. "Let's get you to your subway," he said.

We started walking up the wide, dark avenue. We reached the brightly lit kiosk, which came up out of the sidewalk like some unbelievably malevolent awning or the suction apparatus of a monstrous vacuum cleaner.

"Bye-bye," Caleb said, and kissed Dolores on the nose. "I got to run. See you Monday after school."

"Bye-bye," Dolores said. She bent down and kissed me quickly on the cheek. "Bye-bye, Leo. Be good." She hurried down the steps.

Caleb and I began walking very fast, down the avenue, toward our block. The subway station was near the movie house, and the movie house was dark. We knew we were late; we did not think we were *that* late.

"It was a *very* long show, wasn't it?" Caleb said.

"Yes," I said.

"What did we see? Bettter tell me about *both* pictures. Just in case."

I told him as well as I could as we hurried down the avenue. Caleb had great powers of concentration and could figure out enough from what I said to know what to say if the necessity arose.

But our troubles, that night, came from a very different source than our parents. I had just reached the point in my breathless narration where the good girl is murdered by the Indians and the hero vows revenge. We were hurrying down the long block that led east to our house when we heard a car braking and were blinded by bright lights and were pushed up against a wall.

"Turn around," a voice said. "And keep your hands in the air."

It may seem funny, but I felt as though Caleb and I had conjured up a movie—that if I had not been describing a movie to him, we would not have suddenly found ourselves in the middle of one. Or was it the end? I had never been so frightened in my life.

We did as we were told. I felt the grainy brick beneath my fingers. A hand patted me all over my body, every touch humiliating. Beside me, I heard Caleb catch his breath.

"Turn around," the voice said.

The great lights of the police car had gone out; I could see the car at the curb, the doors open. I did not dare look at Caleb, for I felt that this would, somehow, be used against us. I stared at the two policemen, young, white, tight-lipped and self-important.

They turned a flashlight first on Caleb, then on me. "Where you boys going?"

"Home," Caleb said. I could hear his breathing. "We live in the next block." And he gave the address.

"Where've you been?"

Now I heard the effort Caleb was making not to surrender either to rage or panic. "We just took my girl to the subway station. We were at the movies." And then, forced out of him, weary, dry and bitter, "This here's my brother. I got to get him home. He ain't but ten years old."

"What movie did you see?"

And Caleb told them. I marveled at his memory. But I also knew that the show had let out about an hour or so before. I feared that the policemen might also know this. But they didn't.

"You got any identification?"

"My brother doesn't. I do."

"Let's see it."

Caleb took out his wallet and handed it over.

They looked at his wallet, looked at us, handed it back. "Get on home," one of them said. They got into their car and drove off.

"Thanks," Caleb said. "Thanks, all you scum-bag Christians." His accent was now as irredeemably of the islands as was the accent of our father. I had never heard this sound in his voice before. And then, suddenly, he looked down at me and laughed and hugged me. "Come on, let's get home. Little Leo. Were you scared?"

"Yes," I said. "Were you?"

"Damn right, I was scared. But—damn!—they must have seen that you weren't but ten years old."

"You didn't *act* scared," I said.

We were in our own block, approaching our stoop. "Well. We certainly have a good excuse for being late," he said. He grinned. Then he said, "Leo, I'll tell you something. I'm glad this happened. It had to happen one day, and I'm glad it happened while I was with you—of course, I'm glad you were with *me*, too, because if it hadn't been for you, they'd have pulled me."

"What for?"

"Because I'm black," Caleb said. "That's what for."

I said nothing. I said nothing, because what he said was true, and I knew it. It seemed, now, that I had always known it, though I had never been able to say it. But I did not understand it. I was filled with an awful wonder; it hurt my chest and paralyzed my tongue. *Because you're black.* I tried to think, but I couldn't. I only saw the policemen, those murderous eyes again, those hands. Were they people?

"Caleb," I asked, "are white people people?"

"What are you talking about, Leo?"

"I mean, are white people—*people*? People like us?"

He looked down at me. His face was very strange and sad. It was a face I had never seen before. We were in the house now, and we climbed a few more stairs, very slowly. Then, "All I can tell you, Leo, is—well, *they* don't think they are."

I thought of the landlord. Then I thought of my schoolteacher, a lady named Mrs. Nelson. I liked her very much. I thought she was very pretty. She had long yellow hair, like someone I had seen in the movies, and a nice laugh, and we all liked her, all the kids I knew. The kids who were not in her class wished they were. I liked to write compositions for her, because she seemed really interested. But she was white. Would she hate me all my life because I was black? It didn't seem possible. She didn't hate me now; I was pretty sure of that. And yet, what Caleb had said was true.

"Caleb," I asked, "are all white people the same?"

"I never met a good one."

I asked, "Not even when you were little? In school?"

Caleb said, "Maybe. I don't remember." He smiled at me. "I never met a good one, Leo. But that's not saying that *you* won't. Don't look so frightened."

We were in front of our door. Caleb raised his hand to knock.

I held his hand. "Caleb," I whispered, "what about Mama?"

"What do you mean, what about Mama?"

"Well, Mama." I stared at him; he watched me very gravely. "Mama—Mama's almost white."

"But that don't make her white. You got to be *all* white to be white." He laughed. "Poor Leo. Don't feel bad. I know you don't understand it now. I'll try to explain it to you, little by little." He paused. "But our mama is a colored woman. You can tell she's a colored woman because she's married to a colored *man*, and she's got two colored *children*. Now, you know ain't no white lady going to do a thing like that." He watched me, smiling. "You understand that?" I nodded. "Well, you going to keep me here all night with your questions, or can we go on in now?"

He knocked, and our mother opened the door. "About time," she said drily. She had her hair piled in a knot on the top of her head. I liked her that way. "You must have sat through that movie four or five times. You're going to ruin your eyes, and that'll just be too bad for you, because you know we ain't got no money to be buying you no glasses. Leo, you go on inside and get ready to take your bath."

"Let him come over here a minute," our father said. He was sitting in the one easy chair, near the window. He was drunk, but not as drunk as I had seen him, and this was a good-mood drunk. In this mood, he talked about the islands, his mother and father and kinfolk and friends, the feast days, the singing, the dancing and the sea.

I approached him, and he pulled me to him, smiling, and held me between his thighs. "How's my big man?" he asked, smiling and rubbing his hand, gently, over my hair. "Did you have a good time tonight?"

Caleb sat on a straight chair near him, leaning forward. "Let Leo tell you why we so late. Tell them what happened, Leo."

"We were coming down the block," I began—and I watched my father's face. Suddenly, I did not want to tell him. Something in Caleb's tone had alerted him, and he watched me with a stern and frightened apprehension. My mother came and stood beside him, one hand on his shoulder. I looked at Caleb. "Maybe you could tell it better," I said.

"Go on, start. I'll fill in."

"We were coming down the block," I said, "coming from the movies." I looked at Caleb.

"It's not the way we usually come," Caleb said.

My father and I stared at each other. There was, suddenly, between us, an overwhelming sorrow. It had come from nowhere. "We got stopped by the cops," I said. Then I could not continue. I looked helplessly at Caleb, and Caleb told the story.

As Caleb spoke, I watched my father's face. I don't know how to describe what I saw. I felt his arm tighten, tighten; his lips became bitter, and his eyes grew dull. It was as though—after indescribable, nearly mortal effort, after grim years of fasting and prayer, after the loss of all he had, and after having been promised by the Almighty that he had paid the price and no more would be demanded of his soul, which was harbored now—it was as though in the midst of his joyful feasting and dancing, crowned and robed, a messenger arrived to tell him that a great error had been made, and that it was all to be done again. Before his eyes, then, the banquet and the banquet wines and the banquet guests departed, the robe and crown were lifted, and he was alone, frozen out of his dream, with all that before him which he had thought was behind him.

My father looked as stunned and still and as close to madness as that, and his encircling arm began to hurt me, but I did not complain. I put my hand on his face, and he turned to me; he smiled—he was very beautiful then!—and he put his great hand on top of mine. He turned to Caleb. "That's all that happened? You didn't say nothing?"

"What could I say? It might have been different if I'd been by myself. But I had Leo with me, and I was afraid of what they might do to Leo."

"No, you did right, man. I got no fault to find. You didn't take their badge number?"

Caleb snickered. "What for? You know a friendly judge? We got money for a lawyer? Somebody they going to *listen* to? They get us in that precinct house and make us confess to all kinds of things and sometimes even kill us, and don't nobody give a damn. Don't nobody care what happens to a black man. If they didn't need us for work, they'd have killed us all off a long time ago. They did it to the Indians."

"That's the truth," our mother said. "I wish I could say different, but it's the truth." She stroked our father's shoulder. "We just thank the Lord is wasn't no worse. We just got to say: Well, the boys got home safe tonight."

I asked, "Daddy, how come they do us like they do?"

My father looked at us for a long time. Finally, he said, "Leo, if I could tell you that, maybe I'd be able to make them stop. But don't let them make you afraid. You hear?"

I said, "Yes, sir." But I knew that I was already afraid.

"Let's not talk about it no more," our mother said. "If you two is hungry, I got some pork chops back there."

Caleb grinned at me. "Little Leo might be hungry. He stuffs himself like a pig. But I ain't hungry. Hey, old man—" he nudged my father's shoulder; nothing would be refused us tonight—"why don't we have a taste of your rum? All right?"

Our mother laughed. "I'll go get it," she said. She started out of the room.

"Reckon we can give Leo a little bit, too?" our father asked. He pulled me onto his lap.

"In a big glass of water," our mother said, laughing. She took one last look at us before she went into the kitchen. "My," she said, "I sure am surrounded by some pretty men! My, my, my!"

# Unit 2

## Tell Me How Long the Train's Been Gone

- Comprehension Questions

- Setting

- Discussion Guides

- Writing Exercise

# COMPREHENSION QUESTIONS

For each of the following statements and questions, select the option containing the most complete or most accurate answer.

1. Mr. Proudhammer tells his sons that they are descended from a race of
(g) kings, "kings who had never been taken in battle, kings who had never been slaves." He tells them this because he
   - ☐ a. doesn't understand his own roots.
   - ☐ b. wants them to feel important.
   - ☐ c. wants them to feel insignificant.
   - ☐ d. is a chronic liar.

2. The landlord treats Mr. Proudhammer like
(b) ☐ a. a king.     ☐ c. a peasant.
   ☐ b. a stranger.     ☐ d. an equal.

3. Leo says that his mother is beautiful and thinks her beauty is due to
(a) ☐ a. the mole above her upper lip.
   ☐ b. her black soft hair.
   ☐ c. her light skin color.
   ☐ d. her clothes and jewelry.

4. The reader may infer that the reason Mr. Proudhammer goes out and
(h) gets drunk is that he
   ☐ a. doesn't love his wife and son.
   ☐ b. is a born loser.
   ☐ c. feels bitter and frustrated.
   ☐ d. learned to love rum in Barbados.

5. The boys' relationship with their father was, for the most part,
(c) ☐ a. warm and close.
   ☐ b. changing and unsure.
   ☐ c. suspicious and fearful.
   ☐ d. disrespectful and hateful.

6. The family always splurged on groceries whenever
(a) ☐ a. Mr. Proudhammer received his paycheck.
   ☐ b. Caleb brought home his paycheck.
   ☐ c. company was coming.
   ☐ d. one of the family was sick.

7. After shopping, Leo says, "we all climbed the stairs into that hovel
(k) which, at such moments, was our castle. One very nearly felt the drawbridge rising behind us as our father locked the door." By comparing
their apartment with a castle, at this moment, Leo apparently feels like
  □ a. a bandit returning with his loot.
  □ b. royalty returning home with a trophy.
  □ c. a winner in the olympics .
  □ d. a victorious general.

8. Which of the following choices best defines *opulence* as used in, "Then
(l) we unloaded what we had bought, rather impressed by our *opulence*
though our father was always, by this time, appalled by the money we
had spent." ?
  □ a. Good luck          □ c. Wealth
  □ b. Generosity         □ d. Purchases

9. For the Proudhammers and other Black families living in Harlem, the
(e) world is
  □ a. difficult but rewarding.
  □ b. happy and carefree.
  □ c. easy and slow.
  □ d. hard and unfair.

10. Leo's relationship with his older brother might best be described as
(c) □ a. competitive.          □ c. affectionate .
    □ b. distant .             □ d. suspicious.

11. Mrs. Proudhammer comes across to the reader as
(j) □ a. strong and loving.
    □ b. unhappy and disappointed.
    □ c. vain and self-centered.
    □ d. helpless and insecure.

12. Mr Proudhammer associates the island of Barbados, where he was born,
(d) with
    □ a. humiliation.          □ c. Black pride.
    □ b. despair.              □ d. racism.

13. Which of the following choices best defines *demeanor* as used in, "For
(l) one thing, my *demeanor*, as I came out of the house, very clearly indicated that I had better things to do than play with *them* . . . " ?
    □ a. Behavior              □ c. Manner of dress
    □ b. Conversation          □ d. Secret ambition

14. Leo's actions on the subway and elsewhere show him to be a rather
(j) complicated little boy. Which of these groups of characteristics best
describe him?
- ☐ a. Uncertain, shy and resourceful
- ☐ b. Proud, angry and daring
- ☐ c. Foolish, quarrelsome and pushy
- ☐ d. Confused, demanding and thoughtless

15. Leo's fascination with white people leads the reader to conclude that
(f) ☐ a. he has very little contact with whites.
- ☐ b. he has many white friends at school.
- ☐ c. he prefers white people to Black people.
- ☐ d. he wishes that he were white.

16. Leo tells the Black man who befriends him on the subway train that,
(a) when he grows up, he wants to be
- ☐ a. a school teacher.
- ☐ b. a preacher.
- ☐ c. a writer.
- ☐ d. an actor.

17. Considering the drugstore that sells more than candy and soda pop, and
(f) the party Leo is not supposed to mention to their parents, it would seem
that Caleb's friends are
- ☐ a. too good for the family.
- ☐ b. hardened criminals.
- ☐ c. of a lower class than Caleb.
- ☐ d. somewhat shady.

18. Escorting Dolores home from the party, Leo notes: "We reached the
(k) brightly lit kiosk [subway entrance], which came up out of the sidewalk *like some unbelievably malevolent* [willing evil] *awning* or *the
suction apparatus of a monstrous vacuum cleaner.*" The underlined
phrases are *similes*, comparisons using the words "like" or "as." These
similes make the subway entrance seem
- ☐ a. foreign.          ☐ c. sinister.
- ☐ b. familiar          ☐ d. romantic.

19. On their way home Saturday night, Caleb and Leo are stopped by the
(g) police because
- ☐ a. they seem to be running away from something.
- ☐ b. one of the policemen recognizes Caleb.
- ☐ c. Caleb is drunk.
- ☐ d. they are Black.

20. The policemen treat Caleb and Leo as if they were
(f)  ☐ a. friends.            ☐ c. respectable citizens.
     ☐ b. criminals.          ☐ d. children.

21. When the boys tell they were stopped by the police, their mother says,
(h)  ". . . thank the Lord it wasn't no worse . . . . the boys got home safe to-
     night." What she is thinking, but doesn't say in so many words, is that
     ☐ a. they are probably not telling the truth.
     ☐ b. another night they may not get home safe.
     ☐ c. the boys actually deserve to be arrested.
     ☐ d. there is a reason for this she doesn't know about.

22. Caleb and Leo's encounter with the police that Saturday night teaches
(e)  Leo that
     ☐ a. Black people in Harlem are at the mercy of whites.
     ☐ b. if you tell the truth and obey the law, nothing will happen to you.
     ☐ c. it doesn't pay to be peaceful and law abiding.
     ☐ d. you must stand up for your rights under all circumstances.

23. Which of the following statements spoken by characters in the story
(e)  best expresses a main idea of this story?
     ☐ a. "Mama—Mama's almost white." (Leo)
     ☐ b. "You know I'm going to pay it just as soon as I can." (Mrs.
          Proudhammer)
     ☐ c. "Thank you. You been mighty kind." (Mrs. Proudhammer to the
          storekeeper)
     ☐ d. ". . . don't let them make you afraid. You hear?" Mr. Proud-
          hammer)

24. Leo's memories of growing up in Harlem might best be described as
(i)  ☐ a. nostalgic.           ☐ c. bittersweet
     ☐ b. fond.                ☐ d. cynical.

25. The author's attitude throughout this story suggests that he feels
(i)  ☐ a. tolerant of American society.
     ☐ b. proud of American society.
     ☐ c. indifferent toward American society.
     ☐ d. outraged by American society

---

Comprehension Skills: a — isolating details; b — recalling specific facts; c — retaining
concepts; d — organizing facts; e — understanding the main idea; f — drawing a
conclusion; g — making a judgment; h — making an inference; i — recognizing tone;
j — understanding characters; k — appreciation of literary forms; l — understanding
vocabulary.

# SETTING

## Practice Exercise A

For our father—how shall I describe our father?—was a ruined Barbados peasant, exiled in a Harlem which he loathed, where he never saw the sun or sky he remembered, where life took place neither indoors nor without, and where there was no joy. By which I mean no joy that he remembered. Had he been able to bring with him any of the joy he felt on that far-off island, then the air of the sea and the impulse to dancing would sometimes have transfigured our dreadful rooms. Our lives might have been different.

1. In comparing the island of Barbados with Harlem, the author uses setting to suggest that an important theme of the story is
   - ☐ a. the effect of Harlem on the people who live there.
   - ☐ b. Mr. Proudhammer's declining fortunes.
   - ☐ c. the family's return to Barbados.
   - ☐ d. Mr. Proudhammer's transformation.

2. One word that appears three times in this passage suggests the essential quality that distinguishes the island of Barbados from Harlem in Mr. Proudhammer's mind. Circle the word each time it appears.

## Practice Exercise B

The hall was dark, smelling of cooking, of stale wine, of rotting garbage. We dropped down the stairs, Caleb going two at a time, pausing at each landing, briefly, to glance back up at me. I dropped down behind him as fast as I could. When I reached the street level, Caleb was already on the stoop, joking with some of his friends, who were standing in the doorway—who seemed always to be in the doorway.

1. This setting suggests that Leo's neighborhood has an atmosphere of
   - ☐ a. abandonment.      ☐ c. decay.
   - ☐ b. pride.           ☐ d. hominess.

2. One way an author makes a setting believable is by using many specific details. On the lines provided write the sentence that contains four vivid details about the building Leo lives in.

_____

_____

## Practice Exercise C

The living room was really two living rooms. The far one looked out on the street. There were six or seven people in the room, women and men. They looked exactly like the men and women who frightened me when I saw them standing on the corners, laughing and joking in front of the bars. But they did not seem frightening here. A record player was going, not very loud. They had drinks in their hands, and there were half-empty plates of food around the room. Caleb was sitting on the sofa, with his arm around a girl with a yellow dress.

1. Which element of the party setting makes the greatest impression on Leo?
   - ☐ a. The layout of the apartment
   - ☐ b. The food and drink
   - ☐ c. The music
   - ☐ d. The people

2. Different people view the same setting in different ways. Two sentences remind the reader that we are seeing this setting through the eyes of a small boy. Underline these two sentences.

## Practice Exercise D

I was beginning to be full. But I didn't want to go, although I knew that, now, it was really beginning to be late. While Miss Mildred talked and moved about the kitchen, I listened to the voices coming from the other room, the voices and the music. They were playing a kind of purple, lazy dance music. a music that was already in my bones, along with the wilder music from which the purple music sprang. The voices were not like the music, though they corroborated it. I listened to a girl's voice, gravelly and low, indignant and full of laughter. The room was full of laughter. It exploded, at intervals, and rolled through the living room and hammered at the walls of the kitchen.

1. The atmosphere created by this setting is most like that of
   - ☐ a. your mother's kitchen.
   - ☐ b. a nightclub or bar.
   - ☐ c. a school dance.
   - ☐ d. a neighorhood.

2. In this scene, sounds are used to help create the atmosphere. Circle the phrase near the beginning of the passage that names two of the sounds Leo heard.

## Analyzing Setting

1. At the end of the lesson, we said that the setting of "Tell Me How Long the Train's Been Gone" is actually a participant in the action. Considered in this light, how is setting the antagonist, or opponent, of the main character of this story?

2. Suppose that Baldwin chose a wealthy suburb as the setting for this story. In what ways would this story be different?

3. Baldwin describes the island of Barbados not so much by the way it looks, as by the feeling it evokes in Mr. Proudhammer. Why do you think Baldwin used this technique to depict the setting, instead of simply telling what the island looks like?

## Interpreting the Story

4. Leo says their father "spoke to us of tribes and empires, battles, victories and monarchs of whom we had never heard [because] they were not mentioned in our textbooks." Why didn't Leo's textbooks mention these things? Should they have? What difference would it make to Leo to read about Black history in school?

5. When the Black man on the subway asked Leo what he wanted to be when he grew up, Leo said that he wanted to be an actor. Yet when Miss Mildred asked him the same question, Leo said that he wanted to be a schoolteacher. Why does he give different answers to different people? Which do you think Leo really wants to be?

6. Does Caleb try to poison Leo's mind against white people? Give examples from the story to support your answer.

7. Why doesn't Mr. Proudhammer take his family back to Barbados? Explain your reasons for your answer.

## Analyzing the Author's Technique

8. This story has *one narrator*—Leo—but *two points of view*—Leo as a small boy and Leo as an adult looking back. What insights does Leo the adult provide in this story that Leo the child could not?

9. Do you think Baldwin meant this story to have a message? In other words, did he write the story simply to entertain readers, or to teach them something as well? What might Baldwin want readers to learn from this story? What emotions does he arouse in readers to help them learn?

10. A *metaphor* is an implied comparison between two different things. Baldwin uses elaborate and very beautiful metaphors comparing Mr. Proudhammer with royalty. Why does Baldwin choose to compare Mr. Proudhammer with kings? Wouldn't a more humble metaphor be more appropriate?

## WRITING EXERCISE

Mr. Proudhammer longs for the island of Barbados, where Black men were kings. Sometimes when he's drunk, he talks about the islands, "his mother and father and kinfolk and friends, the feast days, the singing, the dancing and the sea."

Based on Mr. Proudhammer's memories, write a paragraph describing the setting of Barbados—what it looks like, the climate, the people, and their lifestyle. Choose descriptive words and comparisons that help convey the special atmosphere that Mr. Proudhammer associates with the island.

# Introduction

This unit presents two short stories—"My Oedipus Complex" by Frank O'Connor, and "The Jilting of Granny Weatherall" by Katherine Anne Porter—to demonstrate two different uses of point of view.

Oedipus is a character from ancient Greek drama and mythology who unwittingly killed his father and married his mother. It's bad enough to go down in history with a reputation like that, but the good name of Oedipus was to suffer a further blow early in the twentieth century. At that time Sigmund Freud, the pioneering psychiatrist, used the name of Oedipus to describe a theory about the development of children. Small children, Freud contended, go through a stage when they are attracted to the parent of the opposite sex and are hostile toward the other parent. Freud called these feelings the "Oedipus complex" after the unfortunate king in the Greek legend.

Many people are still shocked by the idea of young children having such feelings, but Frank O'Connor was amused by the notion. He responded with a charming little story which he playfully titled "My Oedipus Complex." It's about a five-year-old boy who decides that three's a crowd when Father returns home from the war and claims his share of Mother's attention. Just as Freud had said, the little boy wants to do away with Father and marry Mother. Only somehow Frank O'Connor makes the whole thing seem less outrageous, and more appealing, than Freud ever did.

Frank O'Connor (1903-1966) is best remembered for his witty and moving stories about Irish family life. "Story-telling," he once remarked, "...doesn't deal with problems; it doesn't have any solutions to offer; it just states the human condition." An ardent Irish nationalist, O'Connor joined the Irish Republican Army as a young man, and later served as a director of the famous Abbey Theater in Dublin.

The second story in this unit, "The Jilting of Granny Weatherall," probes the mind of an old lady on her deathbed. Granny Weatherall is nearly eighty years old. She has lived a full life, was married to a good man and raised four children. Yet on the last day of her life, Granny's thoughts keep reverting to the man who had jilted her on her wedding day sixty years before.

Katherine Anne Porter's deft portrayal of Granny's last hours takes the reader inside Granny's mind by presenting the flow of her thoughts as she slips in and out of touch with reality. Her mind wanders back in time, touching down here and there in the past, and occasionally surfaces to the present until a remark made by someone in the room triggers another chain of thoughts and projects her into yet another reverie. For this reason, the storyline is somewhat challenging. It may help you to keep in mind that John, who has been dead for many years, was Granny's husband; George is the man who jilted her; and Cornelia, Jimmy, Lydia and Hapsy are Granny's children. Apparently Hapsy is dead, because Granny seems to anticipate meeting her as death approaches.

The action takes place over the course of a day and an evening. Cornelia keeps a tearful vigil at the bedside; there's a nurse in the room; Doctor Harry comes, goes and returns; Father Connolly comes, goes and returns; Jimmy and Lydia arrive. Granny realizes with a start that her time has come and she isn't ready for it. As her life force ebbs, it seems to concentrate itself into a point of light in the center of her brain; the light flickers and winks, flutters and dwindles as it is engulfed by the encroaching shadow of death. As she watches the darkness curl around the point of light and swallow it up, Granny's last thoughts are not of her loving husband, or her fine children or her full life, but of that terrible day sixty years ago when the bridegroom never came. Overcome by grief, Granny gives a great sigh and blows out the light.

Katherine Anne Porter was born in Indian Creek, Texas, in 1890—a great-great-great-granddaughter of Daniel Boone—and was educated at various convent schools in Texas and Louisiana. Writing about her early life she said: "I was precocious, nervous, rebellious, unteachable, and made life very uncomfortable for myself and I suppose for those around me. As soon as I learned to form letters on paper, at about three years, I began to write stories....For this vocation I was and am willing to live and die, and I consider very few other things of the slightest importance." Porter has been called the American equivalent of Katherine Mansfield ("The Garden Party") and her style is strictly objective without sacrificing sensitivity. "My one aim," she once said, "is to tell a straight story and to give true testimony."

# Point of View

One of the very first things an author has to decide when writing a story is *who* will tell it and *how* it will be told. The author is always in charge, of course; it is always the author speaking, managing things, telling us what is going on. But readers are not interested in authors; they are interested in characters in stories, so most of the time authors will attempt to be as unobtrusive as possible. They try to allow you to be "alone" with the characters so you can enjoy yourself without being bothered by an author's intrusions. They do this by adopting a *point of view*.

An author may become a character in the story, and tell you what is going on that way. Another time, the author may hover in the background and pretend to be seeing everything that is going on, hearing everything that everyone says and even knowing everything that the characters are thinking. These are *points of view*—how the author sees what is going on and is able to tell us about it without our being too aware of his or her presence.

There are many points of view, but essentially there are only the two types that we have just mentioned. One is the *first-person narration,* in which the narrator is a character in the story. The other is *third-person narration,* in which the narrator is not a character in the story, but hovers about like a voice from the beyond, knowing what everyone is saying, doing and thinking.

**1. First-Person Narration.** A first-person narration, or point of view, is easy to identify by the way the author uses first-person pronouns: *I, me, my, we, us, our.* "Yet, mad am *I* not—and very surely *I* do not dream," is the way one first-person begins. Another narrator says, "*Our* whole town went to her funeral." And another says, "*We* huddled around the gas stove in the kitchen."

You can spot the first-person narration in "My Oedipus Complex" because the first-person pronoun *I* is used. But as you think about the point of view, also consider the character who is behind the pronoun *I*.

Father was in the army all through the war—the first war, I mean—so, up to the age of five, I never saw much of him, and what I saw did not worry me. Sometimes I woke and there was a big figure in khaki peering down at me in the candlelight. Sometimes in the early morning I heard the slamming of the front door and the clatter of nailed boots down the cobbles of the lane. These were Father's entrances and exits. Like Santa Claus he came and went mysteriously.

The narrator talks about Father, who is in the army and who makes sudden appearances and disappearances."Up to the age of five,"we learn,"I never saw much of him." Father is "a big figure in khaki," and "like Santa Claus"—all of which leads the reader to infer that this is a man recalling his childhood, talking of a time when he was about five years old.

As the story progresses, the adult narrator seems to slip further and further into the background until it appears that we are hearing the story from the point of view of the little boy himself. It's an engaging story, and a large part of its charm is due to the childlike simplicity, or *naivete*, in the telling of it. In such a case we say that the first-person narrator is a *naive narrator*. The little boy faithfully relates what he sees, but obviously he does not fully understand what is going on. We do, of course, and therein lies the appeal of the story.

A naive narrator is often a child but may also be a simpleton, or a poor, uneducated person or a gullible person set adrift in a sophisticated world. Though telling us all that is going on, the narrator doesn't understand it quite as well as we do as readers.

The reason an author adopts a naive first-person point of view is that it fits the story being told. It enables readers to understand the story better and the points that are being made. In "My Oedipus Complex," the story is about the battle of wills that is being played out between a little boy and his father as each of them competes for the undivided attention of Mother. The situation is easier to understand when we see it as young Larry would. Here he senses that he is losing the battle with Father and he can't understand why.

But as time went on I saw more and more how he managed to alienate Mother and me. What made it worse was that I couldn't grasp his method or see what attraction he had for Mother. In every possible way he was less winning than I. He had a common accent and made noises at his tea. I thought for a while that it might be the newspapers she was interested in, so I made up bits of news of my own to read to her. Then I thought it might be the smoking, which I personally thought attractive, and took his pipes and went round the house dribbling into them till he caught me. I even made noises at my tea, but Mother only told me I was disgusting. It all seemed to hinge round that unhealthy habit of sleeping together, so I made a point of dropping into their bedroom and nosing around, talking to myself, so that they wouldn't know I was watching them, but they were never up to anything that I could see. In the end it beat me.

Notice that, at the beginning of the passage, an adult narrator uses such adult expressions as "managed to alienate" and "I couldn't grasp his method." A small child would not speak like this. But as the passage goes along, it seems more and more as if the narrator is still a little boy talking about how he dribbled into his father's pipes and spied on his parents in their bedroom.

It's all an illusion created by the author, but one that readers enter into willingly for the sake of enjoying the story. The use of *I* tends to convince the reader that this story actually happened. After all, we are more inclined to believe something we hear firsthand than something that is hearsay.

The first-person narrator may be a *protagonist*, or main character, in the story; in this case we experience the greatest sense of involvement because we tend to identify with heroes and heroines. It makes us feel we are living the story ourselves. Other times the first-person narrator is a minor character, as in *Moby Dick*, or a character who doesn't appear in the story at all—someone who describes the events and claims to have witnessed them. There are even stories in which the first-person narrator is a story-teller and begins to spin a yarn—a story within a story. There are endless variations of the first-person point of view, but all of them are easily identified by their use of first-person pronouns.

**2. Third-Person Narration.** A third-person narration, or point of view, is identified by the author's use of third-person pronouns—*he, she, his, her, they*—spoken by a narrator who is obviously outside the story.

You usually get the feeling that this narrator can see and hear everything that is going on, even if it is going on inside a character's mind. What is more, this all-knowing narrator can tell what is going on in several places at once and at all times—present or future. To be all-knowing is to be *omniscient*, and so such a narrator is called an *omniscient narrator*.

The opening paragraph in "The Jilting of Granny Weatherall" is a third-person omniscient narration:

> She flicked her wrist neatly out of Doctor Harry's pudgy careful fingers and pulled the sheet up to her chin. The brat ought to be in knee breeches. Doctoring around the country with spectacles on his nose! "Get along now, take your schoolbooks and go. There's nothing wrong with me."

The narrator describes what's going on between Granny and Doctor Harry, calling them by name and using *she* and *her*, third-person pronouns. The second and third sentences are what Granny is thinking, and only someone who is omniscient could tell us that. Then the narrator reports what Granny says out loud. It is important to notice the quotation marks: when Granny is thinking, there are no quotation marks; when she or someone else speaks, quotation marks are used.

Most of the story, however, is a different type of third-person narration. Instead of being omniscient, the narration is limited almost entirely to Granny. Events are reported through Granny's eyes, so things emerge only as Granny sees them. This is called a *limited point of view* because we get to see the action through the eyes and mind of only one character. In the following passage, notice how limited the point of view is, even though other characters besides Granny appear.

> She meant to wave good-by, but it was too much trouble.... The pillow rose and floated under her, pleasant as a hammock in a light wind...No, somebody was swishing newspapers: no, Cornelia and Doctor Harry were whispering together. She leaped broad awake, thinking they whispered in her ear.
>
> "She was never like this, *never* like this!" "Well what can we expect?" "Yes, eighty years old...."
>
> Well, and what if she was: She still had ears. It was like Cornelia to whisper around doors.... She was always being tactful and kind. Cornelia was dutiful; that was the trouble with her. Dutiful and good: "So good and dutiful," said Granny, "that I'd like to spank her." She saw herself spanking Cornelia and making a fine job of it....
>
> "What'd you say, Mother?"
>
> Granny felt her face tying up in hard knots.
>
> "Can't a body think, I'd like to know?"

This is a very difficult way for an author to write, but Katherine Anne Porter became an expert at it; and used the technique in other stories as well. Granny is very ill, drifting in and out of consciousness, hallucinating a bit, not sure when she is thinking and when she is speaking aloud. The author chose to convey this by using a limited point of view—Granny's. She might have chosen to report Granny's actions from the point of view of the doctor or of Cornelia. Or she could have jumped around among all three characters; this is the privilege of an author using an omniscient narrator. But Porter chose, in this story, to have her narrator stay with Granny throughout. Thus, a limited point of view. Notice that even the dialogue between Cornelia and the doctor is run together as Granny would hear it in her condition.

It is much easier for a writer to adopt a more general omniscient point of view, taking advantage of the freedom that jumping from one character to another affords. A majority of stories, in fact, are written this way—we see things first from the point of view of one character and then from that of another. But there is a drawback to this kind of general omniscience. The author has to intrude too much into the story. An omniscient point of view is a more artificial technique than a limited point of view because people in real life are not all-knowing. It's more difficult for a reader to keep perspective while jumping from inside one character to inside another. Because the story seems to lose some of its realism, the reader loses the sense of "being there."

Sometimes, in using a limited point of view, the author seems to stop the narration and leaves you entirely with the thoughts of a single character. When this happens, the limited point of view becomes an *interior monologue*, the thoughts occurring inside one person. See if you can tell where the narrator "disappears" from the story in this passage and the story becomes interior monologue.

She lay and drowsed, hoping in her sleep that the children would keep out and let her rest a minute. It had been a long day. Not that she was tired. It was always pleasant to snatch a minute now and then. There was always so much to be done, let me see: tomorrow.

Tomorrow was far away and there was nothing to trouble about. Things were finished somehow when the time came; thank God there was always a little margin over for peace; then a person could spread out the plan of life and tuck in the edges orderly. It was good to have everything clean and folded away....

In the first paragraph the author uses *she* and *her* freely, making readers very conscious of the narrator's presence. But then these third-person pronouns disappear and Granny thinks to herself, "let me see." From that point on, there is an illusion of being alone with Granny's thoughts.

The illusion would be even more complete if the second paragraph were written as if it were in the present, thus:

Tomorrow *is* far away and there is nothing to trouble about. Things *are* finished somehow when the time *comes*....

Authors write in the present to make us feel the thoughts are occurring *now*, even as we read them. Carried to an extreme, the author may have the thoughts ramble around in a jumpy and disorderly fashion—just the way people actually think. When this happens, the interior monologue becomes *stream of consciousness*. You witness the streaming-by of all a character's thoughts and impressions. This is not done very often, however, because it is as difficult to read as it is to write effectively. The most famous example of stream of consciousness writing occurs in James Joyce's novel *Ulysses*, where sentences run for pages without punctuation to simulate human thought.

Authors are not obliged to stay with one point of view throughout a story. They may, and frequently do, change the way a story is being told, especially in novels, where there is more room to shift about than there is in a short story. Point of view can be a tricky, slippery thing; an author needs expert writing skill to handle it well. It takes experience and judgment for an author to know what type of narrative and what voice can tell a story best.

As an exercise in recognizing first and third-person narrators, run through the stories in the book and try to put a point of view label on each. Decide which stories are told in the first person and which are told as a third-person narrative. Also try to identify the person (a character or an unknown narrator) who is doing the narration. A summary of the various points of view used is on page 126.

As you read the stories:

- Notice near the beginning of "My Oedipus Complex" how the point-of-view character seems to change from being a grown man to being a small child.

- Find evidence, toward the end of the story, that the little boy in "My Oedipus Complex" is a naive narrator.

- Watch how the narrator takes you inside Granny Weatherall's mind whenever she thinks of George, the man who jilted her.

- Notice how the narration, presented from within Granny's mind, shifts between past and present as she thinks about the day she was jilted.

# My
# Oedipus Complex
# Frank O'Connor

Father was in the Army all through the war—the first war, I mean—so, up to the age of five, I never saw much of him, and what I saw did not worry me. Sometimes I woke and there was a big figure in khaki peering down at me in the candlelight. Sometimes in the early morning I heard the slamming of the front door and the clatter of nailed boots down the cobbles of the lane. These were Father's entrances and exits. Like Santa Claus he came and went mysteriously.

In fact, I rather liked his visits, though it was an uncomfortable squeeze between Mother and him when I got into the big bed in the early morning. He smoked, which gave him a pleasant musty smell, and shaved, an operation of astounding interest. Each time he left a trail of souvenirs—model tanks and Gurkha knives with handles made of bullet cases, and German helmets and cap badges and button-sticks, and all sorts of military equipment—carefully stowed away in a long box on top of the wardrobe, in case they ever came in handy. There was a bit of the magpie about Father; he expected everything to come in handy. When his back was turned, Mother let me get a chair and rummage through his treasures. She didn't seem to think so highly of them as he did.

The war was the most peaceful period of my life. The window of my attic faced southeast. My mother had curtained it, but that had small effect. I always woke with the first light and, with all the responsibilities of the previous day melted, feeling myself rather like the sun, ready to illumine and rejoice. Life never seemed so simple and clear and full of possibilities as then. I put my feet out from under the clothes—I called them Mrs. Left and Mrs. Right—and invented dramatic situations for them in which they discussed the problems of the day. At least Mrs. Right did; she was very demonstrative, but I hadn't the same control of Mrs. Left, so she mostly contented herself with nodding agreement.

They discussed what Mother and I should do during the day, what Santa Claus should give a fellow for Christmas, and what steps should be taken to brighten the home. There was that little matter of the baby, for instance. Mother and I could never agree about that. Ours was the only house in the terrace without a new baby, and Mother said we couldn't afford one till Father came back from the war because they cost seventeen and six. That showed how simple she was. The Geneys up the road had a baby, and everyone knew they couldn't afford seventeen and six. It was probably a cheap baby, and Mother wanted something really good, but I felt she was too exclusive. The Geneys' baby would have done us fine.

Having settled my plans for the day, I got up, put a chair under the attic window, and lifted the frame high enough to stick out my head. The window overlooked the front gardens of the terrace behind ours, and beyond these it looked over a deep valley to the tall, red-brick houses terraced up the opposite hillside, which were all still in shadow, while those at our side of the valley were all lit up, though with long strange shadows that made them seem unfamiliar; rigid and painted.

After that I went into Mother's room and climbed into the big bed. She woke and I began to tell her of my schemes. By this time, though I never seem to have noticed it, I was petrified in my nightshirt, and I thawed as I talked until, the last frost melted, I fell asleep beside her and woke again only when I heard her below in the kitchen, making the breakfast.

After breakfast we went into town; heard Mass at St. Augustine's and said a prayer for Father, and did the shopping. If the afternoon was fine we either went for a walk in the country or a visit to Mother's great friend in the convent, Mother St. Dominic. Mother had them all praying for Father, and every night, going to bed, I asked God to send him back safe from the war to us. Little, indeed, did I know what I was praying for!

One morning, I got into the big bed, and there, sure enough, was Father in his usual Santa Claus manner, but later, instead of uniform, he put on his best blue suit, and Mother was as pleased as anything. I saw nothing to be pleased about, because, out of uniform, Father was altogether less interesting, but she only beamed, and explained that our prayers had been answered, and off we went to Mass to thank God for having brought Father safely home.

The irony of it! That very day when he came in to dinner he took off his boots and put on his slippers, donned the dirty old cap he wore about the house to save him from colds, crossed his legs, and began to talk gravely to Mother, who looked anxious. Naturally, I disliked her looking anxious, because it destroyed her good looks, so I interrupted him.

"Just a moment, Larry!" she said gently.

This was only what she said when we had boring visitors, so I attached no importance to it and went on talking.

"Do be quiet, Larry!" she said impatiently. "Don't you hear me talking to Daddy?"

This was the first time I had heard those ominous words, "talking to Daddy," and I couldn't help feeling that if this was how God answered prayers, he couldn't listen to them very attentively.

"Why are you talking to Daddy?" I asked with as great a show of indifference as I could muster.

"Because Daddy and I have business to discuss. Now, don't interrupt again!"

In the afternoon, at Mother's request, Father took me for a walk. This time we went into town instead of out in the country, and I thought at first, in my usual optimistic way, that it might be an improvement. It was nothing of the sort. Father and I had quite different notions of a walk in town. He had no proper interest in trams, ships, and horses, and the only thing that seemed to divert him was talking to fellows as old as himself. When I wanted to stop he simply went on, dragging me behind him by the hand; when he wanted to stop I had no alternative but to do the same. I noticed that it seemed to be a sign that he wanted to stop for a long time whenever he leaned against a wall. The second time I saw him do it I got wild. He seemed to be settling himself forever. I pulled him by the coat and trousers, but, unlike Mother who, if you were too persistent, got into a wax and said: "Larry, if you don't behave yourself, I'll give you a good slap," Father had an extraordinary capacity for amiable inattention. I sized him up and wondered would I cry, but he seemed to be too remote to be annoyed even by that. Really, it was like going for a walk with a mountain! He either ignored the wrenching and pummeling entirely, or else glanced down with a grin of amusement from his peak. I had never met anyone so absorbed in himself as he seemed.

At teatime, "talking to Daddy" began again, complicated this time by the fact that he had an evening paper, and every few minutes he put it down and told Mother something new out of it. I felt this was foul play. Man for man, I was prepared to compete with him any time for Mother's attention, but when he had it all made up for him by other people it left me no chance. Several times I tried to change the subject without success.

"You must be quiet while Daddy is reading, Larry," Mother said impatiently.

It was clear that she either genuinely liked talking to Father better than talking to me, or else that he had some terrible hold on her which made her afraid to admit the truth.

"Mummy," I said that night when she was tucking me up, "do you think if I prayed hard God would send Daddy back to war?"

She seemed to think about that for a moment.

"No, dear," she said with a smile. "I don't think He would."

"Why wouldn't he, Mummy?"

"Because there isn't a war any longer, dear."

"But, Mummy, couldn't God make another war, if He liked?"

"He wouldn't like to, dear. It's not God who makes wars, but bad people."

"Oh!" I said.

I was disappointed about that. I began to think that God wasn't quite what He was cracked up to be.

Next morning I woke at my usual hour, feeling like a bottle of champagne. I put out my feet and invented a long conversation in which Mrs. Right talked of the trouble she had with her own father till she put him in the Home. I didn't quite know what the Home was but it sounded the right place for Father. Then I got my chair and stuck my head out of the attic window.

Dawn was just breaking, with a guilty air that made me feel I had caught it in the act. My head bursting with stories and schemes, I stumbled in next door, and in the half-darkness scrambled into the big bed. There was no room at Mother's side so I had to get between her and Father. For the time being I had forgotten about him, and for several minutes I sat bolt upright, racking my brains to know what I could do with him. He was taking up more than his fair share of the bed, and I couldn't get comfortable, so I gave him several kicks that made him grunt and stretch. He made room all right, though. Mother waked and felt for me. I settled back comfortably in the warmth of the bed with my thumb in my mouth.

"Mummy!" I hummed, loudly and contentedly.

"Sssh! dear," she whispered. "Don't wake Daddy!"

This was a new development, which threatened to be even more serious than "talking to Daddy." Life without my early-morning conferences was unthinkable.

"Why?" I asked severely.

"Because poor Daddy is tired."

This seemed to me a quite inadequate reason, and I was sickened by the sentimentality of her "poor Daddy." I never liked that sort of gush; it always struck me as insincere.

"Oh!" I said lightly. Then in my most winning tone: "Do you know where I want to go with you today, Mummy?"

"No, dear," she sighed.

"I want to go down the Glen and fish for thornybacks with my new net, and then I want to go out to the Fox and Hounds, and—"

"Don't-wake-Daddy!" she hissed angrily, clapping her hand across my mouth.

But it was too late. He was awake, or nearly so. He grunted and reached for the matches. Then he stared incredulously at his watch.

"Like a cup of tea, dear?" asked Mother in a meek, hushed voice I had never heard her use before. It sounded almost as though she were afraid.

"Tea?" he exclaimed indignantly. "Do you know what the time is?"

"And after that I want to go up the Rathcooney Road," I said loudly, afraid I'd forget something in all those interruptions.

"Go to sleep at once, Larry!" she said sharply.

I began to snivel. I couldn't concentrate, the way that pair went on, and smothering my early-morning schemes was like burying a family from the cradle.

Father said nothing, but lit his pipe and sucked it, looking out into the shadows without minding Mother or me. I knew he was mad. Every time I made a remark Mother hushed me irritably. I was mortified. I felt it wasn't fair; there was even something sinister in it. Every time I had pointed out to her the waste of making two beds when we could both sleep in one, she had told me it was healthier like that, and now here was this man, this stranger, sleeping with her without the least regard for her health!

He got up early and made tea, but though he brought Mother a cup he brought none for me.

"Mummy," I shouted, "I want a cup of tea, too."

"Yes, dear," she said patiently. "You can drink from Mummy's saucer."

That settled it. Either Father or I would have to leave the house. I didn't want to drink from Mother's saucer; I wanted to be treated as an equal in my own home, so, just to spite her, I drank it all and left none for her. She took that quietly, too.

But that night when she was putting me to bed she said gently:

"Larry, I want you to promise me something."

"What is it?" I asked.

"Not to come in and disturb poor Daddy in the morning. Promise?"

"Poor Daddy" again! I was becoming suspicious of everything involving that quite impossible man.

"Why?" I asked.

"Because poor Daddy is worried and tired and he doesn't sleep well."

"Why doesn't he, Mummy?"

"Well, you know, don't you, that while he was at the war Mummy got the pennies from the Post Office?"

"From Miss MacCarthy?"

"That's right. But now, you see, Miss MacCarthy hasn't any more pennies, so Daddy must go out and find us some. You know what would happen if he couldn't?"

"No," I said, "tell us."

"Well, I think we might have to go out and beg for them like the poor old woman on Fridays. We wouldn't like that, would we?"

"No," I agreed. "We wouldn't."

"So you'll promise not to come in and wake him?"

"Promise."

Mind you, I meant that. I knew pennies were a serious matter, and I was all against having to go out and beg like the old woman on Fridays. Mother laid out all my toys in a complete ring round the bed so that, whatever way I got out, I was bound to fall over one of them.

When I woke I remembered my promise all right. I got up and sat on the floor and played—for hours, it seemed to me. Then I got my chair and looked out the attic window for more hours. I wished it was time for Father to wake; I wished someone would make me a cup of tea. I didn't feel in the least like the sun; instead, I was bored and so very, very cold! I simply longed for the warmth and depth of the big featherbed.

At last I could stand it no longer. I went into the next room. As there was still no room at Mother's side I climbed over her and she woke with a start.

"Larry," she whispered, gripping my arm very tightly, "what did you promise?"

"But I did, Mummy," I wailed, caught in the very act. "I was quiet for ever so long."

"Oh, dear, and you're perished!" she said sadly, feeling me all over. "Now, if I let you stay will you promise not to talk?"

"But I want to talk, Mummy," I wailed.

"That has nothing to do with it," she said with a firmness that was new to me. "Daddy wants to sleep. Now, do you understand that?"

I understood it only too well. I wanted to talk, he wanted to sleep—whose house was it, anyway?

"Mummy," I said with equal firmness, "I think it would be healthier for Daddy to sleep in his own bed."

That seemed to stagger her, because she said nothing for a while.

"Now, once and for all," she went on, "you're to be perfectly quiet or go back to your own bed. Which is it to be?"

The injustice of it got me down. I had convicted her out of her own mouth of inconsistency and unreasonableness, and she hadn't even attempted to reply. Full of spite, I gave Father a kick, which she didn't notice but which made him grunt and open his eyes in alarm.

"What time is it?" he asked in a panic-stricken voice, not looking at Mother but at the door, as if he saw someone there.

"It's early yet," she replied soothingly. "It's only the child. Go to sleep again.... Now, Larry," she added, getting out of bed, "you've wakened Daddy and you must go back."

This time, for all her quiet air, I knew she meant it, and knew that my principal rights and privileges were as good as lost unless I asserted them at once. As she lifted me, I gave a screech, enough to wake the dead, not to mind Father. He groaned.

"That damn child! Doesn't he ever sleep?"

"It's only a habit, dear," she said quietly, though I could see she was vexed.

"Well, it's time he got out of it," shouted Father, beginning to heave in the bed. He suddenly gathered all the bedclothes about him, turned to the wall, and then looked back over his shoulder with nothing showing only two small, spiteful, dark eyes. The man looked very wicked.

To open the bedroom door, Mother had to let me down, and I broke free and dashed for the farthest corner, screeching. Father sat bolt upright in bed.

"Shut up, you little puppy!" he said in a choking voice.

I was so astonished that I stopped screeching. Never, never had anyone spoken to me in that tone before. I looked at him incredulously and saw his face convulsed with rage. It was only then that I fully realized how God had codded me, listening to my prayers for the safe return of this monster.

"Shut up, you!" I bawled, beside myself.

"What's that you said?" shouted Father, making a wild leap out of the bed.

"Mick, Mick!" cried Mother. "Don't you see the child isn't used to you?"

"I see he's better fed than taught," snarled Father, waving his arms wildly. "He wants his bottom smacked."

All his previous shouting was as nothing to these obscene words referring to my person. They really made my blood boil.

"Smack your own!" I screamed hysterically. "Smack your own! Shut up! Shut up!"

At this he lost his patience and let fly at me. He did it with the lack of conviction you'd expect of a man under Mother's horrified eyes, and it ended up as a mere tap, but the sheer indignity of being struck at all by a stranger, a total stranger who had cajoled his way back from the war into our big bed as a result of my innocent intercession, made me completely dotty. I shrieked and shrieked, and danced in my bare feet, and Father, looking awkward and hairy in nothing but a short grey army shirt, glared down at me like a mountain out for murder. I think it must have been then that I realized he was jealous too. And there stood Mother in her nightdress, looking as if her heart was broken between us. I hoped she felt as she looked. It seemed to me that she deserved it all.

From that morning out my life was a hell. Father and I were enemies, open and avowed. We conducted a series of skirmishes against one another, he trying to steal my time with Mother and I his. When she was sitting on my bed, telling me a story, he took to looking for some pair of old boots which he alleged he had left behind him at the beginning of the war. While he talked to Mother I played loudly with my toys to show my total lack of concern. He created a terrible scene one evening when he came in from work and found me at his box, playing with his regimental badges, Gurkha knives and button-sticks. Mother got up and took the box from me.

"You mustn't play with Daddy's toys unless he lets you, Larry," she said severely. "Daddy doesn't play with yours."

For some reason Father looked at her as if she had struck him and then turned away with a scowl.

"Those are not toys," he growled, taking down the box again to see had I lifted anything. "Some of those curios are very rare and valuable."

But as time went on I saw more and more how he managed to alienate Mother and me. What made it worse was that I couldn't grasp his method or see what attraction he had for Mother. In every possible way he was less winning than I. He had a common accent and made noises at his tea. I thought for a while that it might be the newspapers she was interested in, so I made up bits of news of my own to read to her. Then I thought it might be the smoking, which I personally thought attractive, and took his pipes and went round the house dribbling into them till he caught me. I even made noises at my tea, but Mother only told me I was disgusting. It all seemed to hinge round that unhealthy habit of sleeping together, so I made a point of dropping into their bedroom and nosing round, talking to myself, so that they wouldn't know I was watching them, but they were never up to any-thing that I could see. In the end it beat me. It seemed to depend on being grown-up and giving people rings, and I realized I'd have to wait.

But at the same time I wanted him to see that I was only waiting, not giving up the fight. One evening when he was being particularly obnoxious, chattering away well above my head, I let him have it.

"Mummy," I said, "do you know what I'm going to do when I grow up?"

"No, dear," she replied. "What?"

"I'm going to marry you," I said quietly.

Father gave a great guffaw out of him, but he didn't take me in. I knew it must only be pretense. And Mother, in spite of everything, was pleased. I felt she was probably relieved to know that one day Father's hold on her would be broken.

"Won't that be nice?" she said with a smile.

"It'll be very nice," I said confidently. "Because we're going to have lots and lots of babies."

"That's right, dear," she said placidly. "I think we'll have one soon, and then you'll have plenty of company."

I was no end pleased about that because it showed that in spite of the way she gave in to Father she still considered my wishes. Besides, it would put the Geneys in their place.

It didn't turn out like that, though. To begin with, she was very preoccupied—I supposed about where she would get the seventeen and six—and though Father took to staying out late in the evenings it did me no particular good. She stopped taking me for walks, became as touchy as blazes, and smacked me for nothing at all. Sometimes I wished I'd never mentioned the confounded baby—I seemed to have a genius for bringing calamity on myself.

And calamity it was! Sonny arrived in the most appalling hullabaloo—even that much he couldn't do without a fuss—and from the first moment I disliked him. He was a difficult child—so far as I was concerned he was always difficult—and demanded far too much attention. Mother was simply silly about him, and couldn't see when he was only showing off. As company he was worse than useless. He slept all day, and I had to go round the house on tiptoe to avoid waking him. It wasn't any longer a question of not waking Father. The slogan now was "Don't-wake-Sonny!" I couldn't understand why the child wouldn't sleep at the proper time, so whenever Mother's back was turned I woke him. Sometimes to keep him awake I pinched him as well. Mother caught me at it one day and gave me a most unmerciful flaking.

One evening, when Father was coming in from work, I was playing trains in the front garden. I let on not to notice him; instead, I pretended to be talking to myself, and said in a loud voice: "If another bloody baby comes into this house, I'm going out."

Father stopped dead and looked at me over his shoulder,

"What's that you said?" he asked sternly.

"I was only talking to myself," I replied, trying to conceal my panic. "It's private."

He turned and went in without a word. Mind you, I intended it as a solemn warning, but its effect was quite different. Father started being quite nice to me. I could understand that, of course. Mother was quite sickening about Sonny. Even at mealtimes she'd get up and gawk at him in the cradle with an idiotic smile, and tell Father to do the same. He was always polite about it, but he looked so puzzled you could see he didn't know what she was talking about. He complained of the way Sonny cried at night, but she only got cross and said that Sonny never cried except when there was something up with him—which was a flaming lie, because Sonny never had anything up with him, and only cried for attention. It was really painful to see how simple-minded she was. Father wasn't attractive, but he had a fine intelligence. He saw through Sonny, and now he knew that I saw through him as well.

One night I woke with a start. There was someone beside me in the bed. For one wild moment I felt sure it must be Mother, having come to her senses and left Father for good, but then I heard Sonny in convulsions in the next room, and Mother saying: "There! There! There!" and I knew it wasn't she. It was Father. He was lying beside me, wide awake, breathing hard and apparently as mad as hell.

After a while it came to me what he was mad about. It was his turn now. After turning me out of the big bed, he had been turned out himself. Mother had no consideration now for anyone but that poisonous pup, Sonny. I couldn't help feeling sorry for Father. I had been through it all myself, and even at that age I was magnanimous. I began to stroke him down and say: "There! There!" He wasn't exactly responsive.

"Aren't you asleep either?" he snarled.

"Ah, come on and put your arm around us, can't you?" I said, and he did, in a sort of way. Gingerly, I suppose, is how you'd describe it. He was very bony but better than nothing.

At Christmas he went out of his way to buy me a really nice model railway.

# The Jilting of Granny Weatherall
## Katherine Anne Porter

She flicked her wrist neatly out of Doctor Harry's pudgy careful fingers and pulled the sheet up to her chin. The brat ought to be in knee breeches. Doctoring around the country with spectacles on his nose! "Get along now, take your schoolbooks and go. There's nothing wrong with me."

Doctor Harry spread a warm paw like a cushion on her forehead where the forked green vein danced and made her eyelids twitch. "Now, now, be a good girl, and we'll have you up in no time."

"That's no way to speak to a woman nearly eighty years old just because she's down. I'd have you respect your elders, young man."

"Well, Missy, excuse me." Doctor Harry patted her cheek. "But I've got to warn you, haven't I? You're a marvel, but you must be careful or you're going to be good and sorry."

"Don't tell me what I'm going to be. I'm on my feet now, morally speaking. It's Cornelia. I had to go to bed to get rid of her."

Her bones felt loose, and floated around in her skin, and Doctor Harry floated like a balloon around the foot of the bed. He floated and pulled down his waistcoat and swung his glasses on a cord. "Well, stay where you are, it certainly can't hurt you."

"Get along and doctor your sick," said Granny Weatherall. "Leave a well woman alone. I'll call for you when I want you.... Where were you forty years ago when I pulled through milk-leg and double pneumonia? You weren't even born. Don't let Cornelia lead you on," she shouted, because Doctor Harry appeared to float up to the ceiling and out. "I pay my own bills, and I don't throw my money away on nonsense!"

She meant to wave good-by, but it was too much trouble. Her eyes closed of themselves, it was like a dark curtain drawn around the bed. The pillow rose and floated under her, pleasant as a hammock in a light wind. She listened to the leaves rustling outside the window. No, somebody was swishing newspapers: no, Cornelia and Doctor Harry were whispering together. She leaped broad awake, thinking they whispered in her ear.

"She was never like this, *never* like this!" "Well, what can we expect?" "Yes, eighty years old...."

Well, and what if she was? She still had ears. It was like Cornelia to whisper around doors. She always kept things secret in such a public way. She was always being tactful and kind. Cornelia was dutiful; that was the trouble with her. Dutiful and good: "So good and dutiful," said Granny, "that I'd like to spank her." She saw herself spanking Cornelia and making a fine job of it.

"What'd you say, Mother?"

Granny felt her face tying up in hard knots.

"Can't a body think, I'd like to know?"

"I thought you might want something."

"I do. I want a lot of things. First off, go away and don't whisper."

She lay and drowsed, hoping in her sleep that the children would keep out and let her rest a minute. It had been a long day. Not that she was tired. It was always pleasant to snatch a minute now and then. There was always so much to be done, let me see: tomorrow.

Tomorrow was far away and there was nothing to trouble about. Things were finished somehow when the time came; thank God there was always a little margin over for peace: then a person could spread out the plan of life and tuck in the edges orderly. It was good to have everything clean and folded away, with the hair brushes and tonic bottles sitting straight on the white embroidered linen: the day started without fuss and the pantry shelves laid out with rows of jelly glasses and brown jugs and white stone-china jars with blue whirligigs and words painted on them: coffee, tea, sugar, ginger, cinnamon, allspice: and the bronze clock with the lion on top nicely dusted off. The dust that lion could collect in twenty-four hours! The box in the attic with all those letters tied up, well, she'd have to go through that tomorrow. All those letters—George's letters and John's letters and her letters to them both—lying around for the children to find afterwards made her uneasy. Yes, that would be tomorrow's business. No use to let them know how silly she had been once.

While she was rummaging around she found death in her mind and it felt clammy and unfamiliar. She had spent so much time preparing for death there was no need for bringing it up again. Let it take care of itself now. When she was sixty she had felt very old, finished, and went around making farewell trips to see her children and grandchildren, with a secret in her mind: This is the very last of your mother, children! Then she made her will and came down with a long fever. That was all just a notion like a lot of other things, but it was lucky too, for she had once for all got over the idea of dying for a long time. Now she couldn't be worried. She hoped she had better sense now. Her father had lived to be one hundred and two years old and had drunk a noggin of strong hot toddy on his last birthday. He told the reporters it was his daily habit, and he owed his long life to that. He had made quite a scandel and was very pleased about it. she believed she'd just plague Cornelia a little.

"Cornelia! Cornelia!" No footsteps, but a sudden hand on her cheek. "Bless you, where have you been?"

"Here, Mother."

"Well Cornelia, I want a noggin of hot toddy."

"Are you cold, darling?"

"I'm, chilly, Cornelia. Lying in bed stops the circulation. I must have told you that a thousand times."

Well, she could just hear Cornelia telling her husband that Mother was getting a little childish and they'd have to humor her. The thing that most annoyed her was that Cornelia thought she was deaf, dumb, and blind. Little hasty glances and tiny gestures tossed around her and over her head saying, "Don't cross her, let her have her way, she's eighty years old," and she sitting there as if she lived in a thin glass cage. Sometimes Granny almost made up her mind to pack up and move back to her own house where nobody could remind her every minute that she was old. Wait, wait, Cornelia, till your own children whisper behind your back!

In her day she had kept a better house and had got more work done. She wasn't too old yet for Lydia to be driving eighty miles for advice when one of the children jumped the track, and Jimmy still dropped in and talked things over: "Now, Mammy, you've a good business head, I want to know what you think of this?..." Old. Cornelia couldn't change the furniture around without asking. Little things, little things! They had been so sweet when they were little. Granny wished the old days were back again with the children young and everything to be done over. It had been a hard pull, but not too much for her. When she thought of all the food she had cooked, and all the clothes she had cut and sewed, and all the gardens she had made—well, the children showed it. There they were, made out of her, and they couldn't get away from that. Sometimes she wanted to see John again and point to them and say, Well, I didn't do so badly, did I? But that would have to wait. That was for tomorrow. She used to think of him as a man, but now all the children were older than their father, and he would be a child beside her if she saw him now. It seemed strange and there was something wrong in the idea. Why, he couldn't possibly recognize her. She had fenced in a hundred acres once, digging the post holes herself and clamping the wires with just a negro boy to help. That changed a woman. John would be looking for a young woman with the peaked Spanish comb in her hair and the painted fan. Digging post holes changed a woman. Riding country roads in the winter when women had their babies was another thing: sitting up nights with sick horses and sick negroes and sick children and hardly ever losing one. John, I hardly ever lost one of them! John would see that in a minute, that would be something he could understand, she wouldn't have to explain anything!

It made her feel like rolling up her sleeves and putting the whole place to rights again. No matter if Cornelia was determined to be everywhere at once, there were a great many things left undone on this place. She would start tomorrow and do them. It was good to be strong enough for everything, even if all you made melted and changed and slipped under your hands, so that by the time you finsihed you almost forgot what you were working for. What was it I set out to do? she asked herself intently, but she could not remember. A fog rose over the valley, she saw it marching across the creek swallowing the trees and moving up the hill like an army of ghosts. Soon it would be at the near edge of the orchard, and then it was time to go in and light the lamps. Come in, children, don't stay out in the night air.

Lighting the lamps had been beautiful. The children huddled up to her and breathed like little calves waiting at the bars in the twilight. Their eyes followed the match and watched the flame rise and settle in a blue curve, then they moved away from her. The lamp was lit, they didn't have to be scared and hang on to mother any more. Never, never, never more. God, for all my life I thank Thee. Without Thee, my God, I could never have done it. Hail, Mary, full of grace.

I want you to pick all the fruit this year and see that nothing is wasted. There's always someone who can use it. Don't let good things rot for want of using. You waste life when you waste good food. Don't let things get lost. It's bitter to lose things. Now, don't let me get to thinking, not when I am tired and taking a little nap before supper....

The pillow rose about her shoulders and pressed against her heart and the memory was being squeezed out of it: oh, push down the pillow, somebody: it would smother her if she tried to hold it. Such a fresh breeze blowing and such a green day with no threats in it. But he had not come, just the same. What does a woman do when she has put on the white veil and set out the white cake for a man and he doesn't come? She tried to remember. No, I swear he never harmed me but in that. He never harmed me but in that... and what if he did? There was the day, the day, but a whirl of dark smoke rose and covered it, crept up and over into the bright field where everything was planted so carefully in orderly rows. That was hell, she knew hell when she saw it. For sixty years she had prayed against remembering him and against losing her soul in the deep pit of hell, and now the two things were mingled in one and the thought of him was a smoky cloud from hell that moved and crept in her head when she had just got rid of Doctor Harry and was trying to rest a minute. Wounded vanity, Ellen, said a sharp voice in the top of her mind. Don't let your wounded vanity get the upper hand of you. Plenty of girls get jilted. You were jilted, weren't you? Then stand up to it. Her eyelids wavered and let in streamers of blue-gray light like tissue paper over her eyes. She must get up and pull the shades down or she'd never sleep. She was in bed again and the shades were not down. How could that happen? Better turn over, hide from the light, sleeping in the light gave you nightmares. "Mother, how do you feel now?" and a stinging wetness on her forehead. But I don't like having my face washed in cold water!

Hapsy? George? Lydia? Jimmy? No, Cornelia, and her features were swollen and full of little puddles. "They're coming, darling, they'll all be here soon." Go wash your face, child, you look funny.

Instead of obeying, Cornelia knelt down and put her head on the pillow. She seemed to be talking but there was no sound. "Well, are you tongue-tied? Whose birthday is it? Are you going to give a party?"

Cornelia's mouth moved urgently in strange shapes. "Don't do that, you bother me, daughter."

"Oh, no, Mother. Oh, no...."

Nonsense. It was strange about children. They disputed your every word.

"No what, Cornelia?"

"Here's Doctor Harry."

"I won't see that boy again. He just left five minutes ago."

"That was this morning, Mother. It's night now. Here's the nurse."

"This is Doctor Harry, Mrs. Weatherall. I never saw you look so young and happy!"

"Ah, I'll never be young again—but I'd be happy if they'd let me lie in peace and get rested."

She thought she spoke up loudly, but no one answered. A warm weight on her forehead, a warm bracelet on her wrist, and a breeze went on whispering, trying to tell her something. A shuffle of leaves in the everlasting hand of God, He blew on them and they danced and rattled. "Mother, don't mind, we're going to give you a little hypodermic." "Look here, daughter, how do ants get in this bed? I saw sugar ants yesterday." Did you send for Hapsy too?

It was Hapsy she really wanted. She had to go a long way back through a great many rooms to find Hapsy standing with a baby on her arm. She seemed to herself to be Hapsy also, and the baby on Hapsy's arm was Hapsy and himself and herself, all at once, and there was no surprise in the meeting. Then Hapsy melted from within and turned flimsy as gray gauze and the baby was a gauzy shadow, and Hapsy came up close and said, "I thought you'd never come," and looked at her very searchingly and said, "You haven't changed a bit!" They leaned forward to kiss, when Cornelia began whispering from a long way off, "Oh, is there anything you want to tell me? Is there anything I can do for you?"

Yes, she had changed her mind after sixty years and she would like to see George. I want you to find George. Find him and be sure to tell him I forgot him. I want him to know I had my husband just the same and my children and my house like any other woman. A good house too and a good husband that I loved and fine children out of him. Better than I hoped for even. Tell him I was given back everything he took away and more. Oh, no, oh, God, no, there was something else besides the house and the man and the children. Oh, surely they were not all? What was it? Something not given back.... Her breath crowded down under her ribs and grew into a monstrous frightening shape with cutting edges; it bored up into her head, and the agony was unbelievable: Yes, John, get the Doctor now, no more talk, my time has come.

When this one was born it should be the last. The last. It should have been born first, for it was the one she had truly wanted. Everything came in good time. Nothing left out, left over. She was strong, in three days she would be as well as ever. Better. A woman needed milk in her to have her full health.

"Mother, do you hear me?"

"I've been telling you—"

"Mother, Father Connolly's here."

"I went to Holy Communion only last week. Tell him I'm not so sinful as all that."

"Father just wants to speak to you."

He could speak as much as he pleased. It was like him to drop in and inquire about her soul as if it were a teething baby, and then stay on for a cup of tea and a round of cards and gossip. He always had a funny story of some sort, usually about an Irishman who made his little mistakes and confessed them, and the point lay in some absurd thing he would blurt out in the confessional showing his struggles between native piety and original sin. Granny felt easy about her soul. Cornelia, where are your manners? Give Father Connolly a chair. She had her secret comfortable understanding with a few favorite saints who cleared a straight road to God for her. All as surely signed and sealed as the papers for the new Forty Acres. Forever... heirs and assigns forever. Since the day the wedding cake was not cut, but thrown out and wasted. The whole bottom dropped out of the world, and there she was blind and sweating with nothing under her feet and the walls falling away. His hand had caught her under the breast, she had not fallen, there was the freshly polished floor with the green rug on it, just as before. He had cursed like a sailor's parrot and said, "I'll kill him for you." Don't lay a hand on him, for my sake leave something to God. "Now, Ellen, you must believe what I tell you...."

So there was nothing, nothing to worry about any more, except sometimes in the night one of the children screamed in a nightmare, and they both hustled out shaking and hunting for the matches and calling, "There, wait a minute, here we are!" John, get the doctor now, Hapsy's time has come. But there was Hapsy standing by the bed in a white cap. "Cornelia, tell Hapsy to take off her cap. I can't see her plain."

Her eyes opened very wide and the room stood out like a picture she had seen somewhere. Dark colors with the shadows rising towards the ceiling in long angles. The tall black dresser gleamed with nothing on it but John's picture, enlarged from a little one, with John's eyes very black when they should have been blue. You never saw him, so how do you know how he looked? But the man insisted the copy was perfect, it was very rich and handsome. For a picture, yes, but it's not my husband. The table by the bed had a linen cover and a candle and a crucifix. The light was blue from Cornelia's silk lampshades. No sort of light at all, just frippery. You had to live forty years with kerosene lamps to appreciate honest electricity. She felt very strong and she saw Doctor Harry with a rosy nimbus around him.

"You look like a saint, Doctor Harry, and I vow that's as near as you'll ever come to it."

"She's saying something."

"I heard you, Cornelia. What's all this carrying-on?"

"Father Connolly's saying—"

Cornelia's voice staggered and bumped like a cart in a bad road. It rounded corners and turned back again and arrived nowhere. Granny stepped up in the cart very lightly and reached for the reins, but a man sat beside her and she knew him by his hands, driving the cart. She did not look in his face, for she knew without seeing, but looked instead down the road where the trees leaned over and bowed to each other and a thousand birds were singing a Mass. She felt like singing too, but she put her hand in the bosom of her dress and pulled out a rosary, and Father Connolly murmured Latin in a very solemn voice and tickled her feet. My God, will you stop that nonsense? I'm a married woman. What if he did run away and leave me to face the priest by myself? I found another a whole world better. I wouldn't have exchanged my husband for anybody except St. Michael himself, and you may tell him that for me with a thank you in the bargain.

Light flashed on her closed eyelids, and a deep roaring shook her. Cornelia, is that lightning? I hear thunder. There's going to be a storm. Close all the windows. Call the children in.... "Mother, here we are, all of us." "Is that you, Hapsy?" "Oh, no, I'm Lydia. We drove as fast as we could." Their faces drifted above her, drifted away. The rosary fell out of her hands and Lydia put it back. Jimmy tried to help, their hands fumbled together, and Granny closed two fingers around Jimmy's thumb. Beads wouldn't do, it must be something alive. She was so amazed her thoughts ran round and round. So, my dear Lord, this is my death and I wasn't even thinking about it. My children have come to see me die. But I can't, it's not time. Oh, I always hated surprises. I wanted to give Cornelia the amethyst set— Cornelia, you're about to have the amethyst set, but Hapsy's to wear it when she wants, and, Doctor Harry, do shut up. Nobody sent for you. Oh, my dear Lord, do wait a minute. I meant to do something about the Forty Acres, Jimmy doesn't need it and Lydia will later on, with that worthless husband of hers. I meant to finish the altar cloth and send six bottles of wine to Sister Borgia for her dyspepsia. I want to send six bottles of wine to Sister Borgia, Father Connolly, now don't let me forget.

Cornelia's voice made short turns and tilted over and crashed. "Oh, Mother, oh, Mother, oh, Mother...."

"I'm not going, Cornelia. I'm taken by surprise. I can't go."

You'll see Hapsy again. What about her? "I thought you'd never come." Granny made a long journey outward, looking for Hapsy. What if I don't find her? What then? Her heart sank down and down, there was no bottom to death, she couldn't come to the end of it. The blue light from Cornelia's lampshade drew into a tiny point in the center of her brain, it flickered and winked like an eye, quietly it fluttered and dwindled. Granny lay curled down within herself, amazed and watchful, staring at the point of light that was herself; her body was now only a deeper mass of shadow in an endless darkness and this darkness would curl around the light and swallow it up. God, give a sign!

For the second time there was no sign. Again no bridegroom and the priest in the house. She could not remember any other sorrow because this grief wiped them all away. Oh, no, there's nothing more cruel than this—I'll never forgive it. She stretched herself with a deep breath and blew out the light.

# Unit 3

## My
## Oedipus Complex

## The Jilting of
## Granny Weatherall

- Comprehension Questions
- Point of View
- Discussion Guides
- Writing Exercise

# COMPREHENSION QUESTIONS

For each of the following statements and questions, select the option containing the most complete or most accurate answer.

1. In "My Oedipus Complex" Larry compares his father's visits during the
(b) war with those of Santa Claus because both of them
    □ a. are jolly.
    □ b. wear red outfits.
    □ c. bring presents.
    □ d. come and go mysteriously.

2. Talking about his father's souvenirs of the war, Larry says: "There was
(l) a bit of the magpie about Father; he expected everything to come in
    handy." From the way that it is used here, a *magpie* probably is a bird
    that
    □ a. hoards things.
    □ b. eats a lot.
    □ c. migrates south in the winter.
    □ d. sings beautifully.

3. Larry envies the Geneys down the street because
(a) □ a. they have a lot of money.
    □ b. Mr. Geney lives at home.
    □ c. they have a dog and cat.
    □ d. they have a baby.

4. The "business" that Mother and Father discuss so gravely probably is
(g) □ a. politics.        □ c. the family finances.
    □ b. their courtship.    □ d. Larry.

5. Now that his father is home to stay, the little boy views him as
(c) □ a. a playmate.      □ c. a hero.
    □ b. a rival.        □ d. an equal.

6. *Personification* gives human qualities to objects and animals. Which of
(k) the following expressions from the story is an example of personification?
    □ a. "Dawn was just breaking, with a guilty air that made me feel I had caught it in the act."
    □ b. "Next morning I woke at my usual hour, feeling like a bottle of champagne."
    □ c. "They really made my blood boil."
    □ d. "There was a bit of the magpie in Father."

7. While Father was away at the war, Larry had become
(f)  □ a. mature beyond his years.
    □ b. lonely and depressed.
    □ c. shy and withdrawn.
    □ d. spoiled and headstrong.

8. Relations between Larry and Father developed into open warfare from
(d) the time when
    □ a. Father came home from the war.
    □ b. Father spanked Larry.
    □ c. Larry came into his parents' bedroom.
    □ d. the new baby arrived.

9. Mother tells Larry, "You mustn't play with Daddy's toys unless he lets
(h) you." The reader may infer from the remark that, in some respects at least, Mother regards both Larry and Father as
    □ a. soldiers.         □ c. children.
    □ b. strangers.       □ d. intruders.

10. Larry cannot understand what Mother sees in Father. "In every possible
(l) way he was less *winning* than I." In this contex, the word *winning* means
    □ a. successful.     □ c. lovable.
    □ b. intelligent.    □ d. good-looking.

11. When Larry announces he is going to marry Mother when he grows up,
(i) Mother seems
    □ a. concerned.     □ c. pleased.
    □ b. puzzled.       □ d. upset.

12. Both Larry and Father agree that Mother's preoccupation with the new
(f) baby is
    □ a. sickening.     □ c. unnatural.
    □ b. touching.      □ d. amusing.

13. At the end of the story the relationship between Larry and his father
(e) might be described as

   ☐ a. co-conspirators.  ☐ c. mortal enemies.
   ☐ b. fellow sufferers.  ☐ d. arch-rivals.

14. Granny accurately describes her daughter Cornelia as
(j)   ☐ a. sweet and innocent.
   ☐ b. selfish and vain.
   ☐ c. unpleasant and irritable.
   ☐ d. dutiful and good.

15. Cornelia gets on Granny's nerves with her
(b)   ☐ a. crying.  ☐ c. complaining.
   ☐ b. praying.  ☐ d. whispering.

16. Granny Weatherall's husband, John, died around the age of
(h)   ☐ a. twenty-five.
   ☐ b. thirty-five to forty.
   ☐ c. sixty to seventy.
   ☐ d. eighty or more.

17. "She [Granny] had to go a long way back through a great many rooms
(k) to find Hapsy standing with a baby on her arm." Here, "rooms" is a
   *metaphor*, a figure of speech that implies a comparison between two
   unlike things. "Rooms" is a metaphor for

   ☐ a. death.  ☐ c. the unknown.
   ☐ b. time.  ☐ d. love.

18. During her lifetime Granny Weatherall seems to have been
(j)   ☐ a. flighty and impractical.
   ☐ b. dainty and delicate.
   ☐ c. strong and capable.
   ☐ d. bitter and unforgiving.

19. Granny says to the doctor, "You look like a saint, Doctor Harry, and I
(i) vow that's as near as you'll ever come to it." The tone of this remark is

   ☐ a. wry humor.
   ☐ b. bitter sarcasm.
   ☐ c. fickle coyness.
   ☐ d. shy sincerity.

20. As the priest administers the last rites, Granny imagines she is stepping
(g) up into a cart. She reaches for the reins, but a man is driving, and she
knows him by his hands. The man is probably
☐ a. Father Connolly.
☐ b. her husband, John.
☐ c. her old flame, George.
☐ d. one of her sons.

21. Granny wants the set of amethyst jewelry
(a) ☐ a. to be buried with her.
☐ b. to go to Lydia.
☐ c. to go to Hapsy.
☐ d. to go to Cornelia.

22. Granny keeps waiting for Hapsy. Near the end, Granny
(d) ☐ a. dies holding Hapsy's hand.
☐ b. sees Hapsy in a dream.
☐ c. looks for Hapsy.
☐ d. becomes angry at Hapsy.

23. The action of this story takes place over a course of
(d) ☐ a. an hour.      ☐ c. three days.
☐ b. a day.      ☐ d. a week.

24. In her last moments of life, Granny Weatherall's feelings about dying are
(c) most similar to her feelings about
☐ a. being jilted on her wedding day.
☐ b. giving birth.
☐ c. being born.
☐ d. losing her husband.

25. The most significant event in Granny Weatherall's long and full life seems
(e) to have been
☐ a. her marriage to John.
☐ b. the time she fenced in a hundred acres herself.
☐ c. the day the bridegroom never came.
☐ d. the time twenty years ago when she prepared for death.

---

Comprehension Skills: a — isolating details; b — recalling specific facts; c — retaining
concepts; d — organizing facts; e — understanding the main idea; f — drawing a
conclusion; g — making a judgment; h — making an inference; i — recognizing tone;
j — understanding characters; k — appreciation of literary forms; l — understanding
vocabulary.

# POINT OF VIEW

## Practice Exercise A

The war was the most peaceful period of my life. The window of my attic faced southeast. My mother had curtained it, but that had small effect. I always woke with the first light and, with all responsibilities of the previous day melted, feeling myself rather like the sun, ready to illumine and rejoice. Life never seemed so simple and clear and full of possibilities as then. I put my feet out from under the clothes—I called them Mrs. Left and Mrs. Right —and invented dramatic situations for them in which they discussed the problems of the day. At least Mrs. Right did; she was very demonstrative, but I hadn't the same control of Mrs. Left, so she mostly contented herself with nodding agreement.

1. What keeps you aware that the narrator is an intelligent adult even though you seem to view the story through the eyes of a child?
   - ☐ a. The use of the pronoun *I*
   - ☐ b. The description of his feet
   - ☐ c. Certain expressions a child wouldn't use
   - ☐ d. A vague feeling the author creates

2. Circle the first sentence of the paragraph that presents Mother's and Father's reactions from the little boy's point of view.

## Practice Exercise B

"Mummy," I said, "do you know what I'm going to do when I grow up?"

"No, dear" she replied. "What?"

"I'm going to marry you," I said quietly.

Father gave a great guffaw out of him, but he didn't take me in. I knew it must only be pretence. And Mother, in spite of everything, was pleased. I felt she was probably relieved to know that one day Father's hold on her would be broken.

"Won't that be nice?" she said with a smile.

"It'll be very nice," I said confidently. "Because we're going to have lots and lots of babies.

"That's right, dear," she said placidly. "I think we'll have one soon, and then you'll have plenty of company."

1. The little boy who narrates the passage above may be called a *naive narrator* because
   - ☐ a. the reader's understanding exceeds that of the little boy.
   - ☐ b. none of the characters understands the situation.
   - ☐ c. neither the reader nor the little boy understand what is going on.
   - ☐ d. the narrator is under ten.

2. On the lines provided, write the first sentence of the paragraph that presents Mother's and Father's reactions from the little boy's point of view.

**Practice Exercise C**

Yes, she had changed her mind after sixty years and she would like to see George. I want you to find George. Find him and be sure to tell him I forgot him. I want him to know I had my husband just the same and my children and my house like any other woman. A good house too and a good husband that I loved and fine children out of him. Better than I hoped for even. Tell him I was given back everything he took away and more. Oh, no, oh, God, no, there was something else besides the house and the man and the children. Oh, surely they were not all? What was it? Something not given back . . . . Her breath crowded down under her ribs and grew into a monstrous frightening shape with cutting edges. . . .

1. The passage above conveys to the reader a feeling of being inside Granny's mind and hearing her thoughts. This technique is called
   □ a. objective point of view.   □ c. third person narration.
   □ b. naive narration.   □ d. interior monologue.

2. Underline the first sentence in which Granny voices her thoughts directly to the reader, in the first person.
   Circle two sentences in which the omniscient narrator addresses the reader, using the third person.

**Practice Exercise D**

Granny felt easy about her soul. Cornelia, where are your manners? Give Father Connolly a chair. She had her secret comfortable understanding with a few favorite saints who cleared a straight road to God for her. All as surely signed and sealed as the papers for the new Forty Acres. Forever. . . heirs and assigns forever. Since the day the wedding cake was not cut, but thrown out and wasted. The whole bottom dropped out of the world, and there she was blind and sweating with nothing under her feet and the walls falling away. His hand had caught her under the breast, she had not fallen, there was a freshly polished floor with the green rug on it, just as before. He had cursed like a sailor's parrot and said, "I'll kill him for you."

1. Granny says: Cornelia, where are your manners? Give Father Connolly a chair. The author does not use quotation marks here because
   □ a. Granny does not understand what she is saying.
   □ b. Granny does not actually say this out loud; she merely thinks it.
   □ c. Granny is speaking out loud throughout the entire passage.
   □ d. The reader understands more than Granny does.

2. About half-way through the passage the point of view shifts from the present to the past. Circle the sentence in which this shift occurs.

# DISCUSSION GUIDES

## Analyzing Point of View

1. Because "My Oedipus Complex" is told from the point of view of a small boy, many facts and ideas are presented incorrectly, as a little boy would see them. What does this force the reader to do?

2. "The Jilting of Granny Weatherall" is told from the limited point of view of Granny—what she sees, hears and thinks. Suppose that, in addition to Granny's point of view, the narrator told the reader what is passing through the minds of all the other characters as well. How would this either improve or weaken the story?

## Interpreting the Story

3. Small children, if we are to believe Frank O'Connor, are shrewd, crafty and self-centered. How are these characteristics expressed in "My Oedipus Complex"? Point to specific passages in the story that depict Larry as shrewd, crafty or self-centered.

4. Larry claims he and Father were open enemies in an all-out war to win Mother's attention. Is this the literal truth? Is Father aware that his son sees him as an arch-rival? Point to passages in the story to support your opinion.

5. What is the turning point in "My Oedipus Complex"? How are the battle lines redrawn and how do the alliances shift at this point?

6. How does Cornelia behave toward her mother? Why does Granny Weatherall object to the way her daughter treats her?

7. Granny wants to tell George, the man who jilted her sixty years ago, that she "was given back everything he took away and more"—a good home, a good husband, and fine children. But then she thinks, "Oh, no, oh, God, no, there was something else besides the house and the man and the children. Oh, surely they were not all? What was it? Something not given back. . ." What do you think was never given back to Granny after George left her?

8. On the last day of her life, how do you think Granny Weatherall feels toward the man who stood her up on her wedding day sixty years ago?

## Analyzing the Author's Technique

9. One could say that Frank O'Connor wrote "My Oedipus Complex" with "tongue-in-cheek." Having read the story, what would you say the expression "tongue-in-cheek" means? How does O'Connor create this effect?

10. Sometimes when Granny Weatherall asks a question, she gets a reply, and sometimes she doesn't. What do you conclude from this? What does this add to the story?

## WRITING EXERCISE

Two people may look at the same thing and each see something different. Take a birthday cake, for example. A grown-up is likely to appraise it with a critical eye: is it lopsided? are the candles evenly distributed? how will it taste? will all the guests like it? A small child, on the other hand, may look at the same cake and behold a dazzling vision of color and lights; a child may think it's the most delicious treat in the world.

**Step One:** Choose an object or an event and write a paragraph describing it *from your own point of view* (use a first-person narrator—*I*). Describe what the object looks like or what happens and how this makes you feel.

**Step Two:** Write a second paragraph describing the same object or event, only this time use a third-person narrator (she, he) with a very different point of view.

Here are some suggestions for objects or events you may want to describe: a Christmas tree, a holiday decoration, a pet, a uniform, a blind date, a wedding.

# POINT OF VIEW IN OTHER STORIES

## Third-person narrations

"Nightfall"

"The Lottery"

"Young Goodman Brown"

"The Kugelmass Episode"

"The Man That Corrupted Hadleyburg"

"The Gentleman from Cracow"

"The Garden Party"

"The Leader of the People"

"The Christian Roommates"

## First-person narrations

"The Wall" (told by the protagonist)

"A Rose for Emily" (told by an unknown townsman)

"The Black Cat" (told by the protagonist)

"Tell Me How Long the Train's Been Gone" (told by the protagonist)

"A Christmas Memory" (told as a memory of the past but written in the present tense as if it is happening now)

Unit 4
**Conflict**

# The Wall

## Jean-Paul Sartre

# Introduction

The terse, objective prose of a history book simply cannot convey the intense personal response which the Spanish Civil War evoked in people around the world. The war erupted in 1936 when various "leftist" factions united in a Popular Front and gained control of the Spanish government in a national election. The leftists, which included anarchists, socialists, Communists, republicans and others, favored a more equal distribution of the country's wealth and resources, which were in the hands of a few large landowners, the military and the clergy. These powerful interest groups referred to as the "rightists," united under the leadership of General Francisco Franco to overthrow the new government and preserve the status quo.

The resulting conflict aroused impassioned support from liberals and leftists in many parts of the world on the side of the republicans—and from fascists, notably Adolf Hitler and Benito Mussolini, on the side of General Franco. The Russians gave support to the left, and thus Spain became a gigantic rehearsal for World War II.

George Orwell, an English journalist best known today as the author of *Animal Farm* and *1984,* was one of thousands who volunteered their services and fought in an International Brigade against the fascist forces. "I had come to Spain," recalled Orwell, "with some notion of writing newspaper articles, but I joined the militia almost immediately, because at that time and in that atmosphere it seemed the only conceivable thing to do."

The "atmosphere" which moved Orwell to risk his life on the front lines seemed to him the embodiment of social equality. He wrote: "Many of the normal motives of civilized life—snobbishness, money-grubbing, fear of the boss, etc.—had simply ceased to exist. The ordinary class division of society had disappeared to an extent that is almost unthinkable in the money-tainted air of England; there was no one there except the peasants and ourselves, and no one owned anyone else as his master. Of course such a state of affairs could not last. It was simply a temporary and local phase in an enormous game that is being played over the whole surface of the earth.

But it lasted long enough to have its effect upon anyone who experienced it.... One realized afterward that one had been in contact with something strange and valuable.... One had breathed the air of equality."

The workers' militias, however, were no match for the better equipped and better organized Falangistas, and the foretaste of socialism which had briefly transformed the lives of the Spanish peasants came to an end in 1939 when General Franco occupied Madrid.

"The Wall," by Jean-Paul Sartre, is set in a Fascist prison camp in the waning phases of the Spanish Civil War. The Falangistas, or Fascists, have apparently occupied the surrounding towns, arresting soldiers, civilians, and even young boys suspected of having leftist sympathies. A popular leftist leader, Ramon Gris, has gone into hiding.

Among those taken prisoner by the Falangistas is Pablo Ibbieta, an anarchist fighting with the leftist forces. After shivering in solitary confinement for five days, Pablo has been brought to a large room where the prisoners are being tried. The trials are perfunctory affairs—a question here, an accusation there. The answers don't seem to matter. Innocent or guilty, the sentence is the same: Death, at daybreak.

Sartre's story is a riveting look into the minds of three condemned prisoners—Pablo, an Irishman named Tom who had joined one of the International Brigades, and Juan, the younger brother of an anarchist—as they await execution by firing squad in front of the wall.

Jean-Paul Sartre (born 1905), a French philosopher, novelist, and playwright, has long been an ardent socialist. Declaring that "commitment is an act, not a word," Sartre has often taken to the streets of Paris to participate in rioting, in the sale of left-wing literature, and in other activities that in his opinion were the way to promote "the revolution."

# Conflict

A story plot might go: "Boy meets girl. Boy marries girl. Boy and girl live happily ever after." It's a story, but one that would never hold your interest because it's missing a key element. The missing element is conflict: "Boy loses girl."

Conflict is the essence of story-telling. Every plot is built around a conflict because conflict creates interest. If the boy and girl never argued with each other, you'd toss the book aside in disgust. It would be boring and monotonous. But just let something come between them and, if the story's any good at all, you'll probably continue reading to learn how things turn out in the end. That's the difference conflict makes: it stimulates interest, it builds suspense, it gives the reader a good reason to keep on reading because it moves the story along. In a novel, conflict usually creates the plot. In a short story where plots are thin, conflict develops incidents and themes.

Of course, conflict can take many forms besides a lovers' quarrel. Conflict can be a mountain climber struggling up a treacherous wall of ice, it can be someone fighting for a place in society, it can be an alcoholic trying to stay on the wagon, or it can be an old person contemplating death. Conflict, in fiction, is generally thought of as occurring in five forms: (1) conflict between people, (2) internal conflict, (3) conflict with the unknown, conflict with nature, and (3) conflict with society.

Every story has at least one kind of conflict, and most have more than one. For instance, a story about a Black person struggling against discrimination would be an example of conflict with society. But this same story might also involve a struggle within a family (conflict with other people), and a struggle against the temptation to give in to overwhelming odds (internal conflict). But no matter what form it may take, conflict always introduces two points of interest. The first, of course, is "Who will win?" Of equal interest, however, is the exposition of the character traits revealed by the way the hero reacts to conflict.

Let's take a closer look at the different kinds of conflict as they are developed in Sartre's "The Wall."

**1. Conflict between People.** Conflict that pits one character against another is the most basic kind of conflict. It is also the easiest to identify. The chief character in a story, the protagonist, confronts an opponent, or antagonist. One character is squared off against another.

In "The Wall," two soldiers and a boy in the Spanish Civil War have been taken prisoner by the enemy and sentenced to die the following morning. They have been joined in their cell by a Belgian doctor who claims he was sent to comfort them in their last hours. Actually, he is there to observe them in a coldly professional manner.

The speaker in the following passage is Pablo Ibbieta, one of the prisoners, who narrates the story. Who is the protagonist and who is the antagonist in this conflict? What is the conflict all about?

> ...I felt him [the Belgian doctor] watching me. I raised my head and returned his look. Impersonally, he said to me, "Doesn't it seem cold to you here?" He looked cold, he was blue.
> "I'm not cold," I told him.
> He never took his hard eyes off me. Suddenly I understood and my hands went to my face: I was drenched in sweat. In this cellar, in the midst of winter, in the midst of drafts, I was sweating. I ran my hands through my hair, gummed together with perspiration; at the same time I saw my shirt was damp and sticking to my skin: I had been dripping for an hour and hadn't felt it. But that swine of a Belgian hadn't missed a thing; he had seen the drops rolling down my cheeks and thought: this is the manifestation of an almost pathological state of terror; and he felt normal and proud of being alive because he was cold. I wanted to stand up and smash his face....

The chief character, or protagonist, in this conflict is the narrator. We know this because the story is being told from his point of view. His opponent, or antagonist, is the Belgian doctor. The conflict that pits Pablo against the Belgian doctor is the most elemental of all conflicts: life versus death. To be specific, life for the Belgian doctor versus death for Pablo.

This conflict brings out some revealing traits in these characters. Obviously, the prospect of his own death has reduced Pablo to "an almost pathological state of terror." His body no longer behaves like the body of a normal person. The cell is cold, yet instead of shivering, he is sweating. The Belgian doctor's reactions are no less revealing. He stares at Pablo "with hard eyes." He purposely calls attention to Pablo's altered condition by asking, "Doesn't it seem cold to you here?" He observes Pablo's agonies with a clinical detachment that is cold-blooded and callous. Whatever the outcome of this confrontation, the reader has gained greater insight into the personalities of both characters.

**2. Internal Conflict.** This kind of conflict is a mental struggle that takes place within a character. When a character is faced with a difficult choice, he or she experiences internal conflict. Internal conflicts also arise when a character must come to terms with some unpleasant reality. In the story you are about to read, Pablo experiences an internal conflict. In the following passage, what is the unpleasant reality facing Pablo?

> He [Tom] kept on chewing his words, with something like distraction. He certainly talked to keep himself from thinking. He smelled of urine like an old prostate case. Naturally, I agreed with him, I could have said everything he said: it isn't *natural* to die. And since I was going to die, nothing seemed natural to me, not this pile of coal dust, or the bench, or Pedro's ugly face. Only it didn't please me to think the same things as Tom. And I knew that, all through the night, every five minutes, we would keep on thinking things at the same time. I looked at him sideways and for the first time he seemed strange to me: he wore death on his face. My pride was wounded: for the past twenty-four hours I had lived next to Tom, I had listened to him, I had spoken to him and I knew we had nothing in common. And now we looked as much alike as twin brothers, simply because we were going to die together.

Something very important to each of us is the fact that we are individuals. We each have our own identity; we are not like anyone else in the world. If anything, we each tend to think of ourselves as just a bit special, different or better than the next person.

Pablo does not particularly like his cell mate Tom. He wants to feel he is different from Tom, and perhaps a better person. But now, facing death has reduced the two men to a remarkable sameness. They were thinking alike and they even looked alike. "It didn't please me to think the same things as Tom" Pablo says. And again, "My pride was wounded...."

Pablo is struggling within himself to maintain his individuality—his precious personal identity. But facing death, he is losing the struggle and is forced to face the old, unpleasant reality that in death there are no individual distinctions.

**3. Conflict with the Unknown.** The protagonist of a story may also struggle against something that is beyond human understanding—an ironic fate, for example, or the nature of death.

Something that is "fated" to happen is going to happen no matter what a person does to prevent it. Conflicts with fate often have an ironic outcome because, in trying to avoid a particular fate, the protagonist unwittingly initiates it. The ancient Greek tale of Oedipus is a classic example of a conflict with fate. As a young man, Oedipus is told by the oracle that he will kill his father and marry his mother. Horrified, Oedipus runs away to escape his fate. Ironically, his journey actually triggers the oracle's prophecy. As it turns out, Oedipus is an adopted son, and while fleeing his native city, he kills an old man who is his real father, and at the end of his journey he marries his mother! "The Wall" wrestles with another unknown besides fate, and that is the mystery of death. In the following passage from the story, Pablo tries to understand what it will mean for him to die. How does this conflict add to your understanding of this character? How does it enhance the story?

> I felt relaxed and over-excited at the same time. I didn't want to think any more about what would happen at dawn, at death. It made no sense. I only found words or emptiness. But as soon as I tried to think of anything else I saw rifle barrels pointing at me. Perhaps I lived through my execution twenty times; once I even thought it was for good: I must have slept a minute. They were dragging me to the wall and I was struggling; I was asking for mercy. I woke up with a start and looked at the Belgian: I was afraid I might have cried out in my sleep. But he was stroking his moustache, he hadn't noticed anything. If I had wanted to, I think I could have slept awhile; I had been awake for forty-eight hours. I was at the end of my rope. But I didn't want to lose two hours of life; they would come to wake me up a dawn, I would follow them, stupefied with sleep and I would have croaked without so much as an "Oof!"; I didn't want that, I didn't want to die like an animal, I wanted to understand.

Here, Pablo is confronted with his own death, but he is unable to come to terms with this reality because he is at a loss to understand it. He pictures rifle barrels aimed at him, and he lives through his execution twenty times. Yet it still makes no sense.

Pablo is struggling to understand what is happening to him because otherwise he will die like an animal, in ignorance. His effort to understand the unknown is in itself proof that he is more than an animal. And his desire to meet death bravely, without making a scene, shows that he is a man of pride and dignity. This is one conflict that can never be resolved, but it is one we must all face sooner or later, and we sympathize with Pablo as he struggles to comprehend the mystery of death.

**4. Conflict with Nature.** A conflict with nature pits human life against the elements. A trapper in Alaska struggling to build a fire before he freezes to death, as in Jack London's story "To Build a Fire," is an example of conflict with nature. So is a fisherman's struggle to land a giant fish or a canoeist's battle against a wild river.

Conflict with nature is a popular theme in literature. Such stories are invariably tense, exciting and suspenseful. What is more, they are excellent vehicles for character development. A conflict with nature tests the limits of a character's strength and will to live. It is usually a humbling experience for the protagonist because it demonstrates just how fragile human life really is. The survivors almost always emerge with a different perspective on life.

**5. Conflict with Society.** When a character in a story is at odds with accepted ways of thinking or living, the result is a conflict with society. This is actually an extension of "conflict between people" since society is made up of people. But dealing with a *society* often seems a larger struggle against something more impersonal than a face-to-face confrontation with another individual.

In literature, this kind of conflict tells as much about the society as it does the protagonist. The reader gets a good idea of what is important to this society—how people live, what they value. And, of course, the reader shares the protagonist's feelings of loneliness and frustration that come from challenging these things.

Pablo Ibbieta is an anarchist involved on one side of the bloody Spanish Civil War. In a sense, the whole story of "The Wall" grows out of this huge social upheaval of a half-century ago. One political ideology is challenging another, and the result is inhuman cruelty and unimaginable suffering throughout Spain. What Pablo and his cell mates are suffering is an incident, or an example of similar incidents—similar conflicts—occurring all over the country at the time.

Conflict in literature, then, can take several forms. A character may struggle against another character, against self, against fate, against nature, and against society. Generally, two or more conflicts are involved in a single story. There are four kinds of conflict in "The Wall," and each one adds a level of meaning to the story. Together, they add up to a memorable reading experience that will stay with you for a long time to come.

As you read the story:

- Be aware of the conflict within Tom when he thinks about his own death.

- Think about the contrast drawn between the Belgian doctor and the condemned prisoners.

- Notice the confrontation towards the end of the story between Pablo and the officer who questions him about Ramon Gris's whereabouts.

- Try to decide whom or what Pablo struggles against at the end of the story.

# The Wall
## Jean-Paul Sartre

They pushed us into a big white room and I began to blink because the light hurt my eyes. Then I saw a table and four men behind the table, civilians, looking over the papers. They had bunched another group of prisoners in the back and we had to cross the whole room to join them. There were several I knew and some others who must have been foreigners. The two in front of me were blond with round skulls; they looked alike. I suppose they were French. The smaller one kept hitching up his pants; nerves.

It lasted about three hours; I was dizzy and my head was empty; but the room was well heated and I found that pleasant enough: for the past 24 hours we hadn't stopped shivering. The guards brought the prisoners up to the table, one after the other. The four men asked each one his name and occupation. Most of the time they didn't go any further—or they would simply ask a question here and there: "Did you have anything to do with the sabotage of munitions?" Or "Where were you the morning of the 9th and what were you doing?" They didn't listen to the answers or at least didn't seem to. They were quiet for a moment and then looking straight in front of them began to write. They asked Tom if it were true he was in the International Brigade; Tom couldn't tell them otherwise because of the papers they found in his coat. They didn't ask Juan anything but they wrote for a long time after he told them his name.

"My brother Jose is the anarchist," Juan said, "you know he isn't here any more. I don't belong to any party, I never had anything to do with politics."

They didn't answer. Juan went on, "I haven't done anything. I don't want to pay for somebody else."

His lips trembled. A guard shut him up and took him away. It was my turn.

"Your name is Pablo Ibbieta?"

"Yes."

The man looked at the papers and asked me, "Where's Ramon Gris?"

"I don't know."

"You hid him in your house from the 6th to the 19th."

"No."

They wrote for a minute and then the guards took me out. In the corridor Tom and Juan were waiting between two guards. We started walking. Tom asked one of the guards, "So?"

"So what?" the guard said.

"Was that the cross-examination or the sentence?"

"Sentence," the guard said.

"What are they going to do with us?"

The answered dryly, "Sentence will be read in your cell."

As a matter of fact, our cell was one of the hospital cellars. It was terrifically cold there because of the drafts. We shivered all night and it wasn't much better during the day. I had spent the previous five days in a cell in a monastery, a sort of hole in the wall that must have dated from the middle ages: since there were a lot of prisoners and not much room, they locked us up anywhere. I didn't miss my cell; I hadn't suffered too much from the cold but I was alone; after a long time it gets irritating. In the cellar I had company. Juan hardly ever spoke: he was afraid and he was too young to have anything to say. But Tom was a good talker and he knew Spanish well.

There was a bench in the cellar and four mats. When they took us back we sat and waited in silence. After a long moment, Tom said, "We're screwed."

"I think so too," I said, "but I don't think they'll do anything to the kid."

"They don't have a thing against him," said Tom. "He's the brother of a militiaman and that's all."

I looked at Juan: he didn't seem to hear. Tom went on, "You know what they do in Saragossa? They lay the men down on the road and run over them with trucks. A Moroccan deserter told us that. They said it was to save ammunition."

"It doesn't save gas," I said.

I was annoyed at Tom: he shouldn't have said that.

"Then there's officers walking along the road," he went on, "supervising it all. They stick their hands in their pockets and smoke cigarettes. You think they finish off the guys? Hell no. They let them scream. Sometimes for an hour. The Moroccan said he damned near puked the first time."

"I don't believe they'll do that here," I said. "Unless they're really short on ammunition."

Day was coming in through four airholes and a round opening they had made in the ceiling on the left, and you could see the sky through it. Through this hole, usually closed by a trap, they unloaded coal into the cellar. Just below the hole there was a big pile of coal dust; it had been used to heat the hospital but since the beginning of the war the patients were evacuated and the coal stayed there, unused; sometimes it even got rained on because they had forgotten to close the trap.

Tom began to shiver. "Good Jesus Christ I'm cold," he said. "Here it goes again."

He got up and began to do exercises. At each movement his shirt opened on his chest, white and hairy. He lay on his back, raised his legs in the air and bicycled. I saw his great rump trembling. Tom was husky but he had too much fat. I thought how rifle bullets or the sharp points of bayonets would soon be sunk into this mass of tender flesh as in a lump of butter. It wouldn't have made me feel like that if he'd been thin.

I wasn't exactly cold, but I couldn't feel my arms and shoulders any more. Sometimes I had the impression I was missing something and began to look around for my coat and then suddenly remembered they hadn't given me a coat. It was rather uncomfortable. They took our clothes and gave them to their soldiers, leaving us only our shirts—and those canvas pants that hospital patients wear in the middle of summer. After a while Tom got up and sat next to me, breathing heavily.

"Warmer?"

"Good Christ, no. But I'm out of wind."

Around eight o'clock in the evening a major came in with two *falangistas*. He had a sheet of paper in his hand. He asked the guard, "What are the names of those three:"

"Steinbock, Ibbieta and Mirbal," the guard said.

The major put on his eyeglasses and scanned the list: "Steinbock... "Steinbock... Oh, yes... You are sentenced to death. You will be shot tomorrow morning." He went on looking. "The other two as well."

That's not possible," Juan said. "Not me."

The major looked at him amazed. "What's your name?"

"Juan Mirbal," he said.

"Well, your name is there," said the major. "You're sentenced."

"I didn't do anything," Juan said.

The major shrugged his shoulders and turned to Tom and me.

"You're Basque?"

"Nobody is Basque."

He looked annoyed. "They told me there were three Basques. I'm not going to waste my time running after them. Then naturally you don't want a priest?"

We didn't even answer.

He said, "A Belgian doctor is coming shortly. He is authorized to spend the night with you." He made a military salute and left.

"What did I tell you," Tom said. "We get it."

"Yes," I said, "it's a rotten deal for the kid."

I said that to be decent but I didn't like the kid. His face was too thin and fear and suffering had disfigured it, twisting all his features. Three days before he was a smart sort of kid, not too bad; but now he looked like an old fairy and I thought how he'd never be young again, even if they were to let him go. It wouldn't have been too hard to have a little pity for him but pity disgusts me, or rather it horrifies me. He hadn't said anything more but he had turned grey; his face and hands were both grey. He sat down again and looked at the ground with round eyes. Tom was good hearted, he wanted to take his arm, but the kid tore himself away violently and made a face.

"Let him alone," I said in a low voice, "you can see he's going to blubber."

Tom obeyed regretfully; he would have liked to comfort the kid, it would have passed his time and he wouldn't have been tempted to think about himself. But it annoyed me: I'd never thought about death because I never had any reason to, but now the reason was here and there was nothing to do but think about it.

Tom began to talk. "So you think you've knocked guys off, do you?" he asked me. I didn't answer. He began explaining to me that he had knocked off six since the beginning of August; he didn't realize the situation and I could tell he didn't *want* to realize it. I hadn't quite realized it myself, I wondered if it hurt much, I thought of bullets, I imagined their burning hail through my body. All that was beside the real question; but I was calm: we had all night to understand. After a while Tom stopped talking and I watched him out of the corner of my eye; I saw he to had turned grey and he looked rotten; I told myself "Now it starts." It was almost dark, a dim glow filtered through the airholes and the pile of coal and made a big stain beneath the spot of sky; I could already see a star through the hole in the ceiling: the night would be pure and icy.

The door opened and two guards came in, followed by a blonde man in a tan uniform. He saluted us. "I am the doctor," he said. "I have authorization to help you in these trying hours."

He had an agreeable and distinguished voice. I said, "What do you want here?"

"I am at your disposal. I shall do all I can to make your last moments less difficult."

"What did you come here for? There are others, the hospital's full of them."

"I was sent here," he answered with a vague look. "Ah! Would you like to smoke?" he added hurriedly, "I have cigarettes and even cigars."

He offered us English cigarettes and *puros*, but we refused. I looked him in the eyes and he seemed irritated. I said to him, "You aren't here on an errand of mercy. Besides, I know you. I saw you with the fascists in the barracks yard the day I was arrested."

I was going to continue, but something surprising suddenly happened to me; the presence of this doctor no longer interested me. Generally when I'm on somebody I don't let go. But the desire to talk left me completely; I shrugged and turned my eyes away. A little later I raised my head; he was watching me curiously. The guards were sitting on a mat. Pedro, the tall thin one, was twiddling his thumbs, the other shook his head from time to time to keep from falling asleep.

"Do you want a light?" Pedro suddenly asked the doctor. The other nodded "Yes": I think he was about as smart as a log, but he surely wasn't bad. Looking in his cold blue eyes it seemed to me that his only sin was lack of imagination. Pedro went out and came back with an oil lamp which he set on the corner of the bench. It gave a bad light but it was better than nothing: they had left us in the dark the night before. For a long time I watched the circle of light the lamp made on the ceiling. I was fascinated. Then suddenly I woke up, the circle of light disappeared and I felt myself crushed under an enormous weight. It was not the thought of death or fear; it was nameless. My cheeks burned and my head ached.

I shook myself and looked at my two friends. Tom had hidden his face in his hands. I could only see the fat white nape of his neck. Little Juan was the worst; his mouth was open and his nostrils trembled. The doctor went to him and put his hand on his shoulder to comfort him, but his eyes stayed cold. Then I saw the Belgian's hand drop stealthily along Juan's arm, down to the wrist. Juan paid no attention. The Belgian took his wrists between three fingers, distractedly, the same time drawing back a little and turning his back to me. But I leaned backward and saw him take a watch from his pocket and look at it for a moment, never letting go of the wrist. After a minute he let the hand fall inert and went and leaned his back against the wall, then, as if he suddenly remembered something very important which had to be jotted down on the spot, he took a notebook from his pocket and wrote a few lines. "Bastard," I thought angrily, "let him come and take my pulse. I'll shove my fist in his rotten face."

He didn't come but I felt him watching me. I raised my head and returned his look. Impersonally, he said to me, "Doesn't it seem cold to you here?" He looked cold, he was blue.

"I'm not cold," I told him.

He never took his hard eyes off me. Suddenly I understood and my hands went to my face: I was drenched in sweat. In this cellar, in the midst of winter, in the midst of drafts, I was sweating. I ran my hands through my hair, gummed together with perspiration; at the same time I saw my shirt was damp and sticking to my skin: I had been dripping for an hour and hadn't felt it. But that swine of a Belgian hadn't missed a thing; he had seen the drops rolling down my cheeks and thought: this is the manifestation of an almost pathological state of terror; and he had felt normal and proud of being alive because he was cold. I wanted to stand up and smash his face but no sooner had I made the slightest gesture than my rage and shame were wiped out; I fell back on the bench with indifference.

I satisfied myself by rubbing my neck with my handkerchief because now I felt the sweat dropping from my hair onto my neck and it was unpleasant. I soon gave up rubbing, it was useless; my handkerchief was already soaked and I was still sweating. My buttocks were sweating too and my damp trousers were glued to the bench.

Suddenly Juan spoke. "You're a doctor?"

"Yes," the Belgian said.

"Does it hurt... very long?"

"Huh? When...? Oh, no," the Belgian said paternally. "Not at all. It's over quickly." He acted as though he were calming a cash customer.

"But I... they told me... sometimes they have to fire twice."

"Sometimes," the Belgian said, nodding. "It may happen that the first volley reaches no vital organs."

"Then they have to reload their rifles and aim all over again?" He thought for a moment and then added hoarsely, "That takes time!"

He had a terrible fear of suffering, it was all he thought about: it was his age. I never thought much about it and it wasn't fear of suffering that made me sweat.

I got up and walked to the pile of coal dust. Tom jumped up and threw me a hateful look: I had annoyed him because my shoes squeaked. I wondered if my face looked as frightened as his: I saw he was sweating too. The sky was superb, no light filtered into the dark corner and I had only to raise my head to see the Big Dipper. But it wasn't like it had been: the night before I could see a great piece of sky from my monastery cell and each hour of the day brought me a different memory. Morning, when the sky was a hard, light blue, I thought of beaches on the Atlantic; at noon I saw the sun and I remembered a bar in Seville where I drank *manzanilla* and ate olives and anchovies; afternoons I was in the shade and I thought of the deep shadow which spreads over half a bull-ring leaving the other half shimmering in sunlight; it was really hard to see the whole world reflected in the sky like that. But now I could watch the sky as much as I pleased, it no longer evoked anything in me. I liked that better. I came back and sat near Tom. A long moment passed.

Tom began speaking in a low voice. He had to talk, without that he wouldn't have been able to recognize himself in his own mind. I thought he was talking to me but he wasn't looking at me. He was undoubtedly afraid to see me as I was, grey and sweating: we were alike and worse than mirrors of each other. He watched the Belgian, the living.

"Do you understand?" he said. "I don't understand."

I began to speak in a low voice too. I watched the Belgian.

"Why? What's the matter?"

"Something is going to happen to us that I can't understand."

There was a strange smell about Tom. It seemed to me I was more sensitive than usual to odors. I grinned. "You'll understand in a while."

"It isn't clear," he said obstinately. "I want to be brave but first I have to know... Listen, they're going to take us into the courtyard. Good. They're going to stand up in front of us. How many?"

"I don't know. Five or eight. Not more."

"All right. There'll be eight. Someone'll holler 'aim!' and I'll see eight rifles looking at me. I'll think how I'd like to get inside the wall, I'll push against it with my back... with every ounce of strength I have, but the wall will stay, like in a nightmare. I can imagine all that. If you only knew how well I can imagine it."

"All right, all right!" I said, "I can imagine it too."

"It must hurt like hell. You know, they aim at the eyes and the mouth to disfigure you," he added mechanically. "I can feel the wounds already; I've had pains in my head and in my neck for the past hour. Not real pains. Worse. This is what I'm going to feel tomorrow morning. And then what?"

I well understood what he meant but I didn't want to act as if I did. I had pains too, pains in my body like a crowd of tiny scars. I couldn't get used to it. But I was like him, I attached no importance to it. "After," I said, "you'll be pushing up daisies."

He began to talk to himself: he never stopped watching the Belgian. The Belgian didn't seem to be listening. I knew what he had come to do; he wasn't interested in what we thought; he came to watch our bodies, bodies dying in agony while yet alive.

"It's like a nightmare," Tom was saying. "You want to think of something, you always have the impression that it's all right, that you're going to understand and then it slips, it escapes you and fades away. I tell myself there will be nothing afterwards. But I don't understand what it means. Sometimes I almost can... and then it fades away and I start thinking about the pains again, bullets, explosions. I'm a materialist, I swear it to you; I'm not going crazy. But something's the matter. I see my corpse; that's not hard but *I'm* the one who see it, with *my* eyes. I've got to think... think that I won't see anything anymore and the world will go on for the others. We aren't made to think that, Pablo. Believe me: I've already stayed up a whole night waiting for something. But this isn't the same: this will creep up behind us, Pablo, and we won't be able to prepare for it."

"Shut up," I said, "Do you want me to call a priest?"

He didn't answer. I had already noticed he had the tendency to act like a prophet and call me Pablo, speaking in a toneless voice. I didn't like that: but it seems all the Irish are that way. I had the vague impression he smelled of urine. Fundamentally, I hadn't much sympathy for Tom and I didn't see why, under the pretext of dying together, I should have any more. It would have been different with some others. With Ramon Gris, for example. But I felt alone between Tom and Juan. I liked that better, anyhow: with Ramon I might have been more deeply moved. But I was terribly hard just then and I wanted to stay hard.

He kept on chewing his words, with something like distraction. He certainly talked to keep himself from thinking. He smelled of urine like an old prostate case. Naturally, I agreed with him, I could have said everything he said: it isn't *natural* to die. And since I was going to die, nothing seemed natural to me, not this pile of coal dust, or the bench, or Pedro's ugly face. Only it didn't please me to think the same things as Tom. And I knew that, all through the night, every five minutes, we would keep on thinking things at the same time. I looked at him sideways and for the first time he seemed strange to me: he wore death on his face. My pride was wounded: for the past twenty-four hours I had lived next to Tom, I had listened to him, I had spoken to him and I knew we had nothing in common. And now we looked as much alike as twin brothers, simply because we were going to die together. Tom took my hand without looking at me.

"Pablo, I wonder... I wonder if it's really true that everything ends."

I took my hand away and said, "Look between your feet, you pig."

There was a big puddle between his feet and drops fell from his pants-leg.

"What is it?" he asked frightened.

"You're pissing in your pants," I told him.

"It isn't true," he said furiously. "I'm not pissing. I don't feel anything."

The Belgian approached us. He asked with false solicitude, "Do you feel ill?"

Tom did not answer. The Belgian looked at the puddle and said nothing.

I don't know what it is," Tom said ferociously. "But I'm not afraid. I swear I'm not afraid."

The Belgian did not answer. Tom got up and went to piss in a corner. He came back buttoning his fly, and sat down without a word. The Belgian was taking notes.

All three of us watched him because he was alive. He had the motions of a living human being, the cares of a living human being; he shivered in the cellar the way the living are supposed to shiver; he had an obedient, well-fed body. The rest of us hardly felt ours—not in the same way anyhow. I wanted to feel my pants between my legs but I didn't dare; I watched the Belgian, balancing on his legs, master of his muscles, someone who could think about tomorrow. There we were, three bloodless shadows; we watched him and we sucked his life like vampires.

Finally he went over to little Juan. Did he want to feel his neck for some professional motive or was he obeying an impulse of charity? If he was acting by charity it was the only time during the whole night.

He caressed Juan's head and neck. The kid let himself be handled, his eyes never leaving him, then suddenly, he seized the hand and looked at it strangely. He held the Belgian's hand between his own two hands and there was nothing pleasant about them, two grey pincers gripping his fat and reddish hand. I suspected what was going to happen and Tom must have suspected it too: but the Belgian didn't see a thing, he smiled paternally. After a moment the kid brought the fat red hand to his mouth and tried to bite it. The Belgian pulled away quickly and stumbled back against the wall. For a second he looked at us with horror, he must have suddenly understood that we were not men like him. I began to laugh and one of the guards jumped up. The other was asleep, his wide open eyes were blank.

I felt relaxed and over-excited at the same time. I didn't want to think any more about what would happen at dawn, at death. It made no sense. I only found words or emptiness. But as soon as I tried to think of anything else I saw rifle barrels pointing at me. Perhaps I lived through my execution twenty times; once I even thought it was for good: I must have slept a minute. They were dragging me to the wall and I was struggling; I was asking for mercy. I woke up with a start and looked at the Belgian: I was afraid I might have cried out in my sleep. But he was stroking his moustache, he hadn't noticed anything. If I wanted to, I think I could have slept a while; I had been awake for forty-eight hours. I was at the end of my rope. But I didn't want to lose two hours of life: they would come to wake me up at dawn, I would follow them, stupefied with sleep and I would have croaked without so much as an "Oof!" I didn't want that, I didn't want to die like an animal, I wanted to understand. Then I was afraid of having nightmares. I got up, walked back and forth, and, to change my ideas, I began to think about my past life. A crowd of memories came back to me pell-mell. There were good and bad ones—or at least I called them that *before*. There were faces and incidents. I saw the face of a little *novillero* who was gored in Valencia during the *Feria*, the face of one of my uncles, the face of Ramon Gris. I remembered my whole life: how I was out of work for three months in 1926, how I almost starved to death. I remembered a night I spent on a bench in Grenada: I hadn't eaten for three days. I was angry, I didn't want to die. That made me smile. How madly I ran after happiness, after women, after liberty. Why? I wanted to free Spain, I admired Piy Margall, I joined the anarchist movement, I spoke in public meetings: I took everything as seriously as if I were immortal.

At that moment I felt that I had my whole life in front of me, and I thought, "It's a damned lie." It was worth nothing because it was finished. I wondered how I'd been able to walk, to laugh with the girls: I wouldn't have moved so much as my little finger if I had only imagined I would die like this. My life was in front of me, shut, closed, like a bag and yet everything inside of it was unfinished. For an instant I tried to judge it. I wanted to tell myself, this is a beautiful life. But I couldn't pass judgment on it; it was only a sketch; I had spent my time counterfeiting eternity, I had understood nothing. I missed nothing: there were so many things I could have missed, the taste of *manzanilla* or the baths I took in summer in a little creek near Cadiz; but death had disenchanted everything.

The Belgian suddenly had a bright idea. "My friends," he told us, "I will undertake—if the military administration will allow it—to send a message for you, a souvenir to those who love you..."

Tom mumbled, "I don't have anybody."

I said nothing. Tom waited an instant then looked at me with curiosity. "You don't have anything to say to Concha?"

"No."

I hated this tender complicity: it was my own fault, I had talked about Concha the night before, I should have controlled myself. I was with her for a year. Last night I would have given an arm to see her again for five minutes. That was why I talked about her, it was stronger than I was. Now I had no more desire to see her, I had nothing more to say to her. I would not even have wanted to hold her in my arms: my body filled me with horror because it was grey and sweating—and I wasn't sure that her body didn't fill me with horror. Concha would cry when she found out I was dead, she would have no taste for life for months afterwards. But I was still the one who was going to die. I thought of her soft, beautiful eyes. When she looked at me something passed from her to me. But I knew it was over: if she looked at me *now* the look would stay in her eyes, it wouldn't reach me. I was alone.

Tom was alone too but not in the same way. Sitting cross-legged, he had begun to stare at the bench with a sort of smile, he looked amazed. He put out his hand and touched the wood cautiously as if he were afraid of breaking something, then drew back his hand quickly and shuddered. If I had been Tom I wouldn't have amused myself by touching the bench; this was some more Irish nonsense, but I too found that objects had a funny look: they were more obliterated, less dense than usual. It was enough for me to look at the bench, the lamp, the pile of coal dust, to feel that I was going to die. Naturally I couldn't think clearly about my death but I saw it everywhere, on things, in the way things fell back and kept their distance, discreetly, as people who speak quietly at the bedside of a dying man. It was *his* death which Tom had just touched on the bench.

In the state I was in, if someone had come and told me I could go home quietly, that they would leave me my life whole, it would have left me cold: several hours or several years of waiting is all the same when you have lost the illusion of being eternal. I clung to nothing, in a way I was calm. But it was a horrible calm—because of my body; my body, I saw with its eyes, I heard with its ears, but it was no longer me; it sweated and trembled by itself and I didn't recognize it any more. I had to touch it and look at it to find out what was happening, as if it were the body of someone else. At times I could still feel it, I felt sinkings, and fallings, as when you're in a plane taking a nosedive, or I felt my heart beating. But that didn't reassure me. Everything that came from my body was all cock-eyed. Most of the time it was quiet and I felt no more than a sort of weight, a filthy presence against me; I had the impression of being tied to an enormous vermin. Once I felt my pants and I felt they were damp; I didn't know whether it was sweat or urine, but I went to piss on the coal pile as a precaution.

The Belgian took out his watch, looked at it. He said, "It's three-thirty."

Bastard! He must have done it on purpose. Tom jumped; we hadn't noticed time was running out; night surrounded us like a shapeless, somber mass, I couldn't even remember that it had begun.

Little Juan began to cry. He wrung his hands, pleaded, "I don't want to die. I don't want to die."

He ran across the whole cellar waving his arms in the air, then fell sobbing on one of the mats. Tom watched him with mournful eyes, without the slightest desire to console him. Because it wasn't worth the trouble: the kid made more noise than we did, but he was less touched: he was like a sick man who defends himself against his illness by fever. It's much more serious when there isn't any fever.

He wept: I could clearly see he was pitying himself; he wasn't thinking about death. For one second, one single second, I wanted to weep myself, to weep with pity for myself. But the opposite happened: I glanced at the kid, I saw his thin sobbing shoulders and I felt inhuman: I could pity neither the others nor myself. I said to myself, "I want to die cleanly."

Tom had gotten up, he placed himself just under the round opening and began to watch for daylight. I was determined to die cleanly and I only thought of that. But ever since the doctor told us the time, I felt time flying, flowing away drop by drop.

It was still dark when I heard Tom's voice: "Do you hear them?"

Men were marching in the courtyard.

"Yes."

"What the hell are they doing? They can't shoot in the dark."

After a while we heard no more. I said to Tom, "It's day."

Pedro got up, yawning, and came to blow out the lamp. He said to his buddy, "Cold as hell."

The cellar was all grey. We heard shots in the distance.

"It's starting," I told Tom. "They must do it in the court in the rear."

Tom asked the doctor for a cigarette. I didn't want one; I didn't want cigarettes or alcohol. From that moment on they didn't stop firing.

"Do you realize what's happening?" Tom said.

He wanted to add something but kept quiet, watching the door. The door opened and a lieutenant came in with four soldiers. Tom dropped his cigarette.

"Steinbock?"

Tom didn't answer. Pedro pointed him out.

"Juan Mirbal?"

"On the mat."

"Get up," the lieutenant said.

Juan did not move. Two soldiers took him under the arms and set him on his feet. But he fell as soon as they released him.

The soldiers hesitated.

"He's not the first sick one," said the lieutenant. "You two carry him; they'll fix it up down there."

He turned to Tom. "Let's go."

Tom went out between two soldiers. Two others followed, carrying the kid by the armpits. He hadn't fainted; his eyes were wide open and tears ran down his cheeks. When I wanted to go out the lieutenant stopped me.

"You Ibbieta?"

"Yes."

"You wait here; they'll come for you later."

They left. The Belgian and the two jailers left too, I was alone. I did not understand what was happening to me but I would have liked it better if they had gotten it over with right away. I heard shots at almost regular intervals; I shook with each one of them. I wanted to scream and tear out my hair. But I gritted my teeth and pushed my hands in my pockets because I wanted to stay clean.

After an hour they came to get me and led me to the first floor, to a small room that smelt of cigars and where the heat was stifling. There were two officers sitting smoking in the armchairs, papers on their knees.

"You're Ibbieta?"

"Yes."

"Where is Ramon Gris?"

"I don't know."

The one questioning me was short and fat. His eyes were hard behind his glasses. He said to me, "Come here."

I went to him. He got up and took my arms, staring at me with a look that should have pushed me into the earth. At the same time he pinched my biceps with all his might. It wasn't to hurt me, it was only a game: he wanted to dominate me. He also thought he had to blow his stinking breath square in my face. We stayed for a moment like that, and I almost felt like laughing. It takes a lot to intimidate a man who is going to die; it didn't work. He pushed me back violently and sat down again. He said, "It's his life against yours. You can have yours if you tell us where he is."

These men dolled up with their riding crops and boots were still going to die. A little later than I, but not too much. They busied themselves looking for names in their crumpled papers, they ran after other men to imprison or suppress them; they had opinions on the future of Spain and on other subjects. Their little activities seemed shocking and burlesqued to me; I couldn't put myself in their place, I thought they were insane. The little man was still looking at me, whipping his boots with the riding crop. All his gestures were calculated to give him the look of a live and ferocious beast.

"So? You understand?"

"I don't know where Gris is," I answered. "I thought he was in Madrid."

The other officer raised his pale hand indolently. This indolence was also calculated. I saw through all their little schemes and I was stupefied to find there were men who amused themselves that way.

"You have a quarter of an hour to think it over," he said slowly. "Take him to the laundry, bring him back in fifteen minutes. If he still refuses he will be executed on the spot."

They knew what they were doing: I had passed the night in waiting; then they had made me wait an hour in the cellar while they shot Tom and Juan and now they were locking me up in the laundry; they must have prepared their game the night before. They told themselves that nerves eventually wear out and they hoped to get me that way.

They were badly mistaken. In the laundry I sat on a stool because I felt very weak and I began to think. But not about their proposition. Of course I knew where Gris was; he was hiding with his cousins, four kilometers from the city. I also knew that I would not reveal his hiding place unless they tortured me (but they didn't seem to be thinking about that). All that was perfectly regulated, definite and in no way interested me. Only I would have liked to understand the reasons for my conduct. I would rather die than give up Gris. Why? I didn't like Ramon Gris any more. My friendship for him had died a little while before dawn at the same time as my love for Concha, at the same time as my desire to live. Undoubtedly I thought highly of him: he was tough. But it was not for this reason that I consented to die in his place; his life had no more value than mine; no life had value. They were going to slap a man up against the wall and shoot him until he died, whether it was I or Gris or somebody else made no difference. I knew he was more useful than I to the cause of Spain but I thought to hell with Spain and anarchy; nothing was important. Yet I was there, I could save my skin and give up Gris and I refused to do it. I found that somehow comic; it was obstinacy. I thought, "I must be stubborn!" And a droll sort of gaiety spread over me.

They came for me and brought me back to the two officers. A rat ran out from under my feet and that amused me. I turned to one of the *falangistas* and said, "Did you see the rat?"

He didn't answer. He was very sober, he took himself seriously. I wanted to laugh but I held myself back because I was afraid that once I got started I wouldn't be able to stop. The *falangista* had a moustache. I said to him again, "You ought to shave off your moustache, idiot." I thought it funny that he would let the hairs of his living being invade his face. He kicked me without great conviction and I kept quiet.

"Well, said the fat officer, "have you thought about it?"

I looked at them with curiosity, as insects of a very rare species. I told them, "I know where he is. He is hidden in the cemetery. In a vault or in the gravediggers' shack."

It was a farce. I wanted to see them stand up, buckle their belts and give orders busily.

They jumped to their feet. "Let's go. Molés, go get fifteen men from Lieutenant Lopez. You," the fat man said, "I'll let you off if you're telling the truth, but it'll cost you plenty if you're making monkeys out of us."

They left in a great clatter and I waited peacefully under the guard of *falangistas*. From time to time I smiled, thinking about the spectacle they would make. I felt stunned and malicious. I imagined them lifting up tombstones, opening the doors of the vaults one by one. I represented this situation to myself as if I had been someone else: this prisoner obstinately playing the hero, these grim *falangistas* with their moustaches and their men in uniform running among the graves; it was irresistibly funny. After half an hour the little fat man came back alone. I thought he had come to give the orders to execute me. The others must have stayed in the cemetery.

The officer looked at me. He didn't look at all sheepish. "Take him into the big courtyard with the others," he said. "After the military operations a regular court will decide what happens to him."

"Then they're not... not going to shoot me?..."

"Not now, anyway. What happens afterwards is none of my business."

I still didn't understand. I asked, "But why?"

He shrugged his shoulders without answering and the soldiers took me away. In the big courtyard there were about a hundred prisoners, women, children and a few old men. I began walking around the central grass-plot, I was stupefied. At noon they let us eat in the mess hall. Two or three people questioned me. I must have known them, but I didn't answer: I didn't even know where I was.

Around evening they pushed about ten new prisoners into the court. I recognized Garcia, the baker. He said, "What damned luck you have! I didn't think I'd see you alive."

"They sentenced me to death," I said, "and then they changed their minds, I don't know why."

"They arrested me at two o'clock," Garcia said.

"Why?" Garcia had nothing to do with politics.

"I don't know," he said. "They arrest everybody who doesn't think the way they do." He lowered his voice. "They got Gris."

I began to tremble. "When?"

"This morning. He messed it up. He left his cousin's on Tuesday because they had an argument. There were plenty of people to hide him but he didn't want to owe anything to anybody. He said, 'I'd go hide in Ibbieta's, place, but they got him, so I'll go hide in the cemetery.' "

"In the cemetery?"

"Yes. What a fool. Of course they went by there this morning, that was sure to happen. They found him in the gravediggers' shack. He shot at them and they got him."

"In the cemetery!"

Everything began to spin and I found myself sitting on the ground: I laughed so hard I cried.

# Unit 4

## The Wall

- **Comprehension Questions**
- **Conflict**
- **Discussion Guides**
- **Writing Exercise**

# COMPREHENSION QUESTIONS

For each of the following statements and questions, select the option containing the most complete or most accurate answer.

1. Pablo, Tom and Juan have been condemned to die because they are
(h) suspected of being
    ☐ a. dangerous killers.    ☐ c. deserters.
    ☐ b. spies.    ☐ d. enemies.

2. The trials at which the prisoners' sentences are decided might best be
(g) described as a
    ☐ a. rough but fair system.    ☐ c. thorough and diligent process.
    ☐ b. cruel farce.    ☐ d. necessity of life.

3. The jail cell where the prisoners are taken after sentencing is actually
(a) ☐ a. the cellar of an old hospital.
    ☐ b. a monastery.
    ☐ c. a tent.
    ☐ d. an abandoned coal mine.

4. Their jail cell is extremely uncomfortable because of the
(a) ☐ a. overcrowding.    ☐ c. rats.
    ☐ b. cold.    ☐ d. dirt.

5. "I thought how rifle bullets or the sharp points of bayonets would soon
(k) be sunk into this mass of tender flesh *as in a lump of butter.*" The
author compares the man's flesh with a lump of butter in order to
convey a feeling of
    ☐ a. disgust and revulsion.    ☐ c. horror and disbelief.
    ☐ b. pity and compassion.    ☐ d. sorrow and remorse.

6. Which of the following best defines *mechanically* as used in, " 'You
(l) know, they aim at the eyes and the mouth to disfigure you,' he added
*mechanically*"?
    ☐ a. Fervently    ☐ c. Angrily
    ☐ b. Unemotionally    ☐ d. Hesitantly

7. One reason that Pablo resents the Belgian doctor is that he is
(c) ☐ a. incompetent            ☐ c. sympathetic toward Juan.
    ☐ b. foreign.               ☐ d. alive and well.

8. "The Belgian approached us. He asked with false *solicitude*, 'Do you
(l) feel ill?' " *Solicitude* means
    ☐ a. cunning.               ☐ c. concern.
    ☐ b. enthusiasm.            ☐ d. solace.

9. Pablo fights to stay awake throughout the night because he
(b) ☐ a. is afraid the guards will kill him.
    ☐ b. is waiting for a chance to escape.
    ☐ c. doesn't want to waste his last hours of life.
    ☐ d. enjoys the company of his fellow prisoners.

10. Based on his recollections as he awaits execution, Pablo Ibbieta seems
(j) to have been
    ☐ a. a man of high ideals.
    ☐ b. a man of wealth and influence.
    ☐ c. an opportunist.
    ☐ d. a madman.

11. The atmosphere that pervades this story is one of
(i) ☐ a. quiet heroism.        ☐ c. wry humor.
    ☐ b. stoic resignation.    ☐ d. cold fear.

12. Pablo enlisted in the fighting because he
(f) ☐ a. believed in a cause.  ☐ c. had nothing better to do.
    ☐ b. was drafted.          ☐ d. needed the money.

13. Before this night, Pablo lived as though
(d) ☐ a. nothing mattered.
    ☐ b. each day was his last.
    ☐ c. each day must be cherished and well spent.
    ☐ d. he would never die.

14. Concha is the narrator's
(h) ☐ a. wife.                 ☐ c. girlfriend.
    ☐ b. sister.               ☐ d. mother.

15. Seen through Pablo's eyes, the mood created by the two officers during
(i) their interrogation of him is one of
- [ ] a. suspense.
- [ ] b. humor.
- [ ] c. excitement.
- [ ] d. terror.

16. Pablo says, "I looked at them [the officers] with curiosity, as insects
(k) of a very rare species." The simile *as insects of very rare species* is used
to express
- [ ] a. detached curiosity.
- [ ] b. bitter hatred.
- [ ] c. disgust.
- [ ] d. intense anger.

17. As the night wears on, Pablo decides that, in the end, friendships become
(c)
- [ ] a. meaningless and unimportant.
- [ ] b. increasingly necessary.
- [ ] c. comforting and inspiring.
- [ ] d. harder and harder to make.

18. From Pablo's story, the reader may conclude that waiting for death is
(f)
- [ ] a. easy compared to actually dying.
- [ ] b. better than dying suddenly.
- [ ] c. as bad as death itself.
- [ ] d. valuable as a religious experience.

19. Pablo refuses to reveal where Ramon Gris can be found because he
(j)
- [ ] a. wants to be remembered as a hero.
- [ ] b. doesn't know.
- [ ] c. will not betray their friendship.
- [ ] d. happens to feel stubborn at the moment.

20. Ramon Gris is
(h)
- [ ] a. a war criminal.
- [ ] b. just another soldier.
- [ ] c. a leader.
- [ ] d. Pablo's relative.

21. Pablo tells the officers that Ramon Gris is hiding in the cemetery in
(b) order to
- [ ] a. save his own skin.
- [ ] b. make monkeys out of his captors.
- [ ] c. get revenge on Gris.
- [ ] d. help bring the war to an end.

22. One may make the judgment that the death of Ramon Gris should be
(g) blamed on
     □ a. Pablo.           □ c. Gris himself.
     □ b. fate.            □ d. the soldiers who shot him.


23. Both Juan Mirdal, the brother of an anarchist, and Garcia, the baker,
(d) were
     □ a. sent to spy on Pablo.
     □ b. executed in the morning.
     □ c. arrested for nothing.
     □ d. working for the International Brigade.


24. An idea expressed in this story is that death is
(e) □ a. normal and inevitable.     □ c. comforting and welcomed.
     □ b. honorable and glorious.     □ d. unnatural and unthinkable.


25. This story makes the reader feel that war is
(e) □ a. cruel and pointless.     □ c. noble and inspiring.
     □ b. exciting and glamorous.     □ d. humdrum and boring.

---

Comprehension Skills: a — isolating details; b — recalling specific facts; c — retaining concepts; d — organizing facts; e — understanding the main idea; f — drawing a conclusion; g — making a judgment; h — making an inference; i — recognizing tone; j — understanding characters; k — appreciation of literary forms; l — understanding vocabulary.

# CONFLICT

## Practice Exercise A

"It's like a nightmare," Tom was saying. "You want to think of something, you always have the impression that it's all right, that you're going to understand and then it slips, it escapes you and fades away. I tell myself there will be nothing afterwards. But I don't understand what it means. Sometimes I almost can. . . and then it fades away and I start thinking about the pains again, bullets, explosions. I'm a materialist, I swear it to you; I'm not going crazy. But something's the matter. I see my corpse; that's not hard but *I'm* the one who sees it, with *my* eyes. I've got to think. . . think that I won't see anything anymore and the world will go on for the others. We aren't made to think that, Pablo.

1. Whenever Tom thinks about death, as in the passage above, a conflict develops. The conflict involves
   ☐ a. fear of hell.       ☐ c. hatred of the enemy.
   ☐ b. fear of suffering.  ☐ d. fear of the unknown.

2. Underline at least one sentence near the beginning of the passage which suggests that Tom is unable to resolve this conflict.

## Practice Exercise B

All three of us watched him [the Belgian doctor] because he was alive. He had the motions of a living human being, the cares of a living human being; he shivered in the cellar the way the living are supposed to shiver; he had an obedient, well-fed body. The rest of us hardly felt ours—not in the same way anyhow. I wanted to feel my pants between my legs but I didn't dare; I watched the Belgian, balancing on his legs, master of his muscles, someone who could think about tomorrow. There we were, three bloodless shadows; we watched him and we sucked his life like vampires.

1. The conflict expressed in the scene above is leaving its mark on the condemned men by making them feel
   ☐ a. Godlike.    ☐ c. less human.
   ☐ b. stoic.      ☐ d. immortal.

2. One sentence contains both a metaphor (an indirect comparison) and a simile (a direct comparison using "like" or "as") that sums up the difference and the conflict between the doctor and the condemned men. Underline this sentence.

## Practice Exercise C

"You're Ibbieta?"

"Yes."

"Where is Ramon Gris?"

"I don't know."

The one questioning me was short and fat. His eyes were hard behind his glasses. He said to me, "Come here."

I went to him. He got up and took my arms, staring at me with a look that should have pushed me into the earth. At the same time he pinched my biceps with all his might. It wasn't to hurt me, it was only a game: he wanted to dominate me. He also thought he had to blow his stinking breath square in my face. We stayed for a moment like that, and I almost felt like laughing. It takes a lot to intimidate a man who is going to die; it didn't work. He pushed me back violently and sat down again.

1. The conflict presented in this passage is an example of
   ☐ a. conflict with nature.        ☐ c. internal conflict.
   ☐ b. conflict between people.      ☐ d. conflict with society.

2. Underline the five-word phrase in the middle of the passage that reveals the underlying motive of Pablo's opponent.

## Practice Exercise D

[Garcia] "They got Gris."

I began to tremble. "When?"

"This morning. He messed it up. He left his cousin's on Tuesday because they had an argument. There were plenty of people to hide him but he didn't want to owe anything to anybody. He said, 'I'd go hide in Ibbieta's place, but they got him, so I'll go hide in the cemetery.'"

"In the cemetery?"

"Yes. What a fool. Of course they went by there this morning, that was sure to happen. They found him in the gravedigger's shack. He shot at them and they got him."

"In the cemetery!"

Everything began to spin and I found myself sitting on the ground: I laughed so hard I cried.

1. Pablo's unseen opponent in this incident is
   ☐ a. fate.                ☐ c. human nature.
   ☐ b. Gris.                ☐ d. the war.

2. One phrase in this passage shows that Ibbieta understands both the tragedy and the absurdity of this conflict. Find the phrase and circle it.

## Analyzing Conflict

1. Tom, Juan and Pablo are all in the same boat. Yet even among them there is conflict. What is the conflict between Pablo and his fellow prisoners?

2. Conflicts are usually resolved in the course of a story. How is the conflict between Pablo and the enemy resolved? the conflict within Pablo? the conflict pitting Pablo against fate? Or, aren't any of the conflicts resolved? Explain your opinion.

3. What sorts of things does conflict reveal about the characters in a story, and about people in real life, that you might not otherwise learn?

## Interpreting the Story

4. Why do you think the Belgian doctor is spending the night with these three condemned prisoners? Does he want to comfort them or give medical care? Does he enjoy watching them suffer? Is he a spy?

5. What does Pablo mean when he says to himself, "I want to die cleanly"?

6. Do you think Pablo will ever be the same again after this experience? Will his love for Concha return? Explain your feelings.

7. What is ironic about the ending of this story?

## Analyzing the Author's Technique

8. Sartre is said to be a proponent of existential philosophy. One idea of existentialism is that human reason cannot explain many mysteries of life so that much in life seems absurd or without meaning. This creates discomfort and anxiety in people. How is this idea expressed in "The Wall"?

9. The setting of "The Wall" is extremely effective. What are some key elements of this setting and what do they contribute to the story? (Keep in mind that atmosphere is also part of the setting.)

10. Plots typically have five parts: (1) the exposition, which simply sets up the story; (2) the complication, or conflict; (3) the crisis, or turning point; (4) the climax, or high point; and (5) the denouement, or wrap-up. "The Wall" certainly has an exposition, and there's lots of conflict, as you've already seen. But what about the other three elements--is there a crisis, a climax, and a denouement? Explain.

## WRITING EXERCISE

For each of the conflicts described, write a few sentences that will serve as a summary for a story based on that conflict. Tell how the conflict is resolved — that is, how the story will end.

1. **Conflict between People.** Ed Bagley and Rutherford Thomas are opoponents for a seat in Congress.

2. **Conflict with Society.** Dana Ebersall and Lydia Castillo, law partners, want to open a low-cost legal clinic. They are opposed by the state bar association, business and civic groups.

3. **Conflict with Nature.** Hinton Northwood and his son Arthur are entertaining an elderly acquaintance, Roy Enfield, on a fishing trip on their yacht. A fog rolls in suddenly, leaving the trio hopelessly lost.

4. **Internal Conflict.** Sylvia Plummer is a cellist with a large symphony orchestra. She falls in love and becomes engaged to marry Guy Matt, a computer technologist, whose job requires that he travel internationally as much as six months of the year. Sylvia also is obliged to travel, with the symphony. Realizing that a marriage under such circumstances has little chance for survival, Sylvia must decide what to do.

5. **Conflict with the Unknown.** Fran Allbright is facing an operation to correct a rare and potentially fatal disease. She may lose her life during the difficult operation. Other cases like hers have been known to recover without treatment, and doctors don't know why.

Unit 5
**Characterization**

# The Christian Roommates

John Updike

# Introduction

"The Christian Roommates" is about eighteen-year-old Orson Ziegler, who comes to Harvard University from a small town in South Dakota. He chose Harvard, he wrote in his college application statement, to take advantage of its "cosmopolitan Eastern environment." But whatever Orson had in mind when he wrote that, his expectations never included the likes of his new roommate, "Hub" Palamountain.

If ever anyone marched to the beat of a different drummer, it is Hub. Patterning himself after Mahatma Gandhi, the assassinated leader of India who preached passive resistance and civil disobedience, Hub follows a strict vegetarian diet. He practices Yoga, uses a small spinning wheel he ordered from Calcutta, and shaves his head, leaving a narrow crest of curly yellow hair that runs down the center and stands up like a rooster's comb—all of which was regarded as highly eccentric, if not subversive, in the sober climate of 1950.

Hub never misses a chance to thumb his nose at authority, in whatever form he finds it. Rather than accept money from his father (a capitalist businessman, presumably), Hub worked in a plywood factory for two years after high school, cleaning gluing machines, to pay his way through college. He refuses to fulfill his science requirement at Harvard, blithely dismissing the entire curriculum as "a mass of hypotheses." He regards the police as agents of a totalitarian regime. And, to his roommate's profound distress, he tears up notices from his local draft board without even opening them.

While Hub was pondering the human condition and swabbing out gluing machines, Orson busied himself in high school with more convential pursuits. Being class president, valedictorian, and captain of both the football and baseball teams left Orson little time to worry about social injustice or civil liberties. In fact, the only liberties Orson had considered with any enthusiasm were the ones he took with his girlfriend.

It's hard to imagine a more unlikely pair of roommates than Orson Ziegler and Hub Palamountain. From the moment Orson walks into their room and meets Hub, sitting on the floor, barefoot, in front of a small spinning wheel, the sparks start flying. Try as he may, Orson can detect no common denominator linking himself with Hub—except that they're both Christians, of a sort. The ensuing conflict is extremely funny for readers, but not for Orson. Before long, Hub's very presence gets under his skin, and by the end of the school year Orson is on the brink of a nervous breakdown. A year ago, Orson had hoped that Harvard would be a valuable experience after spending his entire life in a small provincial town. Valuable, it is; pleasant, it's not.

Like the characters in this story, John Updike also went to Harvard. His earliest ambition was to be a cartoonist for the *New Yorker* magazine, and he chose Harvard because he wanted to draw cartoons for the *Lampoon*. Updike did indeed become a regular contributor to the *New Yorker*, not as a cartoonist, but as a short story writer. His craftsmanship, said one critic, "is unmatched by anyone else now writing the short story."

If he weren't a writer, Updike once mused, he thinks he might like to be a turtle. He told *Life* magazine: "Turtles live quite long and can retreat immediately, and live very close to the grass, the smell of which I've always liked. I also like the sound of rain on a roof, which a turtle must get quite a lot of." Many of Updike's stories involve young people. He says, "I'm still running on energy laid down in childhood. Writing is a way of keeping up that childhood."

# Characterization

A character in a short story is no more than a collection of images—a conversation here, an action there, a tidbit or two touching on appearance or background, and that's about all; mere representations on paper of someone who doesn't even exist. Yet, miraculously, this collection of images takes shape in the mind of the reader as a character, and the character takes on a life of its own.

It's not at all unusual to imagine a character stepping out of the pages of a story and into your living room. You can picture the meeting in great detail—just what you'd say to him or her, and how that character would reply—all on the basis of a few suggestive passages in a story. Spellbound readers have written letters to Sherlock Holmes, one of the greatest fictional characters of all time, on the mistaken assumption that he actually exists— a touching tribute to the author's skill at characterization.

*Characterization* is the creation of imaginary persons that strike the reader as real within the context of the story. The ability to portray fictional characters successfully is the single most important skill of a storyteller. There are two broad methods of characterization, known as expository and dramatic. There are different types of characters, too: flat characters and round characters, static characters and developing characters. They're all in the story that follows this lesson. John Updike is a master at characterization, and we'll take a look at how he does it in "The Christian Roommates."

**1. The Expository Method of Characterization.** The word "exposition" means a setting forth of facts, a detailed explanation. That's what the expository method of characterization consists of: a direct presentation of facts and other information about a character by the narrator or by another character (not by the character himself; that's a different method). Facts such as a character's looks, age, background, social status, and so on, are often presented at the beginning of a story through the expository method.

From this information the reader forms ideas and opinions about the character being introduced.

"The Christian Roommates" begins with an expository paragraph introducing the main character, a college freshman named Orson Ziegler. What impressions do you get of this character from the following account?

> Orson Ziegler came straight to Harvard from the small South Dakota town where his father was the doctor. Orson, at eighteen, was half an inch under six feet tall, with a weight of 164 and an I.Q. of 152. His eczematous cheeks and vaguely irritated squint— as if his face had been for too long transected by the sight of a level horizon—masked a definite self-confidence. As the doctor's son, he had always mattered in the town. In his high school he had been class president, valedictorian, and captain of the football and baseball teams. (The captain of the basketball team had been Lester Spotted Elk, a full-blooded Chippewa with dirty fingernails and brilliant teeth, a smoker, a drinker, a discipline problem, and the only boy Orson ever had met who was better than he at anything that mattered.) Orson was the first native of his town to go to Harvard, and would probably be the last, at least until his son was of age. His future was firm in his mind, the pre-med course here, medical school either at Harvard, Penn, or Yale, and then back to South Dakota, where he had his wife already selected and claimed and primed to wait.

This opening paragraph presents all the information a reader needs to form both a mental picture and a personal opinion of this character. First of all, there's the biographical data. Name: Orson Ziegler. Place of birth: small town in South Dakota. Social status: high—son of the town's only doctor. Next we get the vital statistics. Age: eighteen. Height 5 feet 11½ inches. Weight: 164. I.Q.: a high 152. Appearance: has acne, squints. So much for the factual data.

This is followed by some observations that provide clues to the inner man. There are suggestions that Orson enjoys a rather exaggerated sense of his own importance. "As the doctor's son," we are told, "he had always mattered in the town." He had been a big wheel in high school, president or captain of everything "that mattered." Except in basketball, that is. To Orson's eternal chagrin, the coveted position of captain of the basketball team had been snared by a full-blooded Indian named Lester Spotted Elk who flaunted all the conventional virtues. Aside from this lone challenge to his supremacy, Orson Ziegler feels secure in his status as "most likely to succeed." He has his future all mapped out, and a suitable wife duly selected and waiting in the wings for her cue to take her place, center stage, at Orson's side (and perhaps two steps behind). All in all, these well-chosen comments depict a promising young man who is slightly stuffy and a little bit smug.

This introduction to Orson Ziegler is a good example of the expository method of characterization. The reader wouldn't expect Orson to volunteer any unflattering facts about himself, and it would also be out of character for him to express any keen or penetrating insights. This kind of information could only come from a disinterested narrator or from another character.

**2. The Dramatic Method of Characterization.** The dramatic method of characterization shows the character in action—his behavior, speech, and recorded thoughts—and allows the reader to draw his own conclusions about this character's personality, values, attitudes, and relationships with other characters. This is the *only* method of characterization in drama, of course. When you go to a play, the playwright doesn't come onstage and give the lowdown on the various characters. Instead, the curtain rises on the characters themselves, and people in the audience form their own opinions based on what they see and hear.

When you stop to think about it, it's surprising how much you can learn about a character in this way. Dialect, for example, can pinpoint a character's geographical roots, and also his level of education. A character exhibits certain values, or betrays his prejudices, by the way he treats other characters. And a character's reactions to stress or conflict always afford valuable insights into his or her personality.

In "The Christian Roommates," the reader comes to understand Orson Ziegler better from the way he reacts to his roommate, an unconventional youth named Henry, or "Hub," Palamountain. Whereas Orson is the very picture of conformity, Hub is a walking symbol of rebellion. He's a vegetarian, he reads Greek, he's "into" Yoga, and, at twenty, he's two years older than the rest of the freshman class. Orson has never met anyone like Hub before, and right from the start of their strange relationship he feels threatened by him. In this scene from the story, Hub has returned to their dormitory room carrying a lavish mane of coppery red hair which used to adorn the head of a co-ed. What do you learn about Orson Ziegler from this reaction to his roommate's latest stunt?

"Hub"—the very syllable seemed an expression of pain—"what are you going to do with her hair?"

"Spin it into a rope."

"A *rope*?"

"Yes. It'll be very difficult; her hair is terribly fine."

"And what will you do with the rope?"

"Make a knot of it."

"A *knot*?"

"I think that's the term. I'll coil it and secure it so it can't come undone and give it to her. So she'll always have her hair the way it was when she was nineteen."

"How the hell did you talk this poor girl into it?"

"I didn't talk her into it. I merely offered, and she thought it was a lovely idea. Really, Orson, I don't see why this should offend your bourgeois scruples. Women cut their hair all the time."

"She must think you're insane. She was humoring you."

"As you like. It was a perfectly rational suggestion, and my sanity has never been raised as an issue between us."

"Well, *I* think you're insane. Hub, you're a *nut*."

Poor Orson! Every pained syllable that he utters in this exchange with Hub expresses his outrage and indignation. There's nothing very objectionable about Hub's proposal to spin the girl's shorn hair into a rope that she can save. Unfortunately, however, Orson had once admired those same tresses when they were still attached to their owner's head. Full of youthful illusions regarding the pliancy of a young woman's mind, he jumps to the conclusion that she cut off her hair to humor a madman. There's a note of hysteria in Orson's voice, and he's not just kidding when he says, "Hub, you're a *nut*."

It's obvious from this scene that Orson overreacts to Hub's harmless escapades. Of course, the author could just as easily explain all this to you. But simply reading *about* Orson would be like reading a case study in a psychology textbook. Observing Orson's behavior for yourself brings this character to life. That's why most authors use both the expository method of characterization and the dramatic method in the same story; first they tell you about a particular character, then they present scenes that dramatize that character's traits.

In addition to the *methods* an author uses to develop characterization, it is also useful to consider the *types* of characters that an author creates. These can be broadly divided into two categories: flat characters, and round characters.

**3. Flat Characters.** Flat, or two-dimensional, characters have only one or two striking traits. You can usually sum up a flat character in a word or two—"sullen and morose," for example, might adequately describe one flat character; "happy-go-lucky" might convey the essence of another. When the presentation of a single trait is carried to an extreme, the result is a *caricature*.

Flat characters usually play supporting roles in a story, and they are usually static characters. The word *static* means "not moving or not progressing." Thus, static characters do not grow or progress to a better understanding of themselves or the world around them as a result of events in the story. Things happen *to* such characters without things happening *within* them.

"The Christian Roommates" contains a number of flat characters in supporting roles as fellow students in Orson Ziegler's dormitory. Two such characters are a pair of roommates named Silverstein and Koshland. In a few lines, Updike conveys an image of these two characters that remains essentially unchanged throughout the story. What impression of Silverstein and Koshland does the following description leave you with?

> Silverstein and Koshland, who lived in the room overhead, were Jews from New York City. All Orson knew about non-biblical Jews was that they were a sad race, full of music, shrewdness, and woe. But Silverstein and Koshland were always clowning, always wisecracking. They played bridge and poker

and chess and Go and went to the movies in Boston and drank coffee in the luncheonettes around the Square. They came from the "gifted" high schools of the Bronx and Brooklyn respectively, and treated Cambridge as if it were another borough. Most of what the freshman year sought to teach them they seemed to know already.

"Always clowning, always wisecracking" seems to sum up Silverstein and Koshland. They are bright, fun-loving students who are not faced with any conflicts in the course of the story that might reveal other facets of their personalities. Such characters can be interesting or amusing in their own right, but they lack depth. It's interesting to note that Silverstein and Koshland come across not as two persons, but as one. Like Rosencrantz and Guildenstern, you don't see one without the other. This tends to further dilute their individuality.

**4. Round Characters.** The main character in a story is almost invariably round, or three-dimensional. Such characters are more complex than flat characters. For one thing, they exhibit a greater number of character traits, some good and some bad. For another, we usually learn more about them—their personal history, their self-image, their goals and ambitions—and this helps us to understand them better. And, finally, round characters are also dynamic characters—that is, they are affected in some way by the events of the story.

Orson Ziegler is a round character. Not only do we come to know him well, but we witness a gradual change in Orson in the course of the story. Changes occur in a dynamic character as a response to conflict. And, as you might guess, Orson's conflict is with Hub. Hub's presence in their dormitory room grates on Orson like the sound of fingernails dragged across a blackboard. By the end of the school year, their enforced cohabitation has taken its toll on Orson. How is this demonstrated in the following excerpt?

> The doubt Orson had cast upon [Hub's] sanity bounced back onto himself. As spring slowly broke, he lost the ability to sleep. Figures and facts churned sluggishly in an insomnious mire. His courses became four parallel puzzles.... He felt his mind, which was always more steady than quick, grow slower and slower. His chair threatened to adhere to him, and he would leap up in panic. Sleepless, stuffed with information he could neither forget nor manipulate, he became prey to obsessive delusions....

It looks as if Orson is on the verge of a nervous breakdown. He can't sleep, he can't study, and he is haunted by "obsessive delusions." Quite a change from the self-confident, slightly smug young man we met at the beginning of the story.

Orson's conflict with his roommate comes to a head over a grotesque incident involving, of all things, a parking meter. It's a real learning experience, as they say, for Orson, and for the reader, too. By the end of the story you'll feel you know these characters as well as if you had lived in that dormitory with them. As you read "The Christian Roommates," try to picture in your mind's eye the characters you meet. How does the author present and develop them, and what impressions do they make on you?

As you read the story:

- Notice the expository paragraph in the first part of the story where you are introduced to Orson's roommate, Hub.

- Consider whether the character of Petersen is "flat" or "round."

- Pay particular attention to the parking meter episode and what it reveals about Orson.

- Think about how the character of Orson has changed by the end of the story.

# The Christian Roommates
# John Updike

Orson Ziegler came straight to Harvard from the small South Dakota town where his father was the doctor. Orson, at eighteen, was half an inch under six feet tall, with a weight of 164 and an I.Q. of 152. His eczematous cheeks and vaguely irritated squint—as if his face had been for too long transected by the sight of a level horizon—masked a definite self-confidence. As the doctor's son, he had always mattered in the town. In his high school he had been class president, valedictorian, and captain of the football and baseball teams. (The captain of the basketball team had been Lester Spotted Elk, a full-blooded Chippewa with dirty fingernails and brilliant teeth, a smoker, a drinker, a discipline problem, and the only boy Orson ever had met who was better than he at anything that mattered.) Orson was the first native of his town to go to Harvard, and would probably be the last, at least until his son was of age. His future was firm in his mind, the pre-med course here, medical school either at Harvard, Penn, or Yale, and then back to South Dakota, where he had his wife already selected and claimed and primed to wait. Two nights before he left for Harvard, he had taken her virginity. She had cried, and he had felt foolish, having, somehow, failed. It had been his virginity, too. Orson was sane, sane enough to know that he had lots to learn, and to be, within limits, willing. Harvard processes thousands of such boys and restores them to the world with little apparent damage. Presumably because he was from west of the Mississippi and a Protestant Christian (Methodist), the authorities had given him as a freshman roommate a self-converted Episcopalian from Oregon.

When Orson arrived at Harvard on the morning of Registration Day, bleary and stiff from the series of airplane rides that had begun fourteen hours before, his roommate was already installed. "H. Palamountain" was floridly inscribed in the upper of the two name slots on the door of Room 14. The bed by the window had been slept in, and the desk by the window was neatly loaded with books. Standing sleepless inside the door, inertly clinging to his two heavy suitcases, Orson was conscious of another presence in the room without being able to locate it; optically and mentally, he focused with a slight slowness.

The roommate was sitting on the floor, barefoot, before a small spinning wheel. He jumped up nimbly. Orson's first impression was of the wiry quickness that almost magically brought close to his face the thick-lipped, pop-eyed face of the other boy. He was a head shorter than Orson, and wore, above his bare feet, pegged sky-blue slacks, a lumberjack shirt whose throat was dashingly stuffed with a silk foulard, and a white cap such as Orson had seen before only in photographs of Pandit Nehru. Dropping a suitcase, Orson offered his hand. Instead of taking it, the roommate touched his palms together, bowed his head, and murmured something Orson didn't catch. Then he gracefully swept off the white cap, revealing a narrow crest of curly blond hair that stood up like a rooster's comb. "I am Henry Pala-mountain." His voice, clear and colorless in the way of West Coast voices, suggested a radio announcer. His handshake was metallically firm and seemed to have a pinch of malice in it. Like Orson, he wore glasses. The thick lenses emphasized the hyperthyroid bulge of his eyes and their fishy, searching expression.

"Orson Ziegler," Orson said.

"I know."

Orson felt a need to add something adequately solemn, standing as they were on the verge of a kind of marriage. "Well, Henry"—he lamely lowered the other suitcase to the floor—"I guess we'll be seeing a lot of each other."

"You may call me Hub," the roommate said. "Most people do. However, call me Henry if you insist. I don't wish to diminish your dreadful freedom. You may not wish to call me anything at all. Already I've made three hopeless enemies in the dormitory."

Every sentence in this smoothly enunciated speech bothered Orson, beginning with the first. He himself had never been given a nickname; it was the one honor his classmates had withheld from him. In his adolescence he had coined nicknames for himself—Orrie, Ziggy—and tried to insinuate them into popular usage, without success. And what was meant by "dreadful freedom"? It sounded sarcastic. And why might he not wish to call him anything at all? And how had the roommate had the time to make enemies? Orson asked irritably, "How long have you *been* here?"

"Eight days." Henry concluded every statement with a strange little pucker of his lips, a kind of satisfied silent click, as if to say, "And what do you think of *that*?"

Orson felt that he had been sized up as someone easy to startle. But he slid helplessly into the straight-man role that, like the second-best bed, had been reserved for him. "That *long*?"

"Yes. I was totally alone until the day before yesterday. You see, I hitch-hiked."

"From *Oregon*?"

"Yes. And I wished to allow time enough for any contingency. In case I was robbed, I had sewed a fifty-dollar bill inside my shirt. As it turned out, I made smooth connections all the way. I had painted a large cardboard sign saying 'Harvard.' You should try it sometime. One meets some very interesting Harvard graduates."

"Didn't your parents worry?"

"Of course. My parents are divorced. My father was furious. He wanted me to fly. I told him to give the plane fare to the Indian Relief Fund. He never gives a penny to charity. And, of course, I'm old. I'm twenty."

"You've been in the Army?"

Henry lifted his hands and staggered back as if from a blow. He put the back of his hand to his brow, whimpered "Never," shuddered, straightened up smartly, and saluted. "In fact, the Portland draft board is after me right now." With a preening tug of his two agile hands—which did look, Orson realized, old: bony and veined and red-tipped, like a woman's—he broadened his foulard. "They refuse to recognize any conscientious objectors except Quakers and Mennonites. My bishop agrees with them. They offered me an out if I'd say I was willing to work in a hospital, but I explained that this released a man for combat duty and if it came to that I'd just as soon carry a gun. I'm an excellent shot. I mind killing only on principle."

The Korean War had begun that summer, and Orson, who had been nagged by a suspicion that his duty was to enlist, bristled at such blithe pacifism. He squinted and asked, "What *have* you been doing for two years, then?"

"Working in a plywood mill. As a gluer. The actual gluing is done by machines, but they become swamped in their own glue now and then. It's a kind of excessive introspection—you've read *Hamlet*?"

"Just *Macbeth* and *The Merchant of Venice*."

"Yes. Anyway. They have to be cleaned with solvent. One wears long rubber gloves up to one's elbows. It's very soothing work. The inside of a gluer is an excellent place for resolving Greek quotations in your head. I memorized nearly the whole of the *Phaedo* that way." He gestured toward his desk, and Orson saw that many of the books were green Loeb editions of Plato and Aristotle, in Greek. Their spines were worn; they looked read and reread. For the first time, the thought of being at Harvard frightened him. Orson had been standing between his suitcases and now he moved to unpack. "Have you left me a bureau?"

"Of course. The better one." Henry jumped on the bed that had not been slept in and bounced up and down as if it were a trampoline. "And I've given you the bed with the better mattress," he said, still bouncing, "and the desk that doesn't have the glare from the window."

"Thanks," Orson said.

Henry was quick to notice his tone. "Would you rather have my bed? My desk?" He jumped from the bed and dashed to his desk and scooped a stack of books from it.

Orson had to touch him to stop him, and was startled by the tense muscularity of the arm he touched. "Don't be silly," he said. "They're exactly alike."

Henry replaced his books. "I don't want any bitterness," he said, "or immature squabbling. As the older man, it's my responsibility to yield. I'll give you the shirt off my back." And he began to peel off his lumberjack shirt, leaving the foulard dramatically knotted around his naked throat. He wore no undershirt.

Having won from Orson a facial expression that Orson himself could not see, Henry smiled and rebuttoned the shirt. "Do you mind my name being in the upper slot on the door? I'll remove it. I apologize. I did it without realizing how sensitive you would be."

Perhaps it was all a kind of humor. Orson tried to make a joke. He pointed and asked, "Do I get a spinning wheel, too?"

"Oh, *that*." Henry hopped backward on one bare foot and became rather shy. "That's an experiment. I ordered it from Calcutta. I spin for a half hour a day, after Yoga."

"You do Yoga, too?"

"Just some of the elementary positions. My ankles can't take more than five minutes of the Lotus yet."

"And you say you have a bishop."

The roommate glanced up with a glint of fresh interest. "Say. You listen, don't you? Yes. I consider myself an Anglican Christian Platonist strongly influenced by Gandhi." He touched his palms before his chest, bowed, straightened, and giggled. "My bishop hates me," he said. "The one in Oregon, who wants me to be a soldier. I've introduced myself to the bishop here and I don't think he likes me, either. For that matter, I've antagonized my adviser. I told him I had no intention of fulfilling the science requirement."

"For God's sake, why *not*?"

"You don't really want to know."

Orson felt this rebuff as a small test of strength. "Not really," he agreed.

"I consider science a demonic illusion of human *hubris*. Its phantasmal nature is proved by its constant revision. I asked him, "Why should I waste an entire fourth of my study time, time that could be spent with Plato, mastering a mass of hypotheses that will be obsolete by the time I graduate?"

"My Lord, Henry," Orson exclaimed, indignantly defending the millions of lives saved by medical science, "you can't be serious!"

"Please. Hub. I may be difficult for you, and I think it would help if you were to call me by my name. Now let's talk about you. Your father is a doctor, you received all A's in high school—I received rather mediocre grades myself—and you've come to Harvard because you believe it affords a cosmopolitan Eastern environment that will be valuable to you after spending your entire life in a small provincial town."

"Who the hell told you all this?" The recital of his application statement made Orson blush. He already felt much older than the boy who had written it.

"University Hall," Henry said. "I went over and asked to see your folder. They didn't want to let me at first but I explained that if they were going to give me a roommate, after I had specifically requested to live alone, I had a right to information about you, so I could minimize possible friction."

"And they *let* you?"

"Of course. People without convictions have no powers of resistance." His mouth made its little satisfied click, and Orson was goaded to ask, "Why did *you* come to Harvard?"

"Two reasons." He ticked them off on two fingers. "Raphael Demos and Werner Jaeger."

Orson did not know these names, but he suspected that "Friend of yours?" was a stupid question, once it was out of his mouth.

But Henry nodded, "I've introduced myself to Demos. A charming old scholar, with a beautiful young wife."

"You mean you just went to his house and pushed yourself *in*?" Orson heard his own voice grow shrill; his voice, rather high and unstable, was one of the things about himself that he liked least.

Henry blinked, and looked unexpectedly vulnerable, so slender and bravely dressed, his ugly, yellowish, flat-nailed feet naked on the floor, which was uncarpeted and painted black. "That isn't how I would describe it. I went as a pilgrim. He seemed pleased to talk to me." He spoke carefully, and his mouth abstained from clicking.

That he could hurt his roommate's feelings—that this jaunty apparition had feelings—disconcerted Orson more deeply than any of the surprises he had been deliberately offered. As quickly as he had popped up, Henry dropped to the floor, as if through a trapdoor in the plane of conversation. He resumed spinning. The method apparently called for one thread to be wound around the big toe of a foot and to be kept taut by a kind of absent-minded pedal motion. While engaged in this, he seemed hermetically sealed inside one of the gluing machines that had incubated his garbled philosophy. Unpacking, Orson was slowed and snagged by a complicated mood of discomfort. He tried to remember how his mother had arranged his bureau drawers at home—socks and underwear in one, shirts and handkerchiefs in another. Home seemed infinitely far from him, and he was dizzily conscious of a great depth of space beneath his feet, as if the blackness of the floor were the color of an abyss. The spinning wheel steadily chuckled. Orson's buzz of unease circled and settled on his roommate, who, it was clear, had thought earnestly about profound matters, matters that Orson, busy as he had been with the practical business of being a good student, had hardly considered. It was also clear that Henry had thought unintelligently. This unintelligence ("I received rather mediocre grades myself") was more of a menace than a comfort. Bent above the bureau drawers, Orson felt cramped in his mind, able neither to stand erect in wholehearted contempt nor to lie down in honest admiration. His mood was complicated by the repugnance his roommate's physical presence aroused in him. An almost morbidly clean boy, Orson was haunted by glue, and a tacky ambience resisted every motion of his unpacking.

The silence between the roommates continued until a great bell rang ponderously. The sound was near and yet far, like a heartbeat within the bosom of time, and it seemed to bring with it into the room the muffling foliation of the trees in the Yard, which to Orson's prairie-honed eyes had looked tropically tall and lush; the walls of the room vibrated with leaf shadows, and many minute presences—dust motes, traffic sounds, or angels of whom several could dance on the head of a pin—thronged the air and made it difficult to breathe. The stairways of the dormitory rumbled.

Boys dressed in jackets and neckties crowded the doorway and entered the room, laughing and calling "Hub. Hey, Hub."

"Get up off the floor, dad."

"Jesus, Hub, put your shoes on."

"Pee-*yew*."

"And take off that seductive sarong around your neck."

"Consider the lilies, Hub. They toil not, neither do they spin, and yet I say unto you that Solomon in all his glory was not arrayed like one of these."

"Amen, brothers!"

"Fitch, you should be a preacher."

They were all strangers to Orson. Hub stood and smoothly performed introductions.

In a few days, Orson had sorted them out. That jostling conglomerate, so apparently secure and homogeneous, broke down, under habitual exposure, into double individuals: roommates. There were Silverstein and Koshland, Dawson and Kern, Young and Carter, Petersen and Fitch.

Silverstein and Koshland, who lived in the room overhead, were Jews from New York City. All Orson knew about non-biblical Jews was that they were a sad race, full of music, shrewdness, and woe. But Silverstein and Koshland were always clowning, always wisecracking. They played bridge and poker and chess and Go and went to the movies in Boston and drank coffee in the luncheonettes around the Square. They came from the "gifted" high schools of the Bronx and Brooklyn respectively, and treated Cambridge as if it were another borough. Most of what the freshmen year sought to teach them they seemed to know already. As winter approached, Koshland went out for basketball, and he and his teammates made the floor above bounce to the thump and rattle of scrimmages with a tennis ball and a wastebasket. One afternoon, a section of ceiling collapsed on Orson's bed.

Next door, in Room 12, Dawson and Kern wanted to be writers. Dawson was from Ohio and Kern from Pennsylvania. Dawson had a sulky, slouching bearing, a certain puppyish facial eagerness, and a terrible temper. He was a disciple of Anderson and Hemingway and himself wrote as austerely as a newspaper. He had been raised as an atheist, and no one in the dormitory incited his temper more often than Hub. Orson, feeling that he and Dawson came from opposite edges of that great psychological realm called the Midwest, liked him. He felt less at ease with Kern, who seemed Eastern and subtly vicious. A farm boy driven by an unnatural sophistication, riddled with nervous ailments ranging from conjunctivitis to hemorrhoids, Kern smoked and talked incessantly. He and Dawson maintained between them a battery of running jokes. At night Orson could hear them on the other side of the wall keeping each other awake with improvised parodies and musical comedies based on their teachers, their courses, or their fellow-freshmen. One midnight, Orson distinctly heard Dawson sing, "My name is Orson Ziegler, I come from South Dakota." There was a pause, then Kern sang back, "I tend to be a niggler, and masturbate by quota."

Across the hall, in 15, lived Young and Carter, Negroes. Carter was from Detroit and very black, very clipped in speech, very well dressed, and apt to collapse, at the jab of a rightly angled joke, into a spastic giggling fit that left his cheeks gleaming with tears; Kern was expert at breaking Carter up. Young was a lean, malt-pale colored boy from North Carolina, here on a national scholarship, out of his depth, homesick, and cold. Kern called him Br'er Possum. He slept all day and at night sat on his bed playing the mouthpiece of a trumpet to himself. At first, he had played the full horn in the afternoon, flooding the dormitory and its green envelope of trees with golden, tremulous versions of languorous tunes like "Sentimental Journey" and "The Tennessee Waltz." It had been nice. But Young's sombre sense of tact—a slavish drive toward self-effacement that the shock of Harvard had awakened in him— soon cancelled these harmless performances. He took to hiding from the sun, and at night the furtive spitting sound from across the hall seemed to Orson, as he struggled to sleep, music drowning in shame. Carter always referred to his roommate as "Jonathan," mouthing the sylla- bles fastidiously, as if he were pronouncing the name of a remote being he had just learned about, like Rochefoucauld or Demosthenes.

Cattycorner up the hall, in unlucky 13, Petersen and Fitch kept a strange household. Both were tall, narrow-shouldered, and broad-bottomed; phy- siques aside, it was hard to see what they had in common, or why Harvard had put them together. Fitch, with dark staring eyes and the flat full cranium of Frankenstein's monster, was a child prodigy from Maine, choked with philosophy, wild with ideas, and pregnant with the seeds of the nervous breakdown he was to have, eventually, in April. Petersen was an amiable Swede with a transparent skin that revealed blue veins in his nose. For several summers he had worked as a reporter for the Duluth *Herald*. He had all the newsman's tricks: the side-of-the-mouth quip, the nip of whiskey, the hat on the back of the head, the habit of throwing still-burning cigarettes onto the floor. He did not seem quite to know why he was at Harvard, and in fact did not return at the end of the freshman year. But, while those two drifted toward their respective failures, they made a stran- gely well-suited couple. Each was strong where the other was helpless. Fitch was so uncoordinated and unorganized he could not even type; he would lie on his bed in pajamas, writhing and grimacing, and dictate a tangled humanities paper, twice the requested length and mostly about books that had not been assigned, while Petersen, typing with a hectic two-finger system, would obligingly turn this chaotic monologue into "copy." His patience verged on the maternal. When Fitch appeared for a meal wearing a coat and tie, the joke ran in the dormitory that Petersen had dressed him. In return, Fitch gave Petersen ideas out of the superabundance painfully cramming his big flat head. Petersen had absolutely no ideas; he could neither compare, contrast, nor criticize St. Augustine and Marcus Aurelius. Perhaps having seen, so young, so many corpses and fires and policemen and prostitutes had prematurely blighted his mind. At any rate, mothering Fitch gave him something practical to do, and Orson envied them.

He envied all the roommates, whatever the bond between them— geography, race, ambition, physical size—for between himself and Hub Palamountain he could see no link except forced cohabitation. Not that living with Hub was superficially unpleasant. Hub was tidy, industrious, and ostentatiously considerate. He rose at seven, prayed, did Yoga, spun, and was off to breakfast, often not to be seen again until the end of the day. He went to sleep, generally, at eleven sharp. If there was noise in the room, he would insert rubber plugs in his ears, put a black mask over his eyes, and go to sleep anyway. During the day, he kept a rigorous round of appointments: he audited two courses in addition to taking four, he wrestled three times a week for his physical-training requirement, he wangled tea invitations from Demos and Jaeger and the Bishop of Massachusetts, he attended free evening lectures and readings, he associated himself with Phillips Brooks House and spent two afternoons a week supervising slum boys in a Roxbury redevelopment house. In addition, he had begun to take piano lessons in Brookline. Many days, Orson saw him only at meals in the Union, where the dormitory neighbors, in those first fall months when their acquaintance was crisp and young and differing interests had not yet scattered them, tended to regroup around a long table. In these months there was often a debate about the subject posed under their eyes: Hub's vegetarianism. There he would sit, his tray heaped high with a steaming double helping of squash and lima beans, while Fitch would try to locate the exact point at which vegetarianism became inconsistent. "You eat eggs," he said.

"Yes," Hub said.

"You realize that every egg, from the chicken's point of reference, is a newborn baby?"

"But in fact it is not unless it has been fertilized by a rooster."

"But suppose," Fitch pursued, "as sometimes happens—which I happen to know, from working in my uncle's henhouse in Maine—an egg that *should* be sterile has in fact been fertilized and contains an embryo?"

"If I see it, I naturally don't eat that particular egg," Hub said, his lips making that satisfied concluding snap.

Fitch pounced triumphantly, spilling a fork to the floor with a lurch of his hand. "But *why?* The hen feels the same pain on being parted from an egg whether sterile or fertile. The embryo is unconscious—a vegetable. As a vegetarian, you should eat it with special relish." He tipped back in his chair so hard he had to grab the table edge to keep from toppling over.

"It seems to me," Dawson said, frowning darkly—these discussions, clogging some twist of his ego, often spilled him into a vile temper—"that psychoanalysis of hens is hardly relevant."

"On the contrary," Kern said lightly, clearing his throat and narrowing his pink, infected eyes, "It seems to me that there, in the tiny, dim mind of the hen—the minimal mind, as it were—is where the tragedy of the universe achieves a pinpoint focus. Picture the emotional life of a hen. What does she know of companionship? A flock of pecking, harsh-voiced gossips. Of shelter? A few dung-bespattered slats. Of food? Some flecks of mash and grit insolently tossed on the ground. Of love? The casual assault of a polygamous cock—cock in the Biblical sense. Then, into this heartless world, there suddenly arrives, as if by magic, an egg. An egg of her own. An egg, it must seem to her, that she and God have made. How she must cherish it, its beautiful baldness, its gentle lustre, its firm yet somehow fragile, softly swaying weight."

Carter had broken up. He bent above his tray, his eyes tight shut, his dark face contorted joyfully. "Puhleese," he gasped at last. "You're making my stomach hurt."

"Ah, Carter," Kern said loftily, "if that were only the worst of it. For then, one day, while the innocent hen sits cradling this strange, faceless, oval child, its little weight swaying softly in her wings"—he glanced hopefully at Carter, but the colored boy bit his lower lip and withstood the jab—"an enormous man, smelling of beer and manure, comes and tears the egg from her grasp. And why? Because *he*"—Kern pointed, arm fully extended, across the table, so that his index finger, orange with nicotine, almost touched Hub's nose—"*he*, Saint Henry Palamountain, wants more eggs to eat. 'More eggs!' he cries voraciously, so that brutal steers and faithless pigs can continue to menace the children of American mothers!"

Dawson slammed his silver down, got up from the table, and slouched out of the dining room. Kern blushed. In the silence, Petersen put a folded slice of roast beef in his mouth and said, chewing, "Jesus, Hub, if somebody else kills the animals you might as well eat 'em. They don't give a damn any more."

"You understand nothing," Hub said simply.

"Hey, Hub," Silverstein called down from the far end of the table. "What's the word on milk? Don't calves drink milk? Maybe you're taking milk out of some calf's mouth."

Orson felt impelled to speak. *"No,"* he said, and his voice seemed to have burst, its pitch was so unsteady and excited. "As anybody except somebody from New York would know, milch cows have weaned their calves. What I wonder about, Hub, is your shoes. You wear leather shoes."

"I do." The gaiety left Hub's defense of himself. His lips became prim.

"Leather is the skin of a steer."

"But the animal has already been slaughtered."

"You sound like Petersen. Your purchase of leather goods—what about your wallet and belt, for that matter?—encourages the slaughter. You're as much of a murderer as the rest of us. More of one—because you think about it."

Hub folded his hands carefully in front of him, propping them, almost in prayer, on the table edge. His voice became like that of a radio announcer, but an announcer rapidly, softly describing the home stretch of a race. "My belt, I believe, is a form of plastic. My wallet was given to me by my mother years ago, before I became a vegetarian. Please remember that I ate meat for eighteen years and I still have an appetite for it. If there were any other concentrated source of protein, I would not eat eggs. Some vegetarians do not. On the other hand, some vegetarians eat fish and take liver extract. I would not do this. Shoes are a problem. There is a firm in Chicago that makes non-leather shoes for extreme vegetarians, but they're very expensive and not comfortable. I once ordered a pair. They killed my feet. Leather, you see, 'breathes' in a way no synthetic substitute does. My feet are tender; I have compromised. I apologize. For that matter, when I play the piano I encourage the slaughter of elephants, and in brushing my teeth, which I must do faithfully because a vegetable diet is so heavy in carbohydrates, I use a brush of pig bristles. I am covered with blood, and pray daily for forgiveness." He took up his fork and resumed eating the mound of squash.

Orson was amazed; he had been impelled to speak by a kind of sympathy, and Hub had answered as if he alone were an enemy. He tried to defend himself. "There are perfectly wearable shoes," he said, "Made out of canvas, with crepe-rubber soles."

"I'll look into them," Hub said. "They sound a little sporty to me."

Laughter swept the table and ended the subject. After lunch Orson walked to the library with the beginnings of indigestion; a backwash of emotion was upsetting his stomach. There was a growing confusion inside him he could not resolve. He resented being associated with Hub, and yet felt attacked when Hub was attacked. It seemed to him that Hub deserved credit for putting his beliefs into practice, and that people like Fitch and Kern, in mocking, merely belittled themselves. Yet Hub smiled at their criticism, took it as a game, and fought back in earnest only at Orson, forcing him into a false position. Why? Was it because in being also a Christian he alone qualified for serious rebuke? But Carter went to church, wearing a blue pin-striped suit with a monogrammed handkerchief peaked in the breast pocket, every Sunday; Petersen was a nominal Presbyterian; Orson had once seen Kern sneaking out of Mem Chapel; and even Koshland observed his holidays, by cutting classes and skipping lunch. Why, therefore, Orson asked himself, should Hub pick on him? And why should he care? He had no real respect for Hub. Hub's handwriting was childishly large and careful and his first set of hour exams, even in the course on Plato and Aristotle, had yielded a batch of C's. Orson resented being condescended to by an intellectual inferior. The knowledge that at the table he had come off second best galled him like an unfair grade. His situation with Hub became in his head a diagram in which all his intentions curved off at right angles and his strengths inversely tapered into nothing. Behind the diagram hung the tuck of complacence in Hub's lips, the fishy impudence of his eyes, and the keenly irksome shape and tint of his hands and feet. These images—Hub disembodied—Orson carried with him into the library, back and forth to classes, and along the congested streets around the Square; now and then the glaze of an eye or the flat yellowish nail of a big toe welled up distinctly through the pages of a book and, greatly magnified, slid with Orson into the unconsciousness of sleep. Nevertheless, he surprised himself, sitting one February afternoon in Room 12 with Dawson and Kern, by blurting, "I hate him." He considered what he had said, liked the taste of it, and repeated, "I hate the bastard. I've never hated anybody before in my life." His voice cracked and his eyes warmed with abortive tears.

They had all returned from Christmas vacation to plunge into the weird limbo of reading period and the novel ordeal of midyear exams. This was a dormitory, by and large, of public-school graduates, who feel the strain of Harvard most in their freshman year. The private-school boys, launched by little Harvards like Exeter and Groton, tend to glide through this year and to run aground later on strange reefs, foundering in alcohol, or sinking in a dandified apathy. But the institution demands of each man, before it releases him, a wrenching sacrifice of ballast. At Christmas, Orson's mother thought he looked haggard, and set about fattening him up. On the other hand, he was struck by how much his father had aged and shrunk. Orson spent his first days home listening to the mindless music on the radio, hours of it, and driving through farmland on narrow straight roads already banked bright with plowed snow. The South Dakota sky had never looked so open, so clean; he had never realized before that the high dry sun that made even sub-zero days feel warm at noon was a local phenomenon. He made love to his girl again, and again she cried. He said to her he blamed himself, for ineptitude; but in his heart he blamed her. She was not helping him. Back in Cambridge, it was raining, raining in January, and the entryway of the Coop was full of gray footprints and wet bicycles and Radcliffe girls in slickers and sneakers. Hub had stayed here, alone in their room, and had celebrated Christmas with a fast.

In the monotonous, almost hallucinatory month of rereading, outlining, and memorizing, Orson perceived how little he knew, how stupid he was, how unnatural all learning is, and how futile. Harvard rewarded him with three A's and a B. Hub pulled out two B's and two C's. Kern, Dawson, and Silverstein did well; Petersen, Koshland, and Carter got mediocre grades; Fitch flunked one subject, and Young flunked three. The pale Negro slunk in and out of the dorm as if he were diseased and marked for destruction; he became, while still among them, a rumor. The suppressed whistling of the trumpet mouthpiece was no longer heard. Silverstein and Koshland and the basketball crowd adopted Carter and took him to movies in Boston three or four times a week.

After exams, in the heart of the Cambridge winter, there is a grateful pause. New courses are selected, and even the full-year courses, heading into their second half, sometimes put on, like a new hat, a fresh professor. The days quietly lengthen; there is a snowstorm or two; the swimming and squash teams lend the sports pages of the *Crimson* an unaccustomed note of victory. A kind of foreshadow of spring falls bluely on the snow. The elms are seen to be shaped like fountains. The discs of snow pressed by boots into the sidewalk by Albiani's seem large precious coins; the brick buildings, the arched gates, the archaic lecterns, and the barny mansions along Brattle Street dawn upon the freshman as a heritage he temporarily possesses. The thumb-worn spines of his now familiar textbooks seem proof of a certain knowingness, and the strap of the green book bag tugs at his wrist like a living falcon. The letters from home dwindle in importance. The hours open up. There is more time. Experiments are made. Courtships begin. Conversations go on and on; and an almost rapacious desire for mutual discovery possesses acquaintances. It was in this atmosphere, then, that Orson made his confession.

Dawson turned his head away as if the words had menaced him personally. Kern blinked, lit a cigarette, and asked, "What don't you like about him?"

"Well"—Orson shifted his weight uncomfortably in the black but graceful, shapely but hard Harvard chair—"it's little things. Whenever he gets a notice from the Portland draft board, he tears it up without opening it and scatters it out the window."

"And you're afraid that this incriminates you as an accessory and they'll put you in jail?"

"No—I don't know. It seems exaggerated. He exaggerates everything. You should see how he prays."

"How do you know how he prays?"

"He shows me. Every morning, he gets down on his knees and *throws* himself across the bed, his face in the blanket, his arms way out." He showed them.

"God," Dawson said. "That's marvellous. It's medieval. It's more than medieval. It's Counter-Reformation."

"I mean," Orson said, grimacing in realization of how deeply he had betrayed Hub, "I pray, too, but I don't make a show of myself."

A frown clotted Dawson's expression, and passed.

"He's a saint," Kern said.

"He's *not*," Orson said. "He's not intelligent. I'm taking Chem 1 with him, and he's worse than a child with the math. And those Greek books he keeps on his desk, they look worn because he bought them second-hand."

"Saints don't have to be intelligent,' Kern said. "What saints have to have is energy. Hub has it."

"Look how he wrestles," Dawson said.

"I doubt if he wrestles very *well*," Orson said. "He didn't make the freshman team. I'm sure if we heard him play the piano, it'd be awful."

"You seem to miss the point," Kern said, eyes closed, "of what Hub's all about."

"I know goddam well what he thinks he's all about," Orson said, "but it's fake. It doesn't go. All this vegetarianism and love of the starving Indian—he's really a terribly cold bastard. I think he's about the coldest person I've ever met in my life."

"I don't think Orson thinks that; do you?" Kern asked Dawson.

"No," Dawson said, and his puppyish smile cleared his cloudy face. "That's not what Orson the Parson thinks."

Kern squinted. "Is it Orson the Parson, or Orson the Person?"

"I think Hub is the nub," Dawson said.

"Or the rub," Kern added, and both burst into grinding laughter. Orson felt he was being sacrificed to the precarious peace the two roommates kept between themselves, and left, superficially insulted but secretly flattered to have been given, at last, a nickname of sorts: Orson the Parson.

Several nights later they went to hear Carl Sandburg read in New Lecture Hall—the four adjacent roommates, plus Fitch. To avoid sitting next to Hub, who aggressively led them into a row of seats, Orson delayed, and so sat the farthest away from the girl Hub sat directly behind. Orson noticed her immediately; she had a lavish mane of coppery red hair which hung down loose over the back of her seat. The color of it, and the abundance, reminded him, all at once, of horses, earth, sun, wheat, and home. From Orson's angle she was nearly in profile; her face was small, with a tilted shadowy cheekbone and a pale prominent ear. Toward the pallor of her profile he felt an orgasmic surge; she seemed suspended in the crowd and was floating, a crest of whiteness, toward him. She turned away. Hub had leaned forward and was saying something into her other ear. Fitch overheard it, and gleefully relayed it to Dawson, who whispered to Kern and Orson; *"Hub said to the girl, 'You have beautiful hair.' "*

Several times during the reading, Hub leaned forward to add something more into her ear, each time springing spurts of choked laughter from Fitch, Dawson, and Kern. Meanwhile, Sandburg, his white bangs as straight and shiny as a doll's wig of artificial fibre, incanted above the lectern and quaintly strummed a guitar. Afterward, Hub walked with the girl into the outdoors. From a distance Orson saw her white face turn and crumple into a laugh. Hub returned to his friends with the complacent nick in the corner of his mouth deepened, in the darkness, to a gash.

It was not the next day, or the next week, but within the month that Hub brought back to the room a heap of red hair. Orson found it lying like a diaphanous corpse on a newspaper spread on his bed. "Hub, what the hell is this?"

Hub was on the floor playing with his spinning wheel. "Hair."

*"Human* hair?"

"Of course."

"Whose?"

"A girl's."

"What happened?" The question sounded strange; Orson meant to ask, "What girl's?"

Hub answered as if he had asked that question. "It's a girl I met at the Sandburg reading; you don't know her."

"This is *her* hair?"

"Yes. I asked her for it. She said she was planning to cut it all off this spring anyway."

Orson stood stunned above the bed, gripped by an urge to bury his face and hands in the hair. "You've been *seeing* her?" This effeminate stridence in his voice: he despised it and only Hub brought it out.

"A little. My schedule doesn't allow for much social life, but my adviser has recommended that I relax now and then."

"You take her to movies?"

"Once in a while. She pays her admission, of course."

"Of *course.*"

Hub took him up on his tone. "Please remember I'm here on my savings alone. I have refused all financial assistance from my father."

"Hub"—the very syllable seemed an expression of pain—"what are you going to do with her hair?"

"Spin it into a rope."

"A *rope?*"

"Yes. It'll be very difficult; her hair is terribly fine."

"And what will you do with the rope?"

"Make a knot of it."

"A *knot?*"

"I think that's the term. I'll coil it and secure it so it can't come undone and give it to her. So she'll always have her hair the way it was when she was nineteen."

"How the hell did you talk this poor girl into it?"

"I didn't talk her into it. I merely offered, and she thought it was a lovely idea. Really, Orson, I don't see why this should offend your bourgeois scruples. Women cut their hair all the time."

"She must think you're insane. She was humoring you."

"As you like. It was a perfectly rational suggestion, and my sanity has never been raised as an issue between us."

"Well, *I* think you're insane. Hub, you're a *nut.*"

Orson left the room and slammed the door, and din't return until eleven, when Hub was asleep in his eye mask. The heap of hair had been transferred to the floor beside the spinning wheel, and already some strands were entangled with the machine. In time a rope was produced, a braided cord as thick as a woman's little finger, about a foot long, weightless and waxen. The earthy, horsy'fire in the hair's color had been quenched in the process. Hub carefully coiled it and with black thread and long pins secured and stiffened the spiral into a disc the size of a small saucer. This he presented to the girl one Friday night. The presentation appeared to satisfy him, for, as far as Orson knew, Hub had no further dates with her. Once in a while Orson passed her in the Yard, and without her hair she scarcely seemed female, her small pale face fringed in curt tufts, her ears looking enormous. He wanted to speak to her; some obscure force of pity, or hope of rescue, impelled him to greet this wan androgyne, but the opening word stuck in his throat. She did not look as if she pitied herself, or knew what had been done to her.

Something magical protected Hub; things deflected from him. The doubt Orson had cast upon his sanity bounced back onto himself. As spring slowly broke, he lost the ability to sleep. Figures and facts churned sluggishly in an insomnious mire. His courses became four parallel puzzles. In mathematics, the crucial transposition upon which the solution pivoted consistently eluded him, vanishing into the chinks between the numbers. The quantities in chemistry became impishly unstable; the unbalanced scales clicked down sharply and the system of interlocked elements that fanned from the lab to the far stars collapsed. In the history survey course, they had reached the Enlightenment, and Orson found himself disturbingly impressed by Voltaire's indictment of God, though the lecturer handled it calmly, as one more dead item of intellectual history, neither true nor false. And in German, which Orson had taken to satisfy his language requirement, the words piled on remorselessly, and the existence of languages other than English, the existence of so many, each so vast, intricate, and opaque, seemed to prove cosmic dementia. He felt his mind, which was always more steady than quick, grow slower and slower. His chair threatened to adhere to him, and he would leap up in panic. Sleepless, stuffed with information he could neither forget nor manipulate, he became prey to obsessive delusions; he became convinced that his girl in South Dakota had taken up with another boy and was making love to him happily, Orson having shouldered the awkwardness and blame of taking her virginity. In the very loops that Emily's ballpoint pen described in her bland letters to him he read the pleased rotundity, the inner fatness of a well-loved woman.

He even knew the man. It was Spotted Elk, the black-nailed Chippewa, whose impassive nimbleness had so often mocked Orson on the basketball court, whose terrible ease and speed of reaction had seemed so unjust, and whose defense—he recalled now—Emily had often undertaken. His wife had become a whore, a squaw; the scraggly mute reservation children his father had doctored in the charity clinic became, amid the sliding transparencies of Orson's mind, his own children. In his dreams—or in those limp elisions of imagery which in the absence of sleep passed for dreams—he seemed to be rooming with Spotted Elk, and his roommate, who sometimes wore a mask, invariably had won, by underhanded means, the affection and admiration that were rightfully his. There was a conspiracy. Whenever Orson heard Kern and Dawson laughing on the other side of the wall, he knew it was about him, and about his most secret habits. This ultimate privacy was outrageously invaded; in bed, half-relaxed, he would suddenly see himself bodily involved with Hub's lips, Hub's legs, with Hub's veined, vaguely womanish hands. At first he resisted these visions, tried to erase them; it was like trying to erase ripples on water. He learned to submit to them, to let the attack—for it was an attack, with teeth and sharp acrobatic movements—wash over him, leaving him limp enough to sleep. These dives became the only route to sleep. In the morning he would awake and see Hub sprawled flamboyantly across his bed in prayer, or sitting hunched at his spinning wheel, or gaudily dressed, tiptoeing to the door and with ostentatious care closing it softly behind him; and he would hate him—hate his appearance, his form, his manner, his pretensions with an avidity of detail he had never known in love. The tiny details of his roommate's physical existence—the wrinkles flickering beside his mouth, the slightly withered look about his hands, the complacently polished creases of his leather shoes—seemed a poisonous food Orson could not stop eating. His eczema worsened alarmingly.

By April, Orson was on the verge of going to the student clinic, which had a department called Mental Health. But at this point Fitch relieved him by having, it seemed, his nervous breakdown for him. For weeks, Fitch had been taking several showers a day. Toward the end he stopped going to classes and was almost constantly naked, except for a towel tucked around his waist. He was trying to complete a humanities paper that was already a month overdue and twenty pages too long. He left the dormitory only to eat and to take more books from the library. One night around nine, Petersen was called to the phone on the second-floor landing. The Watertown police had picked Fitch up as he was struggling through the underbrush on the banks of the Charles four miles away. He claimed he was walking to the West, where he had been told there was enough space to contain God, and proceeded to talk with wild animation to the police chief about the differences and affinities between Kierkegaard and Nietzsche. Hub, ever alert for an opportunity to intrude in the guise of doing good, went to the hall proctor—a spindly and murmurous graduate student of astronomy engaged, under Harlow Shapley, in an endless galaxy count—and volunteered himself as an expert on the case, and even conferred with the infirmary psychologist. Hub's interpretation was that Fitch had been punished for *hubris*. The psychologist felt the problem was fundamentally Oedipal. Fitch was sent back to Maine. Hub suggested to Orson that now Petersen would need a roommate next year. "I think you and he would hit it off splendidly. You're both materialists."

"I'm *not* a materialist."

Hub lifted his dreadful hands in half-blessing. "Have it your way. I'm determined to minimize friction."

"Dammit, Hub, all the friction between us comes from *you.*"

"How? What do I do? Tell me, and I'll change. I'll give you the shirt off my back." He began to unbutton, and stopped, seeing that the laugh wasn't going to come.

Orson felt weak and empty, and in spite of himself he cringed inwardly, with a helpless affection for his unreal, unreachable friend. "I don't know, Hub," he admitted. "I don't know what it is you're doing to me."

A paste of silence dried in the air between them.

Orson with an effort unstuck himself. "I think you're right, we shouldn't room together next year."

Hub seemed a bit bewildered, but nodded, saying, "I told them in the beginning that I ought to live alone." And his hurt eyes bulging behind their lenses settled into an invulnerable Byzantine stare.

One afternoon in middle May, Orson was sitting stumped at his desk, trying to study. He had taken two exams and had two to go. They stood between him and release like two towering walls of muddy paper. His position seemed extremely precarious: he was unable to retreat and able to advance only along a very thin thread, a high wire of sanity on which he balanced above an abyss of statistics and formulae, his brain a firmament of winking cells. A push would kill him. There was then a hurried pounding up the stairs, and Hub pushed into the room carrying cradled in his arm a metal object the color of a gun and the size of a cat. It had a red tongue. Hub slammed the door behind him, snapped the lock, and dumped the object on Orson's bed. It was the head of a parking meter, sheared from its post. A keen quick pain cut through Orson's groin. "For God's sake," he cried in his contemptible high voice, "what's *that?*"

"It's a parking meter."

"I *know*, I can *see* that. Where the hell did you *get* it?"

"I won't talk to you until you stop being hysterical," Hub said, and crossed to his desk, where Orson had put his mail. He took the top letter, a special delivery from the Portland draft board, and tore it in half. This time, the pain went through Orson's chest. He put his head in his arms on the desk and whirled and groped in the black-red darkness there. His body was frightening him; his nerves listened for a third psychosomatic slash.

There was a rap on the door; from the force of the knock, it could only be the police. Hub nimbly dashed to the bed and hid the meter under Orson's pillow. Then he pranced to the door and opened it.

It was Dawson and Kern. "What's up?" Dawson asked, frowning as if the disturbance had been created to annoy him.

"It sounded like Ziegler was being tortured," Kern said.

Orson pointed at Hub and explained, "He's castrated a parking meter!"

"I did not," Hub said. "A car went out of control on Mass. Avenue and hit a parked car, which knocked a meter down. A crowd gathered. The head of the meter was lying in the gutter, so I picked it up and carried it away. I was afraid someone might be tempted to steal it."

"Nobody tried to stop you?" Kern asked.

"Of course not. They were all gathered around the driver of the car."

"Was he hurt?"

"I doubt it. I didn't look."

"You didn't *look!*" Orson cried. "You're a great Samaritan."

"I am not prey," Hub said, "to morbid curiosity."

"Where were the police?" Kern asked.

"They hadn't arrived yet."

Dawson asked, "Well why didn't you wait till a cop arrived and give the meter to him?"

"Why should I give it to an agent of the State? It's no more his than mine."

"But it *is.*" Orson said.

"It was a plain act of Providence that placed it in my hands," Hub said, the corners of his lips dented securely. "I haven't decided yet which charity should receive the money it contains."

Dawson asked, "But isn't that stealing?"

"No more stealing than the State is stealing in making people pay money for space in which to park their own cars."

"Hub," Orson said, getting to his feet. "You give it back or we'll both go to jail." He saw himself ruined, the scarcely commenced career of his life destroyed.

Hub turned serenely. "I'm not afraid. Going to jail under a totalitarian regime is a mark of honor. If you had a conscience, you'd understand."

Petersen and Carter and Silverstein came into the room. Some boys from the lower floors follwed them. The story was hilariously retold. The meter was produced from under the pillow and passed around and shaken to demonstrate the weight of pennies it contained. Hub always carried, as a vestige of the lumberjack country he came from, an intricate all-purpose pocket knife. He began to pry open the little money door. Orson came up behind him and got him around the neck with one arm. Hub's body stiffened. He passed the head of the meter and the open knife to Carter, and then Orson experienced sensations of being lifted, of flying, and of lying on the floor, looking up at Hub's face, which was upside down in his vision. He scrambled to his feet and went for him again, rigid with anger and yet, in his heart, happily relaxed; Hub's body was tough and quick and satisfying to grip, though, being a wrestler, he somehow deflected Orson's hands and again lifted and dropped him to the black floor. This time, Orson felt a blow as his coccyx hit the wood; yet even through the pain he perceived, gazing into the heart of this marriage, that Hub was being as gentle with him as he could be. And that he could try in earnest to kill Hub and be in no danger of succeeding was also a comfort. He renewed the attack and again enjoyed the tense defensive skill that made Hub's body a kind of warp in space through which his own body, after an ecstatic instant of contention, was converted to the supine position. He got to his feet and would have gone for

Hub the fourth time, but his fellow-freshmen grabbed his arms and held him. He shook them off and without a word returned to his desk and concentrated down into his book, turning the page. The type looked extremely distinct, though it was trembling too hard to be deciphered.

The head of the parking meter stayed in the room for one night. The next day, Hub allowed himself to be persuaded (by the others; Orson had stopped speaking to him) to take it to the Cambridge police headquarters in Central Square. Dawson and Kern tied a ribbon around it, and attached a note: "Please take good care of my baby." None of them, however, had the nerve to go with Hub to the headquarters, though when he came back he said the chief was delighted to get the meter, and had thanked him, and had agreed to donate the pennies to the local orphans' home. In another week, the last exams were over. The freshmen all went home. When they returned in the fall, they were different: sophomores. Petersen and Young did not come back at all. Fitch returned, made up the lost credits, and eventually graduated *magna cum* in History and Lit. He now teaches in a Quaker prep school. Silverstein is a biochemist, Koshland a lawyer. Dawson writes conservative editorials in Cleveland, Kern is in advertising in New York. Carter, as if obliged to join Young in oblivion, disappeared between his junior and senior years. The dormitory neighbors tended to lose sight of each other, though Hub, who had had his case shifted to the Massachusetts jurisdiction, was now and then pictured in the *Crimson,* and once gave an evening lecture, "Why I Am an Episcopalian Pacifist." As the litigation progressed, the Bishop of Massachusetts rather grudgingly vouched for him, and by the time of his final hearing the Korean War was over, and the judge who heard the case ruled that Hub's convictions were sincere, as witnessed by his willingness to go to jail. Hub was rather disappointed at the verdict, since he had prepared a three-year reading list to occupy him in his cell and was intending to memorize all four Gospels in the original Greek. After graduation, he went to Union Theological Seminary, spent several years as the assistant rector of an urban parish in Baltimore, and learned to play the piano well enough to be the background music in a Charles Street cocktail lounge. He insisted on wearing his clerical collar, and as a consequence gave the bar a small celebrity. After a year of overriding people of less strong convictions, he was allowed to go to South Africa, where he worked and preached among the Bantus until the government requested that he leave the country. From there he went to Nigeria, and when last heard from—on a Christmas card, with French salutations and Negro Magi, which arrived, soiled and wrinkled, in South Dakota in February—Hub was in Madagascar, as a "combination missionary, political agitator, and soccer coach." The description struck Orson as probably facetious, and Hub's childish and confident handwriting, with every letter formed individually, afflicted him with some of the old exasperation. Having vowed to answer the card, he mislaid it, uncharacteristically.

Orson didn't speak to Hub for two days after the parking-meter incident. By then, it seemed rather silly, and they finished out the year sitting side by side at their desks as amiably as two cramped passengers who have endured a long bus trip together. When they parted, they shook hands, and

Hub would have walked Orson to the subway kiosk except that he had an appointment in the opposite direction. Orson received two A's and two B's on his final exams; for the remaining three years at Harvard, he roomed uneventfully with two other colorless pre-med students, named Wallace and Neuhauser. After graduation, he married Emily, attended the Yale School of Medicine, and interned in St. Louis. He is now the father of four children and, since the death of his own father, the only doctor in the town. His life has gone much the way he planned it, and he is much the kind of man he intended to be when he was eighteen. He delivers babies, assists the dying, attends the necessary meetings, plays golf, and does good. He is honorable and irritable. If not as much loved as his father, he is perhaps even more respected. In one particular only—a kind of scar he carries without pain and without any clear memory of the amputation—does the man he is differ from the man he assumed he would become. He never prays.

# Unit 5

## The Christian Roommates

- Comprehension Questions
- Characterization
- Discussion Guides
- Writing Exercise

# COMPREHENSION QUESTIONS

For each of the following statements and questions, select the option containing the most complete or most accurate answer.

1. To Orson, a nickname is a symbol of
(c) ☐ a. acceptance.      ☐ c. disgrace.
     ☐ b. oppression.      ☐ d. courage.

2. Hub refused to enter the army because
(j) ☐ a. he believed the Korean War was a mistake.
     ☐ b. they wouldn't assign him to hospital duty instead of combat.
     ☐ c. he was afraid of dying.
     ☐ d. he objected to killing on principle.

3. Hub had spent the two years between high school and college
(a) ☐ a. traveling abroad.
     ☐ b. working in a plywood mill.
     ☐ c. organizing labor unions.
     ☐ d. leading civil rights demonstrations.

4. The college's basis for pairing off the incoming freshman into room-
(f) mates seems to have been
     ☐ a. carefully thought out.      ☐ c. given religious consideration.
     ☐ b. planned geographically.      ☐ d. done randomly and haphazardly.

5. Orson envied the other pairs of roommates in his dormitory because,
(d) unlike himself and Hub, they all
     ☐ a. came from the East.
     ☐ b. knew each other from high school.
     ☐ c. shared some common bond.
     ☐ d. seemed smarter and more popular.

6. Which of the following choices best described *wangled* as used in,
(l) "During the day. . .Hal [Hub] *wangled* tea invitations from Demos and Jaeger and the Bishop of Massachusetts. . ."?
     ☐ a. Dodged.      ☐ c. Mutilated.
     ☐ b. Finagled.      ☐ d. Devoured.

7. Hub doesn't believe in the slaughter of animals, yet he wears leather
(k) shoes, plays pianos with ivory keys made from the tusks of elephants, and brushes his teeth with a brush made of pig bristles. "I am covered with blood," says Hub, "and pray daily for forgiveness." The phrase *I am covered with blood* is a metaphor meaning

□ a. "I am guilty."  □ c. "I am persecuted."
□ b. "I am wounded."  □ d. "I am invulnerable."

8. Hub celebrated the Christmas holidays by
(a) □ a. going home with Orson to South Dakota.
□ b. staying in his room and fasting.
□ c. chopping down a Christmas tree for the dorm room.
□ d. making a public speech against the commercialization of Christmas.

9. In terms of academic performance, Hub is
(b) □ a. an outstanding student.  □ c. a poor student.
□ b. a mediocre student.  □ d. a cheater.

10. Whenever Hub receives a letter from the Portland draft board, he
(b) □ a. forwards it to his bishop.
□ b. passes it on to his lawyer.
□ c. composes long, rambling replies.
□ d. tears it up.

11. The nickname that Orson eventually winds up with, "Orson the parson,"
(h) implies that the other students see Orson as
□ a. easy-going and carefree.
□ b. clever and amusing.
□ c. straitlaced and puritanical.
□ d. dishonest and deceitful.

12. Orson accuses Hub of being cold and unfeeling. This assessment of Hub
(g) is probably
□ a. accurate.  □ c. an understatement.
□ b. unfair.  □ d. a sound judgment.

13. Hub's attitude toward Orson might best be described as
(i) □ a. hostile.  □ c. respectful.
□ b. smug and superior.  □ d. chummy.

14. The conflict between Orson and Hub should be blamed on
(g)  □ a. Orson.                    □ c. neither of them.
     □ b. Hub.                      □ d. both of them.


15. Two characters in this story seem to upset Orson to a degree that's
(d)  hard to account for. These two characters are
     □ a. Silverstein and Koshland.
     □ b. the two black students.
     □ c. Emily and the girl with red hair.
     □ d. Hub and Lester Spotted Elk.


16. Orson finds that the more his dislike of Hub grows,
(d)  □ a. the more obsessed he becomes about it.
     □ b. the less he thinks about Hub.
     □ c. the better he understands Hub.
     □ d. the more tolerant he becomes of Hub's peculiarities.


17. When Orson and Hub agree not to room together next year, Hub seems
(j)  to feel
     □ a. pleased and relieved.
     □ b. bewildered and hurt.
     □ c. elated and triumphant.
     □ d. angry and bitter.


18. By the middle of May, with two exams behind him and two to go, Orson
(i)  feels
     □ a. nervous and tense.         □ c. silly and carefree.
     □ b. calm and self-assured.     □ d. reckless and irresponsible.


19. On one level, Orson and Hub are simply roommates. In another sense,
(c)  however, their relationship may be compared to
     □ a. a chess match.             □ c. a business partnership.
     □ b. a marriage.                □ d. a professional association.


20. The climax, or emotional high point, of this story comes when
(k)  □ a. Orson and Hub decide not to room together next year.
     □ b. Orson and Hub wrestle with each other.
     □ c. Hub returns the parking meter.
     □ d. Orson marries Emily.

21. As the years passed, Hub grew
(j) ☐ easier to get along with.  ☐ more exasperating than ever.
☐ less certain of himself.  ☐ more like everyone else.

22. "When last heard from . . . Hub was in Madagascar, as a 'combination
(l) missionary, political agitator, and soccer coach.' The description struck
Orson as probably *facetious* . . ." *Facetious* means
☐ a. evenly said in jest ·  ☐ c. untruthful.
☐ b. meant literally.  ☐ d. puzzling.

23. Twenty years later, Orson's feelings toward Hub seem to be
(f) ☐ a. affectionate.  ☐ c. mixed.
☐ b. hostile.  ☐ d. indifferent.

24. Out of ten students in Orson's dorm, three eventually dropped out of
(h) college and one had a nervous breakdown. This leads the reader to
infer that
☐ a. these students were not smart enough.
☐ b. college is a stressful environment.
☐ c. most students dislike Harvard.
☐ d. the students lacked character.

25. Perhaps the most important lesson Orson learns in his freshman year
(e) of college is that
☐ a. all learning is futile.
☐ b. money is the root of all evil.
☐ c. love is fickle.
☐ d. people with different values aren't necessarily "wrong."

Comprehension Skills: a — isolating details; b — recalling specific facts; c — retaining concepts; d — organizing facts; e — understanding the main idea; f — drawing a conclusion; g — making a judgment; h — making an inference; i — recognizing tone; j — understanding characters; k — appreciation of literary forms; l — understanding vocabulary.

# CHARACTERIZATION

## Practice Exercise A

The roommate was sitting on the floor, barefoot, before a small spinning wheel. He jumped up nimbly. Orson's first impression was of the wiry quickness that almost magically brought close to his face the thick-lipped, pop-eyed face of the other boy. He was a head shorter than Orson, and wore, above his bare feet, pegged sky-blue slacks, a lumberjack shirt whose throat was dashingly stuffed with a silk foulard, and a white cap such as Orson had seen before only in photographs of Pandit Nehru. Dropping a suitcase, Orson offered his hand. Instead of taking it, the roommate touched his palms together, bowed his head, and murmured something Orson didn't catch. Then he gracefully swept off the white cap, revealing a narrow crest of curly blond hair that stood up like a rooster's comb. "I am Henry Palamountain."

1. From the way he dresses and the way he acts, Orson's new roommate seems to be
   - ☐ a. a trend setter.
   - ☐ b. an athlete.
   - ☐ c. a nonconformist.
   - ☐ d. a divinity student.

2. The expository method of characterization is a presentation of facts and other information about a character by the narrator or by another character. In the passage above, underline two phrases which reveal through whose eyes we are meeting Henry Palamountain.

## Practice Exercise B

Petersen was an amiable Swede with a transparent skin that revealed blue veins in his nose. For several summers he had worked as a reporter for the Duluth *Herald.* He had all the newsman's tricks: the side-of-the mouth quip, the nip of whiskey, the hat on the back of the head, the habit of throwing still-burning cigarettes onto the floor. He did not seem quite to know why he was at Harvard, and in fact did not return at the end of the freshman year.

1. A flat character can usually be summed up in two or three words. Which of the following brief descriptions most appropriately summarizes Petersen?
   - ☐ a. A witty comic.
   - ☐ b. An imitator.
   - ☐ c. A smart alec.
   - ☐ d. An indifferent student.

2. Underline the long sentence in the passage above which best sums up this character.

## Practice Exercise C

There was then a hurried pounding up the stairs, and Hub pushed into the room carrying cradled in his arm a metal object the color of a gun and the size of a cat. It had a red tongue. Hub slammed the door behind him, snapped the lock, and dumped the object on Orson's bed. It was the head of a parking meter, sheared from its post. A keen quick pain cut through Orson's groin. "For God's sake," he cried in his contemptible high voice, "what's *that*?"

"It's a parking meter."

"I *know*, I can *see* that. Where the hell did you *get* it?"

"I won't talk to you until you stop being hysterical," Hub said, and crossed to his desk, where Orson had put his mail. He took the top letter, a special delivery from the Portland draft board, and tore it in half. This time, the pain went through Orson's chest. He put his head in his arms on the desk and whirled and groped in the black-red darkness there.

1. This scene dramatizes an aspect of Hub's character that is at the heart of the conflict between him and Orson, and that is Hub's
   □ a. flaunting of authority.
   □ b. distaste for organized religion.
   □ c. mediocre scholastic performance.
   □ d. poor manners.

2. Two sentences in different parts of the passage above dramatize the intense anguish Hub's antics cause Orson. Underline these two sentences.

## Practice Exercise D

After graduation he [Orson] married Emily, attended the Yale School of Medicine, and interned in St. Louis. He is now the father of four children and, since the death of his own father, the only doctor in the town. His life has gone much the way he planned it, and he is much the kind of man he intended to be when he was eighteen. He delivers babies, assists the dying, attends the necessary meetings, plays golf, and does good. He is honorable and irritable. If not as much loved as his father, he is perhaps even more respected. In one particular only — a kind of scar he carries without pain and without any clear memory of the amputation — does the man he is differ from the man he assumed he would become. He never prays.

1. This passage shows that Orson is a "round" character because
   □ a. he is an admirable character.
   □ b. we see a lot of him.
   □ c. he is a caricature.
   □ d. he has been changed by events in the story.

2. Circle the short sentence in the passage above which shows how the middle-aged Orson is different from the eighteen-year-old college freshman.

# DISCUSSION GUIDES

## Analyzing Characterization

1. Sometimes Updike comes right out and tells the reader what a certain character is like. In other places, however, the author presents a character through Orson's eyes. What is the advantage of this second technique of characterization?

2. Major characters in a story are usually rounded, three-dimensional characters. Does this generalization apply to Hub? Does Hub change at all in the course of his college years and adult life?

3. An author often pairs a rather average and ordinary character with an unusual, colorful character. In this way, the uniqueness of the one character is highlighted by contrast with the other. This average, ordinary character is said to be a *foil*. Dr. Watson, for instance, acts as a foil for the character of Sherlock Holmes. In "The Christian Roommates," how does Orson serve as a foil for the character of Hub?

## Interpreting the Story

4. Orson notices that when the others tease or attack Hub, Hub smiles at their criticism and takes it as a game. Yet when Orson teases him, Hub fights back in earnest. Is Orson imagining this? If not, how do you account for Hub's behavior toward Orson?

5. When Orson complains that Hub is a phony — his manner of praying is showy, his well-worn Greek books are secondhand, and, furthermore, he's not even a good student — Kern replies, "You seem to miss the point of what Hub's all about." What *is* Hub all about — is he a phony? a saint? just a troubled adolescent? or something else?

6. Orson claims he hates Hub, yet he also confesses to feeling "a helpless affection for his unreal, unreachable friend." What is it about Hub that appeals to Orson in spite of their differences?

7. By spring, Orson is on the verge of a nervous breakdown. Is Hub entirely to blame for this? What other aspects of Orson's freshman year at Harvard might have affected Orson's mental health?

8. How does the author make the reader feel superior to the characters in this story? How does this affect your opinion of them?

9. At the end of the story, the author presents the reader with a brief glimpse of each character twenty years later. Why does Updike do this? Why not end the story with the conclusion of Orson's freshman year?

10. Do you find this story humorous in any way? If so, what scene in particular did you find most amusing, and why?

## WRITING EXERCISE

References to Hub's father are few and brief. We know he is divorced from Hub's mother, that he was "furious" with Hub for hitchhiking to Cambridge from Portland, Oregon, and that "he never gives a penny to charity." That, of course, is Hub's side of the story. It is not entirely clear whether Mr. Palamountain is a money-grubbing capitalist or simply a long-suffering victim of his son's excessive zeal.

As an exercise in characterization, try to imagine what Hub's father might be like. Then:

1. Write a paragraph *describing* Mr. Palamountain — how he dresses, what he does for a living, how he feels about his son.

2. Write a short scene that *dramatizes* one or more of the traits you just described. Your scene should portray Mr. Palamountain interacting with at least one other character — a business associate, a close friend, his ex-wife, or his son, for example.

# Young Goodman Brown

## Nathaniel Hawthorne

# Introduction

"Young Goodman Brown" is the story of a young man, recently married, who kisses his wife good-bye one evening and sets off for a midnight rendezvous with the devil. He is not a wicked person. In fact, there is every reason to believe that Goodman Brown was what is known as "a nice young man"—probably a regular churchgoer, an honest taxpayer, a hard working farmer, and a loving husband. Nonetheless, for whatever reason, young Goodman Brown has secretly made an appointment with the devil. He is to meet the devil in the forest on the outskirts of Salem village and from there follow him to a lurid Witch's Sabbath—a midnight orgy of evil rites. After a night with the forces of evil, Goodman Brown intends to return home the next morning and resume a blameless, Christian life with his pretty wife, Faith.

Things don't quite work out the way he had planned, however. Goodman Brown enters the dark forest in search of evil, and he finds it all right, but the scenes he witnesses that night turn out to be more than he had bargained for.

Goodman Brown was a Puritan, and the Puritans believed that the devil actually walked the earth, persuading men and women to sign away their souls in his book. In fact, the most learned leaders of New England believed in witchcraft, and certain details of this story touch on an episode in history that most Americans would prefer to forget—the Salem witchcraft trials of 1692. The old lady that Goodman Brown meets in the forest, Goody Cloyse, along with Goody Cory and Martha Carrier, who are also mentioned in the story, were among the "witches" of Salem sentenced to death in 1692. (The story, therefore, is probably set around 1691.)

It's hard to believe today that people were once accused, convicted and put to death on the basis of evidence that, by its very nature, could never be proved by the accuser, nor disproved by the accused. This "spectral evidence," as it was called, consisted of testimony by a witness that a specter, or apparition, in the shape and appearance of the accused tempted the witness to sign the devil's book. (Goodman Brown's experience in the forest would have been regarded as spectral evidence of witchcraft.) The catch, of course, was that while the witness could not back up such charges with hard evidence, neither could the accused refute them.

So when a small group of hysterical young girls in Salem village claimed they were possessed by evil spirits, the whole town took them seriously. Basking in the spotlight which their antics attracted, the girls obligingly "named" the witches who were tormenting them. The result was a string of witchcraft trials that quickly mushroomed into new charges and counter-charges as the accused turn accusers to save themselves. The first accusations were aimed at such obvious targets as eccentric and crotchety old women. Soon, however, charges of witchcraft were flying fast and free. Finally, when their accusing fingers pointed to the pious wives of well-known ministers, and even the Governor's wife, the whole affair mercifully collapsed. Within a year after it had started, the witchcraft trials ground to an embarrassing halt, but not before some twenty innocent victims had been put to death, and numerous lives ruined.

The author of "Young Goodman Brown," Nathaniel Hawthorne, was born in 1804, a little more than a century after the Salem witchcraft trials. He was always intrigued by this episode in his town's past, the more so because his great-great-grandfather was a judge who played an active role in the witchcraft trials. Hawthorne felt a sense of inherited guilt for his ancestor's deeds as judge and admitted to being haunted by this "stern, black-browed Puritan" in his family tree.

As you read "Young Goodman Brown," see if you feel the "touch of Puritanic gloom" that others have detected in Hawthorne's writing.

### A Glossary of Words from the Seventeenth Century

**cinquefoil:** a plant with compound leaves, each of five leaflets

**Goodman:** a term of address for a man of humble social status

**Goody:** a contraction of *Goodwife*, used in addressing the wife of a common man, as in Goody Cloyse

**husbandman:** a farmer, but also any man of humble status

**King Philip's War:** King Philip, or Metacomet, was the last Indian leader to resist the white settlers in Southern New England. King Philip's War ended with his death in 1676.

**King William:** William the Third, King of England from 1689 to 1702

**lecture day:** the day of the midweek sermon, usually Thursday

**smallage:** wild celery, credited by witches as having magical powers

**wolf's bane:** a plant with dull yellow flowers, thought to yield a poisonous wine

# Recognizing Themes

People like stories that speak to them personally. That means if you're a student, you're probably interested in stories about other students, or stories about people your own age.

Undoubtedly, however, you have also enjoyed stories that are seemingly worlds removed from your own sphere of interests. Take, for instance, "The Man That Corrupted Hadleyburg" by Mark Twain. The main characters in this story are an elderly couple whose honesty is put to the test when a sack of gold is left on their doorstep. Now you may not be old, like Mr. and Mrs. Richards in the story, and it's highly unlikely that anyone will ever leave a sack of money at your door. Nonetheless, you'll probably still find this story fascinating and thought-provoking. Why? Because of its theme, that the most seemingly honest people can be corrupted, if tempted with the right bait. This attitude, or viewpoint, towards people applies not only to the characters in the story, but to you and every other reader as well. Who, after all, can help wondering how he or she would react in a similar situation? Thus, this story does speak to you personally, through its theme.

When you talk about theme, then, you are referring to the point of the story—the attitude, viewpoint, or personal values that prompted the author to write this story, in this way, in the first place. Themes say something about people in general and about the world we live in. For instance, the theme may be that people are basically good or that people are basically selfish; that the world is a just place or that the world is unjust. A theme is not an indisputable fact. Rather, it is one author's opinion, arrived at through much brooding over human nature.

It's easy to recognize the theme in a fable since it's stated for you at the end. In "The Fox and the Grapes," for example, a fox spies a bunch of grapes hanging above him, just out of reach. He jumps to get them and misses, jumps again and misses. Finally, after many unsuccessful attempts he gives up, saying to himself, "They're probably sour anyway." Then the author, Aesop, presents the moral—and the theme—of his tale, "It is easy to despise what you cannot get." Thus, in one sentence the author sums up the point of the story with an observation on human nature.

Recognizing themes in most stories, however, is not quite as straightforward as this. Most themes are not stated directly. Instead, they are expressed through the main characters, the action, and the symbolism and imagery of the story. The theme, in fact, is the unifying force that ties the various elements of a story together. Let's see how the theme is expressed in "Young Goodman Brown" by Nathaniel Hawthorne.

**1. Expressing Theme through Action and Events.** The action or central event of any good story is carefully chosen by the author to express a particular theme. In fact, some events are so appropriate for expressing theme that, when you come across them in a story, you can almost always count on their being thematically significant.

One of the most common of these is a natural disaster, such as a flood or a hurricane, or even just a raging thunderstorm. An event like this is frequently used by authors to develop the theme of human frailty in the face of nature, or nature's total indifference to man.

Another event that is often a good clue to identifying themes in literature is the journey. A journey can take many forms. In *Moby Dick*, it takes the form of a voyage on a whaling ship. In *Huckleberry Finn*, the journey consists of a raft trip down the Mississippi River. The tale of "Young Goodman Brown" also contains an important journey. The story takes place in old Salem around the late 1600s. The main character, young Goodman Brown, has just kissed his wife good-bye before embarking on a mysterious journey into the forest at sundown. As he enters the forest, he is greeted by a strange man who carries a walking stick carved in the form of a snake, and who is apparently expecting him. In this scene, the fellow traveller urges Goodman Brown to hasten on his journey. What clues do you find in the following passage that might point to the theme of the story?

> "Come, Goodman Brown," cried his fellow-traveller, "this is a dull pace for the beginning of a journey. Take my staff, if you are so soon weary."
>
> "Friend," said the other, exchanging his slow pace for a full stop, "having kept covenant by meeting thee here, it is my purpose now to return whence I came. I have scruples touching the matter thou wot'st of."
>
> "Sayest thou so?" replied he of the serpent, smiling apart. "Let us walk on, nevertheless, reasoning as we go; and if I convince thee not thou shalt turn back. We are but a little way in the forest yet."
>
> "Too far! too far!" exclaimed the goodman, unconsciously resuming his walk. "My father never went into the woods on such an errand, nor his father before him. We have been a race of honest men and good Christians since the days of the martyrs; and shall I be the first of the name of Brown that ever took this path and kept"—
>
> "Such company, thou wouldst say," observed the elder person, interpreting his pause.

Clearly, this is a journey toward some evil end. We infer this from young Goodman Brown's guilty conscience. "I have scruples [misgivings] touching the matter thou wot'st of [knows of]," he says to his fellow-traveler. "My father never went into the woods on such an errand, nor his father before him."

Despite his qualms, however, Goodman Brown is hardly being forced to make this journey. He is not, after all, being dragged kicking and screaming at the end of a chain. He is quite free to turn around and go back home. But Goodman Brown's conscience in this matter is evidently not as strong as some other, conflicting impulse. When his companion suggests they discuss the matter as they walk, he unconsciously resumes his pace.

Young Goodman Brown embarks on this sinister journey an upstanding citizen of good repute. "We have been a race of honest men and good Christians since the days of the martyrs...." What he finds at the end, however, will undoubtedly change him in some way. Journeys in literature are almost always learning experiences. And what young Goodman Brown learns on his journey into the forest is the theme of this story.

**2. Expressing Theme through Symbolism.** A *symbol* is something that has a dual significance. On the one hand, of course, it has a face value. At the same time, however, it also stands for or suggests something else. For instance, the sun is, at face value, a distant ball of fire. Symbolically, however, it can also represent life itself, since without the sun life as we know it would be impossible.

Symbols convey an added layer of meaning that usually contributes to the theme of the story. In the following excerpt from "Young Goodman Brown," the walking stick, or staff, of Goodman Brown's fellow-traveller has symbolic significance. What do you think the staff stands for, and how might it contribute to the theme of the story?

> But, the only thing about [young Goodman Brown's fellow-traveller] that could be fixed upon as remarkable was his staff, which bore the likeness of a great black snake, so curiously wrought that it might almost be seen to twist and wriggle itself like a living serpent.

The staff, we are told, is carved to resemble "a great black snake." Now ever since the serpent in the Garden of Eden tempted Eve to eat the forbidden fruit, snakes have been symbols of evil. The reader might safely assume, therefore, that the man carrying this snakelike staff is evil. And when we consider that the carving almost seems "to twist and wriggle itself like a living serpent," we may conclude that this is a very special staff, that its owner has very special powers to make it come alive, and that its owner is, in fact, the Prince of Evil—the devil himself!

This symbolism fits in nicely with the sinister journey that takes young Goodman Brown into the forest at night. With the devil himself for a travelling companion, it's no wonder he feels guilty about his dark errand.

**3. Expressing Theme through Imagery.** Imagery also develops the theme of a story. The term *imagery* refers to the various kinds of descriptive and figurative language which an author uses to convey feelings and attitudes to the reader—pictures the author paints or conjures up in your mind.

In the following passage from the story, Hawthorne describes the forest through which young Goodman Brown is passing. How does the imagery here affect your feelings about the forest? How does this help suggest the theme of "Young Goodman Brown"?

> The [forest path] grew wilder and drearier and more faintly traced, and vanished at length, leaving him in the heart of the dark wilderness.... The whole forest was peopled with frightful sounds—the creaking of trees, the howling of wild beasts, and the yell of Indians; while sometimes the wind tolled like a distant church bell, and sometimes gave a broad roar around the traveller, as if all Nature were laughing him to scorn.

It's popular nowadays to regard the forest as a place of peace and repose, where one feels closer to God. Not so, however, in this story. The imagery Hawthorne uses to describe this forest conveys a sense of something monstrous and evil.

The forest path is wild and dreary; by and by it vanishes, stranding the traveller "in the heart of the dark wilderness." The woods are alive with fiendish spirits. "The whole forest was peopled with frightful sounds," he says, implying that the sounds themselves have bodies. Needless to say, none of these sounds are comforting. The "creaking of the trees, the howling of wild beasts, and the yell of Indians" together with the wind, which alternately tolls like a church bell and menaces one with its broad roar, are all designed to make a poor traveller's hair stand on end. It seems like all Nature is conspiring to frighten the hapless intruder.

The further young Goodman Brown goes into this forest, the more ominous his mission—whatever it is—becomes. So far, the action (that is, the journey itself), the symbolism, and the imagery all point to a theme involving some terrible evil that young Goodman Brown is seeking out.

**4. Expressing Theme through Character.** The main character in a short story is always used to illustrate the theme. Therefore, a sure clue to finding the theme is to analyze the protagonist. Ask yourself, "Has this character learned anything new in the course of the story? If so, what? And how has this new knowledge changed him (or her)?" When you have answered these questions, you'll probably have hit upon the theme of the story.

In the following passage, young Goodman Brown has arrived at his destination in the forest. It is a Witch's Sabbath, a midnight orgy of evil rites at which Satan himself presides. This is his first such meeting, during which he will be initiated into the fraternity of sinners. Unbeknownst to Goodman Brown, his wife Faith, whom he had regarded as an "angel on earth," is also to be "taken into communion" tonight.

As you read the passage, try to decide what young Goodman Brown learns in the forest this night and what the theme of this story is.

"Bring forth the converts!" cried a voice that echoed through the field and rolled into the forest.

At the word, Goodman Brown stepped forth from the shadow of the trees and approached the congregation, with whom he felt a loathful brotherhood by the sympathy of all that was wicked in his heart. He could have well-nigh sworn that the shape of his own dead father beckoned him to advance, looking downward from a smoke wreath, while a woman, with dim features of despair, threw out her hand to warn him back. Was it his mother? But he had no power to retreat one step, nor to resist, even in thought, when the minister and good old Deacon Gookin seized his arms and led him to the blazing rock. Thither came also the slender form of a veiled female, led between Goody Cloyse, that pious teacher of the catechism, and Martha Carrier, who had received the devil's promise to be queen of hell. A rampant hag was she. And there stood the proselytes beneath the canopy of fire.

"Welcome, my children," said the dark figure, "to the communion of your race. Ye have found thus young your nature and your destiny...."

First of all, young Goodman Brown feels a "loathful brotherhood" with the sinful congregation gathered together in the dark woods. Though he detests it, the wickedness around him is matched by wickedness in his own heart. Not even the shape of his own mother can halt his footsteps as he advances toward his fateful initiation.

Second, it is clear that young Goodman Brown is not consorting with a bunch of ne'er-do-wells. Among the assemblage is his own father, Goody Cloyse who taught him his catechism, the saintly Deacon Gookin, and the minister himself. And last but not least, "the slender form of a veiled female"—his own wife, Faith! All the people whom Goodman Brown has regarded as holy are now revealed to him as sinners.

" 'Welcome, my children,' said the dark figure, 'to the communion of your race. Ye have found thus young your nature and your destiny.' " This, then, is what young Goodman Brown learns—that he is wicked, that everyone else is secretly wicked, though they may take pains to hide it, and that his own destiny and the destiny of the human race is to reside in Hell as the Devil's apostles.

Whether this whole experience was just a bad dream, or whether it actually happened, the resulting effect on young Goodman Brown is the same: he has lost all faith in the goodness of mankind. For the rest of his life, he will look upon his wife, and upon the most pious citizens of old Salem, and wonder whether or not they attended the Witch's Sabbath that night in the forest, and he will always doubt their virtue.

This vision of universal evil, and loss of faith in the goodness of mankind, is the theme of this story. You, too, may have undergone an experience that shook your faith. At the very least, you have undoubtedly learned that no one is perfect. Everyone has flaws, and everyone is tempted to sin; that's what it means to be human. In this sense, the theme of "Young Goodman

Brown" applies to you and to every other reader, and we can all sympathize with Goodman Brown's disillusionment.

As you read the story, notice how the different elements—the action, the symbols, the imagery, and the characters—all help develop the theme.

---

As you read the story:

- Look for clues to the theme in the opening scene where young Goodman Brown says good-bye to his wife as he leaves on his strange journey.

- Consider the symbolic significance of the pink ribbon that flutters down from the sky.

- Notice the imagery which Hawthorne uses to describe the hymn which Goodman Brown hears at the Witch's Sabbath.

- Watch for the transformation in young Goodman Brown as a result of his midnight meeting in the forest.

# Young Goodman Brown
# Nathaniel Hawthorne

Young Goodman Brown came forth at sunset into the street at Salem village; but put his head back, after crossing the threshold, to exchange a parting kiss with his young wife. And Faith, as the wife was aptly named, thrust her own pretty head into the street, letting the wind play with the pink ribbons of her cap while she called to Goodman Brown.

"Dearest heart," whispered she, softly and rather sadly, when her lips were close to his ear, "prithee put off your journey until sunrise and sleep in your own bed tonight. A lone woman is troubled with such dreams and such thoughts that she's afeard of herself sometimes. Pray tarry with me this night, dear husband, of all nights in the year."

"My love and my Faith," replied young Goodman Brown, "of all nights in the year, this one night must I tarry away from thee. My journey, as thou callest it, forth and back again, must needs be done 'twixt now and sunrise. What, my sweet, pretty wife, dost thou doubt me already, and we but three months married?"

"Then God bless you!" said Faith, with the pink ribbons; "and may you find all well when you come back."

"Amen!" cried Goodman Brown. "Say thy prayers, dear Faith, and go to bed at dusk, and no harm will come to thee."

So they parted; and the young man pursued his way until, being about to turn the corner by the meeting-house, he looked back and saw the head of Faith still peeping after him with a melancholy air, in spite of her pink ribbons.

"Poor little Faith!" thought he, for his heart smote him. "What a wretch am I to leave her on such an errand! She talks of dreams, too. Methought as she spoke there was trouble in her face, as if a dream had warned her what work is to be done tonight. But no, no; 't would kill her to think it. Well, she's a blessed angel on earth; and after this one night I'll cling to her skirts and follow her to heaven."

With this excellent resolve for the future Goodman Brown felt himself justified in making more haste on his present evil purpose. He had taken a dreary road, darkened by all the gloomiest trees of the forest, which barely stood aside to let the narrow path creep through, and closed immediately behind. It was all as lonely as could be; and there is this peculiarity in such a solitude, that the traveller knows not who may be concealed by the innumerable trunks and the thick boughs overhead; so that with lonely footsteps he may yet be passing through an unseen multitude.

"There may be a devilish Indian behind every tree," said Goodman Brown to himself; and he glanced fearfully behind him as he added, "What if the devil himself should be at my very elbow!"

His head being turned back, he passed a crook of the road, and, looking forward again, beheld the figure of a man, in grave and decent attire, seated at the foot of an old tree. He arose at Goodman Brown's approach and walked onward side by side with him.

"You are late, Goodman Brown," said he. "The clock of the Old South was striking as I came through Boston, and that is full fifteen minutes agone."

"Faith kept me back a while," replied the young man, with a termor in his voice, caused by the sudden appearance of his companion, though not wholly unexpected.

It was now deep dusk in the forest, and deepest in that part of it where these two were journeying. As nearly as could be discerned, the second traveller was about fifty years old, apparently in the same rank of life as Goodman Brown, and bearing a considerable resemblance to him, though perhaps more in expression than features. Still they might have been taken for father and son. And yet, though the elder person was as simply clad as the younger, and as simple in manner too, he had an indescribable air of one who knew the world, and who would not have felt abashed at the governor's dinner table or in King William's court, were it possible that his affairs should call him thither. But the only thing about him that could be fixed upon as remarkable was his staff, which bore the likeness of a great black snake, so curiously wrought that it might almost be seen to twist and wriggle itself like a living serpent. This, of course, must have been an ocular deception, assisted by the uncertain light.

"Come, Goodman Brown," cried his fellow-traveller, "this is a dull pace for the beginning of a journey. Take my staff, if you are so soon weary."

"Friend," said the other, exchanging his slow pace for a full stop, "having kept covenant by meeting thee here, it is my purpose now to return whence I came. I have scruples touching the matter thou wot'st of."

"Sayest thou so?" replied he of the serpent, smiling apart. "Let us walk on, nevertheless, reasoning as we go; and if I convince thee not thou shalt turn back. We are but a little way in the forest yet."

"Too far! too far!" exclaimed the goodman, unconsciously resuming his walk. "My father never went into the woods on such an errand, nor his father before him. We have been a race of honest men and good Christians since the days of the martyrs; and shall I be the first of the name of Brown that ever took this path and kept—

"Such company, thou wouldst say," observed the elder person, interpreting his pause. "Well said, Goodman Brown! I have been as well acquainted with your family as with ever a one among the Puritans; and that's no trifle to say. I helped your grandfather, the constable, when he lashed the Quaker woman so smartly through the streets of Salem; and it was I that brought your father a pitch-pine knot, kindled at my own hearth, to set fire to an Indian village, in King Philip's war. They were my good friends, both; and many a pleasant walk have we had along this path, and returned merrily after midnight. I would fain be friends with you for their sake."

"If it be as thou sayest," replied Goodman Brown, "I marvel they never spoke of these matters; or, verily, I marvel not, seeing that the least rumor of the sort would have driven them from New England. We are a people of prayer, and good works to boot, and abide no such wickedness."

"Wickedness or not," said the traveller with the twisted staff, "I have a very general acquaintance here in New England. The deacons of many a church have drunk the communion wine with me; the selectmen of divers towns make me their chairman; and a majority of the Great and General Court are firm supporters of my interest. The governor and I, too—But these are state secrets."

"Can this be so?" cried Goodman Brown, with a stare of amazement at his undisturbed companion. "Howbeit, I have nothing to do with the governor and council; they have their own ways, and are no rule for a simple husbandman like me. But, were I to go on with thee, how should I meet the eye of that good old man, our minister, at Salem village? Oh, his voice would make me tremble both Sabbath day and lecture day."

Thus far the elder traveller had listened with due gravity; but now burst into a fit of irrepressible mirth, shaking himself so violently that his snakelike staff actually seemed to wriggle in sympathy.

"Ha! ha! ha!" shouted he again and again; then composing himself, "Well, go on, Goodman Brown, go on; but, prithee, don't kill me with laughing."

"Well, then, to end the matter at once," said Goodman Brown, considerably nettled, "there is my wife, Faith. It would break her dear little heart; and I'd rather break my own."

"Nay, if that be the case," answered the other, "e'en go thy ways, Goodman Brown. I would not for twenty old women like the one hobbling before us that Faith should come to any harm."

As he spoke he pointed his staff at a female figure on the path, in whom Goodman Brown recognized a very pious and exemplary dame, who had taught him his catechism in youth, and was still his moral and spiritual adviser, jointly with the minister and Deacon Gookin.

"A marvel, truly, that Goody Cloyse should be so far in the wilderness at nightfall," said he. "But with your leave, friend, I shall take a cut through the woods until we have left this Christian woman behind. Being a stranger to you, she might ask whom I was consorting with and whither I was going."

"Be it so," said his fellow-traveller. "Betake you to the woods, and let me keep the path."

Accordingly the young man turned aside, but took care to watch his companion, who advanced softly along the road until he had come within a staff's length of the old dame. She, meanwhile, was making the best of her way, with singular speed for so aged a woman, and mumbling some indistinct words—a prayer, doubtless—as she went. The traveller put forth his staff and touched her withered neck with what seemed the serpent's tail.

"The devil!" screamed the pious old lady.

"Then Goody Cloyse knows her old friend?" observed the traveller, confronting her and leaning on his writhing stick.

"Ah, forsooth, and is it your worship indeed?" cried the good dame. "Yea, truly is it, and in the very image of my old gossip, Goodman Brown, the grandfather of the silly fellow that now is. But—would your worship believe it?—my broomstick hath strangely disappeared, stolen, as I suspect, by that unhanged witch, Goody Cory, and that, too, when I was all anointed with the juice of smallage, and cinquefoil, and wolf's bane"—

"Mingled with fine wheat and the fat of a new-born babe," said the shape of old Goodman Brown.

"Ah, your worship knows the recipe," cried the old lady, cackling aloud. "So, as I was saying, being all ready for the meeting, and no horse to ride on, I made up my mind to foot it; for they tell me there is a nice young man to be taken into communion tonight. But now your good worship will lend me your arm, and we shall be there in a twinkling."

"That can hardly be," answered her friend. "I may not spare you my arm, Goody Cloyse; but here is my staff, if you will."

So saying, he threw it down at her feet, where, perhaps, it assumed life, being one of the rods which its owner had formerly lent to the Egyptian magi. Of this fact, however, Goodman Brown could not take cognizance. He had cast up his eyes in astonishment, and, looking down again, beheld neither Goody Cloyse nor the serpentine staff, but his fellow-traveller alone, who waited for him as calmly as if nothing had happened.

"That old woman taught me my catechism," said the young man; and there was a world of meaning in this simple comment.

They continued to walk onward, while the elder traveller exhorted his companion to make good speed and persevere in the path, discoursing so aptly that his arguments seemed rather to spring up in the bosom of his auditor than to be suggested by himself. As they went, he plucked a branch of maple to serve for a walking stick, and began to strip it of the twigs and little boughs, which were wet with evening dew. The moment his fingers touched them they became strangely withered and dried up as with a week's sunshine. Thus the pair proceeded, at a good free pace, until suddenly, in a gloomy hollow of the road, Goodman Brown sat himself down on the stump of a tree and refused to go any farther.

"Friend," said, he stubbornly, "my mind is made up. Not another step will I budge on this errand. What if a wretched old woman do choose to go to the devil when I thought she was going to heaven: is that any reason why I should quit my dear Faith and go after her?"

"You will think better of this by and by," said his acquaintance, composedly. "Sit here and rest yourself a while; and when you feel like moving again, there is my staff to help you along."

Without more words, he threw his companion the maple stick, and was as speedily out of sight as if he had vanished into the deepening gloom. The young man sat a few moments by the roadside, applauding himself greatly, and thinking with how clear a conscience he should meet the minister in his morning walk, nor shrink from the eye of good old Deacon Gookin. And what calm sleep would be his that very night, which was to have been spent so wickedly, but so purely and sweetly now, in the arms of Faith! Amidst these pleasant and praiseworthy meditations, Goodman Brown heard the tramp of horses along the road, and deemed it advisable to conceal himself with the verge of the forest, conscious of the guilty purpose that had brought him thither, though now so happily turned from it.

On came the hoof tramps and the voices of the riders, two grave old voices, conversing soberly as they drew near. These mingled sounds appeared to pass along the road, within a few yards of the young man's hiding-place; but, owing doubtless to the depth of the gloom at that particular spot, neither the travellers nor their steeds were visible. Though their figures brushed the small boughs by the wayside, it could not be seen that they intercepted, even for a moment, the faint gleam from the strip of bright sky athwart which they must have passed. Goodman Brown alternately crouched and stood on tiptoe, pulling aside the branches and thrusting forth his head as far as he durst without discerning so much as a shadow. It vexed him the more, because he could have sworn, were such a thing possible, that he recognized the voices of the minister and Deacon Gookin, jogging along quietly, as they were wont to do, when bound to some ordination or ecclesiastical council. While yet within hearing, one of the riders stopped to pluck a switch.

"Of the two, reverend sir," said the voice like the deacon's, "I had rather miss an ordination dinner than tonight's meeting. They tell me that some of our community are to be here from Falmouth and beyond, and others from Connecticut and Rhode Island, besides several of the Indian powwows, who, after their fashion, know almost as much deviltry as the best of us. Moreover, there is a goodly young woman to be taken into communion."

"Mighty well, Deacon Gookin!" replied the solemn old tones of the minister. "Spur up, or we shall be late. Nothing can be done, you know, until I get on the ground."

The hoofs clattered again; and the voices, talking so strangely in the empty air, passed on through the forest, where no church had ever been gathered or solitary Christian prayed. Whither, then, could these holy men be journeying so deep into the heathen wilderness? Young Goodman Brown caught hold of a tree for support, being ready to sink down on the ground, faint and overburdened with the heavy sickness of his heart. He looked up to the sky, doubting whether there really was a heaven above him. Yet there was the blue arch, and the stars brightening in it.

"With heaven above and Faith below, I will yet stand firm against the devil!" cried Goodman Brown.

While he still gazed upward into the deep arch of the firmament and had lifted his hands to pray, a cloud, though no wind was stirring, hurried across the zenith and hid the brightening stars. The blue sky was still visible, except directly overhead, where this black mass of cloud was sweeping swiftly northward. Aloft in the air, as if from the depths of the cloud, came a confused and doubtful sound of voices. Once the listener fancied that he could distinguish the accents of towns-people of his own, men and women, both pious and ungodly, many of whom he had met at the communion table, and had seen others rioting at the tavern. The next moment, so indistinct were the sounds, he doubted whether he had heard aught but the murmur of the old forest, whispering without a wind. Then came a stronger swell of those familiar tones, heard daily in the sunshine at Salem village, but never until now from a cloud of night. There was one voice, of a young woman, uttering lamentations, yet with an uncertain sorrow, and entreating for some favor, which, perhaps, it would grieve her to obtain; and all the unseen multitude, both saints and sinners, seemed to encourage her onward.

"Faith!" shouted Goodman Brown, in a voice of agony and desperation; and the echoes of the forest mocked him, crying, "Faith! Faith!" as if bewildered wretches were seeking her all through the wilderness.

The cry of grief, rage, and terror was yet piercing the night, when the unhappy husband held his breath for a response. There was a scream, drowned immediately in a louder murmur of voices, fading into far-off laughter, as the dark cloud swept away, leaving the clear and silent sky above Goodman Brown. But something fluttered lightly down through the air and caught on the branch of a tree. The young man seized it, and beheld a pink ribbon.

"My Faith is gone!" cried he, after one stupefied moment. "There is no good on earth; and sin is but a name. Come, devil; for to thee is this world given."

And, maddened with despair, so that he laughed loud and long, did Goodman Brown grasp his staff and set forth again, at such a rate that he seemed to fly along the forest path rather than to walk or run. The road grew wilder and drearier and more faintly traced, and vanished at length, leaving him in the heart of the dark wilderness, still rushing onward with the instinct that guides mortal man to evil. The whole forest was peopled with frightful sounds—the creaking of the trees, the howling of wild beasts, and the yell of Indians; while sometimes the wind tolled like a distant church bell, and sometimes gave a broad roar around the traveller, as if all Nature were laughing him to scorn. But he was himself the chief horror of the scene, and shrank not from its other horrors.

"Ha! ha! ha!" roared Goodman Brown when the wind laughed at him. "Let us hear which will laugh loudest. Think not to frighten me with your deviltry. Come witch, come wizard, come Indian powwow, come devil himself, and here comes Goodman Brown. You may as well fear him as he fear you."

In truth, all through the haunted forest there could be nothing more frightful than the figure of Goodman Brown. On he flew among the black pines, brandishing his staff with frenzied gestures, now giving vent to an inspiration of horrid blasphemy, and now shouting forth such laughter as set all the echoes of the forest laughing like demons around him. The fiend in his own shape is less hideous than when he rages in the breast of man.

Thus sped the demoniac on his course, until, quivering among the trees, he saw a red light before him, as when the felled trunks and branches of a clearing have been set on fire, and throw up their lurid blaze against the sky, at the hour of midnight. He paused, in a lull of the tempest that had driven him onward, and heard the swell of what seemed a hymn, rolling solemnly from a distance with the weight of many voices. He knew the tune; it was a familiar one in the choir of the village meeting-house. The verse died heavily away, and was lengthened by a chorus, not of human voices, but of all the sounds of the benighted wilderness pealing in awful harmony together. Goodman Brown cried out, and his cry was lost to his own ear by its unison with the cry of the desert.

In the interval of silence he stole forward until the light glared full upon his eyes. At one extremity of an open space, hemmed in by the dark wall of the forest, arose a rock, bearing some rude, natural resemblance either to an altar or a pulpit, and surrounded by four blazing pines, their tops aflame, their stems untouched, like candles at an evening meeting. The mass of foliage that had overgrown the summit of the rock was all on fire, blazing high into the night and fitfully illuminating the whole field. Each pendent twig and leafy festoon was in a blaze. As the red light arose and fell, a numerous congregation alternately shone forth, then disappeared in shadow, and again grew, as it were, out of the darkness, peopling the heart of the solitary woods at once.

"A grave and dark-clad company," quoth Goodman Brown.

In truth they were such. Among them, quivering to and fro between gloom and splendor, appeared faces that would be seen next day at the council board of the province, and others which, Sabbath after Sabbath, looked devoutly heavenward, and benignantly over the crowded pews, from the holiest pulpits in the land. Some affirm that the lady of the governor was there. At least there were high dames well known to her, and wives of honored husbands, and widows, a great multitude, and ancient maidens, all of excellent repute, and fair young girls, who trembled lest their mothers should espy them. Either the sudden gleams of light flashing over the obscure field bedazzled Goodman Brown, or he recognized a score of the church members of Salem village famous for their especial sanctity. Good old Deacon Gookin had arrived, and waited at the skirts of that venerable saint, his revered pastor. But, irreverently consorting with these grave, reputable, and pious people, these elders of the church, these chaste dames and dewy virgins, there were men of dissolute lives and women of spotted fame, wretches given over to all mean and filthy vice, and suspected even of horrid crimes. It was strange to see that the good shrank not from the wicked, nor were the sinners abashed by the saints. Scattered also among their pale-faced enemies were the Indian priests, or powwows, who had often scared their native forest with more hideous incantations than any known to English witchcraft.

"But where is Faith?" thought Goodman Brown, and, as hope came into his heart, he trembled.

Another verse of the hymn arose, a slow and mournful strain, such as the pious love, but joined to words which expressed all that our nature can conceive of sin, and darkly hinted at far more. Unfathomable to mere mortals is the lore of fiends. Verse after verse was sung; and still the chorus of the desert swelled between like the deepest tone of a mighty organ; and with the final peal of that dreadful anthem there came a sound, as if the roaring wind, the rushing streams, the howling beasts, and every other voice of the unconcerted wilderness were mingling and according with the voice of guilty man in homage to the prince of all. The four blazing pines threw up a loftier flame, and obscurely discovered shapes and visages of horror on the smoke wreaths above the impious assembly. At the same moment the fire on the rock shot redly forth and formed a glowing arch above its base, where now appeared a figure. With reverence be it spoken, the figure bore no slight similitude, both in garb and manner, to some grave divine of the New England churches.

"Bring forth the converts!" cried a voice that echoed through the field and rolled into the forest.

At the word, Goodman Brown stepped forth from the shadow of the trees and approached the congregation, with whom he felt a loathful brotherhood by the sympathy of all that was wicked in his heart. He could have well-nigh sworn that the shape of his own dead father beckoned him to advance, looking downward from a smoke wreath, while a woman, with dim features of despair, threw out her hand to warn him back. Was it his mother? But he had no power to retreat one step, nor to resist, even in thought, when the minister and good old Deacon Gookin seized his arms and led him to the blazing rock. Thither came also the slender form of a veiled female, led between Goody Cloyse, that pious teacher of the catechism, and Martha Carrier, who had received the devil's promise to be queen of hell. A rampant hag was she. And there stood the proselytes beneath the canopy of fire.

"Welcome, my children," said the dark figure, "to the communion of your race. Ye have found thus young your nature and your destiny. My children, look behind you!"

They turned; and flashing forth, as it were, in a sheet of flame, the fiend worshippers were seen; the smile of welcome gleamed darkly on every visage.

"There," resumed the sable form, "are all whom ye have reverenced from youth. Ye deemed them holier than yourselves, and shrank from your own sin, contrasting it with their lives of righteousness and prayerful aspirations heavenward. Yet here are they all in my worshipping assembly. This night it shall be granted you to know their secret deeds: how hoary-bearded elders of the church have whispered wanton words to the young maids of their households; how many a woman, eager for widows' weeds, has given her husband a drink at bedtime and let him sleep his last sleep in her bosom; how beardless youths have made haste to inherit their fathers' wealth; and how fair damsels—blush not, sweet ones—have dug little graves in the garden, and bidden me, the sole guest, to an infant's funeral. By the sympathy of your human hearts for sin ye shall scent out all the places— whether in church, bed-chamber, street, field, or forest—where crime has been committed, and shall exult to behold the whole earth one stain of guilt, one mighty blood spot. Far more than this. It shall be yours to penetrate, in every bosom, the deep mystery of sin, the fountain of all wicked arts, and which inexhaustibly supplies more evil impulses than human power—than my power at its utmost—can make manifest in deeds. And now, my children, look upon each other."

They did so; and, by the blaze of the hell-kindled torches, the wretched man beheld his Faith, and the wife her husband, trembling before that unhallowed altar.

"Lo, there ye stand, my children," said the figure, in a deep and solemn tone, almost sad with its despairing awfulness, as if his once angelic nature could yet mourn for our miserable race. "Depending upon one another's hearts, ye had still hoped that virtue were not all a dream. Now are ye undeceived. Evil is the nature of mankind. Evil must be your only happiness. Welcome again, my children, to the communion of your race."

"Welcome," repeated the fiend worshippers, in one cry of despair and triumph.

And there they stood, the only pair, as it seemed, who were yet hesitating on the verge of wickedness in this dark world. A basin was hollowed, naturally, in the rock. Did it contain water, reddened by the lurid light? or was it blood? or, perchance, a liquid flame? Herein did the shape of evil dip his hand and prepare to lay the mark of baptism upon their foreheads, that they might be partakers of the mystery of sin, more conscious of the secret guilt of others, both in deed and thought, than they could now be of their own. The husband cast one look at his pale wife, and Faith at him. What polluted wretches would the next glance show them to each other, shuddering alike at what they disclosed and what they saw!

"'Faith! Faith!" cried the husband, "look up to heaven, and resist the wicked one."

Whether Faith obeyed he knew not. Hardly had he spoken when he found himself amid calm night and solitude, listening to a roar of the wind which died heavily away through the forest. He staggered against the rock, and felt it chill and damp; while a hanging twig, that had been all on fire, besprinkled his cheek with the coldest dew.

The next morning young Goodman Brown came slowly into the street of Salem village, staring around him like a bewildered man. The good old minister was taking a walk along the graveyard to get an appetite for breakfast and meditate his sermon, and bestowed a blessing, as he passed, on Goodman Brown. He shrank from the venerable saint as if to avoid an anathema. Old Deacon Gookin was at domestic worship, and the holy words of his prayer were heard through the open window. "What God doth the wizard pray to?" quoth Goodman Brown. Goody Cloyse, that excellent old Christian, stood in the early sunshine at her own lattice, catechizing a little girl who had brought her a pint of morning's milk. Goodman Brown snatched away the child as from the grasp of the fiend himself. Turning the corner by the meeting-house, he spied the head of Faith, with the pink ribbons, gazing anxiously forth, and bursting into such joy at sight of him that she skipped along the street and almost kissed her husband before the whole village. But Goodman Brown looked sternly and sadly into her face, and passed on without a greeting.

Had Goodman Brown fallen asleep in the forest and only dreamed a wild dream of a witch-meeting?

Be it so if you will; but, alas! it was a dream of evil omen for young Goodman Brown. A stern, a sad, a darkly meditative, a distrustful, if not a desperate man did he become from the night of that fearful dream. On the Sabbath day, when the congregation were singing a holy psalm, he could not listen because an anthem of sin rushed loudly upon his ear and drowned all the blessed strain. When the minister spoke from the pulpit with power and fervid eloquence, and, with his hand on the open Bible, of the sacred truths of our religion, and of saint-like lives the triumphant deaths, and of future bliss or misery unutterable, then did Goodman Brown turn pale, dreading lest the roof should thunder down upon the gray blasphemer and his hearers. Often, awaking suddenly at midnight, he shrank from the bosom of Faith; and at morning or eventide, when the family knelt down at prayer, he scowled and muttered to himself, and gazed sternly at his wife, and turned away. And when he had lived long, and was borne to his grave a hoary corpse, followed by Faith, an aged woman, and children and grand-children, a goodly procession, besides neighbors not a few, they carved no hopeful verse upon his tombstone, for his dying hour was gloom.

# Unit 6

## Young
## Goodman Brown

- **Comprehension Questions**
- **Recognizing Themes**
- **Discussion Guides**
- **Writing Exercise**

# COMPREHENSION QUESTIONS

For each of the following statements and questions, select the option containing the most complete or most accurate answer.

1. The errand that takes Goodman Brown into the forest that night is
(b) ☐ a. a visit to a sick friend.
   ☐ b. a business appointment in Boston the next morning.
   ☐ c. a search for a doctor for Faith.
   ☐ d. an appointment with the devil.

2. As Goodman Brown sets off on his journey into the forest, he feels
(j) ☐ a. eager.                    ☐ c. depressed.
   ☐ b. curious.                   ☐ d. guilty.

3. Which of the following best defines the word *innumerable* as used in,
(l) "the traveller knows not who may be concealed by the *innumerable* trunks and the thick boughs overhead. . . " ?
   ☐ a. Countless                  ☐ c. Ghostly
   ☐ b. Heavy                      ☐ d. Threatening

4. The devil made the trip from Boston to Salem in
(a) ☐ a. a few seconds.
   ☐ b. fifteen minutes.
   ☐ c. half an hour.
   ☐ d. twenty-four hours.

5. The atmosphere of the forest may best be described as
(i) ☐ a. inspiring and uplifting.
   ☐ b. awesome and threatening.
   ☐ c. soothing and comforting.
   ☐ d. cold and dreary.

6. The devil's tone of voice as he seeks to persuade Goodman Brown to
(i) attend the meeting in the forest is
   ☐ a. composed.                  ☐ c. menacing.
   ☐ b. pleading.                  ☐ d. whining.

7. From the devil's remarks to young Goodman Brown, the reader must
(f) conclude that the early Puritans were
  □ a. saintly and virtuous.
  □ b. just as wicked as any other group.
  □ c. ignorant and rude.
  □ d. innocent and childlike.

8. "Wickedness or not," said the traveller with the twisted staff, "I have
(1) a very *general* acquaintance here in New England." The word *general*
  as it is used here means
  □ a. limited.          □ c. recent.
  □ b. widespread.       □ d. reluctant.

9. Whether Goodman Brown's experience was real or just a dream, it must
(h) have been inspired by
  □ a. an instinct for self-preservation.
  □ b. an inclination toward devil worship.
  □ c. a strong desire to be like his father.
  □ d. a strong belief in salvation and damnation.

10. The devil appears to Goodman Brown in the form of
(a) □ a. Goody Cloyse.
  □ b. a serpent.
  □ c. Deacon Gookin.
  □ d. Goodman Brown's grandfather.

11. The forest in this story represents
(k) □ a. man's inner goodness.
  □ b. the darkness and evil in man.
  □ c. the conflict between man and woman.
  □ d. man's quest for freedom.

12. Just before Faith's pink ribbons flutter down from the sky, young
(k) Goodman Brown declares, "With heaven above and Faith below, I
  will yet stand firm against the devil." Irony, you may recall, is a literary
  device in which the opposite of what is stated is the actual truth. Young
  Goodman Brown's statement is ironic because
  □ a. there is no devil.
  □ b. Faith is above him at the moment, not below.
  □ c. he had already abandoned his faith.
  □ d. he never, in fact, had any faith.

13. On his way through the forest, Goodman Brown hears the voice of
(b) his wife, Faith, coming from
- ☐ a. a dark cloud.
- ☐ b. a dense bush.
- ☐ c. the mouth of a fox.
- ☐ d. the mouth of the devil.

14. Young Goodman Brown stops delaying and hastens to join the meeting
(d) in the forest when
- ☐ a. he sees Goody Cloyse talking with the devil.
- ☐ b. Faith's pink ribbons flutter down from the sky.
- ☐ c. Deacon Gookin and the minister ride by.
- ☐ d. he learns that his ancestors were acquainted with the devil.

15. The sight of Faith's pink ribbons in the forest
(c) ☐ a. has little effect on Goodman Brown.
- ☐ b. brings Goodman Brown to his senses.
- ☐ c. drives Goodman Brown mad.
- ☐ d. reinforces Goodman Brown's faith in God.

16. The first respected village person Goodman Brown meets in the forest is
(d) ☐ a. Faith.                    ☐ c. Deacon Gookin.
- ☐ b. Goody Cloyse.              ☐ d. the minister.

17. A parody may be defined as a distorted imitation of something, a
(k) mockery. In "Young Goodman Brown," the pulpit-shaped rock, the
flaming pines, and the hymn-singing worshippers are a parody of
- ☐ a. a Puritan church service.
- ☐ b. a New England town meeting.
- ☐ c. a political meeting.
- ☐ d. the proceedings in a courtroom.

18. As a result of his experience in the forest, young Goodman Brown
(e) concludes that
- ☐ a. he alone is sinful.
- ☐ b. neither God nor the devil actually exist.
- ☐ c. it was all a bad dream.
- ☐ d. every man and woman is sinful.

19. Young Goodman Brown's strange experience in the forest leaves him
(j) ☐ a. unchanged.                ☐ c. more pious than before.
- ☐ b. stern and gloomy.          ☐ d. weak and sickly.

20. Young Goodman Brown undergoes a transformation in this story from
(j) ☐ a. believing to suspicious.      ☐ c. poverty to wealth.
    ☐ b. obscurity to fame.            ☐ d. profane to pious.


21. For the rest of his life, Goodman Brown regarded his wife and everyone
(e) else as
    ☐ criminals.              ☐ c. saints.
    ☐ cowards.               ☐ d. secret sinners.


22. Before his experience in the forest, Goodman Brown seems to have been
(c) ☐ a. suspicious by nature.       ☐ c. decent and well-adjusted.
    ☐ b. a non-believer in religion.  ☐ d. a troublemaker.


23. The author seems to be saying in this story that, deep down, people are
(g) ☐ a. fascinated by evil.        ☐ c. immune to temptation.
    ☐ b. disgusted by evil.         ☐ d. powerless to resist temptation.


24. The devil made his first appearance in New England
(g) ☐ a. when he presented himself to young Goodman Brown.
    ☐ b. when he made the acquaintance of young Goodman Brown's
         grandfather.
    ☐ c. when the first Puritan stepped ashore from the first ship.
    ☐ d. when only the Indians lived there.


25. The reader might accurately conclude that religion in early New England
(f) ☐ a. played an important role in the community.
    ☐ b. was of little importance to people.
    ☐ c. was left up to the individual.
    ☐ d. was much the same as it is now.


---

Comprehension Skills: a — isolating details; b — recalling specific facts; c — retaining concepts;  d — organizing facts;  e — understanding the main idea; f — drawing a conclusion; g — making a judgment; h — making an inference; i — recognizing tone; j — understanding characters; k — appreciation of literary forms; l — understanding vocabulary.

## Practice Exercise A

Young Goodman Brown came forth at sunset into the street at Salem village; but put his head back, after crossing the threshold, to exchange a parting kiss with his young wife. And Faith, as the wife was aptly named, thrust her own pretty head into the street, letting the wind play with the pink ribbons of her cap while she called to Goodman Brown.

"Dearest heart," whispered she, softly and rather sadly, when her lips were close to his ear, "prithee put off your journey until sunrise and sleep in your own bed to-night. A lone woman is troubled with such dreams and such thoughts that she's afeard of herself sometimes. Pray tarry with me this night, dear husband, of all nights in the year."

"My love and my Faith," replied young Goodman Brown, "of all nights in the year, this one night must I tarry away from thee. My journey, as thou callest it, forth and back again, must needs be done 'twixt now and sunrise. What, my sweet, pretty wife, dost thou doubt me already, and we but three months married?"

"Then God bless you!" said Faith, with the pink ribbons; "and may you find all well when you come back."

"Amen!" cried Goodman Brown.

1. One fact that suggests the nature of young Goodman Brown's journey immediately is that
   ☐ a. his wife is sorry to see him leave.
   ☐ b. he does not trust his wife.
   ☐ c. he would rather not go at all.
   ☐ d. it must take place at night.

2. On the lines provided, write the sentence spoken by young Goodman Brown's wife which strongly suggests that she is aware of the significance of her husband's absence on this particular night.

_____

_____

_____

_____

_____

_____

## Practice Exercise B

"Faith!" shouted Goodman Brown, in a voice of agony and desperation; and the echoes of the forest mocked him, crying, "Faith! Faith!" as if bewildered wretches were seeking her all through the wilderness.

The cry of grief, rage, and terror was yet piercing the night, when the unhappy husband held his breath for a response. There was a scream, drowned immediately in a louder murmur of voices, fading into far-off laughter, as the dark cloud swept away, leaving the clear and silent sky above Goodman Brown. But something fluttered lightly down through the air and caught on the branch of a tree. The young man seized it, and beheld a pink ribbon.

"My Faith is gone!" cried he, after one stupefied moment. "There is no good on earth; and sin is but a name. Come, devil; for to thee is this world given."

1. The pink ribbon that flutters down from the sky is a symbol in the story. On the one hand, it is simply a pink ribbon like the one his wife wears in her hair; at the same time, however, it also symbolizes
   ☐ a. the devil.                    ☐ c. his loss of faith.
   ☐ b. God.                          ☐ d. his guilty conscience.

2. On the lines provided, write the short sentence that neatly sums up the theme of this story.

_____

_____

_____

_____

_____

_____

_____

_____

Practice Exercise C

Another verse of the hymn arose, a slow and mournful strain, such as the pious love, but joined to words which expressed all that our nature can conceive of sin, and darkly hinted at far more. Unfathomable to mere mortals is the lore of fiends. Verse after verse was sung; and still the chorus of the desert swelled between like the deepest tone of a mighty organ; and with the final peal of that dreadful anthem there came a sound, as if the roaring wind, the rushing streams, the howling beasts, and every other voice of the unconcerted wilderness were mingling and according with the voice of guilty man in homage to the prince of all.

1. Hawthorne uses imagery to describe the hymn that young Goodman Brown hears in the forest. The feeling, or mood, which the hymn creates is
   ☐ a. sinful and irreverent.      ☐ c. hopeful and uplifting.
   ☐ b. wondrous and awesome.    ☐ d. spritely and fanciful.

2. Underline that part of the passage which suggests that mankind and nature were united in evil.

Practice Exercise D

A stern, a sad, a darkly meditative, a distrustful, if not a desperate man did he become from the night of that fearful dream. On the Sabbath day, when the congregation was singing a holy psalm, he could not listen because an anthem of sin rushed loudly upon his ear and drowned all the blessed strain. When the minister spoke from the pulpit with power and fervid eloquence, and, with his hand on the Bible, of the sacred truths of our religion, and of saint-like lives and triumphant deaths, and of future bliss or misery unutterable, then did Goodman Brown turn pale, dreading lest the roof should thunder down upon the gray blasphemer and his hearers. Often, awaking suddenly at midnight, he shrank from the bosom of Faith; and at morning or eventide, when the family knelt down at prayer, he scowled and muttered to himself, and gazed sternly at his wife, and turned away.

1. The new knowledge which young Goodman Brown acquires in the forest leaves him
   ☐ a. happier.
   ☐ b. profoundly disturbed.
   ☐ c. more forgiving of other people's sins.
   ☐ d. stronger.

2. One phrase in this passage has a double meaning. In one sense, it refers to young Goodman Brown's relationship with his wife, while also describing his attitude toward God and religion. Underline this phrase.

# DISCUSSION GUIDES

## Analyzing Themes

1. How does the name of Goodman Brown's wife, Faith, contribute to the theme of the story?

2. How does the theme of "Young Goodman Brown" make this story meaningful to you personally?

## Interpreting the Story

3. Why do you suppose the devil chose to assume the shape of young Goodman Brown's grandfather?

4. Why, when he loved his wife and had only just been married, do you think young Goodman Brown went into the forest that night in the first place?

5. As the devil is about to baptize them, Goodman Brown begs his wife, Faith, to "look up to heaven, and resist the wicked one." Had he not said that, what do you think Faith would have done?

6. How do you explain young Goodman Brown's experience in the forest—was it a dream? a test of his faith? an hallucination? or did it really happen? Why doesn't the author make this clear in the story?

7. Nathaniel Hawthorne's tale of witchcraft is set in old Salem, probably in the late 1600s. Has witchcraft lost any of its appeal since then? Compare "Young Goodman Brown" with such modern stories as *Rosemary's Baby*, *The Exorcist*, and *The Omen*. What do they all have in common? In your opinion, will people ever outgrow the idea of witchcraft?

8. Like young Goodman Brown whose father set fire to an Indian village in King Phillip's war, and whose grandfather lashed a Quaker woman through the streets of Salem, Nathaniel Hawthorne also had stern Puritan ancestors. One of them, in fact, had a hand in the persecution of the Quakers, and another was a judge in the witchcraft trials. Judging from his story of "Young Goodman Brown," how do you think Hawthorne felt about his Puritan ancestors?

9. Some critics have called "Young Goodman Brown" an allegory. An allegory is a story that has a dual meaning—one meaning in the appearance of characters, setting, and events, and another in the ideas they are intended to convey. Do you agree that "Young Goodman Brown" is allegorical? If so, what might be the ideas represented by the character of young Goodman Brown? his wife? her pink ribbons? the forest? the devil? the journey?

10. "Young Goodman Brown" has obvious roots in colonial history. The New England Puritans believed in witchcraft and actually put to death suspected witches on the basis of spectral evidence—that is, testimony based on experiences like that of young Goodman Brown. Do you think Hawthorne intended this story to be read in part as history? Why or why not? Does this story still have meaning for modern readers? Explain.

## WRITING EXERCISE

Every successful television show is based on a theme. For instance, the theme of "The Mary Tyler Moore Show" is a single girl who makes it on her own in the working world. Each episode illustrates this theme by portraying the difficulties and the small triumphs which Mary Richards encounters in both her personal and her professional life.

Choose a television show that you particularly enjoy. In one sentence, identify what you think is the underlying theme of the series. Then, write your own episode that in some way expresses this theme. (Or just write an outline of your episode.) Base your episode on a conflict that your main character faces and resolves. Think up a title for your episode that summarizes the story line and ties in with the theme; for example, "Mary Asks for a Raise."

# The Black Cat

### Edgar Allan Poe

# Introduction

"THE BLACK CAT"—even the title of the story sounds frightening.

Few of us worry anymore about black cats as companions to witches and messengers of evil, but even so, when one is introduced in a story or a movie, we know it is time for our skin to crawl and a cold shiver passes along the spine. It is one of those symbols that instantly creates a somber and frightening tone and mood.

If, however, you are somehow not affected by the imagery of black cats, the first paragraph of the story will soon set you straight. Here the author gets right to work talking about madness, horror, and things beyond belief, and has his narrator tell us, "But tomorrow I die, and today I would unburden my soul." Clearly, if the cat hasn't flipped his whiskers, the narrator has, and you would have to be pretty insensitive to mystery not to be curious about what's going on here.

Like many other Edgar Allan Poe stories, "The Black Cat" begins darkly and sustains this mood until the very end. The story is being told from a prison cell, and on the following day our story teller is to be hanged. How he got into this sad state of affairs is the subject of the story. Because the story has the Poe brand, you can count on its being horrifying and chilling to the heart.

No doubt you have met Poe before, since it is difficult to go very far in school, anywhere in the world, without having read something he has done—he is that popular and that well known. You may know some of his poetry: "The Raven," "Bells," "Annabel Lee," "Lenore," or "Eldorado." He is credited with writing the world's first detective stories: "The Murders in the Rue Morgue" and "The Purloined Letter." And best known of all are his Gothic stories: "The Tell-Tale Heart." "The Pit and the Pendulum," "The Masque of the Red Death," and "The Cask of Amontillado." "The Black Cat" is one of his best Gothic tales.

Gothic novels originated in England in the eighteenth century, about seventy years before Poe started to write, with a book called *The Castle of*

*Otranto* by Horace Walpole. The setting of this book was a Gothic medieval castle which is how this type of story came to be called Gothic. The emphasis in a Gothic story is on plot and setting rather than on such things as theme or character development. Gothic stories feature magic and supernatural happenings, horror, terror, dark and mysterious places, dungeons, cellars, musty attics, evil and deformed characters, and always death which occurs in some unnatural manner. It contains everything, you might say, designed to give readers the delightful shivers.

Though the medieval castle is missing in "The Black Cat," most of the other elements of a Gothic story are present. Watch for them as you read the story and see how many you can identify.

The main character and narrator of "The Black Cat" blames his bizarre actions on the "Fiend Intemperance;" he was an alcoholic, in other words, as Poe was himself in real life. Poe's short life was as strange and as tormented, in many ways, as the lives of the characters of his poems and stories. Although he was a brilliant and promising youth—handsome, athletic, scholarly, and connected to a good family—he was destined to spend most of his life in poverty and misery. The real wonder of his career was that he was able to do as much work as he did, with all of it memorable. He was an innovator in his time; "the finest of finest artists" George Bernard Shaw called him.

The end came for Poe when he was abandoned in a gutter after being dragged about the city of Baltimore in a drunken stupor by a bunch of political thugs who had him vote repeatedly for their candidate. In one of his last lucid moments he was reported to have cried out, "I wish to God somebody would blow my damned brains out!" But it wasn't necessary; he died shortly afterward. He was forty.

"I dwelt alone in a world of moan," he said in his poem "Eulalie." As you read, see if you think this image of his life is reflected in the tone and mood of "The Black Cat."

# Tone and Mood

Tone and mood are a lot like personality—you can't put your finger on them, yet without tone and mood a story is just a report, and without personality an individual is just a robot.

Tone and mood, like personality, are the sum total of many different things all working together to achieve an overall effect. You may be hard put to explain exactly what it is that makes your best friend special to you—you just know that he or she has a nice disposition. Tone and mood are like that, too. You sense the atmosphere created by a particular story, but you can't explain exactly how it got there. Upon closer examination, however, you would see that your best friend's personality is made up of his or her looks, manners, actions, likes and dislikes. Similarly, the tone and mood of a story are the combined effect of setting, character, theme, description, and so on.

Edgar Allan Poe once said that a writer must begin a story with one effect in mind that is to be brought out more than any other—such as terror, passion, or horror. Then, in writing the story, every word must be made to help produce this effect in some way. Every element of the story you are about to read contributes to an atmosphere of horror that builds and intensifies to a ghastly and shocking climax. Let's take a look at how Poe does this.

**1. Tone Versus Mood.** First of all, it's necessary to distinguish between the terms tone and mood.

*Tone* is defined as the *attitude* expressed in a piece of writing. To understand how writers use tone, think about how *you* use tone in your everyday speech to show your attitude—how you feel about something. For instance, you may use an indignant tone when you are defending yourself against an unjust accusation. You may use a triumphant tone when you announce that you made the honor roll or Dean's list, and a sarcastic tone when you thank a friend who turns up to help just as the work is finished. Writers use tone in the same way to how how *they* feel about a particular subject, or to reveal a character's feelings.

The term *mood,* on the other hand, refers to the *atmosphere* that surrounds an incident or scene. You have probably felt the somber atmosphere at a funeral, and the festive atmosphere of New Year's Eve. Writers try to convey a mood, or atmosphere, that is appropriate to their story in order to draw the reader into the little world they have created.

Tone and mood usually work together to achieve a certain effect. In the following passage from "The Black Cat," the narrator describes a terrible act of cruelty to a pet cat. What are the tone and mood in this scene, and how does one affect the other?

> The fury of a demon instantly possessed me. I knew myself no longer. My original soul seemed, at once, to take its flight from my body; and a more than fiendish malevolence, gin-nurtured, thrilled every fibre of my frame. I took from my waistcoat-pocket a penknife, opened it, grasped the poor beast by the throat, and deliberately cut one of its eyes from the socket! I blush, I burn, I shudder, while I pen the damnable atrocity.

The *tone* of the above passage is demonic, as if the speaker were possessed by the devil. The narrator is beside himself with rage. "I knew myself no longer," he says. His usual self has been transformed into a demon that thrills to the most vile and sadistic impulses, such as cutting out the eye of a cat. The *mood* of this scene is one of horror. The "fiendish malevolence" of the narrator and his unspeakable cruelty to the cat are horrifying to imagine and fill the reader with feelings of disgust and revulsion. Clearly, the demonic tone serves to emphasize and reinforce the horrifying mood of this scene.

**2. How Setting Contributes to Tone and Mood.** Just as you are apt to speak in hushed tones and feel a mood of peace in a place of worship, so, too, does the setting of a story influence its tone and mood.

Writers know that certain settings can be relied on to produce certain feelings in readers. So they use a particular setting because it helps build the tone and mood they wish to create. Horror stories such as *Frankenstein,* for instance, are frequently set in crumbling castles because this setting creates a spooky atmosphere that prepares the reader for the strange goings-on inside.

Weather often plays a part in setting, too. The crumbling castle we just mentioned is invariably lit by jagged arrows of lightning from a raging thunderstorm.

Sometimes an author will use a setting that contrasts sharply with the action of a story. A meadow full of flowers on a bright sunny day seems a good setting for a meeting of two young lovers. But by setting the two young lovers in a dingy slum instead of a flowery meadow, the fact of their love may gain added meaning because it is so unexpected in these surroundings. Similarly, it is natural to associate death with a bleak winter's day. But death on a sunny spring day seems twice as cruel because the mood of a sunny spring day suggests life, not death.

In the following passage from "The Black Cat," the setting has a marked effect on the atmosphere of this scene. What is the setting here, and how does it contribute to tone and mood?

> On the day succeeding the fire, I visited the ruins. The walls, with one exception, had fallen in. This exception was found in a compartment wall, not very thick, which stood about the middle of the house, and against which had rested the head of my bed. The plastering had here, in great measure, resisted the action of the fire—a fact which I attributed to its having been recently spread. About this wall a dense crowd were collected, and many persons seemed to be examining a particular portion of it with very minute and eager attention. The words "strange!" "singular!" and other similar expressions, excited my curiosity. I approached and saw, as if graven in *bas-relief* upon the white surface, the figure of a gigantic *cat*. The impression was given with an accuracy truly marvellous. There was a rope about the animal's neck.
>
> When I first beheld this apparition—for I could scarcely regard it as less—my wonder and my terror were extreme.

The setting of this scene is the burned-out shell of a house. Under any circumstances, this is a depressing setting, bringing to mind as it does feelings of great suffering and loss. This particular setting, however, sends an extra shudder through the reader because of the strange and curious image of a cat with a noose around its neck which appears on the one wall of the house left standing after the fire. The *tone* of the passage is one of amazement and disbelief. What, we ask ourselves, could have caused the image of a cat with a noose around its neck to appear on the wall of this ruined house? The *mood* which this scene creates is one of apprehension and, again, horror, because we suspect there is something sinister going on here and we shiver as if with a chill in its presence.

**3. How Character and Theme Influence Tone and Mood.** Character and theme also play their part in establishing atmosphere. A character who engages our sympathy is going to play on our feelings in quite a different way from the character who arouses only scorn and contempt. And since the theme of a story is often revealed in the main character, it too affects tone and mood.

A good example of how this works can be seen in the story you are about to read. Here, the main character is a man whose drinking has brought about disturbing changes in his personality. In the following passage this man, who is also the narrator, describes his extreme dislike for a pet cat. As you read, consider how the character of the narrator influences the tone and mood.

> With my aversion to this cat, however, its partiality for myself seemed to increase. It followed my footsteps with a pertinacity which it would be difficult to make the reader comprehend. Wherever I sat, it would crouch beneath my chair, or spring upon my knees, covering me with its loathsome caresses. If I arose to walk

it would get between my feet and thus nearly throw me down, or, fastening its long and sharp claws in my dress, clamber, in this manner, to my breast. At such times, although I longed to destroy it with a blow, I was yet withheld from so doing, partly by a memory of my former crime, but chiefly—let me confess it at once—by absolute *dread* of the beast.

The character of the narrator in the passage has a disturbing influence on the atmosphere of the story. Obviously, something is wrong with the man. He finds the affectionate caresses of a cat "loathsome." He accuses the animal of purposely getting underfoot so as to trip him, and, what is more, he confesses to having an absolute *dread* of the beast. No one in his right mind would feel this way towards a harmless household pet. Clearly, the man is unsettled.

The tone of the narrator's speech is irrational, and the reader's growing suspicion that here is a madman has a chilling effect on the atmosphere. A theme of this story concerns the narrator's descent into insanity, and this fearsome idea further underscores the mood of horror which we saw in the other two passages.

The black cat is also a main character. Its brooding presence can be felt in every scene, and the tone of its "voice" at the end of the story surpasses in horror all that has gone before.

**4. How the Author's Language Creates Tone and Mood.** Though you may not be conscious of it, the way an author uses language can have a major influence on tone and mood.

Sentence length, for one thing, helps to establish the rhythm of a piece of writing. A series of short, clipped sentences helps to create a feeling of movement and excitement. Long, flowing sentences, on the other hand, are better suited to convey a peaceful atmosphere. Unusual structure is often used to heighten a dramatic effect.

The kind of vocabulary an author uses also affects tone and mood. The vocabulary you use when you're chatting with a friend is different from the vocabulary you'd hear in a sermon. Similarly, an author uses a vocabulary that is suited to the subject matter and the circumstances. Long, expressive words may be necessary to convey feelings and emotions, whereas short, simple words better express action and excitement.

Similes and metaphors affect tone and mood by controlling the associations that come to mind as you read. The simile "fragrant as a rose" obviously conveys pleasant associations. A metaphor such as "the carcass of an old car" brings to mind unpleasant and offensive associations.

Even punctuation affects tone and mood. The use of italics, exclamation points, dashes and even commas affects tone by showing the reader how to read a passage—what to emphasize, where to pause, and so on.

In the following passage from "The Black Cat," Poe's use of language is a major factor in establishing tone and mood. How, exactly, does he do this?

Alas! neither by day nor by night knew I the blessing of Rest any more! During the former the creature left me no moment alone;

and, in the latter, I started, hourly, from dreams of unutterable
fear, to find the hot breath of *the thing* upon my face, and its vast
weight—an incarnate Night-Mare that I had no power to shake
off—incumbent eternally upon my *heart!*

The first word, "Alas" is a heavy and dramatic word suggesting extreme
emotion. "Alas!" is like saying, "Woe is me! What a tale I have to tell!"

He goes on to say that, "neither by day nor by night knew I the blessing of
rest any more!" Notice how this is the reverse construction of a normal
sentence—"knew I" rather than "I knew." This too is designed to heighten
the emotional impact of the statement. Another exclamation point at the
end of the sentence lends added emphasis. Now look at the other, very long,
sentence:

During the former the creature left me no moment alone; and,
in the latter, I started, hourly, from dreams of unutterable fear, to
find the hot breath of *the thing* upon my face.

The sentence is so long that you get out of breath just from reading it. The
adjective *unutterable* is a long word that drags on like the fear that dragged
on for the narrator. By putting *the thing* in italics, the author makes the
poor beast seem unspeakably evil, suggesting that it is not a simple animal
with a name—cat—but an alien, unexplainable *thing!*

and its vast weight—an incarnate Night-Mare that I had no
power to shake off.

The term *vast weight* is an example of hyperbole because it is an exaggeration to describe the weight of a cat as "vast." The word *incarnate* means
that the nightmare seemed to have a real living, bodily form. It is an ornate
word that you would expect to find in a sermon, or in a funeral oration.
There is a feeling of death about it that makes the tone very appropriate to
the sense of the passage. And finally, the sentence ends

incumbent eternally upon my *heart!*

The word *incumbent* means lying or pressing upon. The long phrase
*incumbent eternally* makes you feel the never-ending weight on your own
chest, and by the time you get to *heart!* in italics with an exclamation point
after it, you are breathless and ready to scream. And this is exactly what
Poe intended for you.

The effect of the author's language in this passage, then, is to heighten
the emotional impact of the narrator's tale. The man is terror stricken,
feeling that he has an immense weight upon his heart. He fears for his life
and his sanity. The tone is demented. The mood is gloomy and funereal.

As you read "The Black Cat," notice how tone and mood add to your
enjoyment of the story, and watch how the mood builds and intensifies as
the story goes along.

# The Black Cat
## Edgar Allan Poe

For the most wild, yet mostly homely narrative which I am about to pen, I neither expect nor solicit belief. Mad indeed would I be to expect it, in a case where my very senses reject their own evidence. Yet, mad am I not—and very surely do I not dream. But tomorrow I die, and today I would unburden my soul. My immediate purpose is to place before the world, plainly, succinctly, and without comment, a series of mere household events. In their consequences, these events have terrified—have tortured—have destroyed me. Yet I will not attempt to expound them. To me, they have presented little but Horror—to many they will seem less terrible than *baroques*. Hereafter, perhaps, some intellect may be found which will reduce my phantasm to the common-place—some intellect more calm, more logical and far less excitable than my own, which will perceive, in the circumstances I detail with awe, nothing more than an ordinary succession of very natural causes and effects.

From my infancy I was noted for the docility and humanity of my disposition. My tenderness of heart was even so conspicuous as to make me the jest of my companions. I was especially fond of animals, and was indulged by my parents with a great variety of pets. With these I spent most of my time, and never was so happy as when feeding and caressing them. This peculiarity of character grew with my growth, and, in my manhood, I derived from it one of my principal sources of pleasure. To those who have cherished an affection for a faithful and sagacious dog, I need hardly be at the trouble of explaining the nature or the intensity of the gratification thus derivable. There is something in the unselfish and self-sacrificing love of a brute, which goes directly to the heart of him who has had frequent occasion to test the paltry friendship and gossamer fidelity of mere *Man*.

I married early, and was happy to find in my wife a disposition not uncongenial with my own. Observing my partiality for domestic pets, she lost no opportunity of procuring those of the most agreeable kind. We had birds, gold fish, a fine dog, rabbits, a small monkey, and *a cat*.

This latter was a remarkably large and beautiful animal, entirely black, and sagacious to an astonishing degree. In speaking of his intelligence, my wife, who at heart was not a little tinctured with superstition, made frequent allusion to the ancient popular notion, which regarded all black cats as witches in disguise. Not that she was ever *serious* upon this point—and I mention the matter at all for no better reason than that it happens, just now, to be remembered.

Pluto—this was the cat's name—was my favorite pet and playmate. I alone fed him, and he attended me wherever I went about the house. It was even with difficulty that I could prevent him from following me through the streets.

Our friendship lasted, in this manner, for several years, during which my general temperament and character—through the instrumentality of the Fiend Intemperance—had (I blush to confess it) experienced a radical alteration for the worse. I grew, day by day, more moody, more irritable, more regardless of the feelings of others. I suffered myself to use intemperate language to my wife. At length, I even offered her personal violence. My pets, of course, were made to feel the change in my disposition. I not only neglected, but ill-used them. For Pluto, however, I still retained sufficient regard to restrain me from maltreating him, as I made no scruple of maltreating the rabbits, the monkey, or even the dog, when by accident, or through affection, they came in my way. But my disease grew upon me—for what disease is like Alcohol!—and at length even Pluto, who was now becoming old, and consequently somewhat peevish—even Pluto began to experience the effects of my ill temper.

One night, returning home, much intoxicated, from one of my haunts about town, I fancied that the cat avoided my presence. I seized him; when, in his fright at my violence, he inflicted a slight wound upon my hand with his teeth. The fury of a demon instantly possessed me. I knew myself no longer. My original soul seemed, at once, to take its flight from my body; and a more than fiendish malevolence, gin-nurtured, thrilled every fibre of my frame. I took from my waistcoat-pocket a penknife, opened it, grasped the poor beast by the throat, and deliberately cut one of its eyes from the socket! I blush, I burn, I shudder, while I pen the damnable atrocity.

When reason returned with the morning—when I had slept off the fumes of the night's debauch—I experienced a sentiment half of horror, half of remorse, for the crime of which I had been guilty; but it was, at best, a feeble and equivocal feeling, and the soul remained untouched. I again plunged into excess, and soon drowned in wine all memory of the deed.

In the meantime the cat slowly recovered. The socket of the lost eye presented, it is true, a frightful appearance, but he no longer appeared to suffer any pain. He went about the house as usual, but, as might be expected, fled in extreme terror at my appraoch. I had so much of my old heart left, as to be at first grieved by this evident dislike on the part of a creature which had once so loved me. But this feeling soon gave place to irritation. And then came, as if to my final and irrevocable overthrow, the spirit of PERVERSENESS. Of this spirit philosophy takes no account. Yet I am not more sure that my soul lives, than I am that perverseness is one of the primitive impulses of the human heart—one of the indivisible primary faculties, or sentiments, which give direction to the character of Man. Who has not, a hundred times, found himself committing a vile or a silly action, for no other reason that because he knows he should *not?* Have we not a perpetual inclination, in the teeth of our best judgment, to violate that which is *Law,* merely because we understand it to be such? This spirit of perverseness, I say, came to my final overthrow. It was this unfathomable longing of the soul *to vex itself*—to offer violence to its own nature—to do wrong for the wrong's sake only—that urged me to continue and finally to consummate the injury I had inflicted upon the unoffending brute. One morning, in cold blood, I slipped a noose about his neck and hung it to the limb of a tree;—hung it with the tears streaming from my eyes, and with the bitterest remorse at my heart;—hung it *because* I knew that it had loved me, and *because* I felt it had given me no reason of offense;—hung it *because* I knew that in so doing I was committing a sin—a deadly sin that would so jeopardize my immortal soul as to place it—if such a thing were possible—even beyond the reach of the infinite mercy of the Most Merciful and Most Terrible God.

On the night of the day on which this cruel deed was done, I was aroused from sleep by the cry of fire. The curtains of my bed were in flames. The whole house was blazing. It was with great difficulty that my wife, a servant, and myself, made our escape from the conflagration. The destruction was complete. My entire worldy wealth was swallowed up, and I resigned myself thenceforward to despair.

I am above the weakness of seeking to establish a sequence of cause and effect, between the disaster and the atrocity. But I am detailing a chain of facts—and wish not to leave even a possible link imperfect. On the day succeeding the fire, I visited the ruins. The walls, with one exception, had fallen in. This exception was found in a compartment wall, not very thick, which stood about the middle of the house, and against which had rested the head of my bed. The plastering had here, in great measure, resisted the action of the fire—a fact which I attributed to its having been recently spread. About this wall a dense crowd were collected, and many persons seemed to be examining a particular portion of it with very minute and eager attention. The words "strange!" "singular!" and other similar expressions, excited my curiosity. I approached and saw, as if graven in *bas relief* upon the white surface, the figure of a gigantic *cat.* The impression was given with an accuracy truly marvellous. There was a rope about the animal's neck.

When I first beheld this apparition—for I could scarcely regard it as less—my wonder and my terror were extreme. But at length reflection came to my aid. The cat, I remembered, had been hung in a garden adjacent to the house. Upon the alarm of fire, this garden had been immediately filled by the crowd—by some one of whom the animal must have been cut from the tree and thrown, through an open window, into my chamber. This had probably been done with the view of arousing me from sleep. The falling of other walls had compressed the victim of my cruelty into the substance of the freshly-spread plaster; the lime of which, with the flames, and the *ammonia* from the carcass, had then accomplished the portraiture as I saw it.

Although I thus readily accounted to my reason, if not altogether to my conscience, for the startling fact just detailed, it did not the less fail to make a deep impression upon my fancy. For months I could not rid myself of the phantasm of the cat; and, during this period, there came back into my spirit a half-sentiment that seemed, but was not, remorse. I went so far as to regret the loss of the animal, and to look about me, among the vile haunts which I now habitually frequented, for another pet of the same species, and of somewhat similar appearance, with which to supply its place.

One night as I sat, half stupified, in a den of more than infamy, my attention was suddenly drawn to some black object, reposing upon the head of one of the immense hogheads of Gin, or of Rum, which constituted the chief furniture of the apartment. I had been looking steadily at the top of this hogshead for some minutes, and what now caused me surprise was the fact that I had not sooner perceived the object thereupon. I approached it, and touched it with my hand. It was a black cat—a very large one—fully as large as Pluto, and closely resembling him in every respect but one. Pluto had not a white hair upon any portion of his body; but this cat had a large, although indefinite splotch of white, covering nearly the whole region of the breast.

Upon my touching him, he immediately arose, purred loudly, rubbed against my hand, and appeared delighted with my notice. This, then, was the very creature of which I was in search. I at once offered to purchase it of the landlord; but this person made no claim to it—knew nothing of it—had never seen it before.

I continued my caresses, and, when I prepared to go home, the animal evinced a disposition to accompany me. I permitted it to do so; occasionally stooping and patting it as I proceeded. When it reached the house it domesticated itself at once, and became immediately a great favorite with my wife.

For my own part, I soon found a dislike to it arising within me. This was just the reverse of what I had anticipated; but I know not how or why it was—its evident fondness for myself rather disgusted and annoyed. By slow degrees, these feelings of disgust and annoyance rose into the bitterness of hatred. I avoided the creature; a certain sense of shame, and the remembrance of my former deed of cruelty, preventing me from physically abusing it. I did not, for some weeks, strike, or otherwise violently ill use it; but gradually—very gradually—I came to look upon it with unutterable loathing, and to flee silently from its odious presence, as from the breath of a pestilence.

What added, no doubt, to my hatred of the beast, was the discovery, on the morning after I brought it home, that, like Pluto, it also had been deprived of one of its eyes. This circumstance, however, only endeared it to my wife, who, as I have already said, possessed, in a high degree, that humanity of feeling which had once been my distinguishing trait, and the source of many of my simplest and purest pleasures.

With my aversion to this cat, however, its partiality for myself seemed to increase. It followed my footsteps with a pertinacity which it would be difficult to make the reader comprehend. Whenever I sat, it would crouch beneath my chair, or spring upon my knees, covering me with its loathsome caresses. If I arose to walk it would get between my feet and thus nearly throw me down, or, fastening its long and sharp claws in my dress, clamber, in this manner, to my breast. At such times, although I longed to destroy it with a blow, I was yet withheld from so doing, partly by a memory of my former crime, but chiefly—let me confess it at once—by absolute *dread* of the beast.

This dread was not exactly a dread of physical evil—and yet I should be at a loss how otherwise to define it. I am almost ashamed to own—yes, even in this felon's cell, I am almost ashamed to own—that the terror and horror with which the animal inspired me, had been heightened by one of the merest chimaeras it would be possible to conceive. My wife had called my attention, more than once, to the character of the mark of white hair, of which I have spoken, and which constituted the sole visible difference between the strange beast and the one I had destroyed. The reader will remember that this mark, although large, had been originally very indefinite; but, by slow degrees—degrees nearly imperceptible, and which for a long time my Reason struggled to reject as fanciful—it had, at length, assumed a rigorous distinctness of outline. It was now the representation of an object that I shudder to name—and for this, above all, I loathed, and dreaded, and would have rid myself of the monster *had I dared*—it was now, I say, the image of a hideous—ghastly thing—of the GALLOWS!—oh, mournful and terrible engine of Horror and of Crime—of Agony and of Death!

And now was I indeed wretched beyond the wretchedness of mere Humanity. And *a brute beast*—whose fellow I had contemptuously destroyed—*a brute beast* to work out for *me*—for me a man, fashioned in the image of the High God—so much of insufferable wo! Alas! neither by day nor by night knew I the blessing of Rest any more! During the former the creature left me no moment alone; and, in the latter, I started, hourly, from dreams of unutterable fear, to find the hot breath of *the thing* upon my face, and its vast weight—an incarnate Night-Mare that I had no power to shake off—incumbent eternally upon my *heart!*

Beneath the pressure of torments such as these, the feeble remnant of the good within me succumbed. Evil thoughts became my sole intimates—the darkest and most evil of thoughts. The moodiness of my usual temper increased to hatred of all things and of all mankind; while, from the sudden, frequent, and ungovernable outbursts of a fury to which I now blindly abandoned myself, my uncomplaining wife, alas! was the most usual and the most patient of sufferers.

One day she accompanied me, upon some household errand, into the cellar of the old building which our poverty compelled us to inhabit. The cat followed me down the steep stairs, and, nearly throwing me headlong, exasperated me to madness. Uplifting an axe, and forgetting, in my wrath, the childish dread which had hitherto stayed my hand, I aimed a blow at the animal which, of course, would have proved instantly fatal had it descended as I wished. But this blow was arrested by the hand of my wife. Goaded, by the interference, into a rage more than demoniacal, I withdrew my arm from her grasp and buried the axe in her brain. She fell dead upon the spot, without a groan.

This hideous murder accomplished, I set myself forthwith, and with entire deliberation, to the task of concealing the body. I knew that I could not remove it from the house, either by day or by night, without the risk of being observed by the neighbors. Many projects entered my mind. At one period I thought of cutting the corpse into minute fragments, and destroying them by fire. At another, I resolved to dig a grave for it in the floor of the cellar. Again, I deliberated about casting it in the well in the yard—about packing it in a box, as if merchandize, with the usual arrangements, and so getting a porter to take it from the house. Finally I hit upon what I considered a far better expedient than either of these. I determined to wall it up in the cellar—as the monks of the middle ages are recorded to have walled up their victims.

For a purpose such as this the cellar was well adapted. Its walls were loosely constructed, and had lately been plastered throughout with a rough plaster, which the dampness of the atmosphere had prevented from hardening. Moreover, in one of the walls was a projection, caused by a false chimney, or fireplace, that had been filled up, and made to resemble the rest of the cellar. I made no doubt that I could readily displace the bricks at this point, insert the corpse, and wall the whole up as before, so that no eye could detect anything suspicious.

And in this calculation I was not deceived. By means of a crow-bar I easily dislodged the bricks, and, having carefully deposited the body against the inner wall, I propped it in that position, while, with little trouble, I re-laid the whole structure as it originally stood. Having procured mortar, sand, and hair, with every possible precaution, I prepared a plaster which could not be distinguished from the old, and with this I very carefully went over the new brick-work. When I had finished, I felt satisfied that all was right. The wall did not present the slightest appearance of having been disturbed. The rubbish on the floor was picked up with the minutest care. I looked around triumphantly, and said to myself—"Here at least, then, my labor has not been in vain."

My next step was to look for the beast which had been the cause of so much wretchedness; for I had, at length, firmly resolved to put it to death. Had I been able to meet with it, at the moment, there could have been no doubt of its fate; but it appeared that the crafty animal had been alarmed at the violence of my previous anger, and forebore to present itself in my present mood. It is impossible to describe, or to imagine, the deep, the blissful sense of relief which the absence of the detested creature occasioned in my bosom. It did not make its appearance during the night—and thus for one night at least, since its introduction into the house, I soundly and tranquilly slept; aye, *slept* even with the burden of murder upon my soul!

The second and the third day passed, and still my tormentor came not. Once again I breathed as a freeman. The monster, in terror, had fled the premises forever! I should behold it no more! My happiness was supreme! The guilt of my dark deed disturbed me but little. Some few inquiries had been made, but these had been readily answered. Even a search had been instituted—but of course nothing was to be discovered I looked upon my future felicity as secured.

Upon the fourth day of the assassination, a party of the police came, very unexpectedly, into the house, and proceeded again to make rigorous investigation of the premises. Secure, however, in the inscrutability of my place of concealment, I felt no embarrassment whatever. The officers bade me accompany them in their search. They left no nook or corner unexplored. At length, for the third or fourth time, they descended into the cellar. I quivered not in a muscle. My heart beat calmly as that of one who slumbers in innocence. I walked the cellar from end to end. I folded my arms upon my bosom, and roamed easily to and fro. The police were thoroughly satisfied and prepared to depart. The glee at my heart was too strong to be restrained. I burned to say if but one word, by way of triumph, and to render doubly sure their assurance of my guiltlessness.

"Gentlemen," I said at last, as the party ascended the steps, "I delight to have allayed your suspicions. I wish you all health, and a little more courtesy. By the bye, gentlemen, this—this is a very well constructed house." [In the rabid desire to say something easily, I scarcely knew what I uttered at all.]—"I may say an *excellently* well constructed house. These walls—are you going, gentlemen—these walls are solidly put together;" and here, through the mere phrenzy of bravado, I rapped heavily, with a cane which I held in my hand, upon the very portion of the brick-work behind which stood the corpse of the wife of my bosom.

But may God shield and deliver me from the fangs of the Arch-Fiend! No sooner had the reverberation of my blows sunk into silence, than I was answered by a voice from within the tomb!—by a cry, at first muffled and broken, like the sobbing of a child, and then quickly swelling into one long, loud, and continuous scream, utterly anomalous and inhuman—a howl—a wailing shriek, half of horror and half of triumph, such as might have arisen only out of hell, conjointly from the throats of the damned in their agony and of the demons that exult in the damnation.

Of my own thoughts it is folly to speak. Swooning, I staggered to the opposite wall. For one instant the party upon the stairs remained motionless, through extremity of terror and of awe. In the next, a dozen stout arms were toiling at the wall. It fell bodily. The corpse, already greatly decayed and clotted with gore, stood erect before the eyes of the spectators. Upon its head, with red extended mouth and solitary eye of fire, sat the hideous beast whose craft had seduced me into murder, and whose informing voice had consigned me to the hangman. I had walled the monster up within the tomb!

# Unit 7

## The Black Cat

- Comprehension Questions
- Tone and Mood
- Discussion Guides
- Writing Exercise

# COMPREHENSION QUESTIONS

For each of the following statements and questions, select the option containing the most complete or most accurate answer.

1. When he was a boy, the narrator spent much of his time enjoying
   (a) ☐ a. books.      ☐ c. music.
         ☐ b. pets.       ☐ d. nature.

2. Which of the following best defines *paltry* as used in, "There is some-
   (l) thing in the unselfish and self-sacrificing love of a brute, which goes directly to the heart of him who has had frequent occasion to test the *paltry* friendship and gossamer fidelity of mere *Man*"?
        ☐ a. Practically worthless      ☐ c. Unique
        ☐ b. Valuable       ☐ d. Long-lasting

3. The ugly changes in the narrator's personality began with
   (e) ☐ a. opium addiction.      ☐ c. poverty.
         ☐ b. ill health.       ☐ d. alcoholism.

4. The narrator attributes his downfall to a character trait which he claims
   (c) is "one of the primitive impulses of the human heart," and that is
        ☐ a. greed.      ☐ c. perverseness.
        ☐ b. lust.       ☐ d. fear.

5. The narrator's feelings as he kills Pluto are
   (j) ☐ a. gleeful and triumphant.
        ☐ b. downcast and melancholy.
        ☐ c. at once remorseful and spiteful.
        ☐ d. callous and insensitive.

6. According to the narrator, he kills Pluto because
   (j) ☐ a. he knew he had no reason to.
        ☐ b. the cat was always underfoot.
        ☐ c. he knew his wife loved the cat.
        ☐ d. the cat brought him bad luck.

7. The fire which destroyed the narrator's house occurred
(d)   ☐ a. the night he met Pluto's look-alike in a tavern.
     ☐ b. the night he murdered his wife.
     ☐ c. the night after he hanged Pluto.
     ☐ d. the night he cut out one of Pluto's eyes.

8. On the one wall which still stood after the fire could be seen the
(b) figure of
     ☐ a. the devil.           ☐ c. a skull.
     ☐ b. a cross.           ☐ d. a cat.

9. The image which could be seen on the wall of the house after the fire
(h) was
     ☐ a. a supernatural sign.
     ☐ b. a natural, though unusual, phenomenon.
     ☐ c. an instance of mass hysteria.
     ☐ d. left to the reader's imagination.

10. The reader may assume that the second black cat which followed the
(f) narrator home from the barroom was
     ☐ a. just a stray cat.
     ☐ b. the reincarnation of Pluto.
     ☐ c. a witch in disguise.
     ☐ d. a figment of the narrator's imagination.

11. The narrator says, "I came to look upon the cat with unutterable loath-
(k) ing, and to flee silently from its odious presence, *as from the breath of
a pestilence.*" The phrase *"as from the breath of a pestilence"*
is a simile used to convey associations of
     ☐ a. antiquity.
     ☐ b. brute strength.
     ☐ c. the supernatural.
     ☐ d. death.

12. The black cat that replaces Pluto served to
(c)   ☐ a. comfort the narrator.
     ☐ b. remind the narrator of his former cruelty.
     ☐ c. reform the narrator.
     ☐ d. frighten the narrator's wife.

13. The patch of white on the breast of the second black cat came to
(b) resemble
- ☐ a. a gallows.
- ☐ b. the man's first initial.
- ☐ c. a collar.
- ☐ d. an axe.

14. After the fire destroyed their home, the narrator and his wife lived
(a) ☐ a. with relatives.
- ☐ b. in a barn.
- ☐ c. in an old building.
- ☐ d. at an inn.

15. Throughout their married life, the narrator's wife was for the most
(j) part
- ☐ a. shrewish and hard to live with.
- ☐ b. patient and uncomplaining.
- ☐ c. insane.
- ☐ d. sullen and withdrawn.

16. The narrator disposes of his wife's body by
(b) ☐ a. cutting it into pieces and burning it.
- ☐ b. throwing it down a well.
- ☐ c. burying it in the cellar floor.
- ☐ d. walling it up in the cellar.

17. The mood of the narrator after murdering his wife is
(i) ☐ a. tranquil.           ☐ c. guilt-ridden.
- ☐ b. remorseful.          ☐ d. lonely.

18. The narrator's behavior when the police came to the house might ac-
(g) curately be judged
- ☐ a. irrational.          ☐ c. hostile.
- ☐ b. rude.               ☐ d. suspicious.

19. Which of the following best defines *bravado* as used in, "And here,
(1) through the mere frenzy of *bravado*, I rapped heavily with a cane which
I held in my hand, upon that very portion of the brickwork behind
which stood the corpse of the wife of my bosom"?
- ☐ a. Bravery            ☐ c. Pretended courage
- ☐ b. Cowardice         ☐ d. Insanity

20. The narrator calls the black cat a beast and a monster, "whose craft
(k) had seduced me into murder and whose informing voice had consigned
me to the hangman." Giving human qualities to animals or other non-
human things is a literary device called *personification*. In this case
Poe implies the cat can
☐ a. commit murder and seduction.
☐ b. scheme and talk.
☐ c. hang people.
☐ d. judge and jail people.

21. The narrator might best be described as
(f) ☐ a. a criminal.      ☐ c. a drunk.
     ☐ b. a lunatic.      ☐ d. an innocent victim.

22. The overall atmosphere of this story might best be described as
(i) ☐ a. sunny and cheerful.
     ☐ b. soothing and peaceful.
     ☐ c. useful and instructive.
     ☐ d. morbid and gloomy.

23. It is safe to say that the black cat was
(h) ☐ a. the cause of the narrator's troubles.
     ☐ b. a scapegoat for the narrator's troubles.
     ☐ c. of no more significance than his other pets.
     ☐ d. unrelated to the narrator's problems.

24. From the way the narrator acted with the police, you would probably
(g) judge that he wanted to
     ☐ a. be killed.      ☐ c. live in peace.
     ☐ b. be caught.      ☐ d. kill someone else.

25. The main idea of this story concerns
(e) ☐ a. man's cruelty to animals.
     ☐ b. alcoholism.
     ☐ c. one man's descent into insanity.
     ☐ d. the breakdown of a marriage.

---

Comprehension Skills: a — isolating details; b — recalling specific facts; c — retaining
concepts; d — organizing facts; e — understanding the main idea; f — drawing a
conclusion; g — making a judgment; h — making an inference; i — recognizing tone;
j — understanding characters; k — appreciation of literary forms; l — understanding
vocabulary.

# TONE AND MOOD

**Practice Exercise A**

One night as I sat, half stupefied, in a den of more than infamy, my attention was suddenly drawn to some black object, reposing upon the head of one of the immense hogsheads of Gin, or of Rum, which constituted the chief furniture of the apartment.

1. How would you describe the narrator's state of mind?
   ☐ a. Drunken and debased      ☐ c. Ghostly and unreal
   ☐ b. Evil and scheming        ☐ d. Thieving and murderous

2. Underline the phrase near the beginning of the passage which best suggests the atmosphere of this setting.


**Practice Exercise B**

It was now the representation of an object that I shudder to name — and for this, above all, I loathed, and dreaded, and would have rid myself of the monster *had I dared* — it was now, I say, the image of a hideous — ghastly thing — of the GALLOWS! — oh, mournful and terrible engine of Horror and of Crime — of Agony and of Death!

1. In the passage above, the author uses one long sentence instead of several short ones in order to
   ☐ a. move the action along.      ☐ c. change moods abruptly.
   ☐ b. make it easier to read.      ☐ d. build suspense and dread.

2. On the lines provided, write the long metaphor which the author uses to enhance the mood of this passage. (A metaphor is a suggested comparison, where one object is used to represent or give the feeling of another.)

_____

_____

_____

_____

_____

_____

## Practice Exercise C

"Gentlemen," I said at last, as the party ascended the steps, "I delight to have allayed your suspicions. I wish you all health, and a little more courtesy. By the bye, gentlemen, this—this is a very well-constructed house." [In the rabid desire to say something easily, I scarcely knew what I uttered at all.] —"I may say an *excellently* well constructed house. These walls—are you going, gentlemen—these walls are solidly put together;" and here, through the mere frenzy of bravado, I rapped heavily, with a cane which I held in my hand, upon that very portion of the brick-work behind which stood the corpse of the wife of my bosom.

1. From the tone of this voice in the passage above, the reader gets the impression that the narrator is
   - □ a. saddended and remorseful.
   - □ b. nervous and distraught.
   - □ c. calm and self-assured.
   - □ d. weary and bored.

2. Underline two instances in the passage above in which the narrator reveals his state of mind.

## Practice Exercise D

But may God shield and deliver me from the fangs of the Arch-Fiend! No sooner had the reverberation of my blows sunk into silence, than I was answered by a voice from within the tomb!—by a cry, at first muffled and broken, like the sobbing of a child, and then quickly swelling into one long, loud and continuous scream, utterly anomalous and inhuman—a howl—a wailing shriek, half of horror and half of triumph, such as might have arisen only out of hell, conjointly from the throats of the damned in their agony and of the demons that exult in the damnation.

1. The sound of the shriek which the narrator heard coming from within the tomb can best be described as
   - □ a. beseeching.
   - □ b. whining.
   - □ c. unearthly.
   - □ d. irritating.

2. Underline as many phrases as you can find that suggest and reinforce the atmosphere of death and damnation in this scene.

# DISCUSSION GUIDES

## Analyzing Tone and Mood

1. The tone and mood that Poe creates in the first paragraph of "The Black Cat" is sustained throughout the entire story. What are the advantages of maintaining and intensifying the same feeling in a story?

2. As explained in the lesson, setting is one of the elements that contributes to creating the mood, or atmosphere, of a story. But does a given atmosphere—a gloomy, morbid atmosphere, for example— *require* a particular setting—such as the burned-out shell of a house, or a crumbling castle? Can a horror story be effectively set in a sunny resort town, or a lovely new home in the suburbs? How might a bright, cheerful setting provide an effective background for a story about an insane murderer?

3. Here is a passage from "The Black Cat" as Poe wrote it, followed by a simplified version. What is lost in the "translation"?

   One night, returning home, much intoxicated, from one of my haunts about town, I fancied that the cat avoided my presence. I seized him; when, in his fright at my violence, he inflicted a slight wound upon my hand with his teeth. The fury of a demon instantly possessed me.

   One night, when I came home drunk from my favorite bar, I thought the cat was avoiding me. I grabbed him, and because he was frightened he bit me. I became insanely angry.

4. Stories by Poe are favorites for radio dramatization, often unrevised and unedited. They are also widely used on cassettes and records in high school English classes. What is it about "The Black Cat" that makes it so easy to do in audio alone, without pictures?

## Interpreting the Story

5. Assuming that the narrator is insane, should the reader take everything he says at face value? What parts of the tale might be the product of the narrator's deranged mind?

6. How do you account for the narrator's behavior when the police come to his house? Why does he call attention to the cellar wall where his wife's body is concealed?

7. The narrator insists he is not superstitious. What do *you* think?

Analyzing the Author's Technique

8. Edgar Allan Poe frequently used what are called *Gothic* conventions in his stories. Gothic stories deal with such morbid concerns as murder, horror, mystery, decay, evil, deformity, magic, and the supernatural. The Gothic setting typically includes fens, bogs, ruined castles, forked lightning, owls screeching, and other melodramatic devices. Its characters are frequently "ruined" men, or deranged, or deformed. How many Gothic conventions can you find in "The Black Cat"?

9. Poe uses the "first person" point of view in "The Black Cat"—that is, the reader sees everything through the eyes of the narrator, who tells his own story. How does the author use this point of view to develop character?

10. The black cat in this story is obviously not just another household pet. Many critics feel that the cat has a symbolic significance. In your opinion, what might the author have intended the black cat to symbolize?

## WRITING EXERCISE

The setting of "The Black Cat" is not presented in elaborate detail. In fact, the only setting that is described in any detail at all is the ruined hulk of the narrator's house the morning after the fire. In spite of this lack of detail, however, the tone and mood of the story convey a very definite sense of setting. Based on the impressions which the atmosphere of this story evokes in you, write a descriptive paragraph in which you fill in the details of setting which the author has only sketched. Consider such things as the neighborhood in which he lived, the time of year, what his house looked like, and so on.

Unit 8
**Symbolism**

# A Rose for Emily

William Faulkner

# Introduction

Emily Grierson is one of the strangest women you are likely to meet anywhere in literature. But to tell you just *how* strange she was would be spoiling the very unusual ending of the story. Leave it for now that the year is 1925, or thereabouts, and Emily has just passed away at age 74. It is the occasion of her death that prompts the narrator of the story to tell us about her.

She is the last of the Griersons, an aristocratic family of the Old South, and with her death the last vestiges of the pre-Civil War feudal society—or at least the last vestiges of its aristocracy—have passed from the town of Jefferson forever. "Alive," we are told, "Miss Emily had been a tradition, a duty and a care" for the town, and the narrator goes on to tell us what a real, live tradition was like. It is not a pretty picture.

William Faulkner was one of the great American authors of modern times, having won a Nobel Prize for literature in 1950 and many other international honors. He was a Southerner, a lifelong resident of Oxford, Mississippi, and a yarn-spinner of the sort that that part of the country is famous for. He rarely tells a story himself—in his own voice, that is—but creates a narrator, who is supposedly a witness to the story or even a character in it, to tell the tale for him. Sometimes more than one character in a story speaks to us, giving various points of view. In "A Rose for Emily," the story is told by a resident of Jefferson whom we never meet except through his narration. An interesting exercise for your imagination, as you read the story, might be to try to imagine what this narrator looks like and what kind of person he or she is.

Faulkner himself was descended from the Southern aristocracy in a family reduced by the Civil War to genteel workaday people much like the rest of us. He used Mississippi, its history and its people, black and white, as his window on the world of human nature; and he used them, as he said in his Nobel Prize acceptance speech, "to create out of the materials of the human spirit something which did not exist before."

To do this, he created an entire county in Mississippi out of pure imagination and filled it with people who appear again and again in his stories. Colonel Sartoris, for example, who is a minor charater in "A Rose for Emily," is a main character in a novel titled *Sartoris*. He called it Yoknapatawpha County, and the county seat, Jefferson (a copy of his native Oxford), is where most of his stories are set. It is where Emily Grierson lived and died.

There is a detailed map of Yoknapatawpha County, which appeared in one of Faulkner's novels in 1951, and genealogies of the families that lived there have been developed with great care. The map is labeled "Jefferson, Yoknapatawpha County, Mississippi. Area 2400 square miles. Population: Whites 6298; Negroes 9313. William Faulkner, sole owner and proprietor." It is one of the most famous places in literature.

Faulkner stories are heavily weighted with influences of the past—the effects of the past on the present in which we live. Emily Grierson was a character out of the past who endured into modern times. She was so much a part of the past that she was a symbol of another age and another culture which the people of Jefferson looked back upon with an uncertain longing and nostalgia, just as we like to look back nostalgically at a world before atomic weapons and energy problems. In our minds we make it a better world than it actually was.

Emily, said the narrator, was "dear and inescapable." But as you read the story, try to decide what Faulkner is really saying about the past, or about some parts of it, at least. Then watch how he has the narrator take you backward and forward in time until, at times, you are not quite certain where you are at any one moment. It is an experience that is not always easy reading, but it is an experience that mustn't be missed.

# Symbolism

Outside many courthouses there is a statue of a woman. She is blindfolded, balances a set of scales with one hand and holds a sword in the other. She is the famous symbol of justice. To provide justice, the courts must weigh evidence carefully (the scales), and treat everyone equally (the blindfold) regardless of race, creed, color, sex or social status. Finally, the decisions of justice have the power of law, which explains the sword. The fact that justice is female symbolizes mercy or compassion.

The statue of justice, viewed as a symbol, conveys a great deal of information about our ideas of justice without using words. The statue has emotional appeal as well as intellectual appeal. It leaves us with a better *feeling* for justice than we might get in some other way. This is an important reason why we use symbols in our lives.

The American flag is a symbol of the unity of fifty states that grew out of thirteen. The bald eagle is a symbol of the strength and freedom that we attribute to the American national character.

When the President of the United States travels abroad, he embodies all of the American people; he is, in a very real sense, the United States participating in world councils. His actions reflect on the entire country and all its people, and any gesture or action directed toward the President is a symbolic action toward an entire nation.

So *things* can be symbols, *people* can be symbols, and *actions* can be symbols. Without exception, they stimulate both an idea and an emotion. This is true in many facets of living and is especially true in the arts. Flowing lines in painting or sculpture may symbolize speed or movement. Arches and spires in churches remind us of their heavenly mission. And certain refrains in such musical compositions as Sibelius's *Finlandia* and Chopin's *Polonaise* represent the patriotism of the Finnish and Polish peoples.

Literature also uses symbolism. Earliest legends, passed on by word of mouth, featured heroes and villains that symbolized good and evil forces in life, and provided patriotic examples for the listeners. Some of our common nursery rhymes were, at first, symbolic satires of royal governments. Both "Humpty-Dumpty" and "Rockabye Baby," for example, symbolized royal houses that were headed for a fall.

Often, there is a simple, long-suffering character in a story whom we say is Christ-like. We call him a symbolic Christ figure. Other times a character is so average and so very human that we say he symbolizes all of us, and we call him an "everyman" figure. Tom Sawyer is every man's nostalgic fancy of what boyhood should be. His girlfriend Becky Thatcher is every man's (though not necessarily every woman's) fancy of what girlhood should be.

Much of William Faulkner's writing expresses interest in the concept of time and in ideas related to the passage of time—time and change; the influence of the past on the present; time, death, and decay; resistance to the forces of time. Let's see how he treats these ideas with symbolism in telling the story of Emily Grierson.

**1. The House and Neighborhood: Thing Symbols for Change Brought about by Time.** As we pointed out in the introduction, many of the places in the imaginary county which Faulkner created appear again and again in his stories. Here, the setting is Jefferson, Yoknapatawpha county seat. The following paragraph from the beginning of "A Rose for Emily" is loaded with references to changes in Jefferson brought about by the passage of time. Watch how the narrator takes us back and forth in time and points out changes. What is the idea, and what is the emotion conveyed by the symbolism?

> It was a big, squarish frame house that had once been white, decorated with cupolas and spires and scrolled balconies in the heavily lightsome style of the seventies, set on what had once been our most select street. But garages and cotton gins had encroached and oblitered even the august names of that neighborhood; only Miss Emily's house was left, lifting its stubborn and coquettish decay above the cotton wagons and the gasoline pumps—an eyesore among eyesores. And now Miss Emily had gone to join the representatives of those august names where they lay in the cedar-bemused cemetery among the ranked and anonymous graves of Union and Confederate soldiers who fell at the battle of Jefferson.

There is a lot of time packed into this paragraph. We are told that Miss Emily's house had been built in the 1870s, and we are told what the neighborhood was like then—"our most select street." Now, in the 1920s, garages and cotton gins have replaced all the fine old houses except Emily's, and it is in a state of "stubborn and coquettish decay." With Emily gone the old house will probably go, too. Her passing seems to signal the end of an era, and she is laid to rest among the Confederate and Union soldiers who died sixty years before.

Using an unknown citizen of the town as narrator of the story, and as our vehicle for travel in time, Faulkner skillfully takes us from the story's present (about 1925) to the time Emily's house was built (about 1870). He takes us back to the present to show us the changes brought about by time, and then returns to the past once more, leaving us at the passing of the old South and its aristocracy during the Civil War. The idea is time and change; the emotion is nostalgia.

**2. Emily: A Character Symbol for Tradition Rooted in Time.** Emily Grierson is the central character of the story. She is also the controlling symbol for a number of ideas. In the following paragraphs, she symbolizes old aristocratic traditions. As time goes on and ideas change, notice the town's change in attitude toward Miss Emily and the aristocractic traditions she represents.

> Alive, Miss Emily had been a tradition, a duty, and a care; a sort of hereditary obligation upon the town, dating from that day in 1894 when Colonel Sartoris, the mayor—he who fathered the edict that no Negro woman should appear on the streets without an apron—remitted her taxes, the dispensation dating from the death of her father on into perpetuity. Not that Miss Emily would have accepted charity. Colonel Sartoris invented an involved tale to the effect that Miss Emily's father had loaned money to the town, which the town, as a matter of business, preferred this way of repaying. Only a man of Colonel Sartoris' generation and thought could have invented it, and only a woman could have believed it.
>
> When the next generation, with its more modern ideas, became mayors and aldermen, this arrangement created some little dissatisfaction.

Since 1894, the narrator tells us, Miss Emily "had been a tradition, a duty, and a care...." You almost expect him to add, "like the town's Confederate war memorial and the cemetery with its honored dead." Colonel Sartoris was mayor then, and he treated Emily with the old-style manners.

But times have changed, and new ideas have replaced the old. Colonel Sartoris's treatment of Emily seems as out-of-place and as ridiculous as his edict that Negro women must wear aprons on the street. Time has passed Emily by. Though alive, she is as much a part of a by-gone era as the old aristocratic traditions she represents. With the coming of the new generation of mayors and aldermen, attitudes toward Emily and aristocratic traditions have changed.

Here, too, symbols convey both an idea and an emotion. Miss Emily represents tradition in a time when old ideas are being rejected in favor of new ways of thinking and living. She, and the aristocratic traditions she symbolizes, are casualties of time and change. Miss Emily symbolizes the inevitability of change and its accompanying loss.

The emotion in this case? It depends on your point of view. You may feel sadness for a way of life that is gone forever. Or you may feel joy at the prospect of a new and better way of life, and hope for the future. Or you may feel a combination of these.

**3. Emily: A Character Symbol of a Dead Past.** The past may live fondly in memory and tradition, but for most practical purposes the past is a thing dead and gone. Faulkner expresses this idea in a rather frightening and repelling bit of symbolism as he describes the way Miss Emily appears to the Board of Aldermen who are calling on her:

> They rose when she entered—a small, fat woman in black, with a thin gold chain descending to her waist and vanishing into her belt, leaning on an ebony cane with a tarnished gold head. Her skeleton was small and spare; perhaps that was why what would have been merely plumpness in another was obesity in her. She looked bloated, like a body long submerged in motionless water, and of that pallid hue. Her eyes, lost in the fatty ridges of her face, looked like two small pieces of coal pressed into a lump of dough as they moved from one face to another while the visitors stated their errand.
>
> She did not ask them to sit. She just stood in the door and listened quietly until the spokesman came to a stumbling halt. Then they could hear the invisible watch ticking at the end of the gold chain.
>
> Her voice was dry and cold "I have no taxes in Jefferson."

A few paragraphs before we were told that Miss Emily was "...a tradition, a duty, and a care; a sort of hereditary obligation ...." Now we are face to face with this tradition. She is a bloated corpse; she is pale and pasty, and her voice is dry and cold. An invisible watch ticks from her middle as if it were counting the seconds of life for everyone in the room. It's no wonder the aldermen lost their nerve in front of her. In another paragraph the narrator will tell us, "So she [this symbol of their past] vanquished them ... just as she had vanquished their fathers thirty years before ...."

**4. The Old Men Convey a Concept of Time.** As current events in our lives drift into the past, they tend to become fuzzy and faded in our minds. Precise dates escape us; we tend to blot out painful memories in some cases and exaggerate wrongs and hurts in other cases. But the overall effect is the past becomes a hazy, mellow blur. Faulkner uses a group of old men attending Emily's funeral to demonstrate this effect of time long gone by.

> They held the funeral on the second day, with the town coming to look at Miss Emily beneath a mass of bought flowers, with the crayon face of her father musing profoundly above the bier and the ladies sibilant and macabre; and the very old men—some in their brushed Confederate uniforms—on the porch and the lawn, talking of Miss Emily as if she had been a contemporary of theirs, believing that they had danced with her and courted her perhaps, confusing time with its mathematical progression, as the old do, to whom all the past is not a diminishing road but, instead, a huge meadow which no winter ever quite touches, divided from them now by the narrow bottleneck of the most recent decade of years.

The old men associate Emily with the Civil War and the kind of life that ended with that era. They think she was a contemporary, that they had danced with her or courted her. Actually, she was a little young for them; Emily's father was their contemporary.

This gives the author an opportunity to describe various views of time in a delightful string of comparisons or metaphors. Time, he says, passes in a mathematical progression and is a diminishing road. But for the old, time is reduced from a long road to a short span. To the old, the past is a huge green meadow separated from the present by a bottleneck, Faulkner calls it, of only ten years or so.

The great French writer Jean-Paul Sartre said that Faulkner viewed the world like a man sitting backwards in a convertible. Everything has happened or gone by; he sees nothing in the future. "Faulkner," Sartre said, "uses his extraordinary art to describe a world dying of old age, with us gasping and choking in it."

As you read "A Rose for Emily," watch the imagery and symbolism carefully, and try to decide if you think what Sartre says is true.

---

As you read this story:

- Watch for indications of the ravages of time when the aldermen call on Emily.

- Think carefully about Emily's reaction to her father's death.

- Try to decide what the account of Emily's china-painting lessons tells us about the townspeople.

- Notice how Emily, her servant, and the town change and grow older.

# A Rose for Emily
# William Faulkner

## 1

When Miss Emily Grierson died, our whole town went to her funeral: the
men through a sort of respectful affection for a fallen monument, the women
mostly out of curiosity to see the inside of her house, which no one save an
old manservant—a combined gardener and cook—had seen in at least ten
years.

It was a big, squarish frame house that had once been white, decorated
with cupolas and spires and scrolled balconies in the heavily lightsome
style of the seventies, set on what had once been our most select street. But
garages and cotton gins had encroached and obliterated even the august
names of that neighborhood; only Miss Emily's house was left, lifting its
stubborn and coquettish decay above the cotton wagons and the gasoline
pumps—an eyesore among eyesores. And now Miss Emily had gone to join
the representatives of those august names where they lay in the cedar-
bemused cemetery among the ranked and anonymous graves of Union and
Confederate soldiers who fell at the battle of Jefferson.

Alive, Miss Emily had been a tradition, a duty, and a care; a sort of
hereditary obligation upon the town, dating from that day in 1894 when
Colonel Sartoris, the mayor—he who fathered the edict that no Negro
woman should appear on the streets without an apron—remitted her taxes,
the dispensation dating from the death of her father on into perpetuity. Not
that Miss Emily would have accepted charity. Colonel Sartoris invented an
involved tale to the effect that Miss Emily's father had loaned money to the
town, which the town, as a matter of business, preferred this way of repay-
ing. Only a man of Colonel Sartoris' generation and thought could have
invented it, and only a woman could have believed it.

When the next generation, with its more modern ideas, became mayors
and aldermen, this arrangement created some little dissatisfaction. On the
first of the year they mailed her a tax notice. February came, and there was
no reply. They wrote her a formal letter, asking her to call at the sheriff's
office at her convenience. A week later the mayor wrote her himself,

offering to call or to send his car for her, and received in reply a note on paper of an archaic shape, in a thin, flowing calligraphy in faded ink, to the effect that she no longer went out at all. The tax notice was also enclosed, without comment.

They called a special meeting of the Board of Aldermen. A deputation waited upon her, knocked at the door through which no visitor had passed since she ceased giving china-painting lessons eight or ten years earlier. They were admitted by the old Negro into a dim hall from which a stairway mounted into still more shadow. It smelled of dust and disuse—a close, dank smell. The Negro led them into the parlor. It was furnished in heavy, leather-covered furniture. When the Negro opened the blinds of one window, they could see that the leather was cracked; and when they sat down, a faint dust rose sluggishly about their thighs, spinning with slow motes in the single sun-ray. On a tarnished gilt easel before the fireplace stood a crayon portrait of Miss Emily's father.

They rose when she entered—a small, fat woman in black, with a thin gold chain descending to her waist and vanishing into her belt, leaning on an ebony cane with a tarnished gold head. Her skeleton was small and spare; perhaps that was why what would have been merely plumpness in another was obesity in her. She looked bloated, like a body long submerged in motionless water, and of that pallid hue. Her eyes, lost in the fatty ridges of her face, looked like two small pieces of coal pressed into a lump of dough as they moved from one face to another while the visitors stated their errand.

She did not ask them to sit. She just stood in the door and listened quietly until the spokesman came to a stumbling halt. Then they could hear the invisible watch ticking at the end of the gold chain.

Her voice was dry and cold. "I have no taxes in Jefferson. Colonel Sartoris explained it to me. Perhaps one of you can gain access to the city records and satisfy yourselves."

"But we have. We are the city authorities, Miss Emily. Didn't you get a notice from the sheriff, signed by him?"

"I received a paper, yes," Miss Emily said. "Perhaps he considers himself the sheriff... I have no taxes in Jefferson."

"But there is nothing on the books to show that, you see. We must go by the—"

"See Colonel Sartoris. I have no taxes in Jefferson."

"But, Miss Emily—"

"See Colonel Sartoris." (Colonel Sartoris had been dead almost ten years.) "I have no taxes in Jefferson. Tobe!" The Negro appeared. "Show these gentlemen out."

2

So she vanquished them, horse and foot, just as she had vanquished their fathers thirty years before about the smell. That was two years after her father's death and a short time after her sweetheart—the one we believed would marry her—had deserted her. After her father's death she went out very little; after her sweetheart went away, people hardly saw her at all. A few of the ladies had the temerity to call, but were not received, and the only sign of life about the place was the Negro man—a young man then—going in and out with a market basket.

"Just as if a man—any man—could keep a kitchen properly," the ladies said; so they were not surprised when the smell developed. It was another link between the gross, teeming world and the high and mighty Griersons.

A neighbor, a woman, complained to the mayor, Judge Stevens, eighty years old.

"But what will you have me do about it, madam?" he said.

"Why, send her word to stop it," the woman said. "Isn't there a law?"

"I'm sure that won't be necessary," Judge Stevens said. "It's probably just a snake or a rat that nigger of hers killed in the yard. I'll speak to him about it."

The next day he received two more complaints, one from a man who came in diffident deprecation. "We really must do something about it, Judge. I'd be the last one in the world to bother Miss Emily, but we've got to do something." That night the Board of Aldermen met—three graybeards and one younger man, a member of the rising generation.

"It's simple enough," he said. "Send her word to have her place cleaned up. Give her a certain time to do it in, and if she don't..."

"Dammit, sir," Judge Stevens said, "will you accuse a lady to her face of smelling bad?"

So the next night, after midnight, four men crossed Miss Emily's lawn and slunk about the house like burglars, sniffing along the base of the brickwork and at the cellar openings while one of them performed a regular sowing motion with his hand out of a sack slung from his shoulder. They broke open the cellar door and sprinkled lime there, and in all the outbuildings. As they recrossed the lawn, a window that had been dark was lighted and Miss Emily sat in it, the light behind her, and her upright torso motionless as that of an idol. They crept quietly across the lawn and into the shadow of the locusts that lined the street. After a week or two the smell went away.

That was when people had begun to feel really sorry for her. People in our town, remembering how old lady Wyatt, her great-aunt, had gone completely crazy at last, believed that the Griersons held themselves a little too high for what they really were. None of the young men were quite good enough for Miss Emily and such. We had long thought of them as a tableau, Miss Emily a slender figure in white in the background, her father a spraddled silhouette in the foreground, his back to her and clutching a horsewhip, the two of them framed by the back-flung front door. So when she got to be thirty and was still single, we were not pleased exactly, but vindicated; even with insanity in the family she wouldn't have turned down all of her chances if they had really materialized.

When her father died, it got about that the house was all that was left to her; and in a way, people were glad. At last they could pity Miss Emily. Being left alone, and a pauper, she had become humanized. Now she too would know the old thrill and the old despair of a penny more or less.

The day after his death all the ladies prepared to call at the house and offer condolence and aid, as is our custom. Miss Emily met them at the door, dressed as usual and with no trace of grief on her face. She told them that her father was not dead. She did that for three days, with the ministers calling on her, and the doctors, trying to persuade her to let them dispose of the body. Just as they were about to resort to law and force, she broke down, and they buried her father quickly.

We did not say she was crazy then. We believed she had to do that. We remembered all the young men her father had driven away, and we knew that with nothing left, she would have to cling to that which had robbed her, as people will.

### 3

She was sick for a long time. When we saw her again, her hair was cut short, making her look like a girl, with a vague resemblance to those angels in colored church windows—sort of tragic and serene.

The town had just let the contracts for paving the sidewalks, and in the summer after her father's death they began to work. The construction company came with niggers and mules and machinery, and a foreman named Homer Barron, a Yankee—a big, dark, ready man, with a big voice and eyes lighter than his face. The little boys would follow in groups to hear him cuss the niggers, and the niggers singing in time to the rise and fall of picks. Pretty soon he knew everybody in town. Whenever you heard a lot of laughing anywhere about the square, Homer Barron would be in the center of the group. Presently we began to see him and Miss Emily on Sunday afternoons driving in the yellow-wheeled buggy and the matched team of bays from the livery stable.

At first we were glad that Miss Emily would have an interest, because the ladies all said, "Of course a Grierson would not think seriously of a Northerner, a day laborer." But there were still others, older people, who said that even grief could not cause a real lady to forget *noblesse oblige*—without calling it *noblesse oblige*. They just said, "Poor Emily. Her kinsfolk should come to her." She had some kin in Alabama; but years age her father had fallen out with them over the estate of old lady Wyatt, the crazy woman, and there was no communication between the two families. They had not even been represented at the funeral.

And as soon as the old people said, "Poor Emily," the whispering began. "Do you suppose it's really so?" they said to one another. "Of course it is. What else could..." This behind their hands; rustling of craned silk and satin behind jalousies closed upn the sun of Sunday afternoon as the thin, swift clop-clop-clop of the matched team passed: "Poor Emily."

She carried her head high enough—even when we believed that she was fallen. It was as if she demanded more than ever the recognition of her dignity as the last Grierson; as if it had wanted that touch of earthiness to reaffirm her imperviousness. Like when she bought the rat poison, the arsenic. That was over a year after they had begun to say "Poor Emily," and while the two female cousins were visiting her.

"I want some poison," she said to the druggist. She was over thirty then, still a slight woman, though thinner than usual, with cold, haughty black eyes in a face the flesh of which was strained across the temples and about the eye-sockets as you imagine a light-house-keeper's face ought to look. "I want some poison," she said.

"Yes, Miss Emily. What kind? For rats and such? I'd recom—"

"I want the best you have. I don't care what kind."

The druggist named several. "They'll kill anything up to an elephant. But what you want is—"

"Arsenic," Miss Emily said. "Is that a good one?"

"Is... arsenic? Yes, ma'am. But what you want..."

"I want arsenic."

The druggist looked down at her. She looked back at him, erect, her face like a strained flag. "Why, of course," the druggist said. "If that's what you want. But the law requires you to tell what you are going to use if for."

Miss Emily just stared at him, her head tilted back in order to look him eye for eye, until he looked away and went and got the arsenic and wrapped it up. The Negro delivery boy brought her the package; the druggist didn't come back. When she opened the package at home there was written on the box, under the skull and bones: "For rats."

## 4

So the next day we all said, "She will kill herself"; and we said it would be the best thing. When she had first begun to be seen with Homer Barron, we had said, "She will marry him." Then we said, "She will persuade him yet," because Homer himself had remarked—he liked men, and it was known that he drank with the younger men in the Elks' Club—that he was not a marrying man. Later we said, "Poor Emily" behind the jalousies as they passed on Sunday afternoon in the glittering buggy, Miss Emily with her head high and Homer Barron with his hat cocked and a cigar in this teeth, reins and whip in a yellow glove.

Then some of the ladies began to say that it was a disgrace to the town and a bad example to the young people. The men did not want to interfere, but at last the ladies forced the Baptist minister—Miss Emily's people were Episcopal—to call upon her. He would never divulge what happened during that interview, but he refused to go back again. The next Sunday they again drove about the streets, and the following day the minister's wife wrote to Miss Emily's relations in Alabama.

So she had blood-kin under her roof again and we sat back to watch developments. At first nothing happened. Then we were sure that they were to be married. We learned that Miss Emily had been to the jeweler's and ordered a man's toilet set in silver, with the letters H. B. on each piece. Two days later we learned that she had bought a complete outfit of men's clothing, including a nightshirt, and we said, "They are married." We were really glad. We were glad because the two female cousins were even more Grierson than Miss Emily had ever been.

So we were not surprised when Homer Barron—the streets had been finished some time since—was gone. We were a little disappointed that there was not a public blowing-off, but we believed that he had gone on to prepare for Miss Emily's coming, or to give her a chance to get rid of the cousins. (By that time it was a cabal, and we were all Miss Emily's allies to help circumvent the cousins.) Sure enough, after another week they departed. And, as we had expected all along, within three days Homer Barron was back in town. A neighbor saw the Negro man admit him at the kitchen door at dusk one evening.

And that was the last we saw of Homer Barron. And of Miss Emily for some time. The Negro man went in and out with the market basket, but the front door remained closed. Now and then we would see her at a window for a moment, as the men did that night when they sprinkled the lime, but for almost six months she did not appear on the streets. Then we knew that this was to be expected too; as if that quality of her father which had thwarted her woman's life so many times had been too virulent and too furious to die.

When we next saw Miss Emily, she had grown fat and her hair was turning gray. During the next few years it grew grayer and grayer until it attained an even pepper-and-salt-iron-gray, when it ceased turning. Up to the day of her death at seventy-four it was still that vigorous iron-gray, like the hair of an active man.

From that time on her front door remained closed, save for a period of six or seven years, when she was about forty, during which she gave lessons in china-painting. She fitted up a studio in one of the downstairs rooms, where the daughters and grand-daughters of Colonel Sartoris' contemporaries were sent to her with the same regularity and in the same spirit that they were sent to church on Sundays with a twenty-five-cent piece for the collection plate. Meanwhile her taxes had been remitted.

Then the newer generation became the backbone and the spirit of the town, and the painting pupils grew up and fell away and did not send their children to her with boxes of color and tedious brushes and pictures cut from the ladies' magazines. The front door closed upon the last one and remained closed for good. When the town got free postal delivery, Miss Emily alone refused to let them fasten the metal numbers above her door and attach a mailbox to it. She would not listen to them.

Daily, monthly, yearly we watched the Negro grow grayer and more stooped, going in and out with the market basket. Each December we sent her a tax notice, which would be returned by the post office a week later, unclaimed. Now and then we would see her in one of the downstairs windows—she had evidently shut up the top floor of the house—like the carven torso of an idol in a niche, looking or not looking at us, we could never tell which. Thus she passed from generation to generation—dear, inescapable, impervious, tranquil, and perverse.

And so she died. Fell ill in the house filled with dust and shadows, with only a doddering Negro man to wait on her. We did not even know she was sick; we had long since given up trying to get any information from the Negro. He talked to no one, probably not even to her, for his voice had grown harsh and rusty, as if from disuse.

She died in one of the downstairs rooms, in a heavy walnut bed with a curtain, her gray head propped on a pillow yellow and moldy with age and lack of sunlight.

The Negro met the first of the ladies at the front door and let them in, with their hushed, sibilant voices and their quick, curious glances, and then he disappeared. He walked right through the house and out the back and was not seen again.

The two female cousins came at once. They held the funeral on the second day, with the town coming to look at Miss Emily beneath a mass of bought flowers, with the crayon face of her father musing profoundly above the bier and the ladies sibilant and macabre; and the very old men—some in their brushed Confederate uniforms—on the porch and the lawn, talking of Miss Emily as if she had been a contemporary of theirs, believing that they had danced with her and courted her perhaps, confusing time with its mathematical progression, as the old do, to whom all the past is not a diminishing road but, instead, a huge meadow which no winter ever quite touches, divided from them now by the narrow bottleneck of the most recent decade of years.

Already we knew that there was one room in that region above stairs which no one had seen in forty years, and which would have to be forced. They waited until Miss Emily was decently in the ground before they opened it.

The violence of breaking down the door seemed to fill this room with pervading dust. A thin, acrid pall as of the tomb seemed to lie everywhere upon this room decked and furnished as for a bridal: upon the valance curtains of faded rose color, upon the rose-shaded lights, upon the dressing table, upon the delicate array of crystal and the man's toilet things backed with tarnished silver, silver so tarnished that the monogram was obscured. Among them lay a collar and tie, as if they had just been removed, which, lifted, left upon the surface a pale crescent in the dust. Upon a chair hung the suit, carefully folded; beneath it the two mute shoes and the discarded socks.

The man himself lay in the bed.

For a long while we just stood there, looking down at the profound and fleshless grin. The body had apparently once lain in the attitude of an embrace, but now the long sleep that outlasts love, that conquers even the grimace of love, had cuckolded him. What was left of him, rotted beneath what was left of the nightshirt, had become inextricable from the bed in which he lay; and upon him and upon the pillow beside him lay that even coating of the patient and biding dust.

Then we noticed that in the second pillow was the indentation of a head. One of us lifted something from it, and leaning forward, that faint and invisible dust dry and acrid in the nostrils, we saw a long strand of iron-gray hair.

# Unit 8

## A Rose for Emily

- Comprehension Questions
- Symbolism
- Discussion Guides
- Writing Exercise

# COMPREHENSION QUESTIONS

1. Faulkner calls architecture of the 1870s *heavily lightsome*. This is an
(k) example of a literary device called
   - ☐ a. simile (a description that uses a direct comparison).
   - ☐ b. metaphor (a description that uses an implied comparison).
   - ☐ c. personification (a description that gives human character to non-human things).
   - ☐ d. oxymoron (a description that contains a self-contradiction).

2. We are told that ". . . only Miss Emily's house was left, lifting its *stub-*
(k) *born and coquettish decay* above the cotton wagons and the gasoline
   pumps. . . ." the phrase *stubborn and coquettish decay* is an example of
   - ☐ a. simile (a description that uses a direct comparison).
   - ☐ b. metaphor (a description that uses an implied comparison).
   - ☐ c. personification (a description that gives human character to non-human things).
   - ☐ d. oxymoron (a description that contains a self-contradiction).

3. The author compares Colonel Sartoris's courtly treatment of Emily
(i) with his decree that Black women must wear aprons. Although he
   doesn't say so, we get the feeling that the author is
   - ☐ a. being critical of the Colonel.
   - ☐ b. simply reporting facts as they were.
   - ☐ c. amused by the Colonel's Old-South manner.
   - ☐ d. angry and bitter.

4. When the Aldermen called on Emily, she had
(d) ☐ a. stopped giving china-painting lessons some years before.
   - ☐ b. just begun giving china-painting lessons.
   - ☐ c. been asked to stop giving china-painting lessons.
   - ☐ d. not yet decided to give china-painting lessons.

5. Colonel Sartoris and Judge Stevens are character examples of
(j) ☐ a. the law and spirit of Jefferson.
   - ☐ b. corruption in government.
   - ☐ c. a fading generation.
   - ☐ d. dying southern liberalism.

6. When Emily told the Aldermen to see Colonel Sartoris about her taxes,
(g) it showed that she
 □ a. had a friend in her own generation.
 □ b. didn't have a clear idea of time.
 □ c. had made enemies of the Aldermen.
 □ d. was confused by the Aldermen.

7. The townspeople thought of Emily and her father as a *tableau* framed in
(l) the open doorway. A *tableau* is a
 □ a. memory.            □ c. picture.
 □ b. vision.            □ d. statue.

8. When Emily's father died he left her
(b) □ a. very little.        □ c. quite enough to live on.
   □ b. some wealth.       □ d. enough to keep her in style.

9. Emily began going with Homer Barron
(d) □ a. long before her father died.
   □ b. just before her father died.
   □ c. shortly after her father died.
   □ d. some years after her father died.

10. Emily and her father had
(a) □ a. no emotional ties with relatives.
   □ b. close family ties.
   □ c. great concern for family opinion.
   □ d. no relatives they could call upon.

11. By keeping company with Homer Barron, Emily violated rules of
(g) □ a. law and civic responsibility.
   □ b. love and marriage.
   □ c. class and moral propriety.
   □ d. honesty and loyalty.

12. Regarding Homer Barron, the townspeople
(c) □ a. opposed a marriage to Emily.
   □ b. would have liked Emily to marry him.
   □ c. didn't care what Emily did.
   □ d. forcibly prevented the marriage.

13. The townspeople thought Emily had married Homer Barron when
(b) □ a. she was seen with him in his buggy.
    □ b. he was seen entering her house.
    □ c. her relatives came for the wedding.
    □ d. she bought a toilet set and nightshirt.

14. At the time of her death, Emily's hair was
(a) □ a. a vigorous black.       □ c. iron-gray.
    □ b. pure white.             □ d. faded blond.

15. Right after Emily died, her old servant walked out the back door and
(h) disappeared. This was probably because he
    □ a. had known about Homer for years.
    □ b. had been a slave and was now free.
    □ c. was basically disloyal to Emily.
    □ d. was Emily's accomplice.

16. If dust is "dry and *acrid* in the nostrils," it is dry and
(l) □ a. exhilarating.           □ c. tickling.
    □ b. irritating.             □ d. soothing.

17. In various ways throughout the story, we are made to feel that, for
(e) the townspeople, Emily is a
    □ a. tradition.              □ c. tax evader.
    □ b. liability.              □ d. model citizen.

18. As you review the facts of the story, you must conclude that Emily
(f) had been
    □ a. mentally ill for some time.
    □ b. a bit eccentric all her life.
    □ c. suffering from senility for at least ten years.
    □ d. lovelorn and melancholy since Homer Barron left.

19. An idea dominant in the story is that clinging to the past
(e) □ a. is necessary to assure progress.
    □ b. perpetuates history.
    □ c. can be destructive.
    □ d. assures continuity between generations.

20. By putting the facts together, we can conclude that the smell around
(f) Emily's house was caused by
- ☐ a. age and neglect.
- ☐ b. moldy rugs and furniture.
- ☐ c. rats killed by her servant.
- ☐ d. a decaying body.

21. There was something in Emily's manner that was
(c) ☐ a. intimidating.      ☐ c. endearing.
     ☐ b. frightening.      ☐ d. awe inspiring.

22. By using a citizen of Jefferson as the narrator of the story, the author
(i) has made the tone
- ☐ a. official and investigative.
- ☐ b. conversational and gossipy.
- ☐ c. complaining and angry.
- ☐ d. smug and superior.

23. The shock ending of the story is all the more shocking because the
(k) author
- ☐ a. built suspense from beginning to end.
- ☐ b. used high drama.
- ☐ c. developed a sense of mystery.
- ☐ d. understated everything.

24. Emily's servant is
(j) ☐ a. the hero of the story.
- ☐ b. a main character.
- ☐ c. an important minor character.
- ☐ d. of no consequence to the story.

25. The indentation in the pillow and the gray hair found at the end of the
(h) story suggest that Emily had
- ☐ a. been in bed with the skeleton.
- ☐ b. smothered her lover with the pillow.
- ☐ c. not visited the room for years.
- ☐ d. tried unsuccessfully to get rid of the body.

---

Comprehension Skills: a — isolating details; b — recalling specific facts; c — retaining concepts; d — organizing facts; e — understanding the main idea; f — drawing a conclusion; g — making a judgment; h — making an inference; i — recognizing tone; j — understanding characters; k — appreciation of literary forms; l — understanding vocabulary.

# SYMBOLISM

**Practice Exercise A**

They called a special meeting of the Board of Aldermen. A deputation waited upon her, knocked at the door through which no visitor had passed since she ceased giving china-painting lessons eight or ten years earlier. They were admitted by the old Negro into a dim hall from which a stairway mounted into still more shadow. It smelled of dust and disuse—a close, dank smell. The Negro led them into the parlor. It was furnished in heavy, leather-covered furniture. When the Negro opened the blinds of one window, they could see that the leather was cracked; and when they sat down, a faint dust rose sluggishly about their thighs, spinning with slow motes in the single sun-ray. On a tarnished gilt easel before the fireplace stood a crayon portrait of Miss Emily's father.

1. In the passage above, which of the following best qualifies as a *thing* symbol describing an effect of the passage of time?
   - ☐ a. The door
   - ☐ b. The dust
   - ☐ c. The blinds
   - ☐ d. The sun-ray

2. At the end of the lesson on symbolism, Jean Paul Sartre is quoted as saying: "Faulkner uses his extraordinary art to describe a world dying of old age, with us gasping and choking in it."

   On the lines provided, write at least one part of the passage where this is true.

**Practice Exercise B**

The day after his death all the ladies prepared to call at the house and offer condolence and aid, as is our cutom. Miss Emily met them at the door, dressed as usual and with no trace of grief on her face. She told them that her father was not dead. She did that for three days, with the ministers calling on her, and the doctors, trying to persuade her to let them dispose of the body. Just as they were about to resort to law and force, she broke down, and they buried her father quickly.

We did not say she was crazy then. We believed she had to do that. We remembered all the young men her father had driven away, and we knew that with nothing left, she would have to cling to that which had robbed her, as people will.

1. The character trait displayed here that is most typical of Emily throughout the story is her
   ☐ a. inability to feel grief.
   ☐ b. stubborn resistance to change.
   ☐ c. deep feeling for her father.
   ☐ d. display of emotion.

2. On the lines provided, write the phrase in the passage which best expresses this thought: "Time and death are like thieves that steal your possessions. Some people try to hold onto their possessions by capturing and holding onto the thieves."

_____

_____

_____

_____

_____

_____

_____

_____

## Practice Exercise C

From that time on her front door remained closed, save for a period of six or seven years, when she was about forty, during which she gave lessons in china-painting. She fitted up a studio in one of the downstairs rooms, where the daughters and grand-daughters of Colonel Sartoris' contemporaries were sent to her with the same regularity and in the same spirit that they were sent to church on Sunday with a twenty-five-cent piece for the collection plate. Meanwhile her taxes had been remitted.

Then the newer generation became the backbone and the spirit of the town, and the painting pupils grew up and fell away and did not send their children to her with boxes of color and tedious brushes and pictures cut from the ladies' magazines.

1. In this passage, two generations of townspeople are used to show a change
   □ a. of attitude toward Emily.
   □ b. in town spirit.
   □ c. of taste in art.
   □ d. in feeling for the church.

2. Underline one part of a sentence in the passage which shows that trips to Emily's art classes were more traditional and charitable than educational.

## Practice Exercise D

When the town got free postal delivery, Miss Emily alone refused to let them fasten the metal numbers above her door and attach a mailbox to it. She would not listen to them.

Daily, monthly, yearly we watched the Negro grow grayer and more stooped, going in and out with the market basket. Each December we sent her a tax notice, which would be returned by the post office a week later, unclaimed. Now and then we would see her in one of the downstairs windows—she had evidently shut up the top floor of the house—like the carven torso of an idol in a niche, looking or not looking at us, we could never tell which. Thus she passed from generation to generation—dear, inescapable, impervious, tranquil, and perverse.

1. Which of the following may also be described as dear, inescapable, tranquil, and perverse?
   □ a. Marriage        □ c. Attitudes
   □ b. Civic duty       □ d. Traditions

2. There are four indications in this passage that time is passing. Circle as many of these as you can find.

# DISCUSSION GUIDES

## Analyzing Symbolism

1. How is Emily's father a character symbol in the story?

2. In the Bible, Genesis 3:19, it says " . . . from dust thou art and unto dust shalt thou return." How is this reflected in the symbolism of the story?

3. William Faulkner sometimes used symbolism in the titles of his stories, and sometimes he did not. What might be the symbolism of the rose in "A Rose for Emily"? If you think there is no symbolism in it, explain why you think not. (Some suggestions: Roses are sometimes given in tribute. A rose may be a sign of love. Roses are sent to funerals. An excellent person or beautiful woman may be called a rose.)

## Interpreting the Story

4. When Emily's father died, she refused to allow him to be buried. The narrator said of this: "We believed she had to do that. . . she would have to cling to that which had robbed her, as people will." How may you connect this statement with the shock ending?

5. The story comments specifically on society in the post-Civil War South. What do you think the story has to say about society in general in our time?

6. When the townspeople thought Emily was "fallen," did they mean socially, morally, or what? Do you think they wanted her to "fall"?

7. Why was Emily a "hereditary obligation" on the town when she had done nothing concrete for the town?

## Analyzing the Author's Technique

8. How would the story change if Faulkner told the story himself, in his own voice, rather than through a narrator who is one of the townspeople?

9. From the way he talks, what would you say about the narrator? Is he just an average citizen of Jefferson? How well educated is he? Is the narrator a man or woman? Explain your opinions using examples from the story.

10. There are many passages in the story that appeal to the senses—hearing, smelling, seeing, touching. Find some of these passages and explain what you think they do for the story.

## WRITING EXERCISE

In a sentence or two, describe an idea and an emotion or feeling that you associate with each of these familiar symbols:

1. the Statue of Liberty

2. a plain, gold wedding ring

3. a dove

4. a hawk or eagle

5. burning candles or incense

6. a rock

## Unit 9
## Figurative Language

# A Christmas Memory

## Truman Capote

# Introduction

Between the ages of four and ten, Truman Capote lived with a family of older cousins in Alabama. The household consisted of three elderly ladies and a bachelor brother. One of the three ladies, a shy, retiring person named Sook Faulk, was in charge of Truman, whom she called Buddy. He liked to call her his "friend." The two were extremely fond of one another, feeling themselves kindred spirits in many ways in spite of the vast difference in their ages.

"A Christmas Memory" is set in the early 1930s in the big old house in Monroeville, Alabama, where Truman Capote lived with Miss Sook, as she was called, and the other cousins. This is the same town, incidentally, that would become the setting for *To Kill a Mockingbird* by Truman's childhood friend Harper Lee, in which Truman Capote appeared as the bright little boy Dill who was shuffled from one relative to the next, just as young Truman was.

As you read of the spare country living and the very modest Christmas gifts exchanged in the household, you may get the impression that the family was poor. Quite the opposite was true. Though Miss Sook scrounged for pennies and wore hand-me-downs, the other two ladies ran a dry-goods business and other enterprises in town. Their brother owned and operated several large cotton farms which he supervised on horseback. He refused to have anything to do with cars or other newfangled machinery even though he could well afford them. Together, the family income and holdings must have been substantial.

The story is about the last Christmas that Truman spent with his friend Miss Sook, and about the good times they had preparing for it. It is his favorite story, the author has said, because it is true. This and another story about himself and Miss Sook, "The Thanksgiving Visitor," have been published as small gift books that are always popular during the holiday season. They have both been made into movies for television that are shown over and over again at this special time of year. They keep finding new audiences, and old audiences never tire of them.

Much of Truman Capote's writing is *true* in that his stories frequently relate to experiences he has had, and that he often appears in the stories in either a major or minor role. Other writing Capote has done is reportage—accounts of happenings during his travels, observations about prominent people, local color stories and the like. Each type makes fascinating reading in its own way because of the author's brilliance in making people and places come alive. Capote is one of the true geniuses of descriptive technique, which is why we have chosen one of his stories to illustrate the lesson on descriptive and figurative language.

Truman Capote's reportage style was brought to perfection in his most famous novel, *In Cold Blood*. The author called it a nonfiction novel because, while he used the real people and the real events surrounding a particularly senseless and brutal murder, the artistry of the storytelling is the author's own; this makes it a novel.

After reading "A Christmas Memory," you may want to read "The Thanksgiving Visitor," which sheds more light on the Monroeville household. Then you will surely want to try *In Cold Blood* and perhaps one of the volumes of Truman Capote's collected stories. He is one of the most unusual people of our time, one of the best authors, and someone with whom you will be pleased to become acquainted.

# Figurative Language

Whenever you describe something by comparing it with something else, you are using *figurative language*. If, for instance, it's very cold outside and you're chilled through, you might complain that it's as cold *as the soles of a gravedigger's feet*. You could have simply said that the temperature was ten degrees Fahrenheit with a wind chill factor of forty below, and let it go at that. Such a bald statement of fact, however, lacks the impact of the figurative expression "cold as the soles of a gravedigger's feet."

Poets and authors turn to figurative language to express, in a word or two, feelings and impressions that a whole string of adjectives could not capture. "How *like a winter* has my absence been from thee," wrote Shakespeare because, like winter, being apart from this person made him feel cold, barren and forsaken. Winter also seems bleak, hostile and endless. All this and much more is conveyed in the comparison "How like a winter…"

Comparisons using the words "like" or "as" are called *similes* (pronounced sim'uh leez). They are only one of several kinds of figurative language used by poets, authors and people like you and me to communicate our feelings and impressions. Besides similes other common figures of speech are metaphor, personification, onomatopoeia, alliteration, hyperbole and meiosis. Despite their extravagant names, they are all simply ways to describe something, make a point or share a feeling. Truman Capote uses them masterfully in "A Christmas Memory" to help capture the elusive feelings he associates with a long-ago Christmas in Alabama.

**1. Simile.** A *simile* is a comparison that reveals similarities between otherwise dissimilar things. It is always introduced by *like* or *as*.

In "A Christmas Memory," the author compares an elderly lady to a small hen: "She is small and sprightly, *like a bantam hen*." On the face of it, an old lady is nothing like a bantam hen. Yet, as the author points out, they are both small and sprightly, and you can picture her alert eyes as she takes in her surroundings with quick, hen-like turns of the head. Notice, too, the attitude, or feeling, that this simile conveys. A bantam hen is small and harmless, and so is the lady in this story.

Similes are also introduced by the word *as*. Later in the story we find this elderly woman "weeping into a pillow *as wet as a widow's handkerchief.*" The author could simply have observed that the pillow was wet with tears. But the comparison "as wet as a widow's handkerchief" carries with it a sense of bereavement and loss that appropriately describes what the woman is feeling.

**2. Metaphor.** Like a simile, a *metaphor* (pronounced met'uh-for) also compares two unlike things. Here, however, the comparison is not announced by *like* or *as*; the comparison is implied.

In the following passage, the narrator, Buddy, recalls how he learned of his best friend's death. (His best friend was the elderly lady we just met.) Notice how Buddy uses a long metaphor that describes both the closeness he felt for his friend and his sense of loss in terms of a pair of kites that are flying away:

> A message saying so [that she has died] merely confirms a piece of news some secret vein had already received, severing from me an irreplaceable part of myself, letting it loose like a kite on a broken string. That is why, walking across a school campus on this particular December morning, I keep searching the sky. As if I expected to see, rather like hearts, a lost pair of kites hurrying toward heaven.

The narrator wants to convey the idea that he and his friend were kindred spirits, and he uses simile and metaphor to do this. Using a simile, he compares losing his friend to cutting the string on a kite. He builds on this image, turning the whole paragraph into a metaphor. The kites, by implication, become the kindred souls of the two friends. Buddy imagines his soul hurrying toward heaven with the soul of his friend, and he expresses a feeling of double loss. He has lost his friend in death and feels lost himself without her. This feeling would be almost impossible to describe without using figurative language.

**3. Personification.** *Personification* is a figure of speech which gives the qualities of a person to an animal, an object, or an idea. Its purpose is not to be cute, as when we treat a favorite pet like a person. Rather, it is a comparison that a poet or author uses to show something in an entirely new light, to communicate a certain feeling or attitude towards it and to control the way a reader perceives it. Notice how Truman Capote makes a tree much more than it is using personification.

> A brave handsome brute that survives thirty hatchet strokes before it keels with a creaking rending cry.

The author compares the tree to a "brave handsome brute"—that is, a man in his prime. It takes thirty hatchet strokes to fell this tree, and it goes down "with a creaking rending cry." By assigning human qualities to this pine tree, the author calls forth your admiration for its beauty and strength, and a twinge of pity for its fate. He also tells you how proud he is that this will be his Christmas tree.

**4. Onomatopoeia.** When authors describe something, they want to make readers feel as though they are actually experiencing what is going on. To do this, they use words and images that appeal to our senses—of sight, smell, taste, touch and hearing. Words that mimic sounds, like "buzz" and "hiss," are called *onomatopoeia* (pronounced on′ uh-maht′-uh-pee′ uh). They appeal to our sense of hearing and they help bring a description to life. Here, for example, Capote uses onomatopoeia to describe the sound of pecans being shelled:

> Caarackle! A cheery crunch, scraps of miniature thunder sound
> as the shells collapse and the golden mound of sweet oily ivory
> meat mounts in the milk-glass bowl.

The word "Caarackle!" is a good example of onomatopoeia. You won't find it in the dictionary because it's not actually a word; it's a string of syllables that the author has made up to represent the way a sound really sounds. If you hear the sound that way too, the device has been successful in evoking a sound and a scene. Notice how the rest of this description also appeals to your sense of hearing with descriptions like "a cheery crunch" and "scraps of miniature thunder." The author has relied almost exclusively on sounds, expressed in figures of speech, to bring this scene to life.

**5. Alliteration.** Repeating a sound in a series of words is *alliteration.* Alliteration gives a rhythmic, almost sing-song effect to a passage in which it is used.

The description of the pecans being shelled contains alliteration with its repetition of "m" sounds: "...the golden *m*ound of sweet oily ivory *m*eat *m*ounts in the *m*ilk-glass bowl" Here, the alliterative sounds stretch across the whole sentence and are interspersed with other words; yet the repetitive effect still stands out. Also notice the many *oh, ow,* and *oy* sounds in the sentence: "...g*ol*den m*ou*nd of sweet *oi*ly iv*ory* meat m*ou*nts in the m*il*k-glass b*owl*."

Alliteration may consist of only a pair of words, as in "coils of frazzled tinsel *g*one *g*old with age..." And the repeated sound need not always come at the beginning of the word. Notice how two of the "d" sounds come in the second syllables of words in the following alliterative phrase: "a brief rope of *d*ilapidated, un*d*oubtedly *d*angerous can*d*y-like light bulbs." But wherever it is used, alliteration lends a lilting effect that causes you to pause just long enough to savor the sounds.

**6. Hyperbole.** Hyperbole (pronounced hi-pur′-buh-lee) is simply exaggeration. It is not used to mislead the reader, but to emphasize a point. In "A Christmas Memory," the narrator's friend longs to give him a bicycle for Christmas. "She's said so on several million occasions," he informs us. We all know she couldn't have said it several million times. The exaggeration is intended to show how much his friend wants to give him a bike.

Sometimes hyperbole is used to imply the opposite of what is actually said. For instance, when someone says, "Oh, big deal!" they really mean that it's anything but a big deal. Hyperbole used this way dramatically alters the tone of the statement, usually resulting in a sarcastic or ironic tone. Capote uses hyperbole to imply an opposite meaning in the following passage. Where, precisely, is the hyperbole, and what effect does the author achieve by using it?

> Last summer others in the house contracted to pay us a penny for every twenty-five flies we killed. Oh, the carnage of August: the flies that flew to heaven!

The hyperbole is in the phrase "Oh, the carnage of August." "Carnage" is a rather strong word ordinarily used to describe the bloody slaughter on a battlefield. Yet Capote is not talking about slaughtering people, but about swatting flies! It's a gross exaggeration that distorts the meaning of the word carnage. Actually, the death of flies is bloodless and insignificant—quite the opposite of the literal meaning of carnage. The effect of this hyperbole is to give an ironic tone to the passage. Looking back, the author seems to be saying that he looked at events differently when he was a child from the way he looks at them now.

**7. Meiosis** The opposite of hyperbole is *meiosis* (pronounced my-o'-sis), or understatement. Like hyperbole, meiosis implies something different from what is actually said. When the narrator talks about his friend's oft-repeated wish to give him a bicycle he says, "She's said so on several million occasions." That, as we have seen, is hyperbole, or exaggeration. But if the narrator had said, "She's mentioned it *once or twice*," that would be meiosis—an understatement—because he would be implying, sarcastically, that she had spoken of it many times.

The ultimate purpose of figurative language is to create images in the reader's mind. This *imagery*, as it is called, is the essence of description. The best imagery is both fresh and vivid.... fresh because it describes something familiar in a new and even startling way, and vivid because it forms a picture in our mind's eye.

Truman Capote's descriptions in "A Christmas Memory" are superb because his figurative language creates fresh and vivid images in the reader's mind. In the following passage, Capote describes something very familiar—money. But notice how he communicates his absolute enjoyment of this rare commodity in his life.

> Dollar bills, tightly rolled and green as May buds. Somber fifty-cent pieces, heavy enough to weight a dead man's eyes. Lovely dimes, the liveliest coin, the one that really jingles. Nickels and quarters, worn smooth as creek pebbles. But mostly a hateful heap of bitter-odored pennies.

Figurative language is an important part of this description. "... green *as May buds*" is an effective simile because dollar bills are indeed that peculiar shade of green; moreover, the comparison of dollars with spring buds is a novel one. *"Smooth as creek pebbles"* is another simile that describes exactly how worn nickels and quarters feel. There is personification in the phrase "somber fifty-cent pieces" because somber is ordinarily used to describe people, not things; and there is alliteration in the phrase "*hateful heap*..." It is surely fanciful to describe a fifty-cent piece as "heavy enough to weight a dead man's eyes," yet a half-dollar is exactly the size and heft to weigh down the eyelids of a corpse. All of these images communicate to the reader just how the narrator feels about this small pile of money. This money, saved up over the course of a year, is important to him, and in his imagination each piece has taken on an identity of its own—somber, lively, hateful and so on. The author has used figurative language to create imagery that conveys these feelings.

You don't have to be an expert on figurative language to enjoy good writing. But being able to recognize the different figures of speech helps you to understand how an author uses them to create a certain effect—and how you can use them to similar advantage in your own writing.

As you read the story:

- Ask yourself which of your senses is being appealed to when Buddy and his friend are making their fruitcakes.

- Pay attention to the feeling the author conveys through figurative language when Buddy and his friend get drunk on the last of Haha's whiskey.

- Notice how the author uses figurative language to give a particular feeling to the winter landscape when Buddy and his friend set out to find a Christmas tree.

- Observe how the author describes the special time when Buddy and his friend awaken with the first rays of dawn on Christmas morning.

# A Christmas Memory

# Truman Capote

Imagine a morning in late November. A coming of winter morning more than twenty years ago. Consider the kitchen of a spreading old house in a country town. A great black stove is its main feature; but there is also a big round table and a fireplace with two rocking chairs placed in front of it. Just today the fireplace commenced its seasonal roar.

A woman with shorn white hair is standing at the kitchen window. She is wearing tennis shoes and a shapeless gray sweater over a summery calico dress. She is small and sprightly, like a bantam hen; but, due to a long youthful illness, her shoulders are pitifully hunched. Her face is remarkable—not unlike Lincoln's, craggy like that, and tinted by sun and wind; but it is delicate too, finely boned, and her eyes are sherry-colored and timid. "Oh my," she exclaims, her breath smoking the windowpane, "it's fruitcake weather!"

The person to whom she is speaking is myself. I am seven; she is sixty-something. We are cousins, very distant ones, and we have lived together—well, as long as I can remember. Other people inhabit the house, relatives; and though they have power over us, and frequently make us cry, we are not, on the whole, too much aware of them. We are each other's best friend. She calls me Buddy, in memory of a boy who was formerly her best friend. The other Buddy died in the 1880s, when she was still a child. She is still a child.

"I knew it before I got out of bed," she says, turning away from the window with a purposeful excitement in her eyes. "The courthouse bell sounded so cold and clear. And there were no birds singing; they've gone to warmer country, yes indeed. Oh, Buddy, stop stuffing biscuit and fetch our buggy. Help me find my hat. We've thirty cakes to bake."

It's always the same: a morning arrives in November, and my friend, as though officially inaugurating the Christmas time of year that exhilarates her imagination and fuels the blaze of her heart, announces: "It's fruitcake weather! Fetch our buggy. Help me find my hat."

The hat is found, a straw cartwheel corsaged with velvet roses out-of-doors has faded: it once belonged to a more fashionable relative. Together, we guide our buggy, a dilapidated baby carriage, out to the garden and into a grove of pecan trees. The buggy is mine; that is, it was bought for me when I was born. It is made of wicker, rather unraveled, and the wheels wobble like a drunkard's legs. But it is a faithful object; springtimes, we take it to the woods and fill it with flowers, herbs, wild fern for our porch pots; in the summer, we pile it with picnic paraphernalia and sugar-cane fishing poles and roll it down to the edge of a creek; it has its winter uses, too: as a truck for hauling firewood from the yard to the kitchen, as a warm bed for Queenie, our tough little orange and white rat terrier who has survived distemper and two rattlesnake bites. Queenie is trotting beside it now.

Three hours later we are back in the kitchen hulling a heaping buggyload of windfall pecans. Our backs hurt from gathering them: how hard they were to find (the main crop having been shaken off the trees and sold by the orchard's owners, who are not us) among the concealing leaves, the frosted, deceiving grass. Caarackle! A cheery crunch, scraps of miniature thunder sound as the shells collapse and the golden mound of sweet oily ivory meat mounts in the milk-glass bowl. Queenie begs to taste, and now and again my friend sneaks her a mite, though insisting we deprive ourselves. "We mustn't, Buddy. If we start, we won't stop. And there's scarcely enough as there is. For thirty cakes." The kitchen is growing dark. Dusk turns the window into a mirror: our reflections mingle with the rising moon as we work by the fireside in the firelight. At last, when the moon is quite high, we toss the final hull into the fire and, with joined sighs, watch it catch flame. The buggy is empty, the bowl is brimful.

We eat our supper (cold biscuits, bacon, blackberry jam) and discuss tomorrow. Tomorrow the kind of work I like best begins: buying. Cherries and citron, ginger and vanilla and canned Hawaiian pineapple, rinds and raisins and walnuts and whiskey and oh, so much flour, butter, so many eggs, spices, flavorings: why, we'll need a pony to pull the buggy home.

But before these purchases can be made, there is the question of money. Neither of us has any. Except for skinflint sums persons in the house occasionally provide (a dime is considered very big money); or what we earn ourselves from various activities: holding rummage sales, selling buckets of hand-picked blackberries, jars of homemade jam and apple jelly and peach preserves, rounding up flowers for funerals and weddings. Once we won seventy-ninth prize, five dollars, in a national football contest. Not that we know a fool thing about football. It's just that we enter any contest we hear about: at the moment our hopes are centered on the fifty-thousand-dollar Grand Prize being offered to name a new brand of coffee (we suggested "A.M."; and, after some hesitation, for my friend thought it perhaps sacrilegious, the slogan "A.M.! Amen!"). To tell the truth, our only *really* profitable enterprise was the Fun and Freak Museum we conducted in a back-yard woodshed two summers ago. The Fun was a stereopticon with slide views of Washington and New York lent us by a relative who had been to those places (she was furious when she discovered why we'd borrowed it); the Freak was a three-legged biddy chicken hatched by one of our own hens. Everybody hereabouts wanted to see that biddy: we charged grownups a nickel, kids two cents. And took in a good twenty dollars before the museum shut down due to the decease of the main attraction.

But one way and another we do each year accumulate Christmas savings, a Fruitcake Fund. These moneys we keep hidden in an ancient bead purse under a loose board under the floor under a chamber pot under my friend's bed. The purse is seldom removed from this safe location except to make a deposit, or, as happens every Saturday, a withdrawal; for on Saturdays I am allowed ten cents to go to the picture show. My friend has never been to a picture show, nor does she intend to: "I'd rather hear you tell the story, Buddy. That way I can imagine it more. Besides, a person my age shouldn't squander their eyes. When the Lord comes, let me see him clear." In addition to never having seen a movie, she has never: eaten in a restaurant, traveled more than five miles from home, received or sent a telegram, read anything except funny papers and the Bible, worn cosmetics, cursed, wished someone harm, told a lie on purpose, let a hungry dog go hungry. Here are a few things she has done, does do: killed with a hoe the biggest rattlesnake ever seen in this county (sixteen rattles), dip snuff (secretly), tame humming-birds (just try it) till they balance on her finger, tell ghost stories (we both believe in ghosts) so tingling they chill you in July, talk to herself, take walks in the rain, grow the prettiest japonicas in town, know the recipe for every sort of old-time Indian cure, including a magical wart-remover.

Now, with supper finished, we retire to the room in a faraway part of the house where my friend sleeps in a scrap-quilt-covered iron bed painted rose pink, her favorite color. Silently, wallowing in the pleasures of conspiracy, we take the bead purse from its secret place and spill its contents on the scrap quilt. Dollar bills, tightly rolled and green as May buds. Somber fifty-cent pieces, heavy enough to weight a dead man's eyes. Lovely dimes, the liveliest coin, the one that really jingles. Nickels and quarters, worn smooth as creek pebbles. But mostly a hateful heap of bitter-odored pennies. Last summer others in the house contracted to pay us a penny for every twenty-five flies we killed. Oh, the carnage of August: the flies that flew to heaven! Yet it was not work in which we took pride. And, as we sit counting pennies, it is as though we were back tabulating dead flies. Neither of us has a head for figures; we count slowly, lose track, start again. According to her calculations, we have $12.73. According to mine, exactly $13. "I do hope you're wrong, Buddy. We can't mess around with thirteen. The cakes will fall. Or put somebody in the cemetery. Why, I wouldn't dream of getting out of bed on the thirteenth." This is true: she always spends thirteenths in bed. So, to be on the safe side, we subtract a penny and toss it out the window.

Of the ingredients that go into our fruitcakes, whiskey is the most expen-sive, as well as the hardest to obtain: State laws forbid its sale. But every-body knows you can buy a bottle from Mr. Haha Jones. And the next day, having completed our more prosaic shopping, we set out for Mr. Haha's business address, a "sinful" (to quote public opinion) fish-fry and dancing cafe down by the river. We've been there before, and on the same errand; but in previous years our dealings have been with Haha's wife, an iodine-dark Indian woman with brassy peroxided hair and a dead-tired disposition. Actually, we've never laid eyes on her husband, though we've heard that he's an Indian too. A giant with razor scars across his cheeks. They call him Haha because he's so gloomy, a man who never laughs. As we approach his cafe (a large log cabin festooned inside and out with chains of garish-gay naked light bulbs and standing by the river's muddy edge under the shade of river trees where moss drifts through the branches like gray mist) our steps slow down. Even Queenie stops prancing and sticks close by. People have been murdered in Haha's cafe. Cut to pieces. Hit on the head. There's a case coming up in court next month. Naturally these goings-on happen at night when the colored lights cast crazy patterns and the victrola wails. In the daytime Haha's is shabby and deserted. I knock at the door, Queenie barks, my friend calls: "Mrs. Haha, ma'am? Anyone to home?"

Footsteps. The door opens. Our hearts overturn. It's Mr. Haha Jones himself! And he *is* a giant; he *does* have scars; he *doesn't* smile. No, he glowers at us through Satan-tilted eyes and demands to know: "What you want with Haha?"

For a moment we are too paralyzed to tell. Presently my friend half-finds her voice, a whispery voice at best: "If you please, Mr. Haha, we'd like a quart of your finest whiskey."

His eyes tilt more. Would you believe it? Haha is smiling! Laughing, too. "Which one of you is a drinkin' man?"

"It's for making fruitcakes, Mr. Haha. Cooking."

This sobers him. He frowns. "That's no way to waste good whiskey." Nevertheless, he retreats into the shadowed cafe and seconds later appears carrying a bottle of daisy yellow unlabeled liquor. He demonstrates its sparkle in the sunlight and says: "Two dollars."

We pay him with nickels and dimes and pennies. Suddenly, jangling the coins in his hand like a fistful of dice, his face softens. "Tell you what," he proposes, pouring the money back into our bead purse, "just send me one of them fruitcakes instead."

"Well," my friend remarks on our way home, "there's a lovely man. We'll put an extra cup of raisins in *his* cake."

The black stove, stoked with coal and firewood, glows like a lighted pumpkin. Eggbeaters whirl, spoons spin round in bowls of butter and sugar, vanilla sweetens the air, ginger spices it; melting, nose-tingling odors saturate the kitchen, suffuse the house, drift out to the world on puffs of chimney smoke. In four days our work is done. Thirty-one cakes, dampened with whiskey, bask on window sills and shelves.

Who are they for?

Friends. Not necessarily neighbor friends: indeed, the larger share are intended for persons we've met maybe once, perhaps not at all. People who've struck our fancy. Like President Roosevelt. Like the Reverend and Mrs. J. C. Lucey, Baptist missionaries to Borneo who lectured here last winter. Or the little knife grinder who comes through town twice a year. Or Abner Packer, the driver of the six o'clock bus from Mobile, who exchanges waves with us every day as he passes in a dust-cloud whoosh. Or the young Wistons, a California couple whose car one afternoon broke down outside the house and who spent a pleasant hour chatting with us on the porch (young Mr. Wiston snapped our picture, the only one we've ever had taken).

Is it because my friend is shy with everyone *except* strangers that these strangers, and merest acquaintances, seem to us our truest friends? I think yes. Also, the scrapbooks we keep of thank-you's on White House stationery, time-to-time communications from California and Borneo, the knife grinder's penny post cards, make us feel connected to eventful worlds beyond the kitchen with its view of a sky that stops.

Now a nude December fig branch grates against the window. The kitchen is empty, the cakes are gone; yesterday we carted the last of them to the post office, where the cost of stamps turned our purse inside out. We're broke. That rather depresses me, but my friend insists on celebrating—with two inches of whiskey left in Haha's bottle. Queenie has a spoonful in a bowl of coffee (she likes her coffee chicory-flavored and strong). The rest we divide between a pair of jelly glasses. We're both quite awed at the prospect of drinking straight whiskey; the taste of it brings screwed-up expressions and sour shudders. But by and by we begin to sing, the two of us singing different songs simultaneously. I don't know the words to mine, just: *Come on along, come on along, to the dark-town strutters' ball.* But I can dance: that's what I mean to be, a tap dancer in the movies. My dancing shadow rollicks on the walls; our voices rock the chinaware; we giggle: as if unseen hands were tickling us. Queenie rolls on her back, her paws plow the air, something like a grin stretches her black lips. Inside myself, I feel warm and sparky as those crumbling logs, carefree as the wind in the chimney. My friend waltzes round the stove, the hem of her poor calico skirt pinched between her fingers as though it were a party dress: *Show me the way to go home,* she sings, her tennis shoes squeaking on the floor. *Show me the way to go home.*

Enter: two relatives. Very angry. Potent with eyes that scold, tongues that scald. Listen to what they have to say, the words tumbling together into a wrathful tune: "A child of seven! whiskey on his breath! are you out of your mind? feeding a child of seven! must be loony! road to ruination! remember Cousin Kate? Uncle Charlie? Uncle Charlie's brother-in-law? shame! scandal! humiliation! kneel, pray, beg the Lord!"

Queenie sneaks under the stove. My friend gazes at her shoes, her chin quivers, she lifts her skirt and blows her nose and runs to her room. Long after the town has gone to sleep and the house is silent except for the chimings of clocks and the sputter of fading fires, she is weeping into a pillow already as wet as a widow's handkerchief.

"Don't cry," I say, sitting at the bottom of her bed and shivering despite my flannel nightgown that smells of last winter's cough syrup, "don't cry," I beg, teasing her toes, tickling her feet, "you're too old for that."

"It's because," she hiccups, "I *am* too old. Old and funny."

"Not funny. Fun. More fun than anybody. Listen. If you don't stop crying you'll be so tired tomorrow we can't go cut a tree."

She straightens up. Queenie jumps on the bed (where Queenie is not allowed) to lick her cheeks. "I know where we'll find real pretty trees, Buddy. And holly, too. With berries big as your eyes. It's way off in the woods. Farther than we've ever been. Papa used to bring us Christmas trees from there: carry them on his shoulder. That's fifty years ago. Well, now: I can't wait for morning."

Morning. Frozen rime lusters the grass; the sun, round as an orange and orange as hot-weather moons, balances on the horizon, burnishes the silvered winter woods. A wild turkey calls. A renegade hog grunts in the undergrowth. Soon, by the edge of knee-deep, rapid-running water, we have to abandon the buggy. Queenie wades the stream first, paddles across barking complaints at the swiftness of the current, the pneumonia-making coldness of it. We follow, holding our shoes and equipment (a hatchet, a burlap sack) above our heads. A mile more: of chastising thorns, burs and briers that catch at our clothes; of rusty pine needles brilliant with gaudy fungus and molted feathers. Here, there, a flash, a flutter, an ecstasy of shrillings remind us that not all the birds have flown south. Always, the path unwinds through lemony sun pools and pitch vine tunnels. Another creek to cross: a disturbed armada of speckled trout froths the water round us, and frogs the size of plates practice belly flops; beaver workmen are building a dam. On the farther shore, Queenie shakes herself and trembles. My friend shivers, too: not with cold but enthusiasm. One of her hat's ragged roses sheds a petal as she lifts her head and inhales the pine-heavy air. "We're almost there; can you smell it, Buddy?" she says, as though we were approaching an ocean.

And, indeed, it is a kind of ocean. Scented acres of holiday trees, prickly-leafed holly. Red berries shiny as Chinese bells: black crows swoop upon them screaming. Having stuffed our burlap sacks with enough greenery and crimson to garland a dozen windows, we set about choosing a tree. "It should be," muses my friend, "twice as tall as a boy. So a boy can't steal the star." The one we pick is twice as tall as me. A brave handsome brute that survives thirty hatchet strokes before it keels with a creaking rending cry. Lugging it like a kill, we commence the long trek out. Every few yards we abandon the struggle, sit down and pant. But we have the strength of triumphant huntsmen; that and the tree's virile, icy perfume revive us, goad us on. Many compliments accompany our sunset return along the red clay road to town; but my friend is sly and noncommittal when passers-by praise the treasure perched in our buggy: what a fine tree and where did it come from? "Yonderways," she murmurs vaguely. Once a car stops and the rich mill owner's lazy wife leans out and whines: "Giveya two-bits cash for that ol tree." Ordinarily my friend is afraid of saying no; but on this occasion she promptly shakes her head: "We wouldn't take a dollar." The mill owner's wife persists. "A dollar, my foot! Fifty cents. That's my last offer. Goodness, woman, you can get another one." In answer, my friend gently reflects: "I doubt it. There's never two of anything."

Home: Queenie slumps by the fire and sleeps till tomorrow, snoring loud as a human.

A trunk in the attic contains: a shoebox of ermine tails (off the opera cape of a curious lady who once rented a room in the house), coils of frazzled tinsel gone gold with age, one silver star, a brief rope of dilapidated, undoubtedly dangerous candy-like light bulbs. Excellent decorations, as far as they go, which isn't far enough: my friend wants our tree to blaze "like a Baptist window," droop with weighty snows of ornament. But we can't afford the made-in-Japan splendors at the five-and-dime. So we do what we've always done: sit for days at the kitchen table with scissors and crayons and stacks of colored paper. I make sketches and my friend cuts them out: lots of cats, fish too (because they're easy to draw), some apples, some watermelons, a few winged angels devised from saved-up sheets of Hershey-bar tin foil. We use safety pins to attach these creations to the tree; as a final touch, we sprinkle the branches with shredded cotton (picked in August for this purpose). My friend, surveying the effect, clasps her hands together. "Now honest, Buddy. Doesn't it look good enough to eat?" Queenie tries to eat an angel.

After weaving and ribboning holly wreaths for all the front windows, our next project is the fashioning of family gifts. Tie-dye scarves for the ladies, for the men a home-brewed lemon and licorice and aspirin syrup to be taken "at the first Symptoms of a Cold and after Hunting." But when it comes time for making each other's gift, my friend and I separate to work secretly. I would like to buy her a pearl-handled knife, a radio, a whole pound of chocolate-covered cherries (we tasted some once, and she always swears: "I could live on them, Buddy, Lord yes I could—and that's not taking His name in vain"). Instead, I am building her a kite. She would like to give me a bicycle (she's said so on several million occasions: "If only I could, Buddy. It's bad enough in life to do without something *you* want; but confound it, what gets my goat is not being able to give somebody something you want *them* to have. Only one of these days I will, Buddy. Locate you a bike. Don't ask how. Steal it, maybe"). Instead, I'm fairly certain that she is building me a kite—the same as last year, and the year before: the year before that we exchanged slingshots. All of which is fine by me. For we are champion kite-fliers who study the wind like sailors; my friend, more accomplished than I, can get a kite aloft when there isn't enough breeze to carry clouds.

Christmas Eve afternoon we scrape together a nickel and go to the butcher's to buy Queenie's traditional gift, a good gnawable beef bone. The bone, wrapped in funny paper, is placed high in the tree near the silver star. Queenie knows it's there. She squats at the foot of the tree staring up in a trance of greed: when bedtime arrives she refuses to budge. Her excitement is equaled by my own. I kick the covers and turn my pillow as though it were a scorching summer's night. Somewhere a rooster crows: falsely, for the sun is still on the other side of the world.

"Buddy, are you awake?" It is my friend, calling from her room, which is next to mine; and an instant later she is sitting on my bed holding a candle. "Well, I can't sleep a hoot," she declares. "My mind's jumping like a jack rabbit. Buddy, do you think Mrs. Roosevelt will serve our cake at dinner?" We huddle in the bed, and she squeezes my hand I-love-you. "Seems like your hand used to be so much smaller. I guess I hate to see you grow up. When you're grown up, will we still be friends?" I say always. "But I feel so bad, Buddy. I wanted so bad to give you a bike. I tried to sell my cameo Papa gave me. Buddy—" she hesitates, as though embarrassed—"I made you another kite." Then I confess that I made her one, too; and we laugh. The candle burns too short to hold. Out it goes, exposing the starlight, the stars spinning at the window like a visible caroling that slowly, slowly daybreak silences. Possibly we doze; but the beginnings of dawn splash us like cold water: we're up, wide-eyed and wandering while we wait for others to waken. Quite deliberately my friend drops a kettle on the kitchen floor. I tap-dance in front of closed doors. One by one the household emerges, looking as though they'd like to kill us both; but it's Christmas, so they can't. First, a gorgeous breakfast: just everything you can imagine—from flapjacks and fried squirrel to hominy grits and honey-in-the-comb. Which puts everyone in a good humor except my friend and I. Frankly, we're so impatient to get at the presents we can't eat a mouthful.

Well, I'm disappointed. Who wouldn't be? With socks, a Sunday school shirt, some handkerchiefs, a hand-me-down sweater and a year's subscription to a religious magazine for children. *The Little Shepherd.* It makes me boil. It really does.

My friend has a better haul. A sack of Satsumas, that's her best present. She is proudest, however, of a white wool shawl knitted by her married sister. But she *says* her favorite gift is the kite I built her. And it *is* very beautiful; though not as beautiful as the one she made me, which is blue and scattered with gold and green Good Conduct stars; moreover, my name is painted on it, "Buddy."

"Buddy, the wind is blowing."

The wind is blowing, and nothing will do till we've run to a pasture below the house where Queenie has scooted to bury her bone (and where, a winter hence, Queenie will be buried, too.) There, plunging through the healthy waist-high grass, we unreel our kites, feel them twitching at the string like sky fish as they swim into the wind. Satisfied, sun-warmed we sprawl in the grass and peel Satsumas and watch our kites cavort. Soon I forget the socks and hand-me-down sweater. I'm as happy as if we'd already won the fifty-thousand-dollar Grand Prize in that coffee-naming contest.

"My, how foolish I am!" my friend cries, suddenly alert, like a woman remembering too late she has biscuits in the oven. "You know what I've always thought?" she asks in a tone of discovery, and not smiling at me but a point beyond. "I've always thought a body would have to be sick and dying before they saw the Lord. And I imagined that when He came it would be like looking at the Baptist window: pretty as colored glass with the sun pouring through, such a shine you don't know it's getting dark. And it's been a comfort: to think of that shine taking away all the spooky feeling. But I'll wager it never happens. I'll wager at the very end a body realizes the Lord has already shown Himself. That things as they are"—her hand circles in a gesture that gathers clouds and kites and grass and Queenie pawing earth over her bone—"just what they've always seen, was seeing Him. As for me, I could leave the world with today in my eyes."

This is our last Christmas together.

Life separates us. Those who Know Best decide that I belong in a military school. And so follows a miserable succession of bugle-blowing prisons, grim reveille-ridden summer camps. I have a new home too. But it doesn't count. Home is where my friend is, and there I never go.

And there she remains, puttering around the kitchen. Alone with Queenie. Then alone. ("Buddy dear," she writes in her wild hard-to-read script, "yesterday Jim Macy's horse kicked Queenie bad. Be thankful she didn't feel much. I wrapped her in a Fine Linen sheet and rode her in the buggy down to Simpson's pasture where she can be with all her Bones..."). For a few Novembers she continues to bake her fruitcakes single-handed; not as many, but some: and, of course, she always sends me "the best of the batch." Also, in every letter she encloses a dime wadded in toilet paper: "See a picture show and write me the story." But gradually in her letters she tends to confuse me with her other friend, the Buddy who died in the 1880s; more and more thirteenths are not the only days she stays in bed: a morning arrives in November, a leafless birdless coming of winter morning, when she cannot rouse herself to exclaim: "Oh, my, it's fruitcake weather!"

And when that happens, I know it. A message saying so merely confirms a piece of news some secret vein had already received, severing from me an irreplaceable part of myself, letting it loose like a kite on a broken string. That is why, walking across a school campus on this particular December morning, I keep searching the sky. As if I expected to see, rather like hearts, a lost pair of kites hurrying toward heaven.

# Unit 9

## A Christmas Memory

- Comprehension Questions
- Figurative Language
- Discussion Guides
- Writing Exercise

# COMPREHENSION QUESTIONS

For each of the following statements and questions, select the option containing the most complete or most accurate answer.

1. The narrator's friend calls him "Buddy" after
   (a) □ a. her father.
   □ b. someone she had read about.
   □ c. an acquaintance she admired.
   □ d. a child who had died.

2. Once they decide it's time to make the fruitcakes, the first thing Buddy
   (d) and his friend do is to
   □ a. go to the store.  □ c. gather the pecans.
   □ b. buy the whiskey.  □ d. raise some money.

3. The main attraction in the Fun and Freak Museum was a
   (a) □ a. tap dancer.  □ c. three-legged chicken.
   □ b. slide viewer.  □ d. two-headed turtle.

4. Which of the following best defines *decease* as used in "[We] took in
   (l) a good twenty dollars before the museum shut down due to the *decease*
   of the main attraction?"
   □ a. Disappearance  □ c. Illness
   □ b. Death  □ d. Theft

5. The fact that Buddy's friend spends the thirteenth day of each month in
   (f) bed, and throws out a penny so they won't have $13.00 even, leads the
   reader to conclude that she is
   □ a. cautious.  □ c. scatterbrained.
   □ b. feeble-minded.  □ d. superstitious.

6. Mr. Haha Jones lets Buddy and his friend pay for their whiskey with a
   (f) fruitcake because
   □ a. he can see they don't have much money.
   □ b. he likes fruitcakes.
   □ c. it's Christmas.
   □ d. he doesn't need the money.

7. The fruitcakes are for
(b) ☐ a. members of the family.
    ☐ b. strangers or near strangers.
    ☐ c. a church bazaar.
    ☐ d. close friends.

8. The scolding that Buddy and his friend receive when other members of
(g) the family come in and find them tipsy after finishing Haha's whiskey
    was probably
    ☐ a. undeserved.        ☐ c. unnecessarily harsh.
    ☐ b. well deserved.     ☐ d. intentionally cruel.

9. The other members of the family who live in the house seem
(h) ☐ a. to admire Buddy's friend.
    ☐ b. to look down on Buddy's friend.
    ☐ c. to fear Buddy's friend.
    ☐ d. to love Buddy's friend.

10. Buddy's friend might best be described as
(j) ☐ a. crotchety.        ☐ c. childlike.
    ☐ b. sophisticated.   ☐ d. domineering.

11. Buddy and his friend seem
(h) ☐ a. to live in their own private world.
    ☐ b. to have a large circle of friends.
    ☐ c. to have little in common.
    ☐ d. to feel separated by a generation gap.

12. "My friend is sly and *noncommittal* when passers-by praise the treas-
(1) ure perched in our buggy: what a fine tree and where did it come
    from? 'Yonderways,' she murmurs vaguely." From the way it is used
    here, *noncommittal* means
    ☐ a. helpful.        ☐ c. secretive.
    ☐ b. ignorant.      ☐ d. suspicious.

13. Making the fruitcakes, going after the Christmas tree, fashioning the
(c) holly wreaths for the front windows, and placing Queenie's bone up
    in the tree are all
    ☐ a. chores.       ☐ c. games.
    ☐ b. traditions.    ☐ d. adventures.

14. "Out it [the candle] goes, exposing the starlight, the stars spinning at
(k) the window like a visible caroling that slowly, slowly daybreak silences."
The phrase "like a visible caroling" is an example of
☐ a. metaphor.      ☐ c. meiosis.
☐ b. alliteration.      ☐ d. simile.

15. The Christmas presents Buddy receives are
(c) ☐ a. extravagant.      ☐ c. enjoyable.
☐ b. imaginative.      ☐ d. practical.

16. On Christmas day Buddy and his friend
(b) ☐ a. bake Christmas cookies.
☐ b. build a snowman.
☐ c. go to the movies together.
☐ d. go kite-flying.

17. "We unreel our kites, feel them twitching at the string like sky fish
(k) as they _____ into the wind." The missing word in this metaphor
must be
☐ a. dance.      ☐ c. fly.
☐ b. swim.      ☐ d. run.

18. Buddy's friend decides that the Lord shows himself
(c) ☐ a. in a blaze of light.
☐ b. only after death.
☐ c. in everyday things.
☐ d. only to saints.

19. For Buddy and his friend, the best part of Christmas is
(e) ☐ a. opening the presents.
☐ b. eating all the food.
☐ c. going to church.
☐ d. preparing for the holiday.

20. The decision to send Buddy to a military school was probably
(g) ☐ a. unfortunate.      ☐ c. necessary.
☐ b. wise.      ☐ d. generous.

21. In the years after Buddy goes away, his old friend becomes
(j) ☐ a. bitter and resentful.
     ☐ b. lonely and confused.
     ☐ c. lively and spirited.
     ☐ d. peaceful and contented.


22. Buddy's friend dies
(d) ☐ a. shortly after he leaves for military school.
     ☐ b. before Queenie.
     ☐ c. the following Christmas.
     ☐ d. some years after he leaves home.


23. Buddy's attitude toward the members of the family other than Aunt
(i) Sook seems to be
     ☐ a. loving.              ☐ c. tolerant.
     ☐ b. bitter.              ☐ d. amused.


24. After he left for school Buddy felt his real home was
(e) ☐ a. with Miss Sook.
     ☐ b. in military school.
     ☐ c. in summer camp.
     ☐ d. in his new home.


25. The author's tone as he tells this story might best be described as
(i) ☐ a. wistful.             ☐ c. apologetic.
     ☐ b. rollicking.          ☐ d. superior.


Comprehension Skills: a — isolating details; b — recalling specific facts; c — retaining concepts; d — organizing facts; e — understanding the main idea; f — drawing a conclusion; g — making a judgment; h — making an inference; i — recognizing tone; j — understanding characters; k — appreciation of literary forms; l — understanding vocabulary.

# FIGURATIVE LANGUAGE

## Practice Exercise A

The black stove, stoked with coal and firewood, glows like a lighted pumpkin. Eggbeaters whirl, spoons spin round in bowls of butter and sugar, vanilla sweetens the air, ginger spices it; melting, nose-tingling odors saturate the kitchen, suffuse the house, drift out to the world on puffs of chimney smoke.

1. Which of the reader's senses does this descriptive passage most appeal to?
   - ☐ a. Sight
   - ☐ b. Taste
   - ☐ c. Hearing
   - ☐ d. Smell

2. Underline the simile that appears in the first sentence of the passage above.

## Practice Exercise B

My dancing shadow rollicks on the walls; our voices rock the chinaware; we giggle: as if unseen hands were tickling us. Queenie rolls on her back, her paws plow the air, something like a grin stretches her black lips. Inside myself, I feel warm and sparky as those crumbling logs, carefree as the wind in the chimney. My friend waltzes round the stove, the hem of her poor calico skirt pinched between her fingers as though it were a party dress: *Show me the way to go home*, she sings, her tennis shoes squeaking on the floor. *Show me the way to go home.*

1. The figurative language in this descriptive passage helps contribute to a feeling of
   - ☐ a. devilish revelry.
   - ☐ b. gay abandon.
   - ☐ c. forced enjoyment.
   - ☐ d. enchantment.

2. Queenie does something uniquely human in this scene. On the lines provided, write this example of personification.

_____

_____

_____

**Practice Exercise C**

Morning. Frozen rime [hoarfrost] lusters the grass; the sun, round as an orange and orange as hot-weather moons, balances on the horizon, burnishes the silvered winter woods.

1. The author uses figurative language to make this winter morning landscape seem
   - ☐ a. magical and shining.
   - ☐ b. cold and uninviting.
   - ☐ c. ordinary and unremarkable.
   - ☐ d. strange and unfamiliar.

2. Circle two similes in the passage above.
   Underline two examples of personification in which the sun is described as performing tasks ordinarily done by human beings.

**Practice Exercise D**

Possibly we doze; but the beginnings of dawn splash us like cold water: we're up, wide-eyed and wandering while we wait for the others to waken.

1. The figurative language used in this description depicts the dawn as
   - ☐ a. mysterious.
   - ☐ b. tranquilizing.
   - ☐ c. invigorating.
   - ☐ d. depressing.

2. On the lines provided, write the long alliterative phrase in the passage above. Underline the alliterative sound each time it appears.

_____

_____   _  _____

_____

_____

## Analyzing Figurative Language

1. Figurative language might be called a kind of imaginative shorthand because a good simile or metaphor evokes many feelings and images with a few words. What associations do the following figures of speech from the story bring to mind? a disturbed armada of speckled trout; lugging it [the Christmas tree] like a kill; jangling the coins in his hand like a fistful of dice; my friend wants our tree to blaze "like a Baptist window."

2. Scientists do not use figurative language because it is imprecise: a choice comparison can evoke many different associations. Why are many associations desirable to a writer? What is lost by saying: "The black stove was stoked to an internal temperature of 400 degrees Fahrenheit," instead of "The black stove . . . glowed like a lighted pumpkin"?

## Interpreting the Story

3. Why do you think Buddy and his friend use their savings every Christmas to make fruitcakes for people they hardly know? Why don't they use the money to buy nice gifts for each other?

4. How would you explain the close friendship between a seven-year-old boy and an elderly lady? What do they see in each other?

5. We never actually meet any of the other members of the household, yet they do figure in the story. What exactly do we learn about them? What is your opinion of them?

6. There are hints in the story that Buddy's friend is "different" in some way. The narrator himself says that, at sixty-something, she is still a child. Another relative in the house calls her "looney." What do you think—is Buddy's friend mentally retarded? insane? senile? or something else? Explain your opinion.

7. Why do you think "Those who Know Best"—Buddy's relatives, presumably—decide that Buddy belongs in a military school?

8. Several heroines of Truman Capote's stories have been described as both victims and dreamers. In what ways does Buddy's elderly aunt fit this description?

## Analyzing the Author's Technique

9. The narrator says right at the start that the events related in this story took place twenty years ago. Yet he tells the story in the present tense, as if it were happening right now. What effect does this create?

10. How does the author save this story from becoming sickly sweet or overly sentimental?

## WRITING EXERCISE

Choose *one* holiday tradition that is special to you—decorating, singing, buying gifts, preparing special foods, or something else. Write a paragraph or more describing this tradition. Use figurative language to describe sights, sounds and smells that are a part of your tradition, and to express your feelings about them. Include at least one example of each of the following figures of speech: metaphor, simile, onomatopoeia, personification, alliteration, meiosis and hyperbole.

_____

_____

_____

_____

_____

_____

_____

_____

_____

_____

_____

Unit 10
**Dialogue**

# The Leader of the People

## John Steinbeck

# Introduction

"The Leader of the People" is set in the Salinas River Valley of California, about eighty miles south of San Francisco and not too far inland from the Pacific coast. This is the boyhood home of author John Steinbeck, the country he loved best and the scene of many of his stories and novels. The story is a simple one, easy to read, and occupies something less than twenty-four hours in the life of the Tiflin family.

It is important to remember that three generations are represented in the story. There are historical references and serious statements that reflect the viewpoints of people of different ages. These people are Jody, a small boy; Carl Tiflin and Mrs. Tiflin, Jody's parents; Billy Buck, a ranch hand who is just a little older than Carl Tiflin; and Grandfather, who is well along in years. Grandfather comes to visit the Tiflins at their Salinas Valley ranch. This is all very fine, except that, like many other old people, he tells the same stories over and over again.

The stories Grandfather tells are about fighting Indians and crossing the plains, for he had been a leader of the people in the westward migration of the nineteenth century. Mrs. Tiflin is patient with her father, and tolerant; she realizes that crossing the plains was the most important thing in Grandfather's life, and now that it is over, it is the only thing he has to talk about. Billy Buck treats the old man with polite respect, and Carl Tiflin just wishes Grandfather would find something else to talk about. Only Jody sees his grandfather as heroic; he thinks of the old man as a character out of a storybook about the old Wild West. None of the others sees Grandfather as he was, a leader of the people in a great American epic. And no one, not even Grandfather himself, realizes what he is attempting to accomplish with his stories. Grandfather is an oral historian, like the ancient bards and ballad singers. He is trying to pass on to following generations not just stories of the crossing, but its spirit and meaning. In this second aim he fails.

At the end of the story, however, John Steinbeck provides a rare insight for his readers into the spirit and driving force behind the people who came across the plains to California so long ago. If the crossing of the plains has only been a dry historical fact for you until now, you are likely to find new meaning and new interest in this American drama after reading the story.

The author doesn't put a date on his story; he doesn't name the year, that is, to give readers a setting in time. But there are enough clues to allow you to make that inference for yourself. You are told, for example, that the crossing of the plains is over. Still, there are no modern conveniences on the Tiflin ranch, no paved roads and no electricity. Grandfather arrives by horse and cart. If these clues to the time of the story are not enough for you, you may want to review the facts of American history and apply them to the time frame of the story. For example, when did people in farm areas have electricity or use automobiles?

John Steinbeck wrote many books and stories about different people in different places, but he was at his best when writing about the people he really knew, the Californians. *The Pearl, The Red Pony, Tortilla Flat,* and *Cannery Row* are all well-known and widely-read stories that grew out of his California experiences.

Part of present-day Salinas, California, was settled in the 1930s by migrant workers who fled dust storms and farm foreclosures in the Middle West in that bleak time of our history. From among these people came *The Grapes of Wrath*, Steinbeck's most famous novel, for which he won a Pulitzer Prize. The moving story of George and Lennie in *Of Mice and Men* was also about the migrant farmers, and *In Dubious Battle* was one of the earliest novels to defend the cause of striking agricultural workers. For his great collection of work, John Steinbeck became the fifth American author to be awarded the Nobel Prize in Literature (1962.)

# Dialogue

For many readers, the most interesting part of a story is the conversation between characters, the *dialogue*. It is one thing for an author to tell us what's going on in a story and quite another to hear about it directly from the characters. In the second case it's like eavesdropping on a conversation; we become firsthand witnesses to the action rather than passive listeners to someone else's tale. Or so it seems. The author is in charge all the time, of course, and uses dialogue very artfully to manipulate our feelings and draw us into the story.

A good writer never uses dialogue carelessly. It is never dropped into a story simply as decoration or padding or just for our entertainment, especially in a short story where every word must be made to count. Each time dialogue appears it serves a purpose:

- It establishes the situation and indicates action.
- It presents ideas and establishes themes.
- It helps to present and develop characters.
- It helps create tone and mood.

More often than not, dialogue will perform two or more of these functions simultaneously. For the sake of the lesson, however, we will look at them one at a time.

**1. Situation and Action.** Conversation always represents some kind of action. In a courtroom, at a business meeting, in a classroom, the conversation going on is the entire action. Peace negotiations, councils of war, labor contracts and the proceedings of a congress or parliament, which may affect the lives of millions of people, are all accomplished with dialogue. When you walk into a room filled with people you can tell at once from the conversation what the situation is, what is going on—a celebration, a quarrel, a planning session or, perhaps, just a nice gossipy visit among friends.

In literature, dialogue can show at a glance what *is happening* and it prepares a reader for what *is going to happen* later in the story. Watch how quickly John Steinbeck establishes the situation that will dominate the story in "The Leader of the People" by allowing the reader to "overhear" this bit of dialogue. The Tiflins have just received a letter announcing that Mrs. Tiflin's father is coming to visit for a while.

> Mrs. Tiflin took a hairpin from her head and slit open the flap. Her lips pursed judiciously. Jody saw her eyes snap back and forth over the lines. "He says," she translated, "he says he's going to drive out Saturday to stay for a little while. Why, this is Saturday. The letter must have been delayed." She looked at the postmark. "This was mailed day before yesterday. It should have been here yesterday." She looked up questioningly at her husband, and then her face darkened angrily. "Now what have you got that look on you for? He doesn't come often."
>
> Carl turned his eyes away from her anger. He could be stern with her most of the time, but when occasionally her temper arose, he could not combat it.
>
> "What's the matter with you?" she demanded again.
>
> In his explanation there was a tone of apology Jody himself might have used. "It's just that he talks," Carl said lamely. "Just talks."
>
> "Well, what of it? You talk yourself."
>
> "Sure I do. But your father only talks about one thing."
>
> "Indians!" Jody broke in excitedly. "Indians and crossing the plains!"
>
> Carl turned fiercely on him. "You get out, Mr. Big-Britches! Go on, now! Get out!"

In less than two dozen lines we've learned a great deal about the Tiflin family and we have a very good idea where the story is taking us. In the first place, conflict has been established, and as you may recall from the lesson about conflict ("The Wall"), it is conflict that moves a story along. Carl Tiflin is not happy about his father-in-law's visit. Why? Because "he talks. Just talks." And he talks about Indians, Jody tells us in his brief part of the conversation. "Indians and crossing the plains!" Carl Tiflin's angry reaction to this bit of childish enthusiasm is clearly a clue that Jody has alerted us to a key element in the developing situation.

Jody's enthusiasm, Carl Tiflin's reluctance to hear the old man's stories again, and Mrs. Tiflin's anxiety for her father's feelings are the entire framework of the story, and it has all been established with dialogue.

**2. Ideas and Themes.** One of the reasons people speak is to express thoughts, to pass on information and ideas to others. In the passage just discussed, the conversation ranges from the simple information that the father is coming, to Mrs. Tiflin's expression of anger, and Carl Tiflin's explanation of his annoyance. Dialogue moves very quickly, covering a lot of ground in a short space of time.

As Carl Tiflin and his wife continue their conversation about her father's impending visit, Mrs. Tiflin passes along a thought that will grow in importance, as the story progresses, to become a main theme.

"Jody's damn well right," he heard his father say. "Just Indians and crossing the plains. I've heard that story about how the horses got driven off about a thousand times. He just goes on and on, and he never changes a word in the things he tells."

When Mrs. Tiflin answered her tone was so changed that Jody, outside the window, looked up from his study of the stone. Her voice had become soft and explanatory. Jody knew how her face would have changed to match the tone. She said quietly, "Look at it this way, Carl. That was the big thing in my father's life. He led a wagon train clear across the plains to the coast, and when it was finished, his life was done. It was a big thing to do, but it didn't last long enough. Look!" she continued, "it's as though he was born to do that, and after he finished it, there wasn't anything more for him to do but think about it and talk about it. If there'd been any farther west to go, he'd have gone. He's told me so himself. But at last there was the ocean. He lives right by the ocean where he had to stop."

There are two thoughts here. One describes a foolish old man who repeats stories about Indians and crossing the plains over and over again until people are sick of listening to him. The other thought describes a man who has accomplished a great thing, who had an epic vision of the westward movement of vast numbers of people, and who had been their leader. This vision of westward movement was one of the great driving forces in American history, usually referred to as Manifest Destiny. It was the manifest destiny of the United States, people believed in the nineteenth century, to keep moving westward until the entire continent was occupied from coast to coast.

Steinbeck could have used several paragraphs to explain the idea behind Manifest Destiny and more paragraphs to explain the feelings of the pioneers who lived the vision. He could have used still more space to philosophize about how attitudes change as time passes. But Mr. and Mrs. Tiflin sum this all up very nicely in their conversational exchange. When you read the story, notice how Mrs. Tiflin's father expands on these themes himself, later on.

**3. Characters.** If you know the great musical comedy *My Fair Lady*, (George Bernard Shaw's *Pygmalion*), you may recall that Dr. Henry Higgins could name the place in England where a person was born and raised just by listening to a line or two of conversation. In America, it's easy to place a Bostonian, a Southerner, a New Yorker, a Midwesterner or a Canadian just by having them say, "I parked my car around the corner." But conversation can reveal much more. It points up a person's level of education; his or her manners, temperament, nature and mood at the moment; and whether this is a person you would like to know or one whom you would rather avoid.

Authors use two major devices to tell readers about a character they create. Either they relate a great many facts about the character, or they allow you to observe the character in action. (See the lesson "Understanding Characterization" which accompanies John Updike's "The Christian Roommates.") And a character's conversation is the most revealing of all possible actions. See how much you can tell about Billy Buck, the ranch hand, about Jody, and even about Jody's father, who is not present, from the following conversation, or dialogue.

> Arriving at the used-up haystack, the boy leaned against the barbed wire fence. "Will that be all of it, do you think?" he asked.
> The middle-aged ranch-hand stopped his careful raking and stuck his fork into the ground.... "Nothing left of it that isn't soggy from ground moisture," he said....
> "Ought to be plenty mice," Jody suggested.
> "Lousy with them," said Billy. "Just crawling with mice."
> "Well, maybe, when you get through, I could call the dogs and hunt the mice."
> "Sure, I guess you could," said Billy Buck.... Billy looked up at the top of the hills that surrounded the ranch. "Maybe you better ask your father before you do it," he suggested.
> "Well, where is he? I'll ask him now."
> "He rode up to the ridge ranch after dinner. He'll be back pretty soon."
> Jody slumped against the fence post. "I don't think he'd care."
> As Billy went back to his work he said ominously, "You'd better ask him anyway. You know how he is."

Just before this conversation, Jody is introduced as a little boy, but we could have told as much from his interest in hunting mice. Boys over twelve would not be quite as interested in mice as Jody is, nor would they be as likely to worry about asking permission.

Billy Buck and Jody have an easy way of talking to one another and you have to like Billy for the patience and understanding he has for a small boy. He doesn't *tell* Jody or order him about, and he doesn't speak down to the boy. He makes suggestions to Jody as one adult would to another.

Jody is what you might call "a good kid." He doesn't beg or whine for what he wants, as many children do, but asks in a roundabout way for "opinions." "Will that be all of it do you think?" and "Well, maybe, when you get through, I could call the dogs and hunt the mice." This is a rather mature way of behaving for a youngster. It exhibits considerable understanding of human nature which will be borne out later in Jody's relationship with his grandfather.

Then, from the dialogue, we learn that Jody's father is an active rancher, "He rode up to the ridge ranch after dinner," and that he is not a man to be taken lightly. You do nothing around the ranch without asking him first because, ominously, "You know how he is." This is only a hint about Carl Tiflin, but it prepares us for the rather stern father we will meet shortly. And much more will be learned about him from dialogue later in the story.

**4. Tone and Mood.** We saw in the lesson on tone and mood (Poe's "The Black Cat") that an author has several ways to project tone and establish the mood of a story, the careful selection of language being one of them. Expert use of dialogue is a particularly good use of language for this purpose. Nothing projects tone or expresses mood better than the human voice. You can tell at once, for example, exactly what kind of mood a person is in when you hear the familiar little phrase, "Oh please!" See for yourself how you can change the tone of this expression to convey gratitude, anger, annoyance, fear, supplication, excitement, pleasure and other moods you may think of.

While you can't hear tone in dialogue you read, your experience with words, attitudes and real-life situations usually tips you off to how the voices in a conversation are going—what the tone is. Where this is difficult, or when a group of words may be said in a number of different ways, the author steps in with a few stage directions to guide you further. Then, it's not hard to imagine if the mood surrounding the conversation is tense or relaxed, or angry or happy, or if the mood is changing as the dialogue goes along. Authors often use dialogue to emphasize a rapidly changing mood.

Keeping in mind that, in dialogue, tone is what you hear while mood is what is felt, watch how the tone changes in the course of this bit of dialogue and how the mood in the Tiflin kitchen changes with it. The family is at breakfast awaiting Grandfather's arrival.

> Grandfather hadn't appeared at the table when they sat down. Billy nodded at his empty chair. "He's all right? He isn't sick?"
>
> "He takes a long time to dress," said Mrs. Tiflin. "He combs his whiskers and rubs up his shoes and brushes his clothes."
>
> Carl scattered sugar on his mush. "A man that's led a wagon train across the plains has got to be pretty careful how he dresses."
>
> Mrs. Tiflin turned on him. "Don't do that Carl! Please don't!" There was more of threat than of request in her tone. And the threat irritated Carl.
>
> "Well, how many times do I have to listen to the story of the iron plates, and the thirty-five horses? That time's done. Why can't he forget it, now it's done?" He grew angrier while he talked, and his voice rose. "Why does he have to tell them over and over? He came across the plains. All right! Now it's finished. Nobody wants to hear about it over and over."
>
> The door into the kitchen closed softly. The four at the table sat frozen. Carl laid his mush spoon on the table and touched his chin with his fingers.
>
> Then the kitchen door opened and Grandfather walked in. His mouth smiled tightly and his eyes were squinted. "Good morning," he said, and he sat down and looked at his mush dish.
>
> Carl could not leave it there. "Did—did you hear what I said?" Grandfather jerked a little nod.
>
> "I don't know what got into me, sir. I didn't mean it. I was just being funny."

Guided by the simple directions that the author gives, and by the words themselves, it's rather easy to "hear" the tone of this dialogue change each time someone speaks, and the mood changes too. Let's follow it step by step.

(1) The dialogue begins with an innocent inquiry about Grandfather and a simple explanation of why he is late to breakfast. The tone is quietly conversational, and the mood is calm.

(2) Carl Tiflin injects a sarcastic remark and the mood instantly becomes tense. The author explains that Mrs. Tiflin's response, "Don't do that Carl!" has a threatening tone. This is one of those expressions that can be read many different ways.

(3) Carl's tone quickly becomes angry, and louder as well. The mood remains tense in the kitchen, but now we feel the anger, too.

(4) When Grandfather appears with a quiet "Good morning," there is shocked silence. We can feel the air of embarrassment.

(5) Finally, as Carl stutters and tries to make amends for his rudeness, the tone is once again quiet and conversational, though the mood remains heavy with embarrassment. We can feel the pain of Carl's lame apology.

The one thing that must impress you about dialogue is how much it does for a story in a short space of time. And that's exactly why people like to read dialogue: things are moving quickly and there is action. We get to know characters best during dialogue, just as we get to know people in real life by hearing them speak. Ideas are clarified in conversation, often because the speaker's tone creates mood which, of itself, conveys meaning. Good dialogue, used artfully by a clever author, adds an important touch of reality to a story that draws a reader into the situation. Dialogue traps us into believing in a make-believe situation, which is exactly what we want our reading to do for us.

As you read the story:

- See how, early in the story, the author uses dialogue to compare the natures of Jody, Carl Tiflin and Mrs. Tiflin.

- Think about how dialogue changes to reflect changes in feeling. Notice how the dialogue during breakfast reflects the rather sad turn the story takes.

- Consider how the title, "The Leader of the People," which also is the main theme of the story, is explained in dialogue near the end of the story.

- Notice how the author uses dialogue to wind down the emotional tension at the end of the story.

# The Leader
# of the People
## John Steinbeck

On Saturday afternoon Billy Buck, the ranch-hand, raked together the last of the old year's haystack and pitched small forkfuls over the wire fence to a few mildly interested cattle. High in the air small clouds like puffs of cannon smoke were driven eastward by the March wind. The wind could be heard whishing in the brush on the ridge crests, but no breath of it penetrated down into the ranch cup.

The little boy, Jody, emerged from the house eating a thick piece of buttered bread. He saw Billy working on the last of the haystack. Jody tramped down scuffing his shoes in a way he had been told was destructive to good shoeleather. A flock of white pigeons flew out of the black cypress tree as Jody passed, and circled the tree and landed again. A half-grown tortoise-shell cat leaped from the bunkhouse porch, galloped on stiff legs across the road, whirled and galloped back again. Jody picked up a stone to help the game along, but he was too late, for the cat was under the porch before the stone could be discharged. He threw the stone into the cypress tree and started the white pigeons on another whirling flight.

Arriving at the used-up haystack, the boy leaned against the barbed wire fence. "Will that be all of it, do you think?" he asked.

The middle-aged ranch-hand stopped his careful raking and stuck his fork into the ground. He took off his black hat and smoothed down his hair. "Nothing left of it that isn't soggy from ground moisture," he said. He replaced his hat and rubbed his dry leathery hands together.

"Ought to be plenty mice" Jody suggested.

"Lousy with them," said Billy. "Just crawling with mice."

"Well, maybe, when you get all through, I could call the dogs and hunt the mice."

"Sure, I guess you could," said Billy Buck. He lifted a forkful of the damp ground-hay and threw it into the air. Instantly three mice leaped out and burrowed frantically under the hay again.

Jody sighed with satisfaction. Those plump, sleek, arrogant mice were doomed. For eight months they had lived and multiplied in the haystack.

They had been immune from cats, from traps, from poison and from Jody. They had grown smug in their security, overbearing and fat. Now the time of disaster had come; they would not survive another day.

Billy looked up at the top of the hills that surrounded the ranch. "Maybe you better ask your father before you do it," he suggested.

"Well, where is he? I'll ask him now."

"He rode up to the ridge ranch after dinner. He'll be back pretty soon."

Jody slumped against the fence post. "I don't think he'd care."

As Billy went back to his work he said ominously, "You'd better ask him anyway. You know how he is."

Jody did know. His father, Carl Tiflin, insisted upon giving permission for anything that was done on the ranch, whether it was important or not. Jody sagged farther against the post until he was sitting on the ground. He looked up at the little puffs of wind-driven cloud. "Is it like to rain, Billy?"

"It might. The wind's good for it, but not strong enough."

"Well, I hope it don't rain until after I kill those damn mice." He looked over his shoulder to see whether Billy had noticed the mature profanity. Billy worked on without comment.

Jody turned back and looked at the side-hill where the road from the outside world came down. The hill was washed with lean March sunshine. Silver thistles, blue lupins and a few poppies bloomed among the sage bushes. Halfway up the hill Jody could see Doubletree Mutt, the black dog, digging in a squirrel hole. He paddled for a while and then paused to kick bursts of dirt out between his hind legs, and he dug with an earnestness which belied the knowledge he must have had that no dog had ever caught a squirrel by digging in a hole.

Suddenly, while Jody watched, the black dog stiffened, and backed out of the hole and looked up the hill toward the cleft in the ridge where the road came through. Jody looked up too. For a moment Carl Tiflin on horseback stood out against the pale sky and then he moved down the road toward the house. He carried something white in his hand.

The boy started to his feet. "He's got a letter," Jody cried. He trotted away toward the ranch house, for the letter would probably be read aloud and he wanted to be there. He reached the house before his father did, and ran in. He heard Carl dismount from his creaking saddle and slap the horse on the side to send it to the barn where Billy would unsaddle it and turn it out.

Jody ran into the kitchen. "We got a letter!" he cried.

His mother looked up from a pan of beans. "Who has?"

"Father has. I saw it in his hand."

Carl strode into the kitchen then, and Jody's mother asked, "Who's the letter from, Carl?"

He frowned quickly. "How did you know there was a letter?"

She nodded her head in the boy's direction. "Big-Britches Jody told me."

Jody was embarrassed.

His father looked down at him contemptuously. "He is getting to be a Big-Britches," Carl said. "He's minding everybody's business but his own. Got his big nose into everything."

Mrs. Tiflin relented a little. "Well, he hasn't enough to keep him busy.

Who's the letter from?"

Carl still frowned on Jody. "I'll keep him busy if he isn't careful." He held out a sealed letter. "I guess it's from your father."

Mrs. Tiflin took a hairpin from her head and slit open the flap. Her lips pursed judiciously. Jody saw her eyes snap back and forth over the lines. "He says," she translated, "he says he's going to drive out Saturday to stay for a little while. Why, this is Saturday. The letter must have been delayed." She looked at the postmark. "This was mailed day before yesterday. It should have been here yesterday." She looked up questioningly at her husband, and then her face darkened angrily. "Now what have you got that look on for? He doesn't come often."

Carl turned his eyes away from her anger. He could be stern with her most of the time, but when occasionally her temper arose, he could not combat it.

"What's the matter with you?" she demanded again.

In his explanation there was a tone of apology Jody himself might have used. "It's just that he talks," Carl said lamely. "Just talks."

"Well, what of it? You talk yourself."

"Sure I do. But your father only talks about one thing."

"Indians!" Jody broke in excitedly. "Indians and crossing the plains!"

Carl turned fiercely on him. "You get out, Mr. Big-Britches! Go on, now! Get out!"

Jody went miserably out the back door and closed the screen with elaborate quietness. Under the kitchen window his shamed, downcast eyes fell upon a curiously shaped stone, a stone of such fascination that he squatted down and picked it up and turned it over in his hands.

The voices came clearly to him through the open kitchen window. "Jody's damn well right," he heard his father say. "Just Indians and crossing the plains. I've heard that story about how the horses got driven off about a thousand times. He just goes on and on, and he never changes a word in the things he tells."

When Mrs. Tiflin answered her tone was so changed that Jody, outside the window, looked up from his study of the stone. Her voice had become soft and explanatory. Jody knew how her face would have changed to match the tone. She said quietly, "Look at it this way, Carl. That was the big thing in my father's life. He led a wagon train clear across the plains to the coast, and when it was finished, his life was done. It was a big thing to do, but it didn't last long enough. Look!" she continued. "It's as though he was born to do that, and after he finished it, there wasn't anything more for him to do but think about it and talk about it. If there'd been any farther west to go, he'd have gone. He's told me so himself. But at last there was the ocean. He lives right by the ocean where he had to stop."

She had caught Carl, caught him and entangled him in her soft tone.

"I've seen him," he agreed quietly. "He goes down and stares off west over the ocean." His voice sharpened a little. "And then he goes up to the Horseshoe Club in Pacific Grove, and tells people how the Indians drove off the horses."

She tried to catch him again. "Well, it's everything to him. You might be patient with him and pretend to listen."

Carl turned impatiently away. "Well, if it gets too bad, I can always go down to the bunkhouse and sit with Billy," he said irritably. He walked through the house and slammed the front door after him.

Jody ran to his chores. He dumped the grain to the chickens without chasing any of them. He gathered the eggs from the nests. He trotted into the house with the wood and interlaced it so carefully in the woodbox that two armloads seemed to fill it to overflowing.

His mother had finished the beans by now. She stirred up the fire and brushed off the stove-top with a turkey wing. Jody peered cautiously at her to see whether any rancor toward him remained. "Is he coming today?" Jody asked.

"That's what his letter said."

"Maybe I better walk up the road to meet him."

Mrs. Tiflin clanged the stove-lid shut. "That would be nice," she said. "He'd probably like to be met."

"I guess I'll just do it then."

Outside, Jody whistled shrilly to the dogs. "Come on up the hill," he commanded. The two dogs waved their tails and ran ahead. Along the roadside the sage had tender new tips. Jody tore off some pieces and rubbed them on his hands until the air was filled with the sharp wild smell. With a rush the dogs leaped from the road and yapped into the brush after a rabbit. That was the last Jody saw of them, for when they failed to catch the rabbit, they went back home.

Jody plodded on up the hill toward the ridge top. When he reached the little cleft where the road came through, the afternoon wind struck him and blew up his hair and ruffled his shirt. He looked down on the little hills and ridges below and then out at the huge green Salinas Valley. He could see the white town of Salinas far out in the flat and the flash of its windows under the waning sun. Directly below him, in an oak tree, a crow congress had convened. The tree was black with crows all cawing at once.

Then Jody's eyes followed the wagon road down from the ridge where he stood, and lost it behind a hill, and picked it up again on the other side. On that distant stretch he saw a cart slowly pulled by a bay horse. It disappeared behind the hill. Jody sat down on the ground and watched the place where the cart would reappear again. The wind sang on the hilltops and the puff-ball clouds hurried eastward.

Then the cart came into sight and stopped. A man dressed in black dismounted from the seat and walked to the horse's head. Although it was so far away, Jody knew he had unhooked the check-rein, for the horse's head dropped forward. The horse moved on, and the man walked slowly up the hill beside it. Jody gave a glad cry and ran down the road toward them. The squirrels bumped along off the road, and a road runner flirted its tail and raced over the edge of the hill and sailed out like a glider.

Jody tried to leap into the middle of his shadow at every step. A stone rolled under his foot and he went down. Around a little bend he raced, and there, a short distance ahead, were his grandfather and the cart. The boy dropped from his unseemly running and approached at a dignified walk.

The horse plodded stumble-footedly up the hill and the old man walked beside it. In the lowering sun their giant shadows flickered darkly behind them. The grandfather was dressed in a black broadcloth suit and he wore kid congress gaiters and a black tie on a short, hard collar. He carried his black slouch hat in his hand. His white beard was cropped close and his white eyebrows overhung his eyes like mustaches. The blue eyes were sternly merry. About the whole face and figure there was a granite dignity, so that every motion seemed an impossible thing. Once at rest, it seemed the old man would be stone, would never move again. His steps were slow and certain. Once made, no step could ever be retraced; once headed in a direction, the path would never bend nor the pace increase nor slow.

When Jody appeared around the bend, Grandfather waved his hat slowly in welcome, and he called, "Why, Jody! Come down to meet me, have you?"

Jody sidled near and turned and matched his step to the old man's step and stiffened his body and dragged his heels a little. "Yes, sir," he said. "We got your letter only today."

"Should have been here yesterday," said Grandfather. "It certainly should. How are all the folks?"

"They're fine, sir." He hesitated and then suggested slyly, "Would you like to come on a mouse hunt tomorrow, sir?"

"Mouse hunt, Jody?" Grandfather chuckled. "Have the people of this generation come down to hunting mice? They aren't very strong, the new people, but I hardly thought mice would be game for them."

"No, sir. It's just play. The haystack's gone. I'm going to drive out the mice to the dogs. And you can watch, or even beat the hay a little."

The stern, merry eyes turned down on him. "I see. You don't eat them, then. You haven't come to that yet."

Jody explained, "The dogs eat them, sir. It wouldn't be much like hunting Indians, I guess."

"No, not much—but then later, when the troops were hunting Indians and shooting children and burning teepees, it wasn't much different from your mouse hunt."

They topped the rise and started down into the ranch cup, and they lost the sun from their shoulders. "You've grown," Grandfather said. "Nearly an inch I should say."

"More," Jody boasted. "Where they mark me on the door, I'm up more than an inch since Thanksgiving even."

Grandfather's rich throaty voice said. "Maybe you're getting too much water and turning to pith and stalk. Wait until you head out, and then we'll see."

Jody looked quickly into the old man's face to see whether his feelings should be hurt, but there was no will to injure, no punishing nor putting-in-your-place light in the keen blue eyes. "We might kill a pig," Jody suggested.

"Oh, no! I couldn't let you do that. You're just humoring me. It isn't the time and you know it."

"You know Riley, the big boar, sir?"

"Yes. I remember Riley well."

"Well, Riley ate a hole into that same haystack, and it fell down on him and smothered him."

"Pigs do that when they can," said Grandfather.

"Riley was a nice pig, for a boar, sir. I rode him sometimes, and he didn't mind.'

A door slammed at the house below them, and they saw Jody's mother standing on the porch waving her apron in welcome. And they saw Carl Tiflin walking up from the barn to be at the house for the arrival.

The sun had disappeared from the hills by now. The blue smoke from the house chimney hung in flat layers in the purpling ranch cup. The puff-ball clouds, dropped by the falling wind, hung listlessly in the sky.

Billy Buck came out of the bunkhouse and flung a wash basin of soapy water on the ground. He had been shaving in midweek, for Billy held Grandfather in reverence, and Grandfather said that Billy was one of the few men of the new generation who had not gone soft. Although Billy was in middle age, Grandfather considered him a boy. Now Billy was hurrying toward the house too.

When Jody and Grandfather arrived, the three were waiting for them in front of the yard gate.

Carl said, "Hello, sir. We've been looking for you."

Mrs. Tiflin kissed Grandfather on the side of his beard, and stood still while his big hand patted her shoulder. Billy shook hands solemnly, grinning under his straw moustache. "I'll put up your horse," said Billy, and he led the rig away.

Grandfather watched him go, and then, turning back to the group, he said as he had said a hundred times before, "There's a good boy. I knew his father, old Mule-tail Buck. I never knew why they called him Mule-tail except he packed mules."

Mrs. Tiflin turned and led the way into the house. "How long are you going to stay, Father? Your letter didn't say."

"Well, I don't know. I thought I'd stay about two weeks. But I never stay as long as I think I'm going to."

In a short while they were sitting at the white oilcloth table eating their supper. The lamp with the tin reflector hung over the table. Outside the dining-room windows the big moths battered softly against the glass.

Grandfather cut his steak into tiny pieces and chewed slowly. "I'm hungry," he said. "Driving out here got my appetite up. It's like when we were crossing. We all got so hungry every night we could hardly wait to let the meat get done. I could eat about five pounds of buffalo meat every night."

"It's moving around does it," said Billy. "My father was a government packer. I helped him when I was a kid. Just the two of us could about clean up a deer's ham."

"I knew your father, Billy," said Grandfather. "A fine man he was. They called him Mule-tail Buck. I don't know why except he packed mules."

"That was it," Billy agreed. "He packed mules."

Grandfather put down his knife and fork and looked around the table. "I remember one time we ran out of meat—" His voice dropped to a curious low singsong, dropped into a tonal groove the story had worn for itself. "There was no buffalo, no antelope, not even rabbits. The hunters couldn't even shoot a coyote. That was the time for the leader to be on the watch. I was the leader, and I kept my eyes open. Know why? Well, just the minute the people began to get hungry they'd start slaughtering the team oxen. Do you believe that? I've heard of parties that just ate up their draft cattle. Started from the middle and worked toward the ends. Finally they'd eat the lead pair, and then the wheelers. The leader of a party had to keep them from doing that."

In some manner a big moth got into the room and circled the hanging kerosene lamp. Billy got up and tried to clap it betwen his hands. Carl struck with a cupped palm and caught the moth and broke it. He walked to the window and dropped it out.

"As I was saying," Grandfather began again, but Carl interrupted him. "You'd better eat some more meat. All the rest of us are ready for our pudding."

Jody saw a flash of anger in his mother's eyes. Grandfather picked up his knife and fork. "I'm pretty hungry, all right," he said. "I'll tell you about that later."

When supper was over, when the family and Billy Buck sat in front of the fireplace in the other room, Jody anxiously watched Grandfather. He saw the signs he knew. The bearded head leaned forward; the eyes lost their sternness and looked wonderingly into the fire; the big lean fingers laced themselves on the black knees. "I wonder," he began, "I just wonder whether I ever told you how those thieving Piutes drove off thirty-five of our horses."

"I think you did," Carl interrupted. "Wasn't it just before you went up into the Tahoe country?"

Grandfather turned quickly toward his son-in-law. "That's right. I guess I must have told you that story."

"Lots of times," Carl said cruelly, and he avoided his wife's eyes. But he felt the angry eyes on him, and he said, " 'Course I'd like to hear it again."

Grandfather looked back at the fire. His fingers unlaced and laced again. Jody knew how he felt, how his insides were collapsed and empty. Hadn't Jody been called a Big-Britches that very afternoon? He rose to heroism and opened himself to the term Big-Britches again. "Tell about Indians," he said softly.

Grandfather's eyes grew stern again. "Boys always want to hear about Indians. It was a job for men, but boys want to hear about it. Well, let's see. Did I ever tell you how I wanted each wagon to carry a long iron plate?"

Everyone but Jody remained silent. Jody said, "No. You didn't."

"Well, when the Indians attacked, we always put the wagons in a circle and fought from between the wheels. I thought that if every wagon carried a long plate with rifle holes, the men could stand the plates on the outside of the wheels when the wagons were in the circle and they would be protected. It would save lives and that would make up for the extra weight of the iron. But of course the party wouldn't do it. No party had done it before and they couldn't see why they should go to the expense. They lived to regret it, too."

Jody looked at his mother, and knew from her expression that she was not listening at all. Carl picked at a callus on his thumb and Billy Buck watched a spider crawling up the wall.

Grandfather's tone dropped into its narrative groove again. Jody knew in advance exactly what words would fall. The story droned on, speeded up for the attack, grew sad over the wounds, struck a dirge at the burials on the great plains. Jody sat quietly watching Grandfather. The stern blue eyes were detached. He looked as though he were not very interested in the story himself.

When it was finished, when the pause had been politely respected as the frontier of the story, Billy Buck stood up and stretched and hitched his trousers. "I guess I'll turn in," he said. Then he faced Grandfather. "I've got an old powder horn and a cap and ball pistol down to the bunkhouse. Did I ever show them to you?"

Grandfather nodded slowly. "Yes, I think you did, Billy. Reminds me of a pistol I had when I was leading the people across." Billy stood politely until the little story was done, and then he said "Good night," and went out of the house.

Carl Tiflin tried to turn the conversation then. "How's the country between here and Monterey? I've heard it's pretty dry."

"It is dry," said Grandfather. "There's not a drop of water in the Laguna Seca. But it's a long pull from '87. The whole country was powder then, and in '61 I believe all the coyotes starved to death. We had fifteen inches of rain this year."

"Yes, but it all came too early. We could do with some now." Carl's eye fell on Jody. "Hadn't you better be getting to bed?"

Jody stood up obediently. "Can I kill the mice in the old haystack, sir?"

"Mice? Oh! Sure, kill them all off. Billy said there isn't any good hay left."

Jody exchanged a secret and satisfying look with Grandfather. "I'll kill every one tomorrow," he promised.

Jody lay in his bed and thought of the impossible world of Indians and buffaloes, a world that had ceased to be forever. He wished he could have been living in the heroic time, but he knew he was not of heroic timber. No one living now, save possibly Billy Buck, was worthy to do the things that had been done. A race of giants had lived then, fearless men, men of staunchness unknown in this day. Jody thought of the wide plains and of the wagons moving across like centipedes. He thought of Grandfather on a huge white horse, marshaling the people. Across his mind marched the great phantoms, and they marched off the earth and they were gone.

He came back to the ranch for a moment, then. He heard the dull rushing sound that space and silence make. He heard one of the dogs, out in the doghouse, scratching a flea and bumping his elbow against the floor with every stroke. Then the wind arose again and the black cypress groaned and Jody went to sleep.

He was up half an hour before the triangle sounded for breakfast. His mother was rattling the stove to make the flames roar when Jody went through the kitchen. "You're up early," she said. "Where are you going?"

"Out to get a good stick. We're going to kill the mice today."

"Who is 'we'?"

"Why, Grandfather and I."

"So you've got him in it. You always like to have someone with you in case there's blame to share."

"I'll be right back," said Jody. "I just want to have a good stick ready for after breakfast."

He closed the screen door after him and went out into the cool blue morning. The birds were noisy in the dawn and the ranch cats came down from the hill like blunt snakes. They had been hunting gophers in the dark, and although the four cats were full of gopher meat, they sat in a semicircle at the back door and mewed piteously for milk. Doubletree Mutt and Smasher moved sniffing along the edge of the brush, performing the duty with rigid ceremony, but when Jody whistled, their heads jerked up and their tails waved. They plunged down to him, wriggling their skins and yawning. Jody patted their heads seriously, and moved on to the weathered scrap pile. He selected an old broom handle and a short piece of inch-square scrap wood. From his pocket he took a shoelace and tied the ends of the sticks loosely together to make a flail. He whistled his new weapon through the air and struck the ground experimentally, while the dogs leaped aside and whined with apprehension.

Jody turned and started down past the house toward the old haystack ground to look over the field of slaughter, but Billy Buck, sitting patiently on the back steps, called to him, "You better come back. It's only a couple minutes till breakfast."

Jody changed his course and moved toward the house. He leaned his flail against the steps. "That's to drive the mice out," he said. "I'll bet they're fat. I'll bet they don't know what's going to happen to them today."

"No, nor you either," Billy remarked philosophically, "nor me, nor anyone."

Jody was staggered by this thought. He knew it was true. His imagination twitched away from the mouse hunt. Then his mother came out on the back porch and struck the triangle, and all thoughts fell in a heap.

Grandfather hadn't appeared at the table when they sat down. Billy nodded at his empty chair. "He's all right? He isn't sick?"

"He takes a long time to dress," said Mrs. Tiflin. "He combs his whiskers and rubs up his shoes and brushes his clothes."

Carl scattered sugar on his mush. "A man that's led a wagon train across the plains has got to be pretty careful how he dresses."

Mrs. Tiflin turned on him. "Don't do that, Carl! Please don't!" There was more of threat than of request in her tone. And the threat irritated Carl.

"Well, how many times do I have to listen to the story of the iron plates, and the thirty-five horses? That time's done. Why can't he forget it, now it's done?" He grew angrier while he talked, and his voice rose. "Why does he have to tell them over and over? He came across the plains. All right! Now it's finished. Nobody wants to hear about it over and over."

The door into the kitchen closed softly. The four at the table sat frozen. Carl laid his mush spoon on the table and touched his chin with his fingers.

Then the kitchen door opened and Grandfather walked in. His mouth smiled tightly and his eyes were squinted. "Good morning," he said, and he sat down and looked at his mush dish.

Carl could not leave it there. "Did—did you hear what I said?"

Grandfather jerked a little nod.

"I don't know what got into me, sir. I didn't mean it. I was just being funny."

Jody glanced in shame at his mother, and he saw that she was looking at Carl, and that she wasn't breathing. It was an awful thing that he was doing. He was tearing himself to pieces to talk like that. It was a terrible thing to him to retract a word, but to retract it in shame was infinitely worse.

Grandfather looked sidewise. "I'm trying to get right side up," he said gently. "I'm not being mad. I don't mind what you said, but it might be true, and I would mind that."

"It isn't true," said Carl. "I'm not feeling well this morning. I'm sorry I said it."

"Don't be sorry, Carl. An old man doesn't see things sometimes. Maybe you're right. The crossing is finished. Maybe it should be forgotten, now it's done."

Carl got up from the table. "I've had enough to eat. I'm going to work. Take your time, Billy!" He walked quickly out of the dining room. Billy gulped the rest of his food and followed soon after. But Jody could not leave his chair.

"Won't you tell any more stories?" Jody asked.

"Why, sure I'll tell them, but only when—I'm sure people want to hear them."

"I like to hear them, sir."

"Oh! Of course you do, but you're a little boy. It was a job for men, but only little boys like to hear about it."

Jody got up from his place. "I'll wait outside for you, sir. I've got a good stick for those mice."

He waited by the gate until the old man came out on the porch. "Let's go down and kill the mice now," Jody called.

"I think I'll just sit in the sun, Jody. You go kill the mice."

"You can use my stick if you like."

"No, I'll just sit here a while."

Jody turned disconsolately away, and walked down toward the old haystack. He tried to whip up his enthusiasm with thoughts of the fat juicy mice. He beat the ground with his flail. The dogs coaxed and whined about him, but he could not go. Back at the house he could see Grandfather sitting on the porch, looking small and thin and black.

Jody gave up and went to sit on the steps at the old man's feet.

"Back already? Did you kill the mice?"

"No, sir. I'll kill them some other day."

The morning flies buzzed close to the ground and the ants dashed about in front of the steps. The heavy smell of sage slipped down the hill. The porch boards grew warm in the sunshine.

Jody hardly knew when Grandfather started to talk. "I shouldn't stay here, feeling the way I do." He examined his strong old hands. "I feel as though the crossing wasn't worth doing." His eyes moved up the side-hill and stopped on a motionless hawk perched on a dead limb. "I tell those old stories, but they're not what I want to tell. I only know how I want people to feel when I tell them.

"It wasn't Indians that were important, nor adventures, nor even getting out here. It was a whole bunch of people made into one big crawling beast. And I was the head. It was westering and westering. Every man wanted something for himself, but the big beast that was all of them wanted only westering. I was the leader, but if I hadn't been there, someone else would have been the head. The thing had to have a head.

"Under the little bushes the shadows were black at white noonday. When we saw the mountains at last, we cried—all of us. But it wasn't getting here that mattered, it was movement and westering.

"We carried life out here and set it down the way those ants carry eggs. And I was the leader. The westering was as big as God, and the slow steps that made the movement piled up and piled up until the continent was crossed.

"Then we came down to the sea, and it was done." He stopped and wiped his eyes until the rims were red. "That's what I should be telling instead of stories."

When Jody spoke, Grandfather started and looked down at him. "Maybe I could lead the people some day," Jody said.

The old man smiled. "There's no place to go. There's the ocean to stop you. There's a line of old men along the shore hating the ocean because it stopped them."

"In boats I might, sir."

"No place to go, Jody. Every place is taken. But that's not the worst—no, not the worst. Westering has died out of the people. Westering isn't a hunger any more. It's all done. Your father is right. It is finished." He laced his fingers on his knee and looked at them.

Jody felt very sad. "If you'd like a glass of lemonade I could make it for you."

Grandfather was about to refuse, and then he saw Jody's face. "That would be nice," he said. "Yes, it would be nice to drink a lemonade."

Jody ran into the kitchen where his mother was wiping the last of the breakfast dishes. "Can I have a lemon to make a lemonade for Grandfather?"

His mother mimicked—"And another lemon to make a lemonade for you."

"No, ma'am. I don't want one."

"Jody! You're sick!" Then she stopped suddenly. "Take a lemon out of the cooler," she said softly. "Here, I'll reach the squeezer down to you."

# Unit 10

## The Leader
## of the People

- Comprehension
  Questions

- Dialogue

- Discussion Guides

- Writing Exercise

# COMPREHENSION QUESTIONS

For each of the following statements and questions, select the option containing the most complete or most accurate answer.

1. Jody planned to hunt
(b)   ☐ a. mice in some old hay.
     ☐ b. gophers in the yard.
     ☐ c. deer on the prairie.
     ☐ d. skunks at the chicken coop.

2. When it came to work done on the ranch, Carl Tiflin
(b)   ☐ a. did everything himself.
     ☐ b. had to give permission for everything.
     ☐ d. counted heavily on Jody for help.
     ☐ d. didn't want to be bothered with details.

3. In the phrase "the little *cleft* where the road came through," *cleft*
(l)  means
     ☐ a. closure.       ☐ c. high point.
     ☐ b. opening.      ☐ d. entrance.

4. Several times during the story the author associates a tone of quiet or
(i)  silence with a mood of shame. It occurs in all but one of these situations. Check the one that *does not* apply.
     ☐ a. Jody leaves after being called "Mr. Big-Britches."
     ☐ b. Carl Tiflin tells Grandfather he's heard about the Piute Indians "lots of times."
     ☐ c. Grandfather asks Jody to make him a glass of lemonade.
     ☐ d. Grandfather overhears Carl Tiflin talking about him.

5. The letter from Grandfather arrived
(d)   ☐ a. a week before he did.
     ☐ b. the same day he did.
     ☐ c. at the same instant he did.
     ☐ d. the day after he did.

6. Going to meet his grandfather, "the boy dropped from his *unseemly*
(l)  running." Used this way, *unseemly* means
     ☐ a. exhausting.     ☐ c. improper.
     ☐ b. embarrassing.    ☐ d. foolish.

7. All things considered, the story is probably set between

(f) □ a. 1830 and 1860.
    □ b. 1860 and 1880.
    □ c. 1890 and 1920.
    □ d. 1930 and 1960.

8. When Jody met his grandfather he *"sidled* near and turned and matched
(l) his step to the old man's step." *Sidled* means
    □ a. moved quickly.
    □ b. walked backwards.
    □ c. ran with a snake-like movement.
    □ d. moved sideways.

9. A dominant characteristic of Grandfather repeatedly referred to in
(j) the story is
    □ a. aged foolishness.
    □ b. stern savagery.
    □ c. rock-hard strength.
    □ d. iron-bound stubbornness.

10. Grandfather dressed
(a) □ a. all in black.
    □ b. all in green except for a white hat.
    □ c. in clean jeans and a white shirt.
    □ d. in old and shabby pioneer leathers.

11. Mrs. Tiflin was
 (f) □ a. afraid of her husband.
    □ b. always able to get the better of her husband.
    □ c. always ready to give in to her husband when he showed anger.
    □ d. generally on equal terms with her husband.

12. Grandfather felt that by and large the new generation
(c) □ a. would not work for a living.
    □ b. cared about nothing.
    □ c. had an urge for westering.
    □ d. was softer than the old generation.

13. If Grandfather suddenly appeared before you, he would probably
(g) □ a. command your respect.
    □ b. strike you as a foolish old man.
    □ c. not interest you at all.
    □ d. seem frightening.

14. In the old days, Billy Buck's father was a
(a)  ☐ a. Texas Ranger.
      ☐ b. farmer.
      ☐ c. mule packer.
      ☐ d. wagon train leader.

15. From his actions we must judge Carl Tiflin to be neither
(g)  ☐ a. very strong nor anxious to work.
      ☐ b. caring nor respectful of his family.
      ☐ c. intelligent nor imaginative.
      ☐ d. very tolerant nor patient.

16. The story suggests from time to time that a little boy's feelings are
(h)  ☐ a. very important.
      ☐ b. frequently not considered.
      ☐ c. never considered.
      ☐ d. not very well developed.

17. A metaphor is a figure of speech which implies a comparison between
(k) two unlike things. The author uses this metaphor to describe the pioneers as Jody thought about them: " across his mind marched the great phantoms, and they marched off the earth and they were gone." This metaphor can best be described as
  ☐ a. childlike.        ☐ c. heroic.
  ☐ b. sinister.         ☐ d. overblown.

18. From his actions and conversation, Jody seems
(j)  ☐ a. generally pesty and in the way.
      ☐ b. bright and pretty normal.
      ☐ c. overly sensitive for his age.
      ☐ d. a highly intelligent and gifted child.

19. Jody saw the crossing of the plains
(c)  ☐ a. with the imagination of a little boy.
      ☐ b. with mature understanding.
      ☐ c. in much the same way as his father.
      ☐ d. as his mother did.

20. Jody's hunt
(d)  ☐ a. started after breakfast.
      ☐ b. never took place.
      ☐ c. began at sunset.
      ☐ d. went on all day.

21. By comparing people crossing the plains to "one big crawling beast"
(k) and to "the way those ants carry eggs," Grandfather was saying the
    movement was
    ☐ a. inhumanly difficult.
    ☐ b. ruinous to the environment.
    ☐ c. full of life.
    ☐ d. in harmony with nature.

22. According to Grandfather,
(e) ☐ a. the idea of movement was more important to the pioneers than
         the desire to get to California.
    ☐ b. reaching the ocean was the supreme driving force of the pioneers.
    ☐ c. hunting and fighting Indians represented the spirit of the older
         generation.
    ☐ d. crossing the ocean would be the main goal of Jody's generation.

23. At the end of the story this dialogue takes place: "Jody felt very sad. 'If
(h) you'd like a glass of lemonade I could make it for you.' Grandfather was
    about to refuse, and then he saw Jody's face. 'That would be nice,' he
    said. 'Yes, it would be nice to drink a lemonade.' " We may infer that
    ☐ a. Grandfather wanted to make Jody feel better.
    ☐ b. Grandfather decided he was thirsty after all.
    ☐ c. Jody was bored and looking for something to do.
    ☐ d. Jody was trying to act grown up.

24. Grandfather said, "It's all done. Your father is right. It is finished." This
. (i) was probably said
    ☐ a. wistfully.              ☐ c. angrily.
    ☐ b. proudly.               ☐ d. tearfully.

25. There are three generations of people in the story. An important point
(e) made in the story about the generations is that

    ☐ a. underneath the surface they all see things about the same.
    ☐ b. there is great understanding among people of different ages.
    ☐ c. they all see a great event differently.
    ☐ d. there is no understanding at all among parents, children, and
         grandchildren.

---

Comprehension Skills: a — isolating details; b — recalling specific facts; c — retaining
concepts; d — organizing facts; e — understanding the main idea; f — drawing a
conclusion; g — making a judgment; h — making an inference; i — recognizing tone;
j — understanding characters; k — appreciation of literary forms; l — understanding
vocabulary.

# DIALOGUE

## Practice Exercise A

Jody ran into the kitchen. "We got a letter!" he cried.

His mother looked up from a pan of beans. "Who has?"

"Father has. I saw it in his hand."

Carl strode into the kitchen then, and Jody's mother asked, "Who's the letter from, Carl?"

He frowned quickly. "How did you know there was a letter?"

She nodded her head in the boy's direction. "Big-Britches Jody told me."

Jody was embarrassed.

His father looked down at him contemptuously. "He is getting to be a Big-Britches," Carl said. "He's minding everybody's business but his own. Got his big nose into everything."

Mrs. Tiflin relented a little. "Well, he hasn't enough to keep him busy. "Who's the letter from?"

Carl still frowned on Jody. "I'll keep him busy if he isn't careful."

1. We learn a bit about Carl Tiflin's character from this dialogue. He seems
   - □ a. rough and ignorant.
   - □ b. haughty and arrogant.
   - □ c. gruff and intolerant.
   - □ d. uncertain and nervous.

2. On the lines provided, write the author's two "stage directions" that indicate Jody's excitement.
   Write one "stage direction" that indicates Mrs. Tiflin's tolerance.

_____

_____

_____

_____

_____

_____

## Practice Exercise B

"Won't you tell any more stories?" Jody asked.

"Why, sure I'll tell them, but only when—I'm sure people want to hear them."

"I like to hear them, sir."

"Oh! Of course you do, but you're a little boy. It was a job for men, but only little boys like to hear about it."

"Jody got up from his place. "I'll wait outside for you, sir. "I've got a good stick for those mice."

He waited by the gate until the old man came out on the porch. "Let's go down and kill the mice now," Jody called.

"I think I'll just sit in the sun, Jody. You go kill the mice."

"You can use my stick if you like."

"No, I'll just sit here a while."

1. The fourth sentence of dialogue begins with a single word—"Oh!" If you were reading the story aloud, how would you be most likely to read the word "Oh!" and the rest of the sentence?
   - ☐ a. With an angry bark
   - ☐ b. With a sigh
   - ☐ c. With defiance
   - ☐ d. With a sob in your voice

2. We have said that authors often use "stage directions" with dialogue to indicate how the voices sound. They also use punctuation for this purpose. On the lines provided, write the sentence in which there is punctuation that indicates a pause, or a hesitant way of speaking. Circle the punctuation.

_____

_____

_____

_____

_____

## Practice Exercise C

"It wasn't Indians that were important, nor adventures, nor even getting out here. It was a whole bunch of people made into one big crawling beast. And I was the head. It was westering and westering. Every man wanted something for himself, but the big beast that was all of them wanted only westering. I was the leader, but if I hadn't been there, someone else would have been the head. The thing had to have a head.

"Under the little bushes the shadows were black at white noonday. When we saw the mountains at last, we cried — all of us. But it wasn't getting here that mattered, it was movement and westering.

"We carried life out here and set it down the way those ants carry eggs. And I was the leader. The westering was as big as God, and the slow steps that made the movement piled up and piled up until the continent was crossed.

1. Grandfather has been put down as a silly old man who repeats stories over and over. What is the Grandfather doing here?
   - [ ] a. He is showing that his life had been important.
   - [ ] b. He is trying to show up Carl Tiflin.
   - [ ] c. He is repeating yet another story.
   - [ ] d. He is showing that he realizes he is indeed a foolish old man.

2. The lesson points out that the nineteenth century idea of Manifest Destiny is a major theme of the story. In this dialogue, Grandfather repeats one word that represents the idea of Manifest Destiny: he uses the word five times. Circle the word each time it appears.

## Practice Exercise D

"No place to go, Jody. Every place is taken. But that's not the worst—no, not the worst. Westering has died out of the people. Westering isn't a hunger any more. It's all done. Your father is right. It is finished." He laced his fingers on his knee and looked at them.

Jody felt very sad. "If you'd like a glass of lemonade I could make it for you."

Grandfather was about to refuse, and then he saw Jody's face. "That would be nice," he said. "Yes, it would be nice to drink a lemonade."

1. The dialogue points up a feeling that exists between Jody and his Grandfather at the end of the story. The feeling is best described as
   - [ ] a. pride.
   - [ ] c. embarrassment.
   - [ ] b. sadness.
   - [ ] d. sympathy.

2. The mood has been rather sad and melancholy ever since the scene at the breakfast table. But the mood abruptly changes in the course of this dialogue at the end of the story. Circle the sentence in which the change in mood occurs.

# DISCUSSION GUIDES

## Analyzing Dialogue

1. In literature an *epic* is a long poem, in an elevated style, that centers on great events and the exploits of a heroic character. One literary critic has said that in writing Grandfather's last long speech about the pioneers, Steinbeck had written an epic. In what ways is this true?

2. When we hear people speak on radio, we tend to imagine what they look like from the way they speak. Based on the dialogue, how do you picture Jody, Mr. and Mrs. Tiflin and Billy Buck?

3. Billy Buck is a minor character in the story, and he speaks in short sentences whenever he appears. What purpose do Billy Buck's brief conversations serve in the story — in the beginning, for example, when Jody is talking to him?

## Interpreting the Story

4. In one place, Carl Tiflin speaks to Jody "contemptuously." Another time, Mr. Tiflin speaks to Grandfather "cruelly." What kind of a man is Carl Tiflin?

5. Jody seems to live his life in extreme highs and lows. He is bored, then races into the kitchen all excited. He is shamed and embarrassed and then races happily to meet his Grandfather. What do you think of his behavior?

6. Is Mrs. Tiflin happy with her family and her lot in life?

7. Compare some older person you know with Grandfather.

8. Jody (and Grandfather, too) thought of the people who crossed the plains as "A race of giants . . . men of a staunchness unknown in this day." Is this a true comparison of people in history with living people? Or do people tend to get bigger and better as they fade into history?

## Analyzing the Author's Technique

9. John Steinbeck is famous for his descriptions. Reread the paragraph describing Grandfather when Jody meets him on the road. He fits both the country and the story perfectly. Why is this so?

10. The author uses Grandfather's eyes and hands to develop his character and to demonstrate his changing moods. Find and discuss the passages that do this.

# WRITING EXERCISE

Write a dialogue of a dozen lines or more that might have taken place in one of the following situations. Refer to dialogue in "The Leader of the People" so that you can use author John Steinbeck's writing as your model.

1. Two people are trying to decide what to do on a Saturday night.

2. Three children are discussing a parent's drinking problem when the parent unexpectedly enters the room.

3. A student tries to persuade a friend to invite a classmate to the beach. The friend explains why she feels uncomfortable with their classmate.

4. A small girl has just arrived for a week-long visit at her grandmother's home in the country. The girl and her grandmother are in the kitchen talking.

5. Create your own situation if you prefer.

Unit 11
Science Fiction

# Nightfall

Isaac Asimov

# Introduction

Most of us remember what it's like to be afraid of the dark. As small children we imagined bogeymen floating around the bedroom at night, hovering in dark corners and drifting down shadowy hallways. Even as adults we are not immune to fear of the dark. It's no coincidence that ghosts and U.F.O.'s are almost invariably sighted at night. And whoever heard of conducting a seance in a brightly lit room? There's no question about it—a dark night can make the best of us feel uneasy.

We get used to it, of course. After all, by the time we're eighteen we've survived 6,574 nights with no lingering trauma. But suppose you live on a planet which has no night, a planet flooded with sunlight twenty-four hours a day? You wouldn't have to worry about "things that go bump in the night" because there would be no night. And since there was no night, you wouldn't know about stars. Now take this idea one step further and suppose that, once in two thousand years, the heavenly bodies that make up your planet's solar system line up in such a way as to cause total eclipse. The result? Night, strange and awesome, with its dazzling array of stars!

This is the situation Isaac Asimov envisions in a story called "Nightfall." The planet is Lagash, and if it weren't for its six suns, you'd probably feel right at home there. The inhabitants of Lagash are a lot like us, and their society is advanced enough to have universities, astronomers, observatories and psychologists. Unlike us, however, the people of Lagash go mad under conditions of prolonged darkness. Surprisingly, they never invented artificial light, having had no need for it.

The story opens in an astronomic observatory where Aton 77 and his colleagues are nervously awaiting the eclipse which will blot out Beta, the only one of the planet's six suns left in the sky; the other five suns have set. So when Beta's light is blocked out, Saro City will be in total darkness. This occurs only once every 2,049 years, and there is no historical record of the last eclipse. The scientists have completed their calculations just two months ago, so there has been little time to prepare for the catastrophe. And no one, unfortunately, is taking their predictions seriously—no one, that is, except the Cultists. The Cultists are a small group of religious fanatics who believe in a myth about darkness and something called "Stars" which rob men of their souls.

The predicted eclipse occurs right on schedule. But no one, not even the scientists, could ever have predicted the stunning consequences. "Nightfall," said one critic, "is a penetrating study in mass psychology, a haunting picture of a race doomed by fear of the dark to ever-recurring ruin and destruction."

Good science fiction requires an unusual combination of talents. First of all, it is best if a science fiction writer is a scientist, with a keen insight into the implications of the various branches of science. Equally important, however, is the ability to write well. A science fiction writer must be able to explain enormously complicated scientific principles so that the average person can understand them and also be able to see science imaginatively. And, of course, a science fiction writer must be able to tell a good story.

Happy, Isaac Asimov fulfills all of these requirements. A respected scientist with a Ph.D. in chemistry and an associate professor of biochemistry at the Boston University School of Medicine, Asimov is also the author of over eighty books and some three hundred shorter pieces ranging from pure science and science fiction to history, religion, literature and geography— and all of it fascinating, informative and intriguing. "Nightfall," first published in 1941, is one of his early short stories.

# Science Fiction

"Ninety percent of all science fiction is trash!" declared one of the foremost writers of science fiction today. "But then," he goes on to say, "ninety percent of *everything* is trash."

When you stop to think about it, he's right. An awful lot of popular music is trash, so is a lot of poetry, and so is a lot of fiction. Unfortunately, the best of science fiction has been unjustly lumped together with the worst. To many people, science fiction is just so much "space opera"—the kind of interplanetary adventure story popularized by Buck Rogers, Flash Gordon, and more recently, *Star Wars*. Or they confuse serious science fiction with the "B.E.M. Syndrome"—B.E.M. being the ever-popular "bug-eyed monster" that Hollywood is so fond of dishing up.

To the real enthusiasts however, science fiction is much, much more than galactic cowboys with ray guns, or giant insects ravaging entire cities and carrying off beautiful young ladies!

Isaac Asimov, a respected scientist and science fiction author, has defined science fiction as "that branch of literature which is concerned with the impact of scientific advance upon human beings." Notice that he doesn't say simply "science," but "science as it affects human beings." By this definition, then, the best science fiction is not just about new-fangled gadgets, such as a time machine or a robot, but about how such gadgets might change our lives. Similarly, serious science fiction is not just about life forms on other planets, but rather about what might happen as a result of learning that we are not alone in the universe.

Science fiction stories range from factual to fanciful. One author may speculate on the chilling consequences of technology already in existence, while another may base a story on technology that is still centuries away. But no matter how strange and exotic the story may be, it must still measure up to the same strict standards required of all good fiction. Beyond this, good science fiction generally fulfills four requirements: (1) it is set in the future or on some other planet, (2) it has a scientific basis, (3) it is plausible, and (4) it comments on the nature of people and society. Like all rules, these can be broken, but they hold true often enough to be considered typical of most science fiction.

**1. Science Fiction Is Set in the Future or on Another Planet.** This may seem rather obvious, but it's important to understand why these stories are rarely set in the here and now.

Contrary to what many people think, science fiction does not try to *predict* the future (although some authors have come uncannily close!). What it does do is present an infinite variety of possible tomorrows for us to think about today. Often, the writer of science fiction wishes to call the reader's attention to a potential problem. For instance, a story published in 1940 entitled "Blowups Happen" by Robert A. Heinlein presented a near catastrophe involving a nuclear power plant—years before the first commercial nuclear reactor! As it turned out, of course, nuclear reactors *do* pose a threat. But the author didn't need a crystal ball to arrive at this conclusion—just careful, thoughtful consideration of the available facts plus a healthy dose of imagination!

Science fiction that is set on another planet serves two purposes. First of all, it offers a delightful change of scenery. Just about every reader will be curious to know what the planet looks like and what kind of inhabitants live there. Secondly, by setting the story on another planet, the author can create a different kind of society and use it to comment, indirectly, on our own. We'll take a look at how this is done later in the lesson.

The following passage from "Nightfall," by Isaac Asimov, is from the first part of the story. Aton 77, a famous astronomer, is angrily addressing a newspaper reporter who has come to cover a big story. The story, apparently, is pretty hard to believe and Theremon, the reporter, has ridiculed the scientist in his newspaper columns. What does this passage tell you about the setting of the story?

> The director lifted the copy of the Saro City *Chronicle* on the table and shook it at Theremon furiously. "Even a person of your well-known impudence should have hesitated before coming to me with a request that he be allowed to cover today's events for his paper. Of all newsmen, you!"
>
> Aton dashed the newspaper to the floor, strode to the window and clasped his arms behind his back.
>
> "You may leave," he snapped over his shoulder. He stared moodily out at the skyline where Gamma, the brightest of the planet's six suns, was setting. It had already faded and yellowed into the horizon mists, and Aton knew he would never see it again as a sane man.

This story clearly does not take place on Earth. For one thing, this planet has six suns, not one like our own. For another, the names—Aton and Theremon—are unlike any we find on Earth. We learn elsewhere that last names consist of numbers—Aton 77, Theremon 762, and so on. Yet their society is a lot like ours. They too have scientists, newspapers, and nervy reporters. These are obviously beings that we can identify with. It will be interesting to see in what other ways they are like us, or how they are different. At the moment, however, the reader is more interested in why Aton will never again see Gamma, their brightest sun, as a sane man.

**2. Science Fiction Has a Scientific Basis.** If there's no element of science, then, of course, it's not science fiction. This may seem so obvious that it doesn't even bear mentioning, but a sound scientific hypothesis or premise is the foundation of virtually every good science fiction story.

For example, a story called "No-Sided Professor" by Martin Gardner is about a mathematics professor who invents an amazing "nonlateral surface"—that is, a surface with no sides. In applying his discovery, he accidently contorts himself into another dimension. All of which sounds wildly improbable, except that the author begins his story with a discussion of a related mathematical specialty that actually exists—topology—and an application of this branch of science that you can demonstrate for yourself—the Mobius strip. Convinced of the possiblity of the scientific hypothesis, the reader is prepared to go along with just about anything the author wishes to make of it—including, in this case, tumbling from the fifth dimension smack in the middle of a striptease dancer's Egyptian routine!

Of course, the opposite is also true. If there is a glaring error in the scientific foundation, then it's impossible to believe the rest of the story and the story cannot be good science fiction.

How does the following passage from "Nightfall" help make the story believable?

> "After Genovi 41 discovered that Lagash rotated about the sun Alpha, rather than vice versa—and that was four hundred years ago—astronomers have been working. The complex motions of the six suns were recorded and analyzed and unwoven. Theory after theory was advanced and checked and counterchecked and modified and abandoned and revived and converted to something else. It was a devil of a job....
>
> "It was twenty years ago," he continued after remoistening his own throat, "that it was finally demonstrated that the Law of Universal Gravitation accounted exactly for the orbital motions of the six suns. It was a great triumph."

The Law of Universal Gravitation mentioned above is the same principle that applies to our own universe. As you probably already know, gravity is the "pull" which keeps the Earth, and the other planets orbiting our Sun, from spinning off into space. Apparently, the solar system which Lagash belongs to operates along similar principles. And what is more, astronomers on the planet Lagash once believed that Alpha, one of their suns, rotated around Lagash. This, of course, is what our own astronomers used to believe before Copernicus.

This short passage, then, supplies the reader with two good reasons to believe this story—the Law of Gravitation, which we know to be true, and the fact that progress in this area roughly paralleled our own. Together, they form a valid scientific foundation for the rest of the story.

**3. Science Fiction Is Plausible.** Once the scientific foundation is laid, the "What might happen if...?" element is introduced. This is where the hard facts leave off and the fantasy or imagining begins. But even here, the story must be *plausible*—that is, it must make a certain amount of sense to the reader, and it cannot violate known facts or facts that the author establishes.

For instance, there's nothing wrong with a story about a time machine that can take its passengers ahead or backwards in time. However, a return trip to 1776 can't show Abraham Lincoln signing the Declaration of Independence when we all know Lincoln wasn't born then!

Some of the most plausible science fiction stories speculate on where a current trend will lead. Suppose, for example, that environmental pollution continues unchecked? Or that the population time bomb explodes? A real doomsday story could be based on either of these notions. And no matter how incredible the author's vision of a polluted or overpopulated future seems, it would still sound plausible simply because we can see the beginnings of it around us today.

The story you are about to read is based on a plausible "what if...?" situation. It seems that the planet Lagash has no night as we do; because of its six suns, it is always daylight there. Once in 2,049 years, however, the planet experiences a period of darkness which literally drives everyone crazy. How does the author make this situation sound entirely logical and plausible?

> "What if there were another nonluminous planetary body such as Lagash? If there were... the eternal blaze of the suns would make it invisible—drown it out completely."
>
> Theremon whistled, "What a screwy idea!"
>
> "You think that's screwy? Listen to this: Suppose this body rotated about Lagash at such a distance and in such an orbit and had such a mass that its attraction would exactly account for the deviations of Lagash's orbit from theory—do you know what would happen?"
>
> The columnist shook his head.
>
> "Well, sometimes this body would get in the way of a sun." And Sheerin emptied what remained in the bottle at a draft.
>
> "And it does, I suppose," said Theremon flatly.
>
> "Yes! But only one sun lies in its plane of revolution." He jerked a thumb at the shrunken sun above. "Beta!... The eclipse that results, with the moon seven times the apparent diameter of Beta, covers all of Lagash and lasts well over half a day, so that no spot on the planet escapes the effect. *That eclipse comes once every two thousand and forty-nine years.*"

Of course—an eclipse! *That* would account for the period of darkness. And to people who have never experienced darkness, an eclipse would be a big thing—big enough, maybe, to drive them out of their minds.

At this point, the reader is prepared to accept the whole story as plausible. This is because the author has used scientific facts to lay the groundwork for the story—that a planet with many suns might have no periods of darkness like our nights. Then he goes one step further and ponders how the people on this planet would react to an eclipse. It all makes sense, and it makes good science fiction.

**4. Science Fiction Comments on People and Society.** Isaac Asimov has called science fiction "social experimentation on paper" because it suggests some of the many possible futures that may one day confront us. Science fiction gives us a "sneak preview," so to speak, that can alert us to potential problems.

Often, science fiction exaggerates a single aspect of society in order to show where a trend may lead us. For example, a story called *Chronopolis* by J. G. Ballard is about a city where all timepieces have been banned so that people's lives would never again be regimented by clocks and bells. This, in other words, is where our obsession with time may lead us.

Sometimes science fiction looks at a specific scientific discovery and considers how it might be used—and misused. Take genetic engineering— it's easy to see the advantages it offers in controlling hereditary diseases. But what about the unexpected consequences of tampering with human genes? This is the realm of the science fiction writer.

Science fiction also deals with those qualities of man that never change— hate, love, fear, hunger, curiosity—and how they influence human progress. "Nightfall," for example, is set on another planet. Yet the inhabitants are motivated by many of the same forces as we are, as you can see in the following excerpt. Here, Theremon, the reporter, is telling Aton, the scientist, how the public is reacting to his doomsday prediction. In what ways are the people on Lagash like us, and what do you suppose the author intended by this?

[Theremon:] "...the public is in an ugly humor. They're angry."

Aton twisted his mouth in derision. "Let them be angry."

"Yes, but what about tomorrow?"

"There'll be no tomorrow!"

"But if there is. Say that there is—just to see what happens. That anger might take shape into something serious. After all, you know, business has taken a nose dive these last two months. Investors don't really believe the world is coming to an end, but just the same they're being cagey with their money until it's all over. Johnny Public doesn't believe you, either, but the new spring furniture might as well wait a few months—just to make sure.

"You see the point. Just as soon as this is all over, the business interests will be after your hide. They'll say that if crackpots— begging your pardon—can upset the country's prosperity any time they want simply by making some cockeyed prediction—it's up to the planet to prevent them. The sparks will fly, sir."

Just like in our own society, some of the most influential people on Lagash are businessmen, and their primary concern is making money. If Aton's prediction turns out to be wrong, he will be at the mercy of bankers, investors, manufacturers of spring furniture, and everyone else whose livelihood has been temporarily disrupted.

The implication, of course, is that people right here on Earth would just as soon ignore prophets of doom. Environmentalists who urge us to stop polluting our waterways and our air are notoriously unpopular with businessmen whose factories pollute our waterways and our air. And any scientist bold enough to predict the end of civilization had better be prepared to take a lot of heckling.

But *just suppose* our modern day prophets are right... That's all science fiction asks us to do.

As you read Isaac Asimov's story, think about what we can learn from the experiences of the inhabitants of Lagash.

As you read the story:

- Notice how the author establishes the fact that the story is set on another planet.

- Consider how the Tunnel of Mystery episode lends a scientific basis to the story.

- Notice that Beenay dismisses theories about Earth that we know are true as "cute little notions." Think about how this episode has the effect of making Aton's "cute little notions" about the eclipse sound more plausible.

- Think about Sheerin's comments about the difficulties caused by people's attitudes as the scientists try to prepare the people of Lagash for the eclipse.

# Nightfall
## Isaac Asimov

*"If the stars should appear one night in a thousand years, how would men believe and adore, and preserve for many generations the remembrance of the city of God!"—Emerson*

Aton 77, director of Saro University, thrust out a belligerant lower lip and glared at the young newspaperman in a hot fury.

Theremon 762 took that fury in his stride. In his earlier days, when his now widely syndicated column was only a mad idea in a cub reporter's mind, he had specialized in "impossible" interviews. It had cost him bruises, black eyes, and broken bones; but it had given him an ample supply of coolness and self-confidence.

So he lowered the outthrust hand that had been so pointedly ignored and calmly waited for the aged director to get over the worst. Astronomers were queer ducks, anyway, and if Aton's actions of the last two months meant anything, this same Aton was the queer-duckiest of the lot.

Aton 77 found his voice, and though it trembled with restrained emotion, the careful, somewhat pedantic, phraseology, for which the famous astronomer was noted, did not abandon him.

"Sir," he said, "you display an infernal gall in coming to me with that impudent proposition of yours."

The husky telephotographer of the Observatory, Beenay 25, thrust a tongue's tip across dry lips and interposed nervously, "Now, sir, after—"

The director turned to him and lifted a white eyebrow. "Do not interfere, Beenay. I will credit you with good intentions in bringing this man here; but I will tolerate no insubordination now."

Theremon decided it was time to take a part. "Director Aton, if you'll let me finish what I started saying I think—"

"I don't believe, young man," retorted Aton, "that anything you could say now would count much as compared with your daily columns of these last two months. You have led a vast newspaper campaign against the efforts of myself and my colleagues to organize the world against the menace which it is now too late to avert. You have done your best with your highly personal attacks on me to make the staff of this Observatory objects of ridicule."

The director lifted the copy of the Saro City *Chronicle* on the table and shook it at Theremon furiously. "Even a person of your well-known impudence should have hesitated before coming to me with a request that he be allowed to cover today's events for his paper. Of all newsmen, you!"

Aton dashed the newspaper to the floor, strode to the window and clasped his arms behind his back.

"You may leave," he snapped over his shoulder. He stared moodily out at the skyline where Gamma, the brightest of the planet's six suns, was setting. It had already faded and yellowed into the horizon mists, and Aton knew he would never see it again as a sane man.

He whirled. "No, wait, come here!" He gestured peremptorily. "I'll give you your story."

The newsman had made no motion to leave, and now he approached the old man slowly. Aton gestured outward, "Of the six suns, only Beta is left in the sky. Do you see it?"

The question was rather unnecessary. Beta was almost at zenith; its ruddy light flooding the landscape to an unusual orange as the brilliant rays of setting Gamma died. Beta was at aphelion. It was small; smaller than Theremon had ever seen it before, and for the moment it was undisputed ruler of Lagash's sky.

Lagash's own sun, Alpha, the one about which it revolved, was at the antipodes; as were the two distant companion pairs. The red dwarf Beta—Alpha's immediate companion—was alone, grimly alone.

Aton's upturned face flushed redly in the sunlight. "In just under four hours," he said, "civilization, as we know it, comes to an end. It will do so because, as you see, Beta is the only sun in the sky." He smiled grimly. "Print that! There'll be no one to read it."

"But if it turns out that four hours pass—and another four—and nothing happens?" asked Theremon softly.

"Don't let that worry you. Enough will happen."

"Granted! And *still*—if nothing happens?"

For a second time, Beenay 25 spoke, "Sir, I think you ought to listen to him."

Theremon said, "Put it to a vote, Director Aton."

There was a stir among the remaining five members of the Observatory staff, who till now had maintained an attitude of wary neutrality.

"That," stated Aton flatly, "is not necessary." He drew out his pocket watch. "Since your good friend, Beenay, insists so urgently, I will give you five minutes. Talk away."

"Good! Now, just what difference would it make if you allowed me to take down an eyewitness account of what's to come? If your prediction comes true, my presence won't hurt; for in that case my column would never be written. On the other hand, if nothing comes of it, you will just have to expect ridicule or worse. It would be wise to leave that ridicule to friendly hands."

"Aton snorted. "Do you mean yours when you speak of friendly hands?"

"Certainly!" Theremon sat down and crossed his legs. "My columns may have been a little rough at times, but I gave you people the benefit of the doubt every time. After all, this is not the century to preach 'the end of the world is at hand' to Lagash. You have to understand that people don't believe the 'Book of Revelations' any more, and it annoys them to have scientists turn about face and tell us the Cultists are right after all—"

"No such thing, young man," interrupted Aton. "While a great deal of our data has been supplied us by the Cult, our results contain none of the Cult's mysticism. Facts are facts, and the Cult's so-called 'mythology' *has* certain facts behind it. We've exposed them and ripped away their mystery. I assure you that the Cult hates us now worse than you do."

"I don't hate you. I'm just trying to tell you that the public is in an ugly humor. They're angry."

Aton twisted his mouth in derision. "Let them be angry."

"Yes, but what about tomorrow?"

"There'll be no tomorrow!"

"But if there is. Say that there is—just to see what happens. That anger might take shape into something serious. After all, you know, business has taken a nose dive these last two months. Investors don't really believe the world is coming to an end, but just the same they're being cagey with their money until it's all over. Johnny Public doesn't believe you, either, but the new spring furniture might as well wait a few months—just to make sure.

"You see the point. Just as soon as this is all over, the business interests will be after your hide. They'll say that if crackpots—begging your pardon—can upset the country's prosperity any time they want simply by making some cockeyed prediction—it's up to the planet to prevent them. The sparks will fly, sir."

The director regarded the columnist sternly. "And just what were you proposing to do to help the situation?"

"Well," grinned Theremon, "I was proposing to take charge of the publicity. I can handle things so that only the ridiculous side will show. It would be hard to stand, I admit, because I'd have to make you all out to be a bunch of gibbering idiots, but if I can get people laughing at you, they might forget to be angry. In return for that, all my publisher asks is an exclusive story."

Beenay nodded and burst out, "Sir, the rest of us think he's right. These last two months we've considered everything but the million-to-one chance that there is an error somewhere in our theory or in our calculations. We ought to take care of that, too."

There was a murmur of agreement from the men grouped about the table, and Aton's expression became that of one who found his mouth full of something bitter and couldn't get rid of it.

"You may stay if you wish, then. You will kindly refrain, however, from hampering us in our duties in any way. You will also remember that I am in charge of all activities here, and in spite of your opinions as expressed in your columns, I will expect full co-operation and full respect—"

His hands were behind his back, and his wrinkled face thrust forward determinedly as he spoke. He might have continued indefinitely but for the intrusion of a new voice.

"Hello, hello, hello!" It came in a high tenor, and the plump cheeks of the newcomer expanded in a pleased smile. "What's this morgue-like atmosphere about here? No one's losing his nerve, I hope."

Aton started in consternation and said peevishly, "Now what the devil are you doing here, Sheerin? I thought you were going to stay behind in the Hideout."

Sheerin laughed and dropped his tubby figure into a chair. "Hideout be blowed! The place bored me. I wanted to be here, where things are getting hot. Don't you suppose I have my share of curiosity? I want to see these Stars the Cultists are forever speaking about." He rubbed his hands and added in a soberer tone, "It's freezing outside. The wind's enough to hang icicles on your nose. Beta doesn't seem to give any heat at all, at the distance it is."

The white-haired director ground his teeth in sudden exasperation, "Why do you go out of your way to do crazy things, Sheerin? What kind of good are you around here?"

"What kind of good am I around there?" Sheerin spread his palms in comical resignation. "A psychologist isn't worth his salt in the Hideout. They need men of action and strong, healthy women that can breed children. Me? I'm a hundred pounds too heavy for a man of action, and I wouldn't be a success at breeding children. So why bother them with an extra mouth to feed? I feel better over here."

Theremon spoke briskly, "Just what is the Hideout, sir?"

Sheerin seemed to see the columnist for the first time. He frowned and blew his ample cheeks out. "And just who in Lagash are you, redhead?"

Aton compressed his lips and then muttered sullenly, "That's Theremon 762, the newspaper fellow. I suppose you've heard of him."

The columnist offered his hand. "And, of course, you're Sheerin 501 of Saro University. I've heard of you." Then he repeated, "What is this Hideout, sir?"

"Well," said Sherin, "we have managed to convince a few people of the validity of our prophecy of—er—doom, to be spectacular about it, and those few have taken proper measures. They consist mainly of the immediate members of the families of the Observatory staff, certain of the faculty of Saro University and a few outsiders. Altogether, they number about three hundred, but three quarters are women and children."

"I see! They're supposed to hide where the Darkness and the—er—Stars can't get at them, and then hold out when the rest of the world goes poof."

"If they can. It won't be easy. With all of mankind insane; with the great cities going up in flames—environment will not be conducive to survival. But they have food, water, shelter, and weapons—"

"They've got more," said Aton. "They've got all our records, except for what we will collect today. Those records will mean everything to the next cycle, and *that's* what must survive. The rest can go hang."

Theremon whistled a long, low whistle and sat brooding for several minutes. The men about the table had brought out a multichess board and started a six-member game. Moves were made rapidly and in silence. All eyes bent in furious concentration on the board. Theremon watched them intently and then rose and approached Aton, who sat apart in whispered conversation with Sheerin.

"Listen," he said, "let's go somewhere where we won't bother the rest of the fellows. I want to ask some questions."

The aged astronomer frowned sourly at him, but Sheerin chirped up, "Certainly. It will do me good to talk. It always does. Aton was telling me about your ideas concerning world reaction to a failure of the prediction— and I agree with you. I read your column pretty regularly, by the way, and as a general thing I like your views."

"Please, Sheerin," growled Aton.

"Eh? Oh, all right. We'll go into the next room. It has softer chairs, anyway."

There *were* softer chairs in the next room. There were also thick red curtains on the windows and a maroon carpet on the floor. With the bricky light of Beta pouring in, the general effect was one of dried blood.

Theremon shuddered, "Say, I'd give ten credits for a decent dose of white light for just a second. I wish Gamma or Delta were in the sky."

"What are your questions?" asked Aton. "Please remember that our time is limited. In a little over an hour and a quarter we're going upstairs, and after that there will be no time to talk."

"Well, here it is." Theremon leaned back and folded his hands on his chest. "You people seem so all-fired serious about this that I'm beginning to believe you. Would you mind explaining what it's all about?"

Aton exploded, "Do you mean to sit there and tell me that you've been bombarding us with ridicule without even finding out what we've been trying to say?"

The columnist grinned sheepishly. "It's not that bad, sir. I've got the general idea. You say that there is going to be a world-wide Darkness in a few hours and that all mankind will go violently insane. What I want now is the science behind it."

"No, you don't. No, you don't," broke in Sheerin. "If you ask Aton for that—supposing him to be in the mood to answer at all—he'll trot out pages of figures and volumes of graphs. You won't make head or tail of it. Now if you were to ask *me*, I could give you the layman's standpoint."

"All right; I ask you."

"Then first I'd like a drink." He rubbed his hands and looked at Aton.

"Water?" grunted Aton.

"Don't be silly!"

"Don't you be silly. No alcohol today. It would be too easy to get my men drunk. I can't afford to tempt them."

The psychologist grumbled wordlessly. He turned to Theremon, impaled him with his sharp eyes, and began.

"You realize, of course, that the history of civilization on Lagash displays a cyclic character—but I mean, *cyclic!*"

"I know," replied Theremon cautiously, "that that is the current archaeological theory. Has it been accepted as a fact?"

"Just about. In this last century it's been generally agreed upon. This cyclic character is—or, rather, was—one of *the* great mysteries. We've located series of civilizations, nine of them definitely, and indications of others as well, all of which have reached heights comparable to our own, and all of which, without exception, were destroyed by fire at the very height of their culture.

"And no one could tell why. All centers of culture were thoroughly gutted by fire, with nothing left behind to give a hint as to the cause."

Theremon was following closely. "Wasn't there a Stone Age, too?"

"Probably, but as yet, practically nothing is known of it, except that men of that age were little more than rather intelligent apes. We can forget about that."

"I see. Go on!"

"There have been explanations of these recurrent catastrophes, all of a more or less fantastic nature. Some say that there are periodic rains of fire; some that Lagash passes through a sun every so often; some even wilder things. But there is one theory, quite different from all of these, that has been handed down over a period of centuries."

"I know. You mean this myth of the 'Stars' that the Cultists have in their 'Book of Revelations.' "

"Exactly," rejoined Sheerin with satisfaction. "The Cultists said that every two thousand and fifty years Lagash entered a huge cave, so that all the suns disappeared, and there came *total darkness all over the world!* And then, they say, things called Stars appeared, which robbed men of their souls and left them unreasoning brutes, so that they destroyed the civilization they themselves had built up. Of course, they mix all this up with a lot of religio-mystic notions, but that's the central idea."

There was a short pause in which Sheerin drew a long breath. "And now we come to the Theory of Universal Gravitation." He pronounced the phrase so that the capital letters sounded—and at that point Aton turned from the window, snorted loudly, and stalked out of the room.

The two stared after him, and Theremon said, "What's wrong?"

"Nothing in particular," replied Sheerin. "Two of the men were due several hours ago and haven't shown up yet. He's terrifically short-handed, of course, because all but the really essential men have gone to the Hideout."

"You don't think the two deserted, do you?"

"Who? Faro and Yimot? Of course not. Still, if they're not back within the hour, things would be a little sticky." He got to his feet suddenly, and his eyes twinkled. "Anyway, as long as Aton is gone—"

Tiptoeing to the nearest window, he squatted, and from the low window box beneath withdrew a bottle of red liquid that gurgled suggestively when he shook it.

"I *thought* Aton didn't know about this," he remarked as he trotted back to the table. "Here! We've only got one glass so, as the guest you can have it. I'll keep the bottle." And he filled the tiny cup with judicious care.

Theremon rose to protest, but Sheerin eyed him sternly. "Respect your elders, young man."

The newsman seated himself with a look of pain and anguish on his face. "Go ahead, then, you old villain."

The psychologist's Adams's apple wobbled as the bottle upended, and then, with a satisfied grunt and a smack of the lips, he began again.

"But what do you know about gravitation?"

"Nothing, except that it is a very recent development, not too well established, and that the math is so hard that only twelve men in Lagash are supposed to understand it."

"*Tcha!* Nonsense! Boloney! I can give you all the essential math in a sentence. The Law of Universal Gravitation states that there exists a cohesive force among all bodies of the universe, such that the amount of this force between any two given bodies is proportional to the product of their masses divided by the square of the distance between them."

"Is that all?"

"That's enough! It took four hundred years to develop it."

"Why that long? It sounded simple enough, the way you said it."

"Because great laws are not divined by flashes of inspiration, whatever you may think. It usually takes the combined work of a world full of scientists over a period of centuries. After Genovi 41 discovered that Lagash rotated about the sun Alpha, rather than vice versa—and that was four hundred years ago—astronomers have been working. The complex motions of the six suns were recorded and analyzed and unwoven. Theory after theory was advanced and checked and counterchecked and modified and abandoned and revived and converted to something else. It was a devil of a job."

Theremon nodded thoughtfully and held out his glass for more liquor. Sheerin grudgingly allowed a few ruby drops to leave the bottle.

"It was twenty years ago," he continued after remoistening his own throat, "that it was finally demonstrated that the Law of Universal Gravitation accounted exactly for the orbital motions of the six suns. It was a great triumph."

Sheerin stood up and walked to the window, still clutching his bottle. "And now we're getting to the point. In the last decade, the motions of Lagash about Alpha were computed according to gravity and *it did not account for the orbit observed;* not even when all perturbations due to the other suns were included. Either the law was invalid, or there was another, as yet unknown, factor involved."

Theremon joined Sheerin at the window and gazed out past the wooded slopes to where the spires of Saro City gleamed bloodily on the horizon. The newsman felt the tension of uncertainty grow within him as he cast a short glance at Beta. It glowered redly at zenith, dwarfed and evil.

"Go ahead, sir," he said softly.

Sheerin replied, "Astronomers stumbled about for years, each proposed theory more untenable than the one before—until Aton had the inspiration of calling in the Cult. The head of the Cult, Sor 5, had access to certain data that simplified the problem considerably. Aton set to work on a new track.

"What if there were another nonluminous planetary body such as Lagash? If there were, you know, it would shine only by reflected light, and if it were composed of bluish rock, as Lagash itself largely is, then in the redness of the sky, the eternal blaze of the suns would make it invisible—

drown it out completely."

Theremon whistled, "What a screwy idea!"

"You think *that's* screwy? Listen to this: Suppose this body rotated about Lagash at such a distance and in such an orbit and had such a mass that its attraction would exactly account for the deviations of Lagash's orbit from theory—do you know what would happen?"

The columnist shook his head.

"Well, sometimes this body would get in the way of a sun." And Sheerin emptied what remained in the bottle at a draft.

"And it does, I suppose," said Theremon flatly.

"Yes! But only one sun lies in its place of revolutions." He jerked a thumb at the shrunken sun above. "Beta! And it has been shown that the eclipse will occur only when the arrangement of the suns is such that Beta is alone in its hemisphere and at a maximum distance, at which time the moon is invariably at minimum distance. The eclipse that results, with the moon seven times the apparent diameter of Beta, covers all of Lagash and lasts well over half a day, so that no spot on the planet escapes the effect. *That eclipse comes once every two thousand and forty-nine years.*"

Theremon's face was drawn into an expressionless mask. "And that's my story?"

The psychologist nodded. "That's all of it. First the eclipse—which will start in three quarters of an hour—then universal Darkness, and, maybe, these mysterious Stars—then madness, and end of the cycle."

He brooded. "We had two months' leeway—we at the Observatory—and that wasn't enough time to persuade Lagash of the danger. Two centuries might not have been enough. But our records are at the Hideout, and today we photograph the eclipse. The next cycle will *start off* with the truth, and when the *next* eclipse comes, mankind will at last be ready for it. Come to think of it, that's part of your story, too."

A thin wind ruffled the curtains at the window as Theremon opened it and leaned out. It played coldly with his hair as he stared at the crimson sunlight on his hand. Then he turned in sudden rebellion.

"What is there in Darkness to drive *me* mad?"

Sheerin smiled to himself as he spun the empty liquor bottle with abstracted motions of his hand. "Have you ever experienced Darkness, young man?"

The newsman leaned against the wall and considered. "No. Can't say I have. But I know what it is. Just—uh—" He made vague motions with his fingers, and then brightened. "Just no light. Like in caves."

"Have you ever been in a cave?"

"In a *cave!* Of course not!"

"I thought not. *I* tried last week—just to see—but I got out in a hurry. I went in until the mouth of the cave was just visible as a blur of light, with black everywhere else. I never thought a person my weight could run that fast."

Theremon's lip curled. "Well, if it comes to that, I guess I wouldn't have run, if I had been there."

The psychologist studied the young man with an annoyed frown.

"My, don't you talk big! I dare you to draw the curtain."

Theremon looked his surprise and said, "What for? If we had four or five suns out there we might want to cut the light down a bit for comfort, but now we haven't enough light as it is."

That's the point. Just draw the curtain; then come here and sit down."

"All right." Theremon reached for the tasseled string and jerked. The red curtain slid across the wide window, the brass rings hissing their way along the crossbar, and a dusk-red shadow clamped down on the room.

Theremon's footsteps sounded hollowly in the silence as he made his way to the table, and then they stopped halfway. "I can't see you, sir," he whispered.

"Feel your way," ordered Sheerin in a strained voice.

"But I can't see you, sir." The newsman was breathing harshly. "I can't see anything."

"What did you expect?" came the grim reply. "Come here and sit down!"

The footsteps sounded again, waveringly, approaching slowly. There was the sound of someone fumbling with a chair. Theremon's voice came thinly, "Here I am. I feel...*ulp*... all right."

"You like it, do you?"

"N-no. It's pretty awful. The walls seem to be—" He paused. "They seem to be closing in on me. I keep wanting to push them away. But I'm not going *mad!* In fact, the feeling isn't as bad as it was."

"All right. Draw the curtain back again."

There were cautious footsteps through the dark, the rustle of Theremon's body againt the curtain as he felt for the tassel, and then the triumphant *ro-o-osh* of the curtain slithering back. Red light flooded the room, and with a cry of joy Theremon looked up at the sun.

Sheerin wiped the moistness off his forehead with the back of a hand and said shakily, "And that was just a dark room."

"It can be stood," said Theremon lightly.

"Yes, a dark room can. But were you at the Jonglor Centennial Exposition two years ago?"

"No, it so happens I never got around to it. Six thousand miles was just a bit too much to travel, even for the exposition."

"Well, I was there. You remember hearing about the 'Tunnel of Mystery' that broke all records in the amusement area—for the first month or so, anyway?"

"Yes. Wasn't there some fuss about it?"

"Very little. It was hushed up. You see, that Tunnel of Mystery was just a mile-long tunnel—with no lights. You got into a little open car and jolted along through Darkness for fifteen minutes. It was very popular—while it lasted."

"Popular?"

"Certainly. There's a fascination in being frightened *when it's part of a game*. A baby is born with three instinctive fears: of loud noises, of falling, and of the absence of light. That's why it's considered so funny to jump at someone and shout 'Boo!' That's why it's such fun to ride a roller coaster. And that's why that Tunnel of Mystery started cleaning up. People came out of that Darkness shaking, breathless, half dead with fear, but they kept on paying to get in."

"Wait a while, I remember now. Some people came out dead, didn't they?" There were rumors of that after it shut down."

The psychologist snorted. "Bah! Two or three died. That was nothing! They paid off the families of the dead ones and argued the Jonglor City Council into forgetting it. After all, they said, if people with weak hearts want to go through the tunnel, it was at their own risk—and besides, it wouldn't happen again. So they put a doctor in the front office and had every customer go through a physical examination before getting into the car. That actually *boosted* ticket sales."

"Well then?"

"But, you see, there was something else. People sometimes came out in perfect order, except that they refused to go into buildings—any buildings; including palaces, mansions, apartment houses, tenements, cottages, huts, shacks, lean-tos, and tents."

Theremon looked shocked. "You mean they refused to come in out of the open. Where'd they sleep?"

"In the open."

"They should have *forced* them inside."

"Oh, they did, they did. Whereupon these people went into violent hysterics and did their best to bat their brains out against the nearest wall. Once you got them inside, you couldn't keep them there without a straitjacket and a shot of morphine."

"They must have been crazy."

"Which is exactly what they were. One person out of every ten who went into that tunnel came out that way. They called in the psychologists, and we did the only thing possible. We closed down the exhibit." He spread his hands.

"What was the matter with those people?" asked Theremon finally.

"Essentially the same thing that was the matter with you when you thought the walls of the room were crushing in on you in the dark. There is a psychological term for mankind's instinctive fear of the absence of light. We call it 'claustrophobia,' because the lack of light is always tied up with enclosed places, so that fear of one is fear of the other. You see?"

"And those people of the tunnel?"

"Those people of the tunnel consisted of those unfortunates whose mentality did not quite possess the resiliency to overcome the claustrophobia that overtook them in the Darkness. Fifteen minutes without light is a long time; you only had two or three minutes, and I believe you were fairly upset.

"The people of the tunnel had what is called a 'claustrophobic fixation.' Their latent fear of Darkness and enclosed places had crystallized and become active, and, as far as we can tell, permanent. *That's* what fifteen minutes in the dark will do."

There was a long silence, and Theremon's forehead wrinkled slowly into a frown. "I don't believe it's that bad."

"You mean you don't want to believe," snapped Sheerin. "You're afraid to believe. Look out the window!"

Theremon did so, and the psychologist continued without pausing, "Imagine Darkness—everywhere. No light, as far as you can see. The houses, the trees, the fields, the earth, the sky—*black!* And Stars thrown in, for all I know—whatever *they* are. Can you conceive it?"

"Yes, I can," declared Theremon truculently.

And Sheerin slammed his fist down upon the table in sudden passion. "You lie! You can't conceive that. Your brain wasn't built for the conception any more than it was built for the conception of infinity or of eternity. You can only talk about it. A fraction of the reality upsets you, and when the real thing comes, your brain is going to be presented with a phenomenon outside its limits of comprehension. You will go mad, completely and permanently! There is no question of it!"

He added sadly, "And another couple of millenniums of painful struggle comes to nothing. Tomorrow there won't be a city standing unharmed in all Lagash."

Theremon recovered part of his mental equilibrium. "That doesn't follow. I still don't see that I can go looney just because there isn't a Sun in the sky—but even if I did, and everyone else did, how does that harm the cities? Are we going to blow them down?"

But Sheerin was angry, too. "If you were in Darkness, what would you want more than anything else; what would it be that every instinct would call for? Light, damn you, *light!*"

"Well?"

"And how would you get light?"

"I don't know," said Theremon flatly.

"What's the *only* way to get light, short of the sun?"

"How should I know?"

They were standing face to face and nose to nose.

Sheerin said, "You burn something, mister. Ever see a forest fire? Ever go camping and cook a stew over a wood fire? Heat isn't the only thing burning wood gives off, you know. It gives off light, and people know that. And when it's dark they want light, and they're going to *get it.*"

"So they burn wood?"

"So they burn whatever they can get. They've got to have light. They've got to burn something, and wood isn't handy—so they'll burn whatever is nearest. They'll have their light—and every center of habitation goes up in flames!"

Eyes held each other as though the whole matter were a personal affair of respective will powers, and then Theremon broke away wordlessly. His breathing was harsh and ragged, and he scarcely noted the sudden hubbub that came from the adjoining room behind the closed door.

Sheerin spoke, and it was with an effort that he made it sound matter-of-fact. "I think I heard Yimot's voice. He and Faro are probably back. Let's go in and see what kept them."

"Might as well!" muttered Theremon. He drew a long breath and seemed to shake himself. The tension was broken.

The room was in an uproar, with members of the staff clustering about two young men who were removing outer garments even as they parried the miscellany of questions being thrown at them.

Aton bustled through the crowd and faced the newcomers angrily. "Do you realize that it's less than half an hour before deadline? Where have you two been?"

Faro 24 seated himself and rubbed his hands. His cheeks were red with the outdoor chill. "Yimot and I have just finished carrying through a little crazy experiment of our own. We've been trying to see if we couldn't construct an arrangement by which we could simulate the appearance of Darkness and Stars so as to get an advance notion as to how it looked."

There was a confused murmur from the listeners, and a sudden look of interest entered Aton's eyes. "There wasn't anything said of this before. How did you go about it?"

"Well," said Faro, "the idea came to Yimot and myself long ago, and we've been working it out in our spare time. Yimot knew of a low one-story house down in the city with a domed roof—it had once been used as a museum, I think. Anyway, we bought it—"

"Where did you get the money?" interrupted Aton peremptorily.

"Our bank accounts," grunted Yimot 70. "It cost two thousand credits." Then, defensively, "Well, what of it? Tomorrow, two thousand credits will be two thousand pieces of paper. That's all."

"Sure," agreed Faro. "We bought the place and rigged it up with black velvet from top to bottom so as to get as perfect a Darkness as possible. Then we punched tiny holes in the ceiling and through the roof and covered them with little metal caps, all of which could be shoved aside simultaneously at the close of a switch. At least, we didn't do that part ourselves; we got a carpenter and an electrician and some others—money didn't count. The point was that we could get the light to shine through those holes in the roof, so that we could get a starlike effect."

Not a breath was drawn during the pause that followed. Aton said stiffly:

"You had no right to make a private—"

Faro seemed abashed. "I know, sir—but, frankly, Yimot and I thought the experiment was a little dangerous. If the effect really worked, we half expected to go mad—from what Sheerin says about all this, we thought that would be rather likely. We wanted to take the risk ourselves. Of course, if we found we could retain sanity, it occurred to us that we might develop immunity to the real thing, and then expose the rest of you to the same thing. But things didn't work out at all—"

"Why, what happened?"

It was Yimot who answered "We shut ourselves in and allowed our eyes to get accustomed to the dark. It's an extremely creepy feeling because the total Darkness makes you feel as if the walls and ceiling are crushing in on you. But we got over that and pulled the switch. The caps fell away and the roof glittered all over with little dots of light—"

"Well?"

"Well—nothing. That was the whacky part of it. Nothing happened. It was just a roof with holes in it, and that's just what it looked like. We tried it over and over again—that's what kept us so late—but there just isn't any effect at all."

There followed a shocked silence, and all eyes turned to Sheerin, who sat motionless, mouth open.

Theremon was the first to speak. "You know what this does to this whole theory you've built up, Sheerin, don't you?" He was grinning with relief.

But Sheerin raised his hand. "Now wait a while. Just let me think this through." And then he snapped his fingers, and when he lifted his head there was neither surprise nor uncertainty in his eyes. "Of course—"

He never finished. From somewhere up above there sounded a sharp clang, and Beenay, starting to his feet, dashed up the stairs with a "What the devil!"

The rest followed after.

Things happened quickly. Once up in the dome, Beenay cast one horrified glance at the shattered photographic plates and at the man bending over them; and then hurled himself fiercely at the intruder, getting a death grip on his throat. There was a wild threshing, and as others of the staff joined in, the stranger was swallowed up and smothered under the weight of half a dozen angry men.

Aton came up last, breathing heavily. "Let him up!"

There was a reluctant unscrambling and the stranger, panting harshly, with his clothes torn and his forehead bruised, was hauled to his feet. He had a short yellow beard curled elaborately in the style affected by the Cultists.

Beenay shifted his hold to a collar grip and shook the man savagely. "All right, rat, what's the idea? These plates—"

"I wasn't after *them*," retorted the Cultist coldly. "That was an accident."

Beenay followed his glowering stare and snarled, "I see. You were after the cameras themselves. The accident with the plates was a stroke of luck for you, then. If you had touched Snapping Bertha or any of the others, you would have died by slow torture. As it is—" He drew his fist back.

Aton grabbed his sleeve. "Stop that! Let him go!"

The young technician wavered, and his arm dropped reluctantly. Aton pushed him aside and confronted the Cultist. "You're Latimer, aren't you?"

The Cultist bowed stiffly and indicated the symbol upon his hip. "I am Latimer 25, adjutant of the third class to his serenity, Sor 5."

"And"—Aton's white eyebrows lifted—"you were with his serenity when he visited me last week, weren't you?"

Latimer bowed a second time.

"Now, then, what do you want?"

"Nothing that you would give me of your own free will."

"Sor 5 sent you, I suppose—or is this your own idea?"

"I won't answer that question."

"Will there be any further visitors?"

"I won't answer that, either."

Aton glanced at his timepiece and scowled. "Now, man, what is it your master wants of me? I have fulfilled my end of the bargain."

Latimer smiled faintly, but said nothing.

"I asked him," continued Aton angrily, "for data only the Cult could supply, and it was given to me. For that, thank you. In return, I promised to prove the essential truth of the creed of the Cult."

"There was no need to prove that," came the proud retort. "It stands proven by the 'Book of Revelations.' "

"For the handful that constitute the Cult, yes. Don't pretend to mistake my meaning. I offered to present scientific backing for your beliefs. And I did!"

The Cultist's eyes narrowed bitterly. "Yes, you did—with a fox's subtlety, for your pretended explanation backed our beliefs, and at the same time removed all necessity for them. You made of the Darkness and of the Stars a natural phenomenon, and removed all its real significance. That was blasphemy."

"If so, the fault isn't mine. The facts exist. What can I do but state them?"

"Your 'facts' are a fraud and a delusion."

Aton stamped angrily. "How do *you* know?"

And the answer came with the certainty of absolute faith. "I *know!*"

The director purpled and Beenay whispered urgently. Aton waved him silent. "And what does Sor 5 want us to do? He still thinks, I suppose, that in trying to warn the world to take measures against the menace of madness, we are placing innumerable souls in jeopardy. We aren't succeeding, if that means anything to him."

"The attempt itself has done harm enough, and your vicious effort to gain information by means of your devilish instruments must be stopped. We obey the will of their Stars, and I only regret that my clumsiness prevented me from wrecking your infernal devices."

"It wouldn't have done you too much good," returned Aton. "All our data, except for the direct evidence we intend collecting right now, is already safely cached and well beyond possibility of harm." He smiled grimly. "But that does not affect your present status as an attempted burglar and criminal."

He turned to the men behind him. "Someone call the police at Saro City."

There was a cry of distaste from Sheerin. "Damn it, Aton, what's wrong with you? There's no time for that. Here"—he bustled his way forward— "let me handle this."

Aton stared down his nose at the psychologist. "This is not the time for your monkeyshines, Sheerin. Will you please let me handle this my own way? Right now you are a complete outsider here, and don't forget it."

Sheerin's mouth twisted eloquently. "Now why should we go to the impossible trouble of calling the police—with Beta's eclipse a matter of minutes from now—when this young man here is perfectly willing to pledge his word of honor to remain and cause no trouble whatsover?"

The Cultist answered promptly, "I will do no such thing. You're free to do what you want, but it's only fair to warn you that just as soon as I get my chance I'm going to finish what I came out here to do. If it's my word of honor you're relying on, you'd better call the police."

Sheerin smiled in a friendly fashion. "You're a determined cuss, aren't you? Well, I'll explain something. Do you see that young man at the window? He's a strong, husky fellow, quite handy with his fists, and he's an outsider besides. Once the eclipse starts there will be nothing for him to do except keep an eye on you. Besides him, there will be myself—a little too stout for active fisticuffs, but still able to help."

"Well, what of it?" demanded Latimer frozenly.

"Listen and I'll tell you," was the reply. "Just as soon as the eclipse starts, we're going to take you, Theremon and I, and deposit you in a little closet with one door, to which is attached one giant lock and no windows. You will remain there for the duration."

"And afterward," breathed Latimer fiercely, "there'll be no one to let me out. I know as well as you do what the coming of the Stars means—I know it far better than you. With all your minds gone, you are not likely to free me. Suffocation or slow starvation, is it? About what I might have expected from a group of scientists. But I don't give my word. It's a matter of principle, and I won't discuss it further."

Aton seemed perturbed. His faded eyes were troubled. "Really, Sheerin, locking him—"

"Please!" Sheerin motioned him impatiently to silence. "I don't think for a moment things will go that far. Latimer has just tried a clever little bluff, but I'm not a psychologist just because I like the sound of the word." He grinned at the Cultist. "Come now, you don't really think I'm trying anything as crude as slow starvation. My dear Latimer, if I lock you in the closet, you are not going to see the Darkness, and you are not going to see the Stars. It does not take much of a knowledge of the fundamental creed of the Cult to realize that for you to be hidden from the Stars when they appear means the loss of your immortal soul. Now, I believe you to be an honorable man. I'll accept your word of honor to make no further effort to disrupt proceedings if you'll offer it."

A vein throbbed in Latimer's temple, and he seemed to shrink within himself as he said thickly, "You have it!" And then he added with swift fury, "But it is my consolation that you will all be damned for your deeds of today." He turned on his heel and stalked to the high three-legged stool by the door.

Sheerin nodded to the columnist. "Take a seat next to him, Theremon— just as a formality. Hey, Theremon!"

But the newspaperman didn't move. He had gone pale to the lips. "Look at that!" The finger he pointed toward the sky shook, and his voice was dry and cracked.

There was one simultaneous gasp as every eye followed the pointing finger and, for one breathless moment, stared frozenly.

*Beta was chipped on one side!*

The tiny bit of encroaching blackness was perhaps the width of a fingernail, but to the staring watchers it magnified itself into the crack of doom.

Only for a moment they watched, and after that there was a shrieking confusion that was even shorter of duration and which gave way to an orderly scurry of activity—each man at his prescribed job. At the crucial moment there was no time for emotion. The men were merely scientists with work to do. Even Aton had melted away.

Sheerin said prosaically, "First contact must have been made fifteen minutes ago. A little early, but pretty good considering the uncertainties involved in the calculation." He looked about him and tiptoed to Theremon, who still remained staring out the window, and dragged him away gently.

"Aton is furious," he whispered, "so stay away. He missed first contact on account of this fuss with Latimer, and if you get in his way he'll have you thrown out the window."

Theremon nodded shortly and sat down. Sheerin stared in surprise at him.

"The devil, man," he exclaimed, "you're shaking."

"Eh?" Theremon licked dry lips and then tried to smile. "I don't feel very well, and that's a fact."

The psychologist's eyes hardened. "You're not losing your nerve?"

"No!" cried Theremon in a flash of indignation. "Give me a chance, will you? I haven't really believed this rigmarole—not way down beneath, anyway—till just this minute. Give me a chance to get used to the idea. *You've* been preparing yourself for two months or more."

"You're right, at that," replied Sheerin thoughtfully. "Listen! Have you got a family—parents, wife, children?"

Theremon shook his head. "You mean the Hideout, I suppose. No, you don't have to worry about that. I have a sister, but she's two thousand miles away. I don't even know her exact address."

"Well, then, what about yourself? You've got time to get there, and they're one short anyway, since I left. After all, you're not needed here, and you'd make a darned fine addition—"

Theremon looked at the other wearily. "You think I'm scared stiff, don't you? Well, get this, mister, I'm a newspaperman and I've been assigned to cover a story. I intend covering it."

There was a faint smile on the psychologist's face. "I see. Professional honor, is that it?"

"You might call it that. But, man, I'd give my right arm for another bottle of that sockeroo juice even half the size of the one *you* hogged. If ever a fellow needed a drink, I do."

He broke off. Sheerin was nudging him violently. "Do you hear that? Listen!"

Theremon followed the motion of the other's chin and stared at the Cultist, who oblivious to all about him, faced the window, a look of wild elation on his face, droning to himself the while in singsong fashion.

"What's he saying?" whispered the columnist.

"He's quoting 'Book of Revelations,' fifth chapter," replied Sheerin. Then, urgently, "Keep quiet and listen, I tell you."

The Cultist's voice had risen in a sudden increase of fervor:

" 'And it came to pass that in those days the Sun, Beta, held lone vigil in the sky for ever longer periods as the revolutions passed; until such time as for full half a revolution, it alone, shrunken and cold, shone down upon Lagash.

" 'And men did assemble in the public squares and in the highways, there to debate and to marvel at the sight, for a strange depression had seized them. Their minds were troubled and their speech confused, for the souls of men awaited the coming of the Stars.

" 'And in the city of Trigon, at high noon, Vendret 2 came forth and said unto the men of Trigon, "Lo ye sinners! Though ye scorn the ways of righteousness, yet will the time of reckoning come. Even now the Cave approaches to swallow Lagash; yea, and all it contains."

" 'And even as he spoke the lip of the Cave of Darkness passed the edge of Beta so that to all Lagash it was hidden from sight. Loud were the cries of men as it vanished, and great the fear of soul that fell upon them.

" 'It came to pass that the Darkness of the Cave fell upon Lagash, and there was no light on all the surface of Lagash. Men were even as blinded, nor could one man see his neighbor, though he felt his breath upon his face.

" 'And in this blackness there appeared the Stars, in countless numbers, and to the strains of ineffable music of a beauty so wondrous that the very leaves of the trees turned to tongues that cried out in wonder.

" 'And in that moment the souls of men departed from them, and their abandoned bodies became even as beasts; yea, even as brutes of the wild; so that through the blackened streets of the cities of Lagash they prowled with wild cries.

" 'From the Stars there then reached down the Heavenly Flame, and where it touched, the cities of Lagash flamed to utter destruction, so that of man and of the works of man nought remained.

" 'Even then—' "

There was a subtle change in Latimer's tone. His eyes had not shifted, but somehow he had become aware of the absorbed attention of the other two. Easily, without pausing for breath, the timbre of his voice shifted and the syllables became more liquid.

Theremon, caught by surprise, stared. The words seemed on the border of familiarity. There was an elusive shift in the accent, a tiny change in the vowel stress; nothing more—yet Latimer had become thoroughly unintelligible.

Sheerin smiled slyly. "He shifted to some old-cycle tongue, probably their traditional second cycle. That was the language in which the 'Book of Revelations' had originally been written, you know."

"It doesn't matter; I've heard enough." Theremon shoved his chair back and brushed his hair back with hands that no longer shook. "I feel much better now."

"You do?" Sheerin seemed mildly surprised.

"I'll say I do. I had a bad case of jitters just a while back. Listening to you and your gravitation and seeing that eclipse start almost finished me. But this"—he jerked a contemptuous thumb at the yellow-bearded Cultist— "*this* is the sort of thing my nurse used to tell me. I've been laughing at that sort of thing all my life. I'm not going to let it scare me *now.*"

He drew a deep breath and said with a hectic gaiety, "But if I expect to keep on the good side of myself, I'm going to turn my chair away from the window."

Sheerin said, "Yes, but you'd better talk lower. Aton just lifted his head out of that box he's got it stuck into and gave you a look that should have killed you."

Theremon made a mouth. "I forgot about the old fellow." With elaborate care he turned the chair from the window, cast one distasteful look over his shoulder and said, "It has occurred to me that there must be considerable immunity against this Star madness."

The psychologist did not answer immediately. Beta was past its zenith now, and the square of bloody sunlight that outlined the window upon the floor had lifted into Sheerin's lap. He stared at its dusky color thoughtfully and then bent and squinted into the sun itself.

The chip in its side had grown to a black encroachment that covered a third of Beta. He shuddered, and when he straightened once more his florid cheeks did not contain quite as much color as they had had previously.

With a smile that was almost apologetic, he reversed his chair also. "There are probably two million people in Saro City that are all trying to join the Cult at once in one gigantic revival." Then, ironically, "The Cult is in for an hour of unexampled prosperity. I trust they'll make the most of it. Now, what was it you said?"

"Just this. How do the Cultists manage to keep the 'Book of Revelations' going from cycle to cycle, and how on Lagash did it get written in the first place? There must have been some sort of immunity, for if everyone had gone mad, who would be left to write the book?"

Sheerin stared at his questioner ruefully. "Well, now, young man, there isn't any eyewitness answer to that, but we've got a few damned good notions as to what happened. You see, there are three kinds of people who might remain relatively unaffected. First, the very few who don't see the Stars at all; the blind, those who drink themselves into a stupor at the beginning of the eclipse and remain so to the end. We leave them out—because they aren't really witnesses.

"Then there are children below six, to whom the world as a whole is too new and strange for them to be too frightened at Stars and Darkness. They would be just another item in an already surprising world. You see that, don't you?"

The other nodded doubtfully. "I suppose so."

"Lastly, there are those whose minds are too coarsely grained to be entirely toppled. The very insensitive would be scarcely affected—oh, such people as some of our older, work-broken peasants. Well, the children would have fugitive memories, and that, combined with the confused, incoherent babblings of the half-mad morons, formed the basis for the 'Book of Revelations.'

"Naturally, the book was based, in the first place, on the testimony of those least qualified to serve as historians; that is, children and morons; and was probably extensively edited and re-edited through the cycles."

"Do you suppose," broke in Theremon, "that they carried the book through the cycles the way we're planning on handing on the secret of gravitation?"

Sheerin shrugged. "Perhaps, but their exact method is unimportant. They do it, somehow. The point I was getting at was that the book can't help but be a mass of distortion, even if it is based on fact. For instance, do you remember the experiment with the holes in the roof that Faro and Yimot tried—the one that didn't work?"

"Yes."

"You know why it didn't w—" He stopped and rose in alarm, for Aton was approaching, his face a twisted mask of consternation. *"What's happened?"*

Aton drew him aside and Sheerin could feel the fingers on his elbow twitching.

"Not so loud!" Aton's voice was low and tortured. "I've just gotten word from the Hideout on the private line."

Sheerin broke in anxiously. "They are in trouble?"

"Not *they*." Aton stressed the pronoun significantly. "They sealed themselves off just a while ago, and they're going to stay buried till day after tomorrow. They're safe. But the *city,* Sheerin—it's a shambles. You have no idea—" He was having difficulty in speaking.

"Well?" snapped Sheerin impatiently. "What of it? It will get worse. What are you shaking about?" Then, suspiciously, "How do you feel?"

Aton's eyes sparked angrily at the insinuation, and then faded to anxiety once more. "You don't understand. The Cultists are active. They're rousing the people to storm the Observatory—promising them immediate entrance into grace, promising them salvation, promising them anything. What are we to do, Sheerin?"

Sheerin's head bent, and he stared in long abstraction at his toes. He tapped his chin with one knuckle, then looked up and said crisply, "Do? What is there to do? Nothing at all! Do the men know of this."

"No, of course not!"

"Good! Keep it that way. How long till totality?"

"Not quite an hour."

"There's nothing to do but gamble. It will take time to organize any really formidable mob, and it will take more time to get them out here. We're a good five miles from the city—"

He glared out the window, down the slopes to where the farmed patches gave way to clumps of white houses in the suburbs; down to where the metropolis itself was a blur on the horizon—a mist in the waning blaze of Beta.

He repeated without turning, "It will take time. Keep on working and pray that totality comes first."

Beta was cut in half, the line of division pushing a slight concavity into the still-bright portion of the Sun. It was like a gigantic eyelid shutting slantwise over the light of a world.

The faint clatter of the room in which he stood faded into oblivion, and he sensed only the thick silence of the fields outside. The very insects seemed frightened mute. And things were dim.

He jumped at the voice in his ear. Theremon said, "Is something wrong?"

"Eh? Er—no. Get back to the chair. We're in the way." They slipped back to their corner, but the psychologist did not speak for a time. He lifted a finger and loosened his collar. He twisted his neck back and forth but found no relief. He looked up suddenly.

"Are you having any difficulty in breathing?"

The newspaperman opened his eyes wide and drew two or three long breaths. "No. Why?"

"I looked out the window too long, I suppose. The dimness got me. Difficulty in breathing is one of the first symptoms of a claustrophobic attack."

Theremon drew another long breath. "Well, it hasn't got me yet. Say, here's another of the fellows."

Beenay had interposed his bulk between the light and the pair in the corner, and Sheerin squinted up at him anxiously. "Hello, Beenay."

The astronomer shifted his weight to the other foot and smiled feebly. "You won't mind if I sit down awhile and join in on the talk? My cameras are set, and there's nothing to do till totality." He paused and eyed the Cultist, who fifteen minutes earlier had drawn a small, skin-bound book from his sleeve and had been poring intently over it ever since. "That rat hasn't been making trouble, has he?"

Sheerin shook his head. His shoulders were thrown back and he frowned his concentration as he forced himself to breathe regularly. He said, "Have you had any trouble breathing, Beenay?"

Beenay sniffed the air in his turn. "It doesn't seem stuffy to me."

"A touch of claustrophobia," explained Sheerin apologetically.

"Oh-h-h! It worked itself differently with me. I get the impression that my eyes are going back on me. Things seem to blur and—well, nothing is clear. And it's cold, too."

"Oh, it's cold, all right. That's no illusion." Theremon grimaced. "My toes feel as if I've been shipping them crosscountry in a refrigerating car."

"What we need," put in Sheerin, "is to keep our minds busy with extraneous affairs. I was telling you a while ago, Theremon, why Faro's experiments with the holes in the roof came to nothing."

"You were just beginning," replied Theremon. He encircled a knee with both arms and nuzzled his chin against it.

"Well, as I started to say, they were misled by taking the 'Book of Revelations' literally. There probably wasn't any sense in attaching any physical significance to the Stars. It might be, you know, that in the presence of total Darkness, the mind finds it absolutely necessary to create light. This illusion of light might be all the Stars there really are."

"In other words," interposed Theremon, "you mean the Stars are the results of the madness and not one of the causes. Then, what good will Beenay's photographs be?"

"To prove that it is an illusion, maybe; or to prove the opposite, for all I know. Then again—"

But Beenay had drawn his chair closer, and there was an expression of sudden enthusiasm on his face. "Say, I'm glad you two got on to this subject." His eyes narrowed and he lifted one finger. "I've been thinking about these Stars and I've got a really cute notion. Of course, it's strictly ocean foam, and I'm not trying to advance it seriously, but I think it's interesting. Do you want to hear it?"

He seemed half reluctant, but Sheerin leaned back and said, "Go ahead! I'm listening."

"Well, then, supposing there were other suns in the universe." He broke off a little bashfully. "I mean suns that are so far away that they're too dim to see. It sounds as if I've been reading some of that fantastic fiction, I suppose."

"Not necessarily. Still, isn't that possibility eliminated by the fact that, according to the Law of Gravitation, they would make themselves evident by their attractive forces?"

"Not if they were far enough off," rejoined Beenay, "really far off—maybe as much as four light years, or even more. We'd never be able to detect perturbations then, because they'd be too small. Say that there were a lot of suns that far off; a dozen or two, maybe."

Theremon whistled melodiously. "What an idea for a good Sunday supplement article. Two dozen suns in a universe eight light years across. Wow! That would shrink *our* universe into insignificance. The readers would eat it up."

"Only an idea," said Beenay with a grin, "but you see the point. During eclipse, these dozen suns would become visible, because there'd be no *real* sunlight to drown them out. Since they're so far off, they'd appear small, like so many little marbles. Of course, the Cultists talk of millions of Stars, but that's probably exaggeration. There just isn't any place in the universe you could put a million suns—unless they touch one another."

Sheerin had listened with gradually increasing interest. "You've hit something there, Beenay. And exaggeration is just exactly what would happen. Our minds, as you probably know, can't grasp directly any number higher than five; above that there is only the concept of 'many.' A dozen would become a million just like that. A damn good idea!"

"And I've got another cute little notion," Beenay said. "Have you ever thought what a simple problem gravitation would be if only you had a sufficiently simple system? Supposing you had a universe in which there was a planet with only one sun. The planet would travel in a perfect ellipse and the exact nature of the gravitational force would be so evident it could be accepted as an axiom. Astronomers on such a world would start off with gravity probably before they even invent the telescope. Naked-eye observation would be enough."

"But would such a system be dynamically stable?" questioned Sheerin doubtfully.

"Sure! They call it the 'one-and-one' case. It's been worked out mathematically, but it's the philosophical implications that interest me."

"It's nice to think about," admitted Sheerin, "as a pretty abstraction—like a perfect gas or absolute zero."

"Of course," continued Beenay, "there's the catch that life would be impossible on such a planet. It wouldn't get enough heat and light, and if it rotated there would be total Darkness half of each day. You couldn't expect life—which is fundamentally dependent upon light—to develop under those conditions. Besides—"

Sheerin's chair went over backward as he sprang to his feet in a rude interruption. "Aton's brought out the lights."

Beenay said, "Huh," turned to stare, and then grinned halfway around his head in open relief.

There were half a dozen foot-long, inch-thick rods cradled in Aton's arms.

He glared over them at the assembled staff members.

"Get back to work, all of you. Sheerin, come here and help me!"

Sheerin trotted to the older man's side and, one by one, in utter silence, the two adjusted the rods in makeshift metal holders suspended from the walls.

With the air of one carrying through the most sacred item of a religious ritual, Sheerin scraped a large, clumsy match into spluttering life and passed it to Aton, who carried the flame to the upper end of one of the rods.

It hesitated there a while, playing futilely about the tip, until a sudden, crackling flare cast Aton's lined face into yellow highlights. He withdrew the match and a spontaneous cheer rattled the window.

The rod was topped by six inches of wavering flame! Methodically, the other rods were lighted, until six independent fires turned the rear of the room yellow.

The light was dim, dimmer even than the tenuous sunlight. The flames reeled crazily, giving birth to drunken, swaying shadows. The torches smoked devilishly and smelled like a bad day in the kitchen. But they emitted yellow light.

There is something to yellow light—after four hours of somber, dimming Beta. Even Latimer had lifted his eyes from his book and stared in wonder.

Sheerin warmed his hands at the nearest, regardless of the soot that gathered upon them in a fine, gray powder, and muttered ecstatically to himself. "Beautiful! Beautiful! I never realized before what a wonderful color yellow is."

But Theremon regarded the torches suspiciously. He wrinkled his nose at the rancid odor, and said, "What are those things?"

"Wood," said Sheerin shortly.

"Oh, no, they're not. They aren't burning. The top inch is charred and the flame just keeps shooting up out of nothing."

"That's the beauty of it. This is a really efficient artifical-light mechanism. We made a few hundred of them, but most went to the Hideout, of course. You see"—he turned and wiped his blackened hands upon his handkerchief—"you take the pithy core of coarse water reeds, dry them thoroughly and soak them in animal grease. Then you set fire to it and the grease burns, little by little. These torches will burn for almost half an hour without stopping. Ingenious, isn't it? It was developed by one of our own young men at Saro University."

After the momentary sensation, the dome had quieted. Latimer had carried his chair directly beneath a torch and continued reading, lips moving in the monotonous recital of invocations to the Stars. Beenay had drifted away to his cameras once more, and Theremon seized the opportunity to add to his notes on the article he was going to write for the Saro City *Chronicle* the next day—a procedure he had been following for the last two hours in a perfectly methodical, perfectly conscientious and, as he was well aware, perfectly meaningless fashion.

But, as the gleam of amusement in Sheerin's eyes indicated, careful note taking occupied his mind with something other than the fact that the sky was gradually turning a horrible deep purple-red, as if it were one gigantic, freshly peeled beet; and so it fulfilled its purpose.

The air grew, somehow, denser. Dusk, like a palpable entity, entered the room, and the dancing circle of yellow light about the torches etched itself into ever-sharper distinction against the gathering grayness beyond. There was the odor of smoke and the presence of little chuckling sounds that the torches made as they burned; the soft pad of one of the men circling the table at which he worked, on hesitant tiptoes; the occasional indrawn breath of someone trying to retain composure in a world that was retreating into the shadow.

It was Theremon who first heard the extraneous noise. It was a vague, unorganized *impression* of sound that would have gone unnoticed but for the dead silence that prevailed within the dome.

The newsman sat upright and replaced his notebook. He held his breath and listened; then, with considerable reluctance, threaded his way between the solarscope and one of Beenay's cameras and stood before the window.

The silence ripped to fragments at his startled shout:

*"Sheerin!"*

Work stopped! The psychologist was at his side in a moment. Aton joined him. Even Yimot 70, high in his little lean-back seat at the eyepiece of the gigantic solar-scope, paused and looked downward.

Outside, Beta was a mere smoldering splinter, taking one last desperate look at Lagash. The eastern horizon, in the direction of the city, was lost in Darkness, and the road from Saro to the Observatory was a dull-red line bordered on both sides by wooden tracts, the trees of which had somehow lost individuality and merged into a continuous shadowy mass.

But it was the highway itself that held attention, for along it there surged another, and infinitely menacing, shadowy mass.

Aton cried in a cracked voice, "The madmen from the city! They've come!"

"How long to totality?" demanded Sheerin.

"Fifteen minutes, but... but they'll be here in five."

"Never mind, keep the men working. We'll hold them off. This place is built like a fortress. Aton, keep an eye on our young Cultist just for luck. Theremon, come with me."

Sheerin was out the door, and Theremon was at his heels. The stairs stretched below them in tight, circular sweeps about the central shaft, fading into a dank and dreary grayness.

The first momentum of their rush had carried them fifty feet down, so that the dim, flickering yellow from the open door of the dome had disappeared and both up above and down below the same dusky shadow crushed in upon them.

Sheerin paused, and his pudgy hand clutched at his chest. His eyes bulged and his voice was a dry cough. "I can't... breathe... go down... yourself. Close all doors—"

Theremon took a few downward steps, then turned. "Wait! Can you hold out a minute?" He was panting himself. The air passed in and out his lungs like so much molasses, and there was a little germ of screeching panic in his mind at the thought of making his way into the mysterious Darkness below by himself.

Theremon, after all, was afraid of the dark!

"Stay here," he said. "I'll be back in a second." He dashed upward two steps at a time, heart pounding—not altogether from the exertion—tumbled into the dome and snatched a torch from its holder. It was foul smelling, and the smoke smarted his eyes almost blind, but he clutched that torch as if he wanted to kiss it for joy, and its flame streamed backward as he hurtled down the stairs again.

Sheerin opened his eyes and moaned as Theremon bent over him. Theremon shook him roughly. "All right, get a hold on yourself. We've got light."

He held the torch at tiptoe height and, propping the tottering psychologist by an elbow, made his way downward in the middle of the protecting circle of illumination.

The offices on the ground floor still possessed what light there was, and Theremon felt the horror about him relax.

"Here," he said brusquely, and passed the torch to Sheerin. "You can hear *them* outside."

And they could. Little scraps of hoarse, wordless shouts.

But Sheerin was right; the Observatory was built like a fortress. Erected in the last century, when the neo-Gavottian style of architecture was at its ugly height, it had been designed for stability and durability, rather than for beauty.

The windows were protected by the grill work of inch-thick iron bars sunk deep into the concrete sills The walls were solid masonry that an earthquake couldn't have touched, and the main door was a huge oaken slab reinforced with iron at the strategic points. Theremon shot the bolts and they slid shut with a dull clang.

At the other end of the corridor, Sheerin cursed weakly. He pointed to the lock of the back door which had been nearly jimmied into uselessness.

"That must be how Latimer got in," he said.

"Well, don't stand there," cried Theremon impatiently. "Help me drag up the furniture—and keep that torch out of my eyes. The smoke's killing me."

He slammed the heavy table up against the door as he spoke, and in two minutes had built a barricade which made up for what it lacked in beauty and symmetry by the sheer inertia of its massiveness..

Somewhere, dimly, far off, they could hear the battering of naked fists upon the door; and the screams and yells from outside had a sort of half reality.

That mob had set off from Saro City with only two things in mind: the attainment of Cultist salvation by the destruction of the Observatory, and a maddening fear that all but paralyzed them. There was no time to think of ground cars, or of weapons, or of leadership, or even of organization. They made for the Observatory on foot and assaulted it with bare hands.

And now that they were there, the last flash of Beta, the last ruby-red drop of flame, flickered feebly over a humanity that had left only stark, universal fear!

Theremon groaned, "Let's get back to the dome!"

In the dome, only Yimot, at the solarscope, had kept his place. The rest were clustered about the cameras, and Beenay was giving his instructions in a hoarse, strained voice.

"Get it straight, all of you, I'm snapping Beta just before totality and changing the plate. That will leave one of you to each camera. You all know about... about times of exposure—"

There was a breathless murmur of agreement.

Beenay passed a hand over his eyes. "Are the torches still burning? Never mind, I see them!" He was leaning hard against the back of a chair. "Now remember, don't... don't try to look for good shots. Don't waste time trying to get t-two stars at a time in the scope field. One is enough. And... and if you feel yourself going, *get away from the camera.*"

At the door, Sheerin whispered to Theremon, "Take me to Aton. I don't see him."

The newsman did not answer immediately. The vague form of the astronomers wavered and blurred, and the torches overhead had become only yellow splotches.

"It's dark," he whimpered.

Sheerin held out his hand, "Aton." He stumbled forward. "Aton!"

Theremon stepped after and seized his arm. "Wait, I'll take you." Somehow he made his way across the room. He closed his eyes against the Darkness and his mind against the chaos within it.

No one heard them or paid attention to them. Sheerin stumbled against the wall. "Aton!"

The psychologist felt shaking hands touching him, then withdrawing, and a voice muttering, "Is that you, Sheerin?"

"Aton!" He strove to breathe normally. "Don't worry about the mob. The place will hold them off."

Latimer, the Cultist, rose to his feet, and his face twisted in desperation. His word was pledged, and to break it would mean placing his soul in mortal peril. Yet that word had been forced from him and had not been given freely. The Stars would come soon; he could not stand by and allow— And yet his word was pledged.

Beenay's face was dimly flushed as it looked upward at Beta's last ray, and Latimer, seeing him bend over his camera, made his decision. His nails cut the flesh of his palms as he tensed himself.

He staggered crazily as he started his rush. There was nothing before him but shadows; the very floor beneath his feet lacked substance. And then someone was upon him and he went down with clutching fingers at his throat.

He doubled his knee and drove it hard into his assailant. "Let me up or I'll kill you."

Theremon cried out sharply and muttered through a blinding haze of pain, "You double-crossing rat!"

The newsman seemed conscious of everything at once. He heard Beenay croak, "I've got it. At your cameras, men!" and then there was the strange awareness that the last thread of sunlight had thinned out and snapped.

Simultaneously he heard one last choking gasp from Beenay, and a queer little cry from Sheerin, a hysterical giggle that cut off in a rasp—and a sudden silence, a strange, deadly silence from outside.

And Latimer had gone limp in his loosening grasp. Theremon peered into the Cultist's eyes and saw the blankness of them, staring upward, mirroring the feeble yellow of the torches. He saw the bubble of froth upon Latimer's lips and heard the low animal whimper in Latimer's throat.

With the slow fascination of fear, he lifted himself on one arm and turned his eyes toward the blood-curdling blackness of the window.
Through it shone the Stars!

Not Earth's feeble thirty-six hundred Stars visible to the eye—Lagash was in the center of a giant cluster. Thirty thousand mighty suns shown down in a soul-searing splendor that was more frighteningly cold in its awful indifference than the bitter wind that shivered across the cold, horribly bleak world.

Theremon staggered to his feet, his throat constricting him to breathlessness, all the muscles of his body writhing in a tensity of terror and sheer fear beyond bearing. He was going mad, and knew it, and somewhere deep inside a bit of sanity was screaming, struggling to fight off the hopeless flood of black terror. It was very horrible to go mad and know that you were going mad—to know that in a little minute you would be here physically and yet all the real essence would be dead and drowned in the black madness. For this was the Dark—the Dark and the Cold and the Doom. The bright walls of the universe were shattered and their awful black fragments were falling down to crush and squeeze and obliterate him.

He jostled someone crawling on hands and knees, but stumbled somehow over him. Hands groping at his tortured throat, he limped toward the flame of the torches that filled all his mad vision.

"Light!" he screamed.

Aton, somewhere, was crying, whimpering horribly like a terribly frightened child. "Stars—all the Stars—we didn't know at all . We didn't know anything. We thought six stars is a universe is something the Stars didn't notice is Darkness forever and ever and ever and the walls are breaking in and we didn't know we couldn't know and anything—"

Someone clawed at the torch, and it fell and snuffed out. In the instant, the awful splendor of the indifferent Stars leaped nearer to them.

On the horizon outside the window, in the direction of Saro City, a crimson glow began growing, strengthening in brightness, that was not the glow of a sun.

The long night had come again.

# Unit 11

## Nightfall

- Comprehension Questions
- Science Fiction
- Discussion Guides
- Writing Exercise

# COMPREHENSION QUESTIONS

For each of the following statements and questions, select the option containing the most complete or most accurate answers.

1. Before Theremon, the reporter, came to the observatory to interview
(h) Aton, he and his newspaper had
   - ☐ a. ridiculed the scientists.
   - ☐ b. taken the eclipse very seriously.
   - ☐ c. worshipped the Cultist.
   - ☐ d. ignored the whole story.

2. Businessmen on Lagash were hostile towards Aton because
(f) ☐ a. they didn't believe him.
   - ☐ b. they thought he was a crackpot.
   - ☐ c. they were Cultists.
   - ☐ d. his predictions were hurting business.

3. Aton and his fellow scientists had known that an eclipse was coming for
(d) ☐ a. at least a year.        ☐ c. two months.
   - ☐ b. many years now.        ☐ d. the past week.

4. The main difference between the planet Lagash and the planet Earth is
(d) that
   - ☐ a. Earth has a moon and Lagash does not.
   - ☐ b. Lagash is always bathed in sunlight and Earth is not.
   - ☐ c. Earth has eclipses of the sun and Lagash does not.
   - ☐ d. Lagash moves in an orbit and Earth does not.

5. Choose the word which explains what *credits* are as used in this context:
(l) "Theremon shuddered, 'Say, I'd give ten *credits* for a decent dose of white light for just a second.' "
   - ☐ a. Wishes        ☐ c. Money
   - ☐ b. Guesses       ☐ d. Wagers

6. When Theremon asks Aton to explain what's going on, Sheerin says, "If
(l) you ask Aton for that. . . he'll trot out pages of figures and volumes of graphs. You won't make head or tail of it. Now if you were to ask me, I could give you the *layman's* standpoint.' " From the way it's used in this sentence, *layman* means a
   - ☐ a. nonprofessional        ☐ c. spectator
   - ☐ b. scientist              ☐ d. nonbeliever

7. Archeologists had found that civilization on Lagash
(e) □ a. was relatively recent.
   □ b. started over and over again in regular cycles.
   □ c. showed a long, steady history of uninterrupted progress.
   □ d. was highly sophistocated compared to other civilizations.


8. Aton and other scientists at the observatory hope that their records of
(e) the eclipse will
   □ a. put an end to the Cultists.
   □ b. prepare the people in the next cycle.
   □ a. make them famous.
   □ d. preserve their sanity.


9. The popularity of the Tunnel of Mystery amusement ride showed that
(f) the people on Lagash
   □ a. liked to be frightened.
   □ b. were basically unstable.
   □ c. acted childlike in many ways.
   □ d. behaved primitively.


10. The Stars drove people mad because
(g) □ a. they were magical.
   □ b. they gave off poisonous rays.
   □ c. people's brains couldn't comprehend this phenomenon.
   □ d. people had been told beforehand that this is what would happen.


11. The person in the story who *best* understands how the eclipse affects
(g) people's minds is
   □ a. Theremon, the reporter.     □ c. Aton, the scientist.
   □ b. Sheerin, the psychologist.  □ d. Latimer, the Cultist.


12. The reason there won't be a city standing unharmed in all Lagash is that
(h) □ a. an earthquake will topple them.
   □ b. the inhabitants will set fire to everything.
   □ c. the eclipse will trigger a huge tidal wave.
   □ d. the end of the world will come.


13. Latimer, the Cultist, has come to the observatory in order to
(a) □ a. convert the scientists.
   □ b. destroy the equipment.
   □ c. help prove that the Stars exist.
   □ d. get a better view of the Stars.

14. The mood of the scientists inside the observatory as they prepare for the
(i) eclipse is one of

    ☐ a. hopeless despair      ☐ c. nervous anticipation

    ☐ b. religious fervor.      ☐ d. confusion and commotion.

15. In general, Aton, Theremon, and the other characters in this story are
(j) ☐ a. strange and alien to us.

    ☐ b. better than people on Earth.

    ☐ c. ignorant and backwards.

    ☐ d. a lot like you and me.

16. The Cultist religion is based on theories and ideas that are
(c) ☐ a. factual.

    ☐ b. just folklore.

    ☐ c. partly myth and partly fact.

    ☐ d. meaningless.

17. According to Sheerin, which of the following would be affected by
(b) the stars?

    ☐ a. Blind people      ☐ c. Morons

    ☐ b. Small children      ☐ d. Intelligent people

18. The Cultists recruited new followers just before the eclipse by promising
(a) them

    ☐ a. immunity to the Stars.      ☐ c. salvation.

    ☐ b. wealth.      ☐ d. power.

19. What invention does Aton introduce as the eclipse nears totality?
(a) ☐ a. Fire      ☐ c. A wide-angle lens

    ☐ b. A timepiece      ☐ d. Torches

20. "Dusk, like a palpable entity, entered the room. . . ." This is an example
(k) of a figure of speech called

    ☐ a. hyperbole (an exaggeration).

    ☐ b. alliteration (repeating initial sounds).

    ☐ c. personification (ascribing human traits to nonhuman things).

    ☐ d. meiosis (understatement).

21. A main conflict in this story concerns
(c) □ a. Aton versus Sheerin.
    □ b. Theremon versus Sheerin.
    □ c. citizens versus Cultists.
    □ d. scientists versus Cultists.

22. Public opinion toward the Cultists progresses from
(d) □ a. unpopular to popular.
    □ b. faithful to unfaithful.
    □ c. tolerant to intolerant.
    □ d. unknown to well known.

23. The tone of Aton's voice when he beholds the Stars expresses his
(i) □ a. wonder and delight.
    □ b. astonishment and terror.
    □ c. disappointment and displeasure.
    □ d. apathy and lack of interest.

24. At the very end of the story, the crimson glow that could be seen on the
(f) horizon from the observatory window comes from the
    □ a. burning city.        □ c. setting sun.
    □ b. rising sun.          □ d. Stars.

25. The moral of this story might be
(g) □ a. the universe is greater than the human mind can imagine.
    □ b. science and religion don't mix.
    □ c. forewarned is forearmed.
    □ d. science has all the answers.

Comprehension Skills: a — isolating details; b — recalling specific facts; c — retaining concepts; d — organizing facts; e — understanding the main idea; f — drawing a conclusion; g — making a judgment; h — making an inference; i — recognizing tone; j — understanding characters; k — appreciation of literary forms; l — understanding vocabulary.

# SCIENCE FICTION

## Practice Exercise A

Aton gestured outward, "Of the six suns, only Beta is left in the sky. Do you see it?"

The question was rather unnecessary. Beta was almost at zenith; its ruddy light flooding the landscape to an unusual orange as the brilliant rays of setting Gamma died. Beta was at aphelion. It was small; smaller than Theremon had ever seen it before, and for the moment it was undisputed ruler of Lagash's sky.

1. If you were standing beside Aton and Theremon, the most striking difference which you, as an Earth person, couldn't help notice would be
   ☐ a. the small size of Beta.
   ☐ b. the absence of Gamma.
   ☐ c. the ruddy, orange light flooding the landscape.
   ☐ d. the fact that there is only one sun in the sky.

2. Circle all the words and phrases in the passage above which suggest that this story takes place on another planet.

## Practice Exercise B

"What was the matter with those people?" asked Theremon finally.

"Essentially the same thing that was the matter with you when you thought the walls of the room were crushing in on you in the dark. There is a psychological term for mankind's instinctive fear of the absence of light. We call it 'claustrophobia,' because the lack of light is always tied up with enclosed places, so that fear of one is fear of the other. You see?"

"And those people of the tunnel?". . .

"The people of the tunnel had what is called a 'claustrophobic fixation.' Their latent fear of Darkness and enclosed places had crystallized and become active, and, as far as we can tell, permanent. *That's* what fifteen minutes in the dark will do."

1. Like the inhabitants of Lagash, most people on Earth also fear the dark to some extent. This common bond makes the story seem
   ☐ a. more believable.        ☐ c. far-fetched.
   ☐ b. more exciting.          ☐ d. weird and mysterious.

2. Circle a scientific term used in the passage above to lend validity to this episode.

## Practice Exercise C

"And I've got another cute little notion," Beenay said. "Have you ever thought what a simple problem gravitation would be if only you had a sufficiently simple system? Supposing you had a universe in which there was a planet with only one sun. The planet would travel in a perfect ellipse and the exact nature of the gravitational force would be so evident it could be accepted as an axiom. Astronomers on such a world would start off with gravity probably before they even invent the telescope. Naked eye observation would be enough.". . .

"It's nice to think about," admitted Sheerin, "as a pretty abstraction—like a perfect gas or absolute zero."

"Of course," continued Beenay, "there's the catch that life would be impossible on such a planet. It wouldn't get enough heat and light, and if it rotated there would be total Darkness half of each day. You couldn't expect life — which is fundamentally dependent upon light — to develop under those conditions. . . ."

1. The author uses this little episode to show that
   □ a. our knowledge is sometimes limited by our point of view.
   □ b. scientists on Lagash are not very bright.
   □ c. facts never lie.
   □ d. life can develop only under a single set of conditions.

2. Underline at least one phrase in the passage which reveals that the system Beenay is referring to is Earth! Several things Beenay "theorizes" about are descriptions of things we know to be true about the Earth.

## Practice Exercise D

"We had two months' leeway — we at the Observatory — and that wasn't enough time to persuade Lagash of the danger. Two centuries might not have been enough. But our records are at the Hideout, and today we photograph the eclipse. The next cycle will start off with the truth, and when the *next* eclipse comes, mankind will at last be ready for it. Come to think of it, that's part of your story, too."

1. The speaker here is expressing an attitude about people in general that applies to the inhabitants of Earth as well as Lagash. The attitude expressed is that
   * □ a. people are willing and ready to face the worst that is in store for them.
   □ b. people are incapable of preparing for a catastrophe.
   □ c. civilization is too advanced to be endangered by natural phenomena.
   □ d. people prefer to ignore unpleasant realities if they possibly can.

2. Underline the single sentence that best expresses the speaker's attitude about the difficulty of convincing people of the truth of a new idea.

# DISCUSSION GUIDES

## Analyzing Science Fiction

1. Do you find anything implausible about "Nightfall"? If so, explain what it is. How does something that seems implausible affect your enjoyment of the story?

2. "The ultimate role of science fiction," claims one critic, "is to act as an interpreter of science to humanity." How can science fiction — which is, after all, fiction — do this? What aspect of science has Asimov explained for you in "Nightfall"?

3. Far from being "escape literature," insists Asimov, science fiction is "an escape into reality." What do you think he meant by this?

## Interpreting the Story

4. According to Sheerin, the psychologist, mankind is instinctively afraid of the dark — on the planet Lagash, at least. Do you think this is true of people on Earth? Give reasons to support your answer.

5. Why, in your opinion, did Fara and Yimot's experiment simulating darkness and stars fail to produce the expected effect?

6. Why does Latimer, the Cultist who tried to sabotage the observatory, hate Aton so much? After all, Aton provided scientific proof substantiating the basic beliefs of the Cultists.

7. In the story, there's a basic conflict between science, represented by Aton and the other astronomers, and religion, represented by the Cultists. Does a similar conflict exist in our own culture? Explain. Must scientific advancement conflict with religion?

## Analyzing the Author's Technique

8. What is ironic about the quotation by Emerson which Asimov uses to introduce this story?

9. Why do you think Asimov used characters who speak much like us for his story instead of more outlandish creatures?

10. Review the last page or two of the story. How does Asimov convey to the reader the terrible impact of the stars on those viewing them?

# WRITING EXERCISE

Dreaming up alien creatures is a science fiction writer's stock in trade. There's more to it, though, than just adding antennae, a third eye, and scales. The new life form, however fantastic, must be *believable*. This means if a being has a tail, there must be a persuasive biological reason why this appendage evolved. Similarly, if the creature has ESP (extrasensory perception), it must be because this trait helps it to survive.

Naturally, any life form must be specially adapted to existence in its own particular environment. For instance, a planet with a low gravity is apt to have tall, spindly inhabitants, and a planet with a higher gravity is more likely to spawn short, squat beings.

The author of "Nightfall," Isaac Asimov, never tells the reader exactly what the inhabitants of Lagash look like. We may assume they look just like us. But, given the fact that Lagash has no night as we do, this is bound to be reflected in its life forms.

Based on information given in the story, write a short composition describing what *you* think the inhabitants of Lagash look like. Use your imagination, by all means, but back up your details with rational explanations. Your description should include: the color of their skin and hair, their body build, how they move about, what they eat, and whatever else you think is important.

Unit 12
**Humor**

# The Kugelmass
# Episode

## Woody Allen

# Introduction

"The Kugelmass Episode" is one of the most improbable and impossible stories you will ever read, and also one of the funniest. Sidney Kugelmass is a lecherous, middle-aged professor of humanities at City College of New York—uptown branch, he hastens to point out, which, to New Yorkers, implies just a touch more academic prestige than the downtown business school or the upstart colleges in Brooklyn and Queens. Kugelmass is unhappy, neurotic, and anxiety-ridden because his life has turned out pretty much as he has designed it. He has made his own bed and finds himself extremely uncomfortable sleeping in it.

He describes his second wife, Daphne, as a troglodyte who has swollen up like a beach ball, and, unfortunately, Kugelmass has a decided preference for women who are young, beautiful, sensual and exciting. "She had promise," is the nicest thing Kugelmass can tell his analyst about Daphne. But, we find out, Kugelmass married Daphne for her money in order to help meet alimony and child-support payments to his first wife—a bit of planning without foresight that he now finds frustrating.

"I'm a man who needs romance. I need softness, I need flirtation," Kugelmass whines to Dr. Mandel. "I'm an analyst, not a magician," Dr. Mandel replies.

At that point Kugelmass decides that a magician is exactly what he does need. It will take a magician to put a little romance and flirtation in his life without Daphne finding out about it. It isn't long, then, before he gets a call from The Great Persky, a small-time magician in Brooklyn, who promises that for a double sawbuck ($20) he will project Kugelmass into any short story or novel he chooses, where he can "carry on as much as he likes" with a beautiful heroine.

Kugelmass chooses to meet Emma Bovary in the classic nineteenth-century French novel *Madame Bovary* by Gustave Flaubert. In some ways, Emma is just like Kugelmass. She is bored with her marriage to a stodgy doctor, and she has dabbled in romantic affairs with two other men, Leon and Rodolphe.

Persky works his magic well and manages to get Kugelmass into the book when Dr. Bovary is away from home and between appearances of Leon and Rodolphe. "By showing up in the right chapters, I've got the situation knocked," says Kugelmass.

Emma Bovary finds Kugelmass exciting, and the romantic encounters that follow are all that he ever dreamed of. But then, intrigued by Kugelmass's stories of such twentieth-century marvels as Hollywood, fast cars, and O.J. Simpson, Emma decides that she wants to come to New York with Kugelmass. She feels she can be a great actress and win an Academy Award. Persky works his magic again, and Emma and Kugelmass, riding in the Bovary carriage, arrive at the Plaza Hotel where Kugelmass has reserved a suite for the weekend. Once in New York, however, the same fickle fate that always seems to plague Kugelmass takes control once more.

The story is pure fantasy and just the kind of hilarious fun that you would expect from the exorbitantly fertile imagination of Woody Allen. Most of us think of Woody Allen as an actor-director, but he was a writer long before he was either of these and, of course, he still writes or collaborates in writing screenplays for his films.

"The Kugelmass Episode" first appeared in *New Yorker* magazine in 1977 and was published again in Doubleday's *Prize Stories 1978, The O. Henry Awards*. Because the story contains some trendy slang, a few Jewish expressions and references to places in New York which are more familiar to New Yorkers than to outlanders, you may find it helpful to look at the following words and expressions which are listed in the order in which they appear in the story.

## Glossary of Words and Expressions

**kugel (as in Kugelmass):** In Yiddish, a kugel is a pudding.

**analyst:** psychoanalyst; a practitioner who helps people suffering under mental stress

**trade quips at '21':** Club 21 is a New York restaurant.


**Brooklyn:** one of the five boroughs of New York City

**What's your scam?** What's your con game?

**It's the emess:** It's the truth; on the level

**a double sawbuck:** $20

**troglodyte:** a cave dweller

**Bloomingdale's:** a department store presently in favor with upper-middle-class shoppers

**the ball and chain:** my wife

**Rupert Murdoch:** a publisher of sensational newspapers and magazines who became the owner of the *New York Post*


***Women's Wear Daily:*** the newspaper of the fashion industry


**FAO Schwartz:** a toy store

**the Sherry:** the Sherry Netherland, a New York hotel where visiting celebrities often stay

**Halston, Saint Laurent, Ralph Lauren:** clothing designers

**the Guggenheim:** an art museum

**SoHo:** an "in" district of nightspots just below Greenwich Village

**Dom Pérignon and black eggs:** expensive champagne and caviar

**Comp Lit:** comparative literature

***International Herald Tribune:*** an American newspaper published in France

**The Monkey in *Portnoy's Complaint:*** a promiscuous young woman with an exceptional appetite for sex, in the book by Philip Roth

# Humor

Many people don't realize that there is an art to being funny and that it is a very difficult art to master. There are probably fewer than one hundred good comedians in the whole country and perhaps not as many good humorous writers. *Great* humorists can be numbered on the fingers of one hand.

Just as in any art, writing successful humor requires talent, intelligence, sensitivity to the world and the people in it, and a penetrating insight into human actions, motives and feelings. On top of all this, the humorist must have a highly developed sense of the ridiculous. That is, a humorist must be able to look at an ordinary situation and see how it would be funny if it were changed just a bit, made more obvious, exaggerated, understated, made larger, made smaller, reversed, twisted or otherwise rendered peculiar in some way. An audience, or in our case the reader, is surprised by the strange turn of events and laughs or chuckles inside.

We are also amused by fantasy, a situation that is only possible if we allow our imaginations to play with it. Sudden changes or reversals—a build-up to a letdown, for example—can be funny when handled by an expert humorist. Humor is often achieved by making something—an object or an idea—absurd, ludicrous or illogical. In any case our reaction is, "Now isn't that ridiculous," and the result is laughter.

For the professional humorist there are "rules" for humor. They are not absolute rules and many good humorists break them at will, but they are found often enough in the best humor that we can make a list of them.

- Good humor will stimulate your imagination so that you are willing to join in the fun.
- Good humor is fresh and spontaneous. People don't laugh at old jokes or at humor that is dragged out and labored.
- The audience must understand the situation and be able to identify with the object of the humor. You are generally made to feel a bit superior to a person who is the object of humor.

- You will probably be interested in the character involved in the humorous situation, and you will sympathize with him or her without feeling unduly sorry. When you begin to feel sorry for a character or if you are upset by a situation, the story will not be funny.
- Humor must not be serious or threatening. A drunk scene may not be funny to you if you suffer with an alcoholic in the family. Satire is often biting and reminds us of our more serious weaknesses. While there is always an element of light satire in pure humor, it is never sustained or made threatening to our egos.
- Humor must give pleasure. Not everyone is amused by the same things. If you are pleased enough to smile or laugh, the humor is successful as far as you are concerned. But the appreciation of humor is a very personal matter, and thus, humorists must often pick their material carefully to suit a particular audience.

Let's see how all of this works for Woody Allen's humor in "The Kugelmass Episode." Watch how the opening paragraphs put you in the mood to enjoy what promises to be a funny story.

> Kugelmass, a professor of humanities at City College, was unhappily married for the second time. Daphne Kugelmass was an oaf. He also had two dull sons by his first wife, Flo, and was up to his neck in alimony and child support.
>
> "Did I know it would turn out so badly?" Kugelmass whined to his analyst one day. "Daphne had promise. Who suspected she'd let herself go and swell up like a beach ball? Plus she had a few bucks, which is not in itself a healthy reason to marry a person, but it doesn't hurt, with the kind of operating nut I have. You see my point?"

Here is a man in psychoanalysis, partly because he is unhappily married. His wife is fat and oafish, his sons are a disappointment and he is in financial difficulties with heavy alimony and child-support payments. So what's funny about that?

Well, from the outset, Woody Allen tickles us with far-fetched images of an unattractive middle-class couple who, nevertheless, are somehow familiar. We have met, or have seen or have heard of people like this before, so we can identify with them. The name Kugelmass sounds a bit improbable, especially if you know that a kugel, in Yiddish, is a pudding. He is a humanities professor at City College of New York, but not exactly the kind of person you expect a professor of humanities to be. His wife has the first name of a Greek goddess, Daphne, but added to the name "Daphne" is "Kugelmass"— Daphne Kugelmass—and she looks like a beach ball.

Kugelmass becomes a proper object for humor when we find out that he has married Daphne for her money, and he speaks of his marriage like an accountant examining a balance sheet. We can understand his motives, but we don't have to sympathize with him too much, or feel sorry for him.

Whatever is coming he will bring on himself. We can feel a bit smug and even superior to this humanities professor with feet of clay.

Kugelmass, we learn, is a lecherous middle-aged man on the prowl for new romance in his life. But he wants it to be safe. Above all he doesn't want Daphne to find out, or she'll complete the financial ruin that his first wife started. The Great Persky, a small-time magician in Brooklyn, hears about Kugelmass's search for "a little exotica" and undertakes to help by putting Kugelmass in a magic box. The charge is "a double sawbuck," twenty dollars in advance.

> "Now here's the point." Persky said. "If I throw any novel into this cabinet with you, shut the doors and tap it three times, you will find yourself projected into that book."
> Kugelmass made a grimace of disbelief.
> "It's the emess," Persky said. "My hand to God. Not just a novel either. A short story, a play, a poem. You can meet any of the women created by the world's best writers. Whoever you dreamed of. You could carry on all you like with a real winner. Then when you've had enough you give a yell, and I'll see you're back here in a split second."

This is food for the imagination, indeed. How would you like to spend a little time with your favorite hero or heroine in any story you choose? "It's the emess (the truth, on the level)," says Persky. We know it's not true—it's absurd, in fact—but that's what makes it funny to think about. Kugelmass chooses to meet a French lady of careless virtue, Emma Bovary, from the novel *Madame Bovary* by Gustave Flaubert. Since Emma Bovary lived in France during the last century, there is a rather severe generation gap for Kugelmass to overcome, as well as a language barrier. But this is no problem for the humorist; it is just that much more material for his fun. Here is how Woody Allen handles these problems as Kugelmass drops in on Emma for the first time.

> Emma turned in surprise. "Goodness, you startled me," she said. "Who are you?" She spoke in the same fine English translation as the paperback.
> It's simply devastating, he thought. Then, realizing that it was he whom she had addressed, he said, "Excuse me. I'm Sidney Kugelmass. I'm from City College. A professor of humanities. CCNY? Uptown. I—oh, boy!"

Emma speaks not in French, as she should if this were a plausible situation, but in a paperback English translation. The problem is solved with a ludicrous assumption. The humor comes from the absurdity of the idea. Then, as Kugelmass tries to introduce himself, we can imagine how tongue-tied we might be ourselves trying to explain our presence to a lady from a hundred years ago whom we have just accosted. We sympathize with Kugelmass, but we don't feel sorry for him. It is, after all, a funny situation to be in.

Humor is frequently achieved with a big build-up followed by a sudden and surprising letdown. This is one form of the comic reversal. There are several of these in the following passage. See if you can find them.

> After the wine they went for a stroll in the lovely French countryside. "I've always dreamed that some mysterious stranger would appear and rescue me from the monotony of this crass rural existence," Emma said, clasping his hand. They passed a small church. "I love what you have on," she murmured. "I've never seen anything like it around here. It's so...so modern."
>
> "It's called a leisure suit," he said romantically. "It was marked down." Suddenly he kissed her. For the next hour they reclined under a tree and whispered together and told each other deeply meaningful things with their eyes. Then Kugelmass sat up. He had just remembered he had to meet Daphne at Bloomingdale's.

This is a tried and true comic technique that has been used by comedians for years. You have seen it used in TV comedy shows, in Saturday morning cartoons and in old Marx Brothers and Laurel and Hardy movies. The key to the comedy is a sudden and surprising change of tone and mood.

Here, Kugelmass and Emma are strolling hand-in-hand through the French countryside. Romantic tension builds. They speak of his clothes— "It's called a leisure suit.... It was marked down." Suddenly the romantic bubble bursts and we are reminded of pudgy, bald Kugelmass in his bargain-basement clothes. But he kisses her and they spend the next hour telling each other "deeply meaningful things with their eyes." Another romantic build-up. And again the bubble is burst as he remembers his appointment with Daphne at a New York department store. "OK, Persky!" he will yell, "I got to be at Bloomingdale's by three-thirty."

Neither leisure suits nor Bloomingdale's by themselves are funny. But when they are suddenly dropped into a romantic nineteenth-century French setting and completely turn the situation around, they do become very funny.

It's very possible, however, that you don't find any of this funny. Perhaps you cannot understand or identify with the setting or the characters. The setting is New York City, Kugelmass is a Jewish New Yorker, and he speaks of landmarks that are most familiar to native New Yorkers — Bloomingdale's, City College, the Bushwick section of Brooklyn, the Plaza Hotel. The places, the accents and attitudes of the people all have comic connotations that make the story seem funnier to people who have lived in New York. Some people may find Kugelmass more offensive than funny, and for them the humor would seem inappropriate.

We don't all like the same things, and we don't all find the same things funny. But look at one more example of Woody Allen's comic art. Sidney Kugelmass has just returned from his first romantic meeting with Emma Bovary in her novel. Every student who has ever struggled through an assigned novel for an English class should be able to recognize the comic possibilities of this passage.

Kugelmass hailed a cab and sped off to the city. His heart danced on point. I am in love, he thought, I am the possessor of a wonderful secret. What he didn't realize was that at this very moment students in various classrooms across the country were saying to their teachers, "Who is this character on page 100? A bald Jew is kissing Madame Bovary?" A teacher in Sioux Falls, South Dakota, sighed and thought, Jesus, these kids, with their pot and acid. What goes through their minds!

Once again, the author develops a romantic notion based on a fantastic and impossible situation, and then drops his comic bombshell by carrying the situation to its impossible, logically illogical, funny conclusion. Kugelmass has been transported into the novel *Madame Bovary* by The Great Persky's wonderful machine. The logical result of this impossible situation is that Kugelmass and Emma will be spotted together in the novel by students in Sioux Falls and elsewhere. It is also logical for the teacher, who hasn't seen Kugelmass in the book, to think his students are having an adverse reaction to drugs. Ridiculous? Of course. By this time everything is completely twisted beyond all reason, but we are so caught up in the fun that the story becomes more hilarious with each new complication.

Enjoying humor is the final test and ultimate proof of whether or not it has been successful as far as you are concerned. If you have found the sample passages as funny as most people do, then you have just joined the Woody Allen fan club or renewed your membership. In any case, read on. The story gets funnier.

As you read the story:

- Try to determine what is *really* bothering Kugelmass as he tells his analyst what he wants in life.

- Notice what modern American novelties Emma and Kugelmass talk about before she comes to New York.

- Watch for the Stanford professor's reaction to the strange goings-on in Emma's book.

- Decide what is funny about the predicament Kugelmass is in at the end of the story.

# The Kugelmass Episode
## Woody Allen

Kugelmass, a professor of humanities at City College, was unhappily married for the second time. Daphne Kugelmass was an oaf. He also had two dull sons by his first wife, Flo, and was up to his neck in alimony and child support.

"Did I know it would turn out so badly?" Kugelmass whined to his analyst one day. "Daphne had promise. Who suspected she'd let herself go and swell up like a beach ball? Plus she had a few bucks, which is not in itself a healthy reason to marry a person, but it doesn't hurt, with the kind of operating nut I have. You see my point?"

Kugelmass was bald and as hairy as a bear, but he had soul.

"I need to meet a new woman," he went on. "I need to have an affair. I may not look the part, but I'm a man who needs romance. I need softness, I need flirtation. I'm not getting younger, so before is too late I want to make love in Venice, trade quips at '21' and exchange coy glances over red wine and candlelight. You see what I'm saying?"

Dr. Mandel shifted in his chair and said, "An affair will solve nothing. You're so unrealistic. Your problems run much deeper."

"And also this affair must be discreet," Kugelmass continued. "I can't afford a second divorce. Daphne would really sock it to me."

"Mr. Kugelmass—"

"But it can't be anyone at City College, because Daphne also works there. Not that anyone on the faculty at CCNY is any great shakes, but some of those coeds ...."

"Mr. Kugelmass—"

"Help me. I had a dream last night. I was skipping through a meadow holding a picnic basket and the basket was marked 'Options.' And then I saw there was a hole in the basket."

"Mr. Kugelmass, the worst thing you could do is act out. You must simply express your feelings here, and together we'll analyze them. You have been in treatment long enough to know there is no overnight cure. After all, I'm an analyst, not a magician."

"Then perhaps what I need is a magician," Kugelmass said, rising from his chair. And with that he terminated his therapy.

A couple of weeks later, while Kugelmass and Daphne were moping around in their apartment one night like two pieces of old furniture, the phone rang.

"I'll get it," Kugelmass said. "Hello."

"Kugelmass?" a voice said. "Kugelmass, this is Persky."

"Who?"

"Persky. Or should I say The Great Persky?"

"Pardon me?"

"I hear you're looking all over town for a magician to bring a little exotica into your life? Yes or no?"

"Sh-h-h," Kugelmass whispered. "Don't hang up. Where are you calling from, Persky?"

Early the following afternoon, Kugelmass climbed three flights of stairs in a broken-down apartment house in the Bushwick section of Brooklyn. Peering through the darkness of the hall, he found the door he was looking for and pressed the bell. I'm going to regret this, he thought to himself.

Seconds later, he was greeted by a short, thin, waxy-looking man.

"*You're* Persky the Great?" Kugelmass said.

"The Great Persky. You want a tea?"

"No, I want romance. I want music. I want love and beauty."

"But not tea, eh? Amazing. OK, sit down."

Persky went to the back room, and Kugelmass heard the sounds of boxes and furniture being moved around. Persky reappeared, pushing before him a large object on squeaky roller-skate wheels. He removed some old silk handkerchiefs that were lying on its top and blew away a bit of dust. It was a cheap-looking Chinese cabinet, badly lacquered.

"Persky," Kugelmass said, "what's your scam?"

"Pay attention," Persky said. "This is some beautiful effect. I developed it for a Knights of Phythias date last year, but the booking fell through. Get into the cabinet."

"Why, so you can stick it full of swords or something?"

"You see any swords?"

Kugelmass made a face and, grunting, climbed into the cabinet. He couldn't help noticing a couple of ugly rhinestones glued onto the raw plywood just in front of his face. "If this is a joke," he said.

"Some joke. Now, here's the point. If I throw any novel into this cabinet with you, shut the doors and tap it three times, you will find yourself projected into that book."

Kugelmass made a grimace of disbelief.

"It's the emess," Persky said. "My hand to God. Not just a novel, either. A short story, a play, a poem. You can meet any of the women created by the world's best writers. Whoever you dreamed of. You could carry on all you like with a real winner. Then when you've had enough you give a yell, and I'll see you're back here in a split second."

"Persky, are you some kind of outpatient?"

"I'm telling you it's on the level," Persky said.

Kugelmass remained skeptical. "What are you telling me—that this cheesy homemade box can take me on a ride like you're describing?"

"For a double sawbuck."

Kugelmass reached for his wallet. "I'll believe this when I see it," he said.

Persky tucked the bills in his pants pocket and turned toward his bookcase. "So who do you want to meet? Sister Carrie? Hester Prynne? Ophelia? Maybe someone by Saul Bellow? Hey, what about Temple Drake? Although for a man your age she'd be a workout."

"French. I want to have an affair with a French lover."

"Nana?"

"I don't want to have to pay for it."

"What about Natasha in *War and Peace*?"

"I said French. I know! What about Emma Bovary? That sounds to me perfect."

"You got it, Kugelmass. Give me a holler when you've had enough." Persky tossed in a paperback copy of Flaubert's novel.

"You sure this is safe?" Kugelmass asked as Persky began shutting the cabinet doors.

"Safe. Is anything safe in this crazy world?" Persky rapped three times on the cabinet and then flung open the doors.

Kugelmass was gone. At the same moment, he appeared in the bedroom of Charles and Emma Bovary's house at Yonville. Before him was a beautiful woman, standing alone with her back turned to him as she folded some linen. I can't believe this, thought Kugelmass, staring at the doctor's ravishing wife. This is uncanny. I'm here. It's her.

Emma turned in surprise. "Goodness, you startled me," she said. "Who are you?" She spoke in the same fine English translation as the paperback.

It's simply devastating, he thought. Then, realizing that it was he whom she had addressed, he said, "Excuse me. I'm Sidney Kugelmass. I'm from City College. A professor of humanities. CCNY? Uptown. I—oh, boy!"

Emma Bovary smiled flirtatiously and said, "Would you like a drink? A glass of wine, perhaps?"

She is beautiful, Kugelmass thought. What a contrast with the troglodyte who shared his bed! He felt a sudden impulse to take this vision into his arms and tell her she was the kind of woman he had dreamed of all his life.

"Yes, some wine," he said hoarsely. "White. No, red. No, white. Make it white."

"Charles is out for the day," Emma said, her voice full of playful implication.

After the wine, they went for a stroll in the lovely French countryside. "I've always dreamed that some mysterious stranger would appear and rescue me from the monotony of this crass rural existence,' Emma said, clasping his hand. They passed a small church. "I love what you have on," she murmured. "I've never seen anything like it around here. It's so . . . so modern."

"It's called a leisure suit," he said romantically. "It was marked down." Suddenly he kissed her. For the next hour they reclined under a tree and whispered together and told each other deeply meaningful things with their eyes. Then Kugelmass sat up. He had just remembered he had to meet Daphne at Bloomingdale's. "I must go," he told her. "But don't worry, I'll be back."

"I hope so," Emma said.

He embraced her passionately, and the two walked back to the house. He held Emma's face cupped in his palms, kissed her again and yelled, "OK, Persky! I got to be at Bloomingdale's by three-thirty."

There was an audible pop, and Kugelmass was back in Brooklyn.

"So? Did I lie?" Persky asked triumphantly.

"Look, Persky, I'm right now late to meet the ball and chain at Lexington Avenue, but when can I go again? Tomorrow?"

"My pleasure. Just bring a twenty. And don't mention this to anybody."

"Yeah. I'm going to call Rupert Murdoch."

Kugelmass hailed a cab and sped off to the city. His heart danced on point. I am in love, he thought, I am the possessor of a wonderful secret. What he didn't realize was that at this very moment students in various classrooms across the country were saying to their teachers, "Who is this character on page 100? A bald Jew is kissing Madame Bovary?" A teacher in Sioux Falls, South Dakota, sighed and thought, Jesus, these kids, with their pot and acid. What goes through their minds!

Daphne Kugelmass was in the bathroom-accessories department at Bloomingdale's when Kugelmass arrived breathlessly. "Where've you been?" she snapped. "It's four-thirty."

"I got held up in traffic," Kugelmass said.

Kugelmass visited Persky the next day, and in a few minutes was again passed magically to Yonville. Emma couldn't hide her excitement at seeing him. The two spent hours together, laughing and talking about their different backgrounds. Before Kugelmass left, they made love. "My God, I'm doing it with Madame Bovary!" Kugelmass whispered to himself. "Me, who failed freshman English."

As the months passed, Kugelmass saw Persky many times and developed a close and passionate relationship with Emma Bovary. "Make sure and always get me into the book before page 120," Kugelmass said to the magician one day. "I always have to meet her before she hooks up with this Rodolphe character."

"Why?" Persky asked. "You can't beat his time?"

"Beat his time. He's landed gentry. Those guys have nothing better to do than flirt and ride horses. To me, he's one of those faces you see in the pages of *Women's Wear Daily*. With the Helmut Berger hairdo. But to her he's hot stuff."

"And her husband suspects nothing?"

"He's out of his depth. He's a lacklustre little paramedic who's thrown in his lot with a jitterbug. He's ready to go to sleep by ten, and she's putting on her dancing shoes. Oh, well.... See you later."

And once again Kugelmass entered the cabinet and passed instantly to the Bovary estate at Yonville. "How you doing, cupcake?" he said to Emma.

"Oh, Kugelmass," Emma sighed. "What I have to put up with. Last night at dinner, Mr. Personality dropped off to sleep in the middle of the dessert course. I'm pouring my heart out about Maxim's and the ballet, and out of the blue I hear snoring."

"It's OK, darling. I'm here now," Kugelmass said, embracing her. I've earned this, he thought, smelling Emma's French perfume and burying his nose in her hair. I've suffered enough. I've paid enough analysts. I've searched till I'm weary. She's young and nubile, and I'm here a few pages after Leon and just before Rodolphe. By showing up during the correct chapters, I've got the situation knocked.

Emma, to be sure, was just as happy as Kugelmass. She had been starved for excitement, and his tales of Broadway night life, of fast cars and Hollywood and TV stars, enthralled the young French beauty.

"Tell me again about O.J. Simpson," she implored that evening, as she and Kugelmass strolled past Abbe Bournisien's church.

"What can I say? The man is great. He sets all kinds of rushing records. Such moves. They can't touch him."

"And the Academy Awards?" Emma said wistfully. "I'd give anything to win one."

"First you've got to be nominated."

"I know. You explained it. But I'm convinced I can act. Of course, I'd want to take a class or two. With Strasberg maybe. Then, if I had the right agent—"

"We'll see, we'll see. I'll speak to Persky."

That night, safely returned to Persky's flat, Kugelmass brought up the idea of having Emma visit him in the big city.

"Let me think about it," Persky said. "Maybe I could work it. Stranger things have happened." Of course, neither of them could think of one.

"Where the hell do you go all the time?" Daphne Kugelmass barked at her husband as he returned home late that evening. "You got a chippie stashed somewhere?"

"Yeah, sure, I'm just the type," Kugelmass said wearily. "I was with Leonard Popkin. We were discussing Socialist agriculture in Poland. You know Popkin. He's a freak on the subject."

"Well, you've been very odd lately," Daphne said. "Distant. Just don't forget about my father's birthday. On Saturday?"

"Oh, sure, sure," Kugelmass said, heading for the bathroom.

"My whole family will be there. We can see the twins. And Cousin Hamish. You should be more polite to Cousin Hamish—he likes you."

"Right, the twins," Kugelmass said, closing the bathroom door and shutting out the sound of his wife's voice. He leaned against it and took a deep breath. In a few hours, he told himself, he would be back in Yonville again, back with his beloved. And this time, if all went well, he would bring Emma back with him.

At three-fifteen the following afternoon, Persky worked his wizardry again. Kugelmass appeared before Emma, smiling and eager. The two spent a few hours at Yonville with Binet and then remounted the Bovary carriage. Following Persky's instructions, they held each other tightly, closed their eyes and counted to ten. When they opened them, the carriage was just drawing up at the side door of the Plaza Hotel, where Kugelmass had optimistically reserved a suite earlier in the day.

"I love it! It's everything I dreamed it would be,' Emma said as she swirled joyously around the bedroom, surveying the city from their window. "There's FAO Schwarz. And there's Central Park, and the Sherry is which one? Oh, there—I see. It's too divine."

On the bed there were boxes from Halston and Saint Laurent. Emma unwrapped a package and held up a pair of black velvet pants against her perfect body.

"The slacks suit is by Ralph Lauren," Kugelmass said. "You'll look like a million bucks in it. Come on, sugar, give us a kiss."

"I've never been so happy!" Emma squealed as she stood before the mirror. "Let's go out on the town. I want to see *Chorus Line* and the Guggenheim and this Jack Nicholson character you always talk about. Are any of his flicks showing?"

"I cannot get my mind around this," a Stanford professor said. "First a strange character named Kugelmass, and now she's gone from the book. Well, I guess the mark of a classic is that you can reread it a thousand times and always find something new."

The lovers passed a blissful weekend. Kugelmass had told Daphne he would be away at a symposium in Boston and would return Monday. Savoring each moment, he and Emma went to the movies, had dinner in Chinatown, passed two hours at a discotheque and went to bed with a TV movie. They slept till noon on Sunday, visited SoHo and ogled celebrities at Elaine's. They had caviar and champagne in their suite on Sunday night and talked until dawn. That morning, in the cab taking them to Persky's apartment, Kugelmass thought, I can't bring her here too often, but now and then it will be a charming contrast with Yonville.

At Persky's, Emma climbed into the cabinet, arranged her new boxes of clothes neatly around her and kissed Kugelmass fondly. 'My place next time" she said with a wink. Persky rapped three times on the cabinet. Nothing happened.

"Hmm," Persky said, scratching his head. He rapped again, but still no magic. "Something must be wrong," he mumbled.

"Persky, you're joking!" Kugelmass cried. "How can it not work?"

"Relax, relax. Are you still in the box, Emma?"

"Yes."

Persky rapped again—harder this time.

"I'm still here, Persky."

"I know, darling. Sit tight."

"Persky, we *have* to get her back," Kugelmass whispered. "I'm a married man, and I have a class in three hours. I'm not prepared for anything more than a cautious affair at this point."

"I can't understand it," Persky muttered. "It's such a reliable little trick."

But he could do nothing. "It's going to take a little while," he said to Kugelmass. "I'm going to have to strip it down. I'll call you later."

Kugelmass bundled Emma into a cab and took her back to the Plaza. He barely made it to his class on time. He was on the phone all day, to Persky and to his mistress. The magician told him it might be several days before he got to the bottom of the trouble.

"How was the symposium?" Daphne asked him that night.

"Fine, fine," he said, lighting the filter end of a cigarette.

"What's wrong? You're as tense as a cat."

"Me? Ha, that's a laugh. I'm as calm as a summer night. I'm just going to take a walk." He eased out the door, hailed a cab and flew to the Plaza.

"This is no good," Emma said. "Charles will miss me."

"Bear with me, sugar," Kugelmass said. He was pale and sweaty. He kissed her again, raced to the elevators, yelled at Persky over a pay phone in the Plaza lobby and just made it home before midnight.

"According to Popkin, barley prices in Krakow have not been this stable since 1971," he said to Daphne, and smiled wanly as he climbed into bed.

The whole week went by like that. On Friday night, Kugelmass told Daphne there was another symposium he had to catch, this one in Syracuse. He hurried back to the Plaza, but the second weekend there was nothing like the first. "Get me back into the novel or marry me," Emma told Kugelmass. "Meanwhile, I want to get a job or go to class, because watching TV all day is the pits."

"Fine, we can use the money," Kugelmass said. "You consume twice your weight in room service."

"I met an off-Broadway producer in Central Park yesterday, and he said I might be right for a project he's doing," Emma said.

"Who is this clown?" Kugelmass asked.

"He's not a clown. He's sensitive and kind and cute. His name's Jeff Something-or-Other, and he's up for a Tony."

Later that afternoon, Kugelmass showed up at Persky's drunk.

"Relax," Persky told him. "You'll get a coronary."

"Relax. The man says relax. I've got a fictional character stashed in a hotel room, and I think my wife is having me tailed by a private shamus."

"OK, OK. We know there's a problem." Persky crawled under the cabinet and started banging on something with a large wrench.

"I'm like a wild animal," Kugelmass went on. "I'm sneaking around town, and Emma and I have had it up to here with each other. Not to mention a hotel tab that reads like the defense budget."

"So what should I do? This is the world of magic," Persky said. "It's all nuance."

"Nuance, my foot. I'm pouring Dom Pérignon and black eggs into this little mouse, plus her wardrobe, plus she's enrolled at the Neighborhood Playhouse and suddenly needs professional photos. Also, Persky, Professor Fivish Kopkind, who teaches Comp Lit and who has always been jealous of me, has identified me as the sporadically appearing character in the Flaubert book. He's threatened to go to Daphne. I see ruin and alimony jail. For adultery with Madame Bovary, my wife will reduce me to beggary."

"What do you want me to say? I'm working on it night and day. As far as your personal anxiety goes, that I can't help you with. I'm a magician, not an analyst."

By Sunday afternoon, Emma had locked herself in the bathroom and refused to respond to Kugelmass's entreaties. Kugelmass stared out the window at the Wollman Rink and contemplated suicide. Too bad this is a low floor, he thought, or I'd do it right now. Maybe if I ran away to Europe and started life over ... Maybe I could sell the *International Herald Tribune*, like those young girls used to.

The phone rang. Kugelmass lifted it to his ear mechanically.

"Bring her over," Persky said. "I think I got the bugs out of it."

Kugelmass's heart leaped. "You're serious?" he said. "You got it licked?"

"It was something in the transmission. Go figure."

"Persky, you're a genius. We'll be there in a minute. Less than a minute."

Again the lovers hurried to the magician's apartment, and again Emma Bovary climbed into the cabinet with her boxes. This time there was no kiss. Persky shut the doors, took a deep breath and tapped the box three times. There was the reassuring popping noise, and when Persky peered inside, the box was empty. Madame Bovary was back in her novel. Kugelmass heaved a great sigh of relief and pumped the magician's hand.

"It's over," he said. "I learned my lesson. I'll never cheat again, I swear it." He pumped Persky's hand again and made a mental note to send him a necktie.

Three weeks later, at the end of a beautiful spring afternoon, Persky answered his doorbell. It was Kugelmass, with a sheepish expression on his face.

"OK, Kugelmass," the magician said. "Where to this time?"

"It's just this once," Kugelmass said. "The weather is so lovely, and I'm not getting any younger. Listen, you've read *Portnoy's Complaint*? Remember The Monkey?"

"The price is now twenty-five dollars, because the cost of living is up, but I'll start you off with one freebie, due to all the trouble I caused you."

"You're good people," Kugelmass said, combing his few remaining hairs as he climbed into the cabinet again. "This'll work all right?"

"I hope. But I haven't tried it much since all that unpleasantness."

"Sex and romance," Kugelmass said from inside the box. "What we go through for a pretty face."

Persky tossed in a copy of *Portnoy's Complaint* and rapped three times on the box. This time, instead of a popping noise there was a dull explosion, followed by a series of crackling noises and a shower of sparks. Persky leaped back, was seized by a heart attack and dropped dead. The cabinet burst into flames, and eventually the entire house burned down.

Kugelmass, unaware of this catastrophe, had his own problems. He had not been thrust into *Portnoy's Complaint*, or into any other novel, for that matter. He had been projected into an old textbook, *Remedial Spanish*, and was running for his life over a barren, rocky terrain as the word tener ("to have")—a large and hairy irregular verb—raced after him on its spindly legs.

# Unit 12

## The Kugelmass Episode

- **Comprehension Questions**
- **Humor**
- **Discussion Guides**
- **Writing Exercise**

## COMPREHENSION QUESTIONS

For each of the following statements and questions, select the option containing the most complete or most accurate answer.

1. Dr. Mandel was Kugelmass's
(a) □ a. family doctor.        □ c. analyst.
   □ b. dentist.              □ d. chiropractor.


2. Kugelmass says he wants
(c) □ a. romance in his life.
   □ b. a date with a City College coed.
   □ c. excitement and danger.
   □ d. financial security.


3. Kugelmass considers his marrage to Daphne
(g) □ a. acceptable.          □ c. challenging.
   □ b. better than some.     □ d. dull.


4. Kugelmass said that Daphne's money helped him with his *operating nut.*
(l) This is a slang business expression which in this context seems to mean
   □ a. expenses.             □ c. bookkeeping.
   □ b. inventory.            □ d. insurance.


5. Persky was
(a) □ a. an analyst.          □ c. a writer.
   □ b. a magician.           □ d. a lawyer.


6. Emma is from the novel
(b) □ a. *Emma.*              □ c. *Lady Chatterly's Lover.*
   □ b. *Madame Bovary.*      □ d. *The Magic Mountain.*


7. Emma spoke to Kugelmass
(b) □ a. in French.
   □ b. with a New York accent.
   □ c. in fine English.
   □ d. in English with a French accent.

8. Kuglemass visited Emma in France

(d) ☐ a. many times.      ☐ c. only once.
    ☐ b. twice.            ☐ d. infrequently.

9. Daphne Kugelmass

(c) ☐ a. did not suspect her husband.
    ☐ b. was suspicious of her husband.
    ☐ c. approved of her husband's conduct.
    ☐ d. wished to share her husband's adventures.

10. Emma is best described as

(j) ☐ a. loving and considerate.
    ☐ b. sympathetic and understanding.
    ☐ c. sloppy and careless.
    ☐ d. fickle and demanding.

11. Charles is identified as Emma's husband. It is left to the reader to infer

(h) that Léon and Rodolphe are her
    ☐ a. servants.      ☐ c. guards.
    ☐ b. lovers.         ☐ d. relatives.

12. After entertaining Emma in New York, Kuglemass

(e) ☐ a. became tired of her.
    ☐ b. appreciated Daphne more.
    ☐ c. loved her more dearly.
    ☐ d. still preferred coeds.

13. Living in New York, Emma

(j) ☐ a. becomes sophisticated.
    ☐ b. retains her French dignity.
    ☐ c. acts like a stage-struck girl.
    ☐ d. becomes morose and withdrawn.

14. When Persky's machine broke down, Emma

(d) ☐ a. went into hiding.
    ☐ b. returned to the Plaza Hotel.
    ☐ c. remained in her room.
    ☐ d. stayed with Persky.

15. Persky's machine can't return Emma to Yonville. Kugelmass becomes
(k) frightened and excited. Persky says, "I can't understand it. It's such a
reliable little trick." The humor comes from
   ☐ a. exaggeration.       ☐ c. understatement.
   ☐ b. letdown.            ☐ d. slapstick.

16. When Emma was unable to return to her novel, the relationship with
(i) Kugelmass became
   ☐ a. close and intimate.     ☐ c. distant and reserved.
   ☐ b. calm and settled.      ☐ d. strained and hectic.

17. Emma said that watching TV all day is the pits. This is apt to strike you
(k) funny because
   ☐ a. authors rarely use slang.
   ☐ b. the expression is unexpected from a French lady.
   ☐ c. watching TV all day is a human failing.
   ☐ d. slang is always comical.

18. Kugelmass thinks his wife is having him *tailed by a private shamus*. This
(l) is slang for
   ☐ a. followed by a detective.
   ☐ b. checked by a credit agency.
   ☐ c. investigated by the F.B.I.
   ☐ d. sued by a lawyer.

19. Kugelmass ended his therapy because
(e) ☐ a. he disliked his analyst.
   ☐ b. he ran out of money.
   ☐ c. he wanted an easy solution to his problems.
   ☐ d. he had worked through all his problems.

20. After getting to know Emma and Kugelmass, you may conclude that
(f) they
   ☐ a. are contented and happy people.
   ☐ b. can never be satisfied with their lives.
   ☐ c. are a good influence on each other.
   ☐ d. can find happiness if they try.

21. Dr. Mandel says, "I'm not a magician." Persky says, "I'm not an analyst."
(g) You may judge from this that
- ☐ a. they don't want to help Kugelmass.
- ☐ b. Kugelmass won't cooperate.
- ☐ c. together they can help Kugelmass.
- ☐ d. neither one can help Kugelmass.

22. Emma meets "an off-Broadway producer" in Central Park. She says he
(h) is sensitive and kind. He is probably
- ☐ a. from another novel.
- ☐ b. forward but sincere.
- ☐ c. a typical New York theater type.
- ☐ d. feeding Emma a line.

23. When Kugelmass considers suicide or running away to Europe, the tone
(i) of the story
- ☐ a. becomes threatening.
- ☐ b. turns serious.
- ☐ c. is moralistic.
- ☐ d. remains humorous.

24. You may conclude from the story that Kugelmass is
(f)
- ☐ a. selfish.
- ☐ b. generous toward women.
- ☐ c. generous with everyone.
- ☐ d. rich.

25. The ending of the story emphasizes the idea that
(e)
- ☐ a. love can be dangerous.
- ☐ b. some people never learn a lesson.
- ☐ c. magic can be a force for evil.
- ☐ d. you should not tempt fate.

---

Comprehension Skills: a — isolating details; b — recalling specific facts; c — retaining concepts; d — organizing facts; e — understanding the main idea; f — drawing a conclusion; g — making a judgment; h — making an inference; i — recognizing tone; j — understanding characters; k — appreciation of literary forms; l — understanding vocabulary.

# HUMOR

**Practice Exercise A**

Kugelmass was bald and as hairy as a bear, but he had soul.

"I need to meet a new woman," he went on. "I need to have an affair.
I may not look the part, but I'm a man who needs romance. I need softness,
I need flirtation. I'm not getting younger, so before it's too late I want to
make love in Venice, trade quips at '21' and exchange coy glances over red
wine and candlelight. You see what I'm saying?"

1. The humor in this passage comes from the comic contrast between our
   view of Kugelmass and
   ☐ a. Kugelmass's view of us.     ☐ c. Kugelmass's view of himself.
   ☐ b. his analyst's view of him.     ☐ d. his wife's view of him.

2. Kugelmass expresses many "needs" and wants. But one phrase seems to
   get to the root of his problem. Circle the phrase that tells what is *really*
   bothering Kugelmass.

**Practice Exercise B**

Emma, to be sure, was just as happy as Kugelmass. She had been starved
for excitement, and his tales of Broadway night life, of fast cars and Hollywood and TV stars, enthralled the young French beauty.

"Tell me again about O. J. Simpson," she implored that evening, as she
and Kugelmass strolled past Abbe Bournisien's church.

"What can I say? The man is great. He sets all kinds of rushing records.
Such moves. They can't touch him."

1. The element of comic surprise occurs when we find that a nineteenth-
   century French beauty is interested in
   ☐ a. a football player.     ☐ c. night life.
   ☐ b. excitement.     ☐ d. Kugelmass.

2. Emma has a need that will cause problems for Kugelmass later. On the
   lines provided, write the expression that describes her need.

_____

_____

_____

## Practice Exercise C

"I cannot get my mind around this," a Stanford professor said. "First a strange character named Kugelmass, and now she's gone from the book. Well, I guess the mark of a classic is that you can reread it a thousand times and always find something new."

1. What is happening in this passage may best be described as
   - ☐ a. interesting.
   - ☐ b. stimulating.
   - ☐ c. phony.
   - ☐ d. absurd.

2. A Stanford professor of English may be expected to be very knowledgeable and sophisticated about literature. But this professor is confused. On the lines provided, write the sentence in which the professor makes a shallow observation to explain his confusion.

_____

_____

_____

## Practice Exercise D

Persky tossed in a copy of *Portnoy's Complaint* and rapped three times on the box. This time, instead of a popping noise there was a dull explosion. . . . Persky leaped back, was seized by a heart attack and dropped dead. . . .

Kugelmass, unaware of this catastrophe, had his own problems. He had not been thrust into *Portnoy's Complaint,* or into any other novel, for that matter. He had been projected into an old textbook, *Remedial Spanish,* and was running for his life over a barren, rocky terrain as the word *tener* ("to have")—a large and hairy irregular verb—raced after him on its spindly legs.

1. One thing that makes this ending funny is the thought that
   - ☐ a. Kugelmass probably got what he deserved.
   - ☐ b. Persky failed again.
   - ☐ c. here, finally, is a real catastrophe.
   - ☐ d. textbooks are generally comical.

2. Circle the sentence which describes Kugelmass's comic fate which results from Persky's accident.

# DISCUSSION GUIDES

## Analyzing Humor

1. Woody Allen called Daphne an "oaf." Kugelmass said, "Who suspected she'd swell up like a beach ball?" Why is this funny, while saying that Daphne is a fat, stupid pig is not funny?

2. What makes The Great Persky a funny character?

3. The scenes with Kugelmass and Daphne in them are not very funny. Why not?

4. Kugelmass was bald, hairy and middle-aged. Why would the story not be as funny if he were young, dashing and handsome?

## Interpreting the Story

5. Poetic justice is loosely defined as the ideal distribution of rewards and punishments in the outcome of a story. The characters get their just deserts, in other words. What is the poetic justice in this story?

6. There is usually an element of mild satire in comedy and humor. Woody Allen is clearly poking fun at certain things and certain people. What and who are objects of satire in the story?

7. All of the characters except Emma are New York Jews. Is the story one big ethnic slur, therefore? Explain your opinion. Is there a difference between this story and jokes that deride Jews, Blacks, Poles, Italians and others? If so, what is the difference?

8. Humor is funniest when you can identify with the main character. In what ways can most of us identify with Kugelmass?

## Analyzing the Author's Technique

9. Woody Allen uses New York City as a setting for this story as he does for many of his movies. Other authors are also fond of using New York in their work. What does New York add to a funny story? What can a setting in New York contribute to a serious story or a tragic story?

10. There is a lot of conversation in the story among the characters, and most of it is heavily laced with modern slang. Even Emma Bovary uses modern slang expressions. In between conversational quotations, the author uses very correct narrative English. Why do you suppose Woody Allen didn't write the story all one way?

## WRITING EXERCISE

The following jokes are missing punch lines. Write a punch line for each joke. There are several possible funny endings in each case. One possible punch line for each joke is given in the answer key at the end of the book.

1. "Bob is divorcing Ethel because of a bowl of cereal."
   "That's silly. Why would anyone get a divorce over a bowl of cereal?"

2. "The President just solved the energy crisis."
   "He did? How?"

3. A comic birthday card: I wanted to give you a pair of genuine alligator shoes for your birthday, but

4. A letter to the editor: Dear Editor, I read your magazine every month with great relish, and

5. When I bite into a steak, I want it to be so rare that

6. "A spaceship landed in my backyard, and an alien creature got out."
   "It did! What did the creature look like?"
   "Sort of like a roast beef with eyes like stuffed olives and ears that stuck out like baked sweet potatoes."
   "Gee, where is he now?"

# The Man That Corrupted Hadleyburg

## Mark Twain

# Introduction

It is impossible to pick up a newspaper or listen to a news report without learning of some new corruption, somewhere, in business, in government, or in someone's private life. There is no doubt about it—the whole world is corrupt.

The whole world? Well, the whole world except *us*, of course—you, me, our families and our good friends and neighbors. People like us. We're totally honest and incorruptible—aren't we?

Mark Twain would have replied, "Maybe, but then maybe not," because he was highly skeptical about most human beings, their motives, and their actions. It was a skepticism that showed clearly in all of his work. He was especially suspicious of pretentious people—those who felt they were better than anyone else, being a cut or two above the crowd in wealth, social position, or in what they fancied to be their own virtue. So he took great delight, in his writing, in giving this kind of person his comeuppance. The method he used was satire.

The mythical town of Hadleyburg was full of people who were convinced of their total honesty. They saw themselves as an island of incorruptibility in an otherwise corrupt world. From the time they were babies, the children of Hadleyburg were brought up to be honest in all their dealings; no temptation to cheat or steal was ever put in their way. So honest were these people that it became a point of pride with them. And so prideful were they about their reputation for honesty that they became vain, forgetting that vanity is as much a sin as being dishonest. They also forgot, or perhaps they never knew, that vain people can never be honest with themselves or recognize their true natures.

Foremost and most self-righteous of all among this righteous population were the town's leading citizens. These became a target for the revenge of an unknown stranger who, upon passing through Hadleyburg, had been deeply offended in some way. How he took his revenge is the subject of the story—he plotted the sure corruption of the incorruptibles.

The people of Hadleyburg are a typical assortment of Mark Twain characters. On the good side are such people as Jack Halliday, the good-natured loafer; the Reverend Burgess, who had been wrongly accused of scandal by the town; and the late Barclay Goodson, who had been the "best-hated" man for accurately and publicly identifying his neighbors as "honest, narrow, self-righteous and stingy." On the bad side are the town's greedy and grasping leading citizens—businessman, banker, lawyer and a patent medicine quack.

Somewhere in between good and bad are the main characters of the story, Edward and Mary Richards. These two are hard-working, honest and well-liked people. They are unique among the town's nineteen leading citizens in that they are included with the cream of society not for their wealth—they have none of that—but for their basic decency. They are the people in the story who are most like you and me, honest at heart until overwhelming temptation is put in their way.

"The Man That Corrupted Hadleyburg" is a satire of small-town America. It begins with the kind of tongue-in-cheek, wry humor for which Mark Twain is so famous, but you will find that the end is all pathos and bitterness. In his later years, Twain was subjected to a series of personal and financial losses that turned his familiar humorous criticism of American manners into something more biting; the man himself became cynical and impatient with life. "The Man That Corrupted Hadleyburg" was written in these later, darker years.

In the following lesson you will learn how to recognize some of the elements of satire. You will also be shown how to tell when a story changes from satire into something else. As you read "The Man That Corrupted Hadleyburg," see if you can tell where the story ceases to be satire and becomes an account of human tragedy.

# Satire

"Nothing so needs reforming as other people's habits!" observed Mark Twain, and few people would deny that, by and large, human behavior leaves much to be desired.

It is a fact, however, that criticism is notoriously hard to peddle. Sermons go in one ear and out the other, and the latest newspaper editorial condemning this political scandal or that human action typically summons up a big "ho-hum" from most readers. No matter how well intentioned the critic or how constructive the criticism, most of us would just as soon remain in blissful ignorance of our faults.

How, then, does a critic reach an audience so unreceptive to his message? Well, one of the best ways is through *satire*. Satire is a style of writing that blends criticism with humor and wit. There are all shades and degrees of satire, from gentle barbs to venomous stings, but it's always attractively packaged in a comic wrapping.

Behind all satire is the belief that the least flattering motivations of individuals and institutions are probably the true ones. Satirists probe to find the *real* motives for people's actions and, by dramatizing the difference between appearance and reality, they seek to prod readers into an awareness of unpleasant truths—about themselves in particular and about society in general.

In the story you are about to read, the author presents a whole town that *appears* to be totally honest but is *in reality* completely corrupt. Within this satiric framework, Mark Twain takes aim at some favorite targets of satire—human greed, hypocrisy and vanity. Like many satirists, Twain relies heavily on such literary devices as sarcasm and irony to make his point.

**1. Greed and Hypocrisy Exposed with Sarcasm.** Money, it has been said, is the root of all evil. There's no denying that some people would sell their grandmother for a sack of gold. Satirists have no quarrel, however, with the person who is openly greedy. What they *do* object to is greed masquerading as virtue because this is hypocritical. People or institutions that pretend to be more virtuous than they really are are fair game for the satirist.

In "The Man That Corrupted Hadleyburg," a trap is set with a sack of gold as bait to test the honesty of an entire town. Supposedly, the money belongs to the man who once did a great service for the late Barclay Goodson, the town's most hated citizen. In fact, however, no one in town ever did Barclay Goodson a good turn, and no one is entitled to the money. Undeterred by this small technicality, one of the leading citizens of Hadleyburg, Edward Richards, devises an elaborate story to justify his greed:

> ...of course he had done that service—that was settled; but what *was* that service? He must recall it....
>
> ...And sure enough, by-and-by he found it. Goodson, years and years ago, came near marrying a very sweet and pretty girl, named Nancy Hewitt, but in some way or other the match had been broken off; the girl died.... Soon after the girl's death the village found out, or thought it had found out, that she carried a spoonful of negro blood in her veins. Richards worked at these details a good while, and in the end he thought he remembered things concerning them which must have gotten mislaid in his memory through long neglect. He seemed to dimly remember that it was *he* that found out about the negro blood; ...that he thus saved Goodson from marrying the tainted girl.... It was all clear and simple now, and the more he went over it the more luminous and certain it grew; and at last, when he nestled to sleep satisfied and happy, he remembered the whole thing just as if it had been yesterday. In fact, he dimly remembered Goodson's *telling* him his gratitude once.

Satire, as we said, exposes hypocrisy wherever it finds it. Greed almost always inspired hypocrisy simply because no one likes to admit that he or she is greedy. In the passage above, poor Mr. Richards performs feats of mental gymnastics to support his claim to the sack of gold. First, he dreams up a "favor" he did for Goodson, and then he actually convinces himself that the story he has woven out of thin air is true— "...the more he went over it the more luminous and certain it grew...."

What makes this passage satiric is the sarcastic tone which the author uses. *Sarcasm* is a figure of speech used to suggest the opposite of what is actually said, and the passage above is heavy with sarcasm. The so-called "favor" which Richards imagines he performed for Goodson was to break up the man's engagement to "a very sweet and pretty girl"—a deed that is not a favor at all, but a terrible wrong. The more Richards pursues this flight of fancy, the more sarcastic the author's tone. The business about Nancy Hewitt becomes "all clear and simple now" when, of course, Richards has just finished distorting the facts beyond all recognition. And to top it off, Richards "dimly remembers Goodson *telling* him his gratitude once," although the reader has a pretty strong suspicion that Goodson probably told Richards something entirely different. Here and throughout the story, the author uses sarcasm to poke fun at human pretensions.

**2. Vanity Exposed with Irony.** People who are vain, who have an excessively high opinion of themselves, are often the butt of satire, possibly because it's so tempting to deflate an overblown ego.

Vanity turns out to be the downfall of the citizens of Hadleyburg, a town famed for its honesty. Their reputation becomes a point of tremendous pride among the citizens. Thus, when a stranger drops off a sack of gold with instructions that it be delivered to its rightful owner, their vanity knows no bounds. Everybody shakes hands with everybody else, slaps one another on the back, and congratulates each other on this display of confidence in their honesty. A public meeting is held at the Town Hall to award the money, and everyone cheers when the moderator proclaims:

> "To-day your purity is beyond reproach.... To-day there is not a person in your community who could be beguiled to touch a penny not his own...."

The irony of the situation, of course, is that all of these supposedly honest people have been scheming to get the sack of gold for themselves. Irony is an effective vehicle for satire because, like sarcasm, it emphasizes the difference between what appears to be true and what actually is true.

**3. The Corruption of Truth Exposed with Sarcasm.** Lawyers are an easy target for satire because they represent an ideal—justice—and ideals are very hard to live up to. Here again, you have an appearance that is not always borne out by the reality. Half of the people involved in any lawsuit are bound to come away convinced there has been a miscarriage of justice simply because they lost. They'll blame it on the winning lawyer for twisting the facts and confusing the jury.

In "The Man That Corrupted Hadleyburg," Mark Twain capitalizes on these sentiments with a satiric attack on a lawyer named Wilson. Wilson is one of the "incorruptible" citizens of Hadleyburg who tries to get his hands on the sack of gold. When his claim is challenged, he responds in typical lawyer fashion with a fancy speech. This prompts Twain to remark,

> There is nothing in the world like a persuasive speech to fuddle the mental apparatus and upset the convictions and debauch the emotions of an audience not practiced in the tricks and delusions of oratory.

Satire, as we said, is at the same time critical and humorous, and this passage conveys both these qualities. The criticism, of course, is directed at Lawyer Wilson, who makes speeches not to reveal the truth, as a lawyer is supposed to do, but to confuse and even twist the truth. The humor lies in the sarcastic jibes Twain makes about the art of oratory and the intelligence of the average audience. Wilson's victory, it seems, is not won by clarifying matters but by deliberately confusing them. "There is nothing in the world like a persuasive speech," the narrator begins, and you'd expect this kind of sentence to finish something like, "... to set the story straight." Instead, he blames Wilson's speech for "fuddling the mental apparatus, upsetting the convictions and debauching [that is, corrupting] the emotions of the audience"—hardly fitting conduct for a lawyer! But then again, if his audience weren't so gullible, they'd see right through his slick speeches.

**4. Recognizing What Is and What Isn't Satire.** It's difficult sometimes to recognize what is and what isn't satire. Satire always includes sharp criticism couched in its humor, and it is always aimed at someone or something. The wacky humor of a comedian like Steve Martin is usually not satiric because it is broadly slapstick and it has no victim. The humor of satire, on the other hand, is often quite subtle and always has a victim. It has been said that the ability to recognize irony (and its close cousin, sarcasm) is one of the surest tests of a reader's intelligence and sophistication. This is because a reader must appreciate both the face value of the message *and* the overtones that carry the opposite meaning. Readers who fail to see both meanings miss the point of satire completely.

On the other hand, the critical side of satire must not be so heavyhanded that it ceases to be funny. A vicious personal attack is not satire, but *invective*. Invective is a literary term used to refer to harsh, abusive language. It's easy to recognize invective because it's so bitter and emotional, as if the author is expressing a deep personal grievance. Satiric criticism is usually more detached and unemotional. It is not directed against a particular individual so much as against a kind of behavior that all of us might be guilty of at one time or another. Furthermore, the character being criticized must not be so unfortunate as to command our sympathy. To criticize someone who is aware of his defects and feels bad about them is like kicking a man when he's down—it's not funny, it's pathetic.

The story you are about to read is satiric in many ways. You should be aware, however, that the last part of the story *is not* satire. Here, for example, is a passage that at first glance may seem satiric, but closer examination reveals that it is not. In this passage, Mr. and Mrs. Richards have just come into a large sum of money that they are not, strictly speaking, entitled to. They know it and they feel unbearably guilt-stricken.

> At home the Richardses had to endure congratulations and compliments until midnight. Then they were left to themselves. They looked a little sad, and they sat silent and thinking. Finally Mary sighed and said,
>
> "Do you think we are to blame, Edward—*much* to blame?" and her eyes wandered to the accusing triplet of big bank-notes lying on the table, where the congratulators had been gloating over them and reverently fingering them. Edward did not answer at once; then he brought out a sigh and said, hesitatingly:
>
> "We—we couldn't help it, Mary. It—well, it was ordered. *All* things are."

Here again you have people pretending to be something they're not. Mr. and Mrs. Richards are pretending to be entitled to the money when in fact they are not. In this case, however, the reader takes no pleasure in seeing them exposed; they are already aware of their guilt, and they are obviously suffering because of it. There is no humor or satisfaction to be had here.

As you read "The Man That Corrupted Hadleyburg," notice how the author combines criticism with humor to attack basic human frailties. Keep in mind, however, that the ending is not satiric. Satire must maintain a delicate balance between criticism and humor, and when you start feeling too sorry for the victims, you can be pretty sure that the scale has tipped.

As you read the story:

- Notice how the citizens of Hadleyburg feel about themselves when they learn that the newspapers have spread their story across the entire country.

- Try to identify the human weakness that becomes obvious whenever the townspeople view the sack of gold.

- Be aware of Harkness's motivations in buying the sack of gold from the stranger for $40,000.

- Think about why the ending of the story is not satiric.

# The Man That Corrupted Hadleyburg
## Mark Twain

It was many years ago. Hadleyburg was the most honest and upright town in all the region round about. It had kept that reputation unsmirched during three generations, and was prouder of it than of any other of its possessions. It was so proud of it, and so anxious to insure its perpetuation, that it began to teach the principles of honest dealing to its babies in the cradle, and made the like teachings the staple of their culture thenceforward through all the years devoted to their education. Also, throughout the formative years temptations were kept out of the way of the young people, so that their honesty could have every chance to harden and solidify, and become a part of their very bone. The neighboring towns were jealous of this honorable supremacy, and affected to sneer at Hadleyburg's pride in it and call it vanity; but all the same they were obliged to acknowledge that Hadleyburg was in reality an incorruptible town; and if pressed they would also acknowledge that the mere fact that a young man hailed from Hadleyburg was all the recommendation he needed when he went forth from his natal town to seek for responsible employment.

But at last, in the drift of time, Hadleyburg had the ill luck to offend a passing stranger—possibly without knowing it, certainly without caring, for Hadleyburg was sufficient unto itself, and cared not a rap for strangers or their opinions. Still, it would have been well to make an exception in this one's case, for he was a bitter man and revengeful. All through his wanderings during a whole year he kept his injury in mind, and gave all his leisure moments to trying to invent a compensating satisfaction for it. He contrived many plans, and all of them were good, but none of them was quite sweeping enough; the poorest of them would hurt a great many individuals, but what he wanted was a plan which would comprehend the entire town, and not let so much as one person escape unhurt. At last he had a fortunate idea, and when it fell into his brain it lit up his whole head with an evil joy. He began to form a plan at once, saying to himself, "That is the thing to do—I will corrupt the town."

Six months later he went to Hadleyburg, and arrived in a buggy at the house of the old cashier of the bank about ten at night. He got a sack out of the buggy, shouldered it, and staggered with it through the cottage yard, and knocked at the door. A woman's voice said "Come in," and he entered, and set his sack behind the stove in the parlor, saying politely to the old lady who sat reading the *Missionary Herald* by the lamp:

"Pray keep your seat, madam, I will not disturb you. There—now it is pretty well concealed; one would hardly know it was there. Can I see your husband a moment, madam?"

No, he was gone to Brixton, and might not return before morning.

"Very well, madam, it is no matter. I merely wanted to leave that sack in his care, to be delivered to the rightful owner when he shall be found. I am a stranger; he does not know me; I am merely passing through the town tonight to discharge a matter which has been long in my mind. My errand is now completed, and I go pleased and a little proud, and you will never see me again. There is a paper attached to the sack which will explain everything. Good-night, madam."

The old lady was afraid of the mysterious big stranger, and was glad to see him go. But her curiosity was roused, and she went straight to the sack and brought away the paper. It began as follows:

"TO BE PUBLISHED; *or, the right man sought out by private inquiry— either will answer. This sack contains gold coin weighing a hundred and sixty pounds four ounces—*"

"Mercy on us, and the door not locked!"

Mrs. Richards flew to it all in a tremble and locked it, then pulled down the window shades and stood frightened, worried, and wondering if there was anything else she could do toward making herself and the money more safe. She listened awhile for burglars, then surrendered to curiosity and went back to the lamp and finished reading the paper:

"*I am a foreigner, and am presently going back to my own country, to remain there permanently. I am grateful to America for what I have received at her hands during my stay under her flag; and to one of her citizens—a citizen of Hadleyburg—I am especially grateful for a great kindness done me a year or two ago. Two great kindnesses; in fact. I will explain. I was a gambler. I say I WAS. I was a ruined gambler. I arrived in this village at night, hungry and without a penny. I asked for help—in the dark; I was ashamed to beg in the light. I begged of the right man. He gave me twenty dollars—that is to say, he gave me life, as I considered it. He also gave me fortune; for out of that money I have made myself rich at the gaming-table. And finally, a remark which he made to me has remained with me to this day, and has at last conquered me; and in conquering has saved the remnant of my morals; I shall gamble no more. Now I have no idea who that man was, but I want him found, and I want him to have this money, to give away, throw away or keep, as he pleases. It is merely my way of testifying my gratitude to him. If I could stay, I would find him myself; but no matter, he will be found. This is an honest town, an incorruptible town, and I know I can trust it without fear. This man can be identified by the remark which he made to me; I feel persuaded that he will remember it.*

*"And now my plan is this: If you prefer to conduct the inquiry privately, do so. Tell the contents of this present writing to any one who is likely to be the right man. If he shall answer, 'I am the man; the remark I made was so-and-so,' apply the test—to wit: open the sack, and in it you will find a sealed envelope containing that remark. If the remark mentioned by the candidate tallies with it, give him the money, and ask no further questions, for he is certainly the right man.*

*"But if you shall prefer a public inquiry, then publish this present writing in the local paper—with these instructions added, to wit: Thirty days from now, let the candidate appear at the town hall at eight in the evening (Friday), and hand his remark, in a sealed envelope, to the Rev. Mr. Burgess (if he will be kind enough to act); and let Mr. Burgess there and then destroy the seals on the sack, open it, and see if the remark is correct; if correct, let the money be delivered, with my sincere gratitude, to my benefactor thus identified."*

Mrs. Richards sat down, gently, quivering with excitement and was soon lost in thinking—after this pattern: "What a strange thing it is!... And what a fortune for that kind man who set his bread afloat upon the waters!... If he had only been my husband that did it!—for we are so poor, so old and poor!..." Then, with a sigh—"But it was not my Edward; no, it was not he that gave the stranger twenty dollars. It is a pity too; I see it now...." Then, with a shudder—"But it is *gambler's* money! the wages of sin: we couldn't take it; we couldn't touch it. I don't like to be near it; it seems a defilement." She moved to a farther chair.... "I wish Edward would come, and take it to the bank; a burglar might come at any moment; it is dreadful to be here all alone with it."

At eleven Mr. Richards arrived, and while his wife was saying, "I am *so* glad you've come!" he was saying, "I'm so tired—tired clear out; it is dreadful to be poor, and have to make these dismal journeys at my time of life. Always at the grind, grind, grind, on a salary—another man's slave, and he sitting at home in his slippers, rich and comfortable."

"I am so sorry for you, Edward, you know that; but be comforted; we have our livelihood; we have our good name—"

"Yes, Mary, and that is everything. Don't mind my talk—it's just a moment's irritation and doesn't mean anything. Kiss me—there, it's all gone now, and I am not complaining any more. What have you been getting? What's in the sack?"

Then his wife told him the great secret. It dazed him for a moment; then he said:

"It weighs a hundred and sixty pounds? Why, Mary, it's for-ty thou-sand dollars—think of it—a whole fortune! Not ten men in this village are worth that much. Give me the paper."

He skimmed through it and said:

"Isn't it an adventure! Why, it's a romance; it's like the impossible things one reads about in books, and never sees in life." He was well stirred up now; cheerful, even gleeful. He tapped his old wife on the cheek, and said, humorously, "Why, we're rich, Mary, rich; all we've got to do is to bury the money and burn the papers. If the gambler ever comes to inquire, we'll merely look coldly upon him and say: 'What is this nonsense you are talking: We have never heard of you and your sack of gold before;' and then he would look foolish, and—"

"And in the mean time, while you are running on with your jokes, the money is still here, and it is fast getting along toward burglar-time."

"True, Very well, what shall we do—make the inquiry private? No, not that: it would spoil the romance. The public method is better. Think what a noise it will make! And it will make all the other towns jealous; for no stranger would trust such a thing to any town but Hadleyburg, and they know it. It's a great card for us. I must get to the printing office now, or I shall be too late."

"But stop—stop—don't leave me here alone with it, Edward!"

But he was gone. For only a little while, however. Not far from his own house he met the editor-proprietor of the paper, and gave him the document, and said, "Here is a good thing for you, Cox—put it in."

"It may be too late, Mr. Richards, but I'll see."

At home again he and his wife sat down to talk the charming mystery over; they were in no condition for sleep. The first question was, Who could the citizen have been who gave the stranger the twenty dollars? It seemed a simple one; both answered it in the same breath—

"Barclay Goodson."

"Yes," said Richards, "he could have done it, and it would have been like him, but there's not another in the town."

"Everybody will grant that, Edward—grant it privately, anyway. For six months, now, the village has been its own proper self once more—honest, narrow, self-righteous, and stingy."

"It is what he always called it, to the day of his death—said it right out publicly, too."

"Yes, and he was hated for it."

"Oh, of course; but he didn't care. I reckon he was the best-hated man among us, except the Reverend Burgess."

"Well, Burgess deserves it—he will never get another congregation here. Mean as the town is, it knows how to estimate *him*. Edward, doesn't it seem odd that the stranger should appoint Burgess to deliver the money?"

"Well, yes—it does. That is—that is—"

"Why so much that-*is*-ing? Would *you* select him?"

"Mary, maybe the stranger knows him better than this village does."

"Much *that* would help Burgess!"

The husband seemed perplexed for an answer; the wife kept a steady eye upon him, and waited. Finally Richards said, with the hesitancy of one who is making a statement which is likely to encounter doubt:

"Mary, Burgess is not a bad man."

His wife was certainly surprised.

"Nonsense!" she exclaimed.

"He is not a bad man. I know. The whole of his unpopularity had its foundation in that one thing—the thing that made so much noise."

"That 'one thing,' indeed! As if that 'one thing' wasn't enough, all by itself."

"Plenty. Plenty. Only he wasn't guilty of it."

"How you talk! Not guilty of it! Everybody knows he *was* guilty."

"Mary, I give you my word—he was innocent."

"I can't believe it, and I don't. How do you know?"

"It is a confession. I am ashamed, but I will make it. I was the only man who knew he was innocent. I could have saved him, and—and—well, you know how the town was wrought up—I hadn't the pluck to do it. It would have turned everybody against me. I felt mean, ever so mean; but I didn't dare; I hadn't the manliness to face that."

Mary looked troubled, and for a while was silent. Then she said, stammeringly:

"I—I don't think it would have done for you to—to—One mustn't—er—public opinion—one has to be so careful—so—" It was a difficult road, and she got mired; but after a little she got started again. "It was a great pity, but—Why, we couldn't afford it, Edward—we couldn't indeed. Oh, I wouldn't have had you do it for anything!"

"It would have lost us the good will of so many people, Mary; and then—and then—"

"What troubles me now is, what *he* thinks of us, Edward."

"He? *He* doesn't suspect that I could have saved him."

"Oh," exclaimed the wife, in a tone of relief, "I am glad of that. As long as he doesn't know that you could have saved him, he—he—well, that makes it a great deal better. Why, I might have known he didn't know, because he is always trying to be friendly with us, as little encouragement as we give him. More than once people have twitted me with it. There's the Wilsons, and the Wilcoxes, and the Harknesses, they take a mean pleasure in saying, '*Your friend* Burgess,' because they know it pesters me. I wish he wouldn't persist in liking us so; I can't think why he keeps it up."

"I can explain it. It's another confession. When the thing was new and hot, and the town made a plan to ride him on a rail, my conscience hurt me so that I couldn't stand it, and I went privately and gave him notice, and he got out of the town and stayed out till it was safe to come back."

"Edward! If the town had found it out—"

"*Don't!* It scares me yet, to think of it. I repented of it the minute it was done; and I was even afraid to tell you, lest your face might betray it to somebody. I didn't sleep any that night, for worrying. But after a few days I saw that no one was going to suspect me, and after that I got to feeling glad I did it. And I feel glad yet, Mary—glad through and through."

"So do I, now, for it would have been a dreadful way to treat him. Yes, I'm glad; for really you did owe him that, you know. But, Edward, suppose it should come out yet, some day!"

"It won't."

"Why!"

"Because everybody thinks it was Goodson."

"Of course they would!"

"Certainly. And of course *he* didn't care. They persuaded poor old Sawlsberry to go and charge it on him, and he went blustering over there and did it. Goodson looked him over, like as if he was hunting for a place on him that he could despise the most, then he says, 'So you are the Committee of Inquiry, are you?' Sawlsberry said that was about what he was. 'Hm. Do they require particulars, or do you reckon a kind of a *general* answer will do?' 'If they require particulars, I will come back, Mr. Goodson; I will take the general answer first.' 'Very well, then, tell them to go to hell—I reckon that's general enough. And I'll give you some advice, Sawlsberry; when you come back for the particulars, fetch a basket to carry the relics of yourself home in.' "

"Just like Goodson; it's got all the marks. He had only vanity; he thought he could give advice better than any other person."

"It settled the business, and saved us, Mary. The subject was dropped."

"Bless you, I'm not doubting *that.*"

Then they took up the gold-sack mystery again, with strong interest. Soon the conversation began to suffer breaks—interruptions caused by absorbed thinkings. The breaks grew more and more frequent. At last Richards lost himself wholly in thought. He sat long, gazing vacantly at the floor, and by-and-by he began to punctuate his thoughts with little nervous movements of his hands that seemed to indicate vexation. Meantime his wife too had relapsed into a thoughtful silence, and her movements were beginning to show a troubled discomfort. Finally Richards got up and strode aimlessly about the room, ploughing his hands through his hair, much as a somnambulist might do who was having a bad dream. Then he seemed to arrive at a definite purpose; and without a word he put on his hat and passed quickly out of the house. His wife sat brooding, with a drawn face, and did not seem to be aware that she was alone. Now and then she murmured, "Lead us not in t... but—but—we are so poor, so poor!... Lead us not into... Ah, who would be hurt by it?—and no one would ever know.... Lead us..." The voice died out in mumblings. After a little she glanced up and muttered in a half frightened, half-glad way—

"He is gone! But, oh dear, he may be too late—too late.... Maybe not—maybe there is still time." She rose and stood thinking, nervously clasping and unclasping her hands. A slight shudder shook her frame, and she said, out of a dry throat, "God forgive me—it's awful to think such things—but... Lord, how we are made—how strangely we are made!"

She turned the light low, and slipped stealthily over and kneeled down by the sack and felt of its ridgy sides with her hands, and fondled them lovingly; and there was a gloating light in her poor old eyes. She fell into fits of absence; and came half out of them at times to mutter, "If we had only waited!—oh, if we had only waited a little, and not been in such a hurry!"

Meantime Cox had gone home from his office and told his wife all about the strange thing that had happened, and they had talked it over eagerly, and guessed that the late Goodson was the only man in the town who could have helped a suffering stranger with so noble a sum as twenty dollars. Then there was a pause, and the two became thoughtful and silent. And by-and-by nervous and fidgety. At last the wife said, as if to herself:

"Nobody knows this secret but the Richardses... and us... nobody."

The husband came out of his thinkings with a slight start, and gazed wistfully at his wife, whose face was become very pale; then he hesitatingly rose, and glanced furtively at his hat, then at his wife—a sort of mute inquiry. Mrs. Cox swallowed once or twice, with her hand at her throat, then in place of speech she nodded her head. In a moment she was alone, and mumbling to herself.

And now Richards and Cox were hurrying through the deserted streets, from opposite directions. They met, panting, at the foot of the printing-office stairs; by the night-light there they read each other's face. Cox whispered:

"Nobody knows about this but us?"

The whispered answer was,

"Not a soul—on honor, not a soul!"

"If it isn't too late to—"

The men were starting upstairs; at this moment they were overtaken by a boy, and Cox asked:

"Is that you, Johnny?"

"Yes, sir."

"You needn't ship the early mail—nor *any* mail; wait till I tell you."

"It's already gone, sir."

"*Gone?*" It had the sound of an unspeakable disappointment in it.

"Yes, sir. Time-table for Brixton and all the towns beyond changed today, sir—had to get the papers in twenty minutes earlier than common. I had to rush; if I had been two minutes later—"

The men turned and walked slowly away, not waiting to hear the rest. Neither of them spoke during ten minutes; then Cox said, in a vexed tone:

"What possessed you to be in such a hurry, *I* can't make out."

"The answer was humble enough:

"I see it now, but somehow I never thought, you know, until it was too late. But the next time—"

"Next time be hanged! It won't come in a thousand years."

Then the friends separated without a good-night, and dragged themselves home with the gait of mortally stricken men. At their homes their wives sprang up with an eager "Well?"—then saw the answer with their eyes and sank down sorrowing, without waiting for it to come in words. In both houses a discussion followed of a heated sort—a new thing; there had been discussions before, but not heated ones, not ungentle ones. The discussions tonight were a sort of seeming plagiarisms of each other. Mrs. Richards said,

"If you had only waited, Edward—if you had only stopped to think; but no, you must run straight to the printing office and spread it all over the world."

"It *said* publish it."

"That is nothing; it also said do it privately, if you liked. There, now—is that true, or not?"

"Why, yes—yes, it is true; but when I thought what a stir it would make, and what a compliment it was to Hadleyburg that a stranger should trust it so—"

"Oh, certainly, I know all that; but if you had only stopped to think, you would have seen that you *couldn't* find the right man, because he is in his grave, and hasn't left chick nor child nor relation behind him; and as long as the money went to somebody that awfully needed it, and nobody would be hurt by it, and—and—"

She broke down, crying. Her husband tried to think of some comforting thing to say, and presently came out with this:

"But after all, Mary, it must be for the best—it *must* be; we know that. And we must remember that it was so ordered—"

"Ordered! Oh, everything's *ordered*, when a person has to find some way out when he has been stupid. Just the same, it was *ordered* that the money should come to us in this special way, and it was you that must take it on yourself to go meddling with the designs of Providence—and who gave you the right? It was wicked, that is what it was—just blasphemous presumption, and no more becoming to a meek and humble professor of—"

"But, Mary, you know how we have been trained all our lives long, like the whole village, till it is absolutely second nature to us to stop not a single moment to think when there's an honest thing to be done—"

"Oh, I know it, I know it—it's been one everlasting training and training and training in honesty—honesty shielded, from the very cradle, against every possible temptation, and so it's *artificial* honesty, and weak as water when temptation comes, as we have seen this night. God knows I never had shade nor shadow of a doubt of my petrified and indestructible honesty until now—and now, under the very first big and real temptation, I— Edward, it is my belief that this town's honesty is as rotten as mine is; as rotten as yours is. It is a mean town, a hard, stingy town, and hasn't a virtue in the world but this honesty it is so celebrated for and so conceited about; and so help me, I do believe that if ever the day comes that its honesty falls under great temptation, its grand reputation will go to ruin like a house of cards. There, now, I've made confession, and I feel better; I am a humbug, and I've been one all my life, without knowing it. Let no man call me honest again—I will not have it."

"I—Well, Mary, I feel a good deal as you do; I certainly do. It seems strange, too, so strange. I never could have believed it—never."

A long silence followed; both were sunk in thought. At last the wife looked up and said:

"I know what you are thinking, Edward."

Richards had the embarrassed look of a person who is caught.

"I am ashamed to confess it, Mary, but—"

"It's no matter, Edward, I was thinking the same question myself."

"I hope so. State it."

"You were thinking, if a body could only guess out *what the remark was* that Goodson made to the stranger."

"It's perfectly true. I feel guilty and ashamed. And you?"

"I'm past it. Let us make a pallet here; we've got to stand watch till the bank vault opens in the morning and admits the sack. ...Oh, dear, oh, dear—if we hadn't made the mistake!"

The pallet was made, and Mary said:

"The open sesame—what could it have been? I do wonder what that remark could have been? But come; we will get to bed now."

"And sleep?"

"No, think."

"Yes, think."

By this time the Coxes too had completed their spat and their reconciliation, and were turning in—to think, to think, and toss, and fret, and worry over what the remark could possibly have been which Goodson made to the stranded derelict: that golden remark; that remark worth forty thousand dollars, cash.

The reason that the village telegraph office was open later than usual that night was this: The foreman of Cox's paper was the local representative of the Associated Press. One might say its honorary representative, for it wasn't four times a year that he could furnish thirty words that would be accepted. But this time it was different. His despatch stating what he had caught got an instant answer:

*"Send the whole thing—all the details—twelve hundred words."*

A colossal order! The foreman filled the bill; and he was the proudest man in the State. By breakfast-time the next morning the name of Hadleyburg the Incorruptible was on every lip in America, from Montreal to the Gulf, from the glaciers of Alaska to the orange groves of Florida; and millions and millions of people were discussing the stranger and his money-sack, and wondering if the right man would be found, and hoping some more news about the matter would come soon—right away.

## II

Hadleyburg village woke up world-celebrated—astonished—happy—vain. Vain beyond imagination. Its nineteen principal citizens and their wives went about shaking hands with each other, and beaming, and smiling, and congratulating, and saying *this* thing adds a new word to the dictionary—*Hadleyburg,* synonym for *incorruptible*—destined to live in dictionaries forever! And the minor and unimportant citizens and their wives went around acting in much the same way. Everybody ran to the bank to see the gold-sack; and before noon grieved and envious crowds began to flock in from Brixton and all the neighboring towns; and that afternoon and next day reporters began to arrive from everywhere to verify the sack and its history and write the whole thing up anew, and make dashing free-hand pictures of the sack and of Richards's house, and the bank, and the Presbyterian church, and the Baptist church, and the public square, and the town hall where the test would be applied and the money delivered; and damnable portraits of the Richardses, and Pinkerton the banker, and Cox, and the foreman, and Reverend Burgess, and the postmaster—and even of Jack Halliday, who was the loafing, goodnatured, no-account, irreverent fisherman, hunter, boys' friend, stray-dog's friend, typical "Sam Lawson"[1] of the town. The little mean, smirking, oily Pinkerton showed the sack to all comers, and rubbed his sleek palms together pleasantly, and enlarged upon the town's fine old reputation for honesty and upon this wonderful endorsement of it, and hoped and believed that the example would now spread far and wide over the American world, and be epoch-making in the matter of moral regeneration. And so on, and so on.

[1]A lazy, humorous Yankee character who appears in some Harriet Beecher Stowe stories.

By the end of a week things had quieted down again; the wild intoxication of pride and joy had sobered to a soft, sweet, silent delight—a sort of deep, nameless, unutterable content. All faces bore a look of peaceful, holy happiness.

Then a change came. It was a gradual change: so gradual that its beginnings were hardly noticed; maybe were not noticed at all, except by Jack Halliday, who always noticed everything; and always made fun of it, too, no matter what it was. He began to throw out chaffing remarks about people not looking quite so happy as they did a day or two ago; and next he claimed that the new aspect was deepening to positive sadness; next, that it was taking on a sick look; and finally he said that everybody was become so moody, thoughtful, and absent-minded that he could rob the meanest man in town of a cent out of the bottom of his breeches pocket and not disturb his revery.

At this stage—or at about this stage—a saying like this was dropped at bedtime—with a sigh, usually—by the head of each of the nineteen principal households: "Ah, what *could* have been the remark that Goodson made!"

And straightway—with a shudder—came this, from the man's wife:

"Oh, *don't!* What horrible thing are you mulling in your mind? Put it away from you, for God's sake!"

But that question was wrung from those men again the next night—and got the same retort. But weaker.

And the third night the men uttered the question yet again—with anguish, and absently. This time—and the following night—the wives fidgeted feebly, and tried to say something. But didn't.

And the night after that they found their tongues and responded—longingly,

"Oh, if we *could* only guess!"

Halliday's comments grew daily more and more sparklingly disagreeable and disparaging. He went diligently about, laughing at the town, individually and in mass. But his laugh was the only one left in the village: it fell upon a hollow and mournful vacancy and emptiness. Not even a smile was findable anywhere. Halliday carried a cigar box around on a tripod, playing that it was a camera, and halted all passers and aimed the thing and said, "Ready!—now look pleasant, please," but not even this capital joke could surprise the dreary faces into any softening.

So three weeks passed—one week was left. It was Saturday evening—after supper. Instead of the aforetime Saturday evening flutter and bustle and shopping and larking, the streets were empty and desolate. Richards and his old wife sat apart in their little parlor—miserable and thinking. This was become their evening habit now: the life-long habit which preceded it, of reading, knitting, and contented chat, or receiving or paying neighborly calls, was dead and gone and forgotten, ages ago—two or three weeks ago; nobody talked now, nobody read, nobody visited—the whole village sat at home, sighing, worrying, silent. Trying to guess out that remark.

The postman left a letter. Richards glanced listlessly at the superscription and the post-mark—unfamiliar, both—and tossed the letter on the table and resumed his might-have-beens and his hopeless dull miseries where he had left them off. Two or three hours later his wife got wearily up and was going away to bed without a good-night—custom now—but she stopped near the letter and eyed it awhile with a dead interest, then broke it open, and began to skim it over. Richards, sitting there with his chair tilted back against the wall and his chin between his knees, heard something fall. It was his wife. He sprang to her side, but she cried out:

"Leave me alone, I am too happy. Read the letter—read it!"

He did. He devoured it, his brain reeling. The letter was from a distant State, and it said:

*I am a stranger to you, but no matter: I have something to tell. I have just arrived home from Mexico, and learned about that episode. Of course you do not know who made that remark, but I know, and I am the only person living who does know. It was* GOODSON. *I knew him well, many years ago. I passed through your village that very night, and was his guest till the midnight train came along. I overheard him make that remark to the stranger in the dark—it was in Hale Alley. He and I talked of it the rest of the way home, and while smoking in his house. He mentioned many of your villagers in the course of his talk—most of them in a very uncomplimentary way, but two or three favorably: among these latter yourself. I say 'favorably'—nothing stronger. I remember his saying he did not actually* LIKE *any person in the town—not one; but that you—I* THINK *he said you— am almost sure, had done him a very great service once, possibly without knowing the full value of it, and he wished he had a fortune, he would leave it to you when he died, and a curse apiece for the rest of the citizens. Now, then, if it was you that did him that service, you are his legitimate heir, and entitled to the sack of gold. I know that I can trust to your honor and honesty, for in a citizen of Hadleyburg these virtues are an unfailing inheritance, and so I am going to reveal to you the remark, well satisfied that if you are not the right man you will seek and find the right one and see that poor Goodson's debt of gratitude for the service referred to is paid. This is the remark:* 'YOU ARE FAR FROM BEING A BAD MAN: GO, AND REFORM.'*

"HOWARD L. STEPHENSON"

"Oh, Edward, the money is ours, and I am so grateful, *oh*, so grateful— kiss me, dear, it's forever since we kissed—and we needed it so—the money—and now you are free of Pinkerton and his bank, and nobody's slave any more; it seems to me I could fly for joy."

It was a happy half our that the couple spent there on the settee caressing each other; it was the old days come again—days that had begun with their courtship and lasted without a break till the stranger brought the deadly money. By-and-by the wife said:

"Oh, Edward, how lucky it was you did him that grand service, poor Goodson! I never liked him, but I love him now. And it was fine and beautiful of you never to mention it or brag about it." Then, with a touch of reproach, "But you ought to have told *me*, Edward, you ought to have told your wife, you know."

"Well, I—er—well, Mary, you see—"

"Now stop hemming and hawing, and tell me about it, Edward. I always loved you, and now I'm proud of you. Everybody believes there was only one good generous soul in this village, and now it turns out that you—Edward, why don't you tell me?"

"Well—er—er— Why, Mary, I can't!"

"You *can't? Why* can't you?"

"You see, he—well, he—he made me promise I wouldn't."

The wife looked him over, and said, very slowly,

"Made—you—promise? Edward, what do you tell me that for?"

"Mary, do you think I would lie?"

She was troubled and silent for a moment, then she laid her hand within his and said:

"No ... no. We have wandered far enough from our bearings—God spare us that! In all your life you have never uttered a lie. But now—now that the foundations of things seem to be crumbling from under us, we—we—" She lost her voice for a moment, then said, brokenly, "Lead us not into temptation.... I think you made the promise, Edward. Let it rest so. Let us keep away from that ground. Now—that is all gone by; let us be happy again; it is no time for clouds."

Edward found it something of an effort to comply, for his mind kept wandering—trying to remember what the service was that he had done Goodson.

The couple lay awake the most of the night, Mary happy and busy, Edward busy, but not so happy. Mary was planning what she would do with the money. Edward was trying to recall that service. At first his conscience was sore on account of the lie he had told Mary—if it was a lie. After much reflection—suppose it *was* a lie? What then: Was it such a great matter? Aren't we *acting* lies? Then why not *tell* them? Look at Mary—look what she had done. While he was hurrying off on his honest errand, what was she doing? Lamenting because the papers hadn't been destroyed and the money kept! Is theft better than lying?

*That* point lost its sting—the lie dropped into the background and left comfort behind it. The next point came to the front: *had* he rendered that service? Well, here was Goodson's own evidence as reported in Stephenson's letter; there could be no better evidence than that—it was even *proof* that he had rendered it. Of course. So that point was settled.... No, not quite. He recalled with a wince that this unknown Mr. Stephenson was just a trifle unsure as to whether the performer of it was Richards or some other—and, oh dear, he had to put Richards on his honor! He must himself decide wither that money must go—and Mr. Stephenson was not doubting that if he was the wrong man he would go honorably and find the right one. Oh, it was odious to put a man in such a situation—ah, why couldn't Stephenson have left out that doubt! What did he want to intrude that for?

Further reflection. How did it happen that *Richards's* name remained in Stephenson's mind as indicating the right man, and not some other man's name? That looked good. Yes, that looked very good. In fact, it went on looking better and better, straight along—until by-and-by it grew into positive *proof*. And then Richards put the matter at once out of his mind, for he had a private instinct that a proof once established is better left so.

He was feeling reasonably comfortable now, but there was still one other detail that kept pushing itself on his notice: of course he had done that service—that was settled; but what *was* that service? He must recall it—he would not go to sleep till he had recalled it; it would make his peace of mind perfect. And so he thought and thought. He thought of a dozen things— possible services, even probable services—but none of them seemed adequate, none of them seemed large enough, none of them seemed worth the money—worth the fortune Goodson had wished he could leave in his will. And besides, he couldn't remember having done them, anyway. Now, then—now, then—what *kind* of a service would it be that would make a man so inordinately grateful? Ah—the saving of his soul! That must be it. Yes, he could remember, now, how he once set himself the task of converting Goodson, and labored at it as much as—he was going to say three months; but upon closer examination it shrunk to a month, then to a week, then to a day, then to nothing. Yes, he remembered now, and with unwelcome vividness, that Goodson had told him to go to thunder and mind his own business—*he* wasn't hankering to follow Hadleyburg to heaven!

So that solution was a failure—he hadn't saved Goodson's soul. Richards was discouraged. Then after a little came another idea: had he saved Goodson's property? No, that wouldn't do—he hadn't any. His life? This is it! Of course. Why, he might have thought of it before. This time he was on the right track, sure. His imagination was hard at work in a minute, now.

Thereafter during a stretch of two exhausting hours he was busy saving Goodson's life. He saved it in all kinds of difficult and perilous ways. In every case he got it saved satisfactorily up to a certain point; then, just as he was beginning to get well persuaded that it had really happened, a troublesome detail would turn up which made the whole thing impossible. As in the matter of drowning, for instance. In that case he had swum out and tugged Goodson ashore in an unconscious state with a great crowd looking on and applauding, but when he had got it all thought out and was just beginning to remember all about it a whole swarm of disqualifying details arrived on the ground: the town would have known of it, it would glare like a limelight in his own memory instead of being an inconspicuous service which he had possibly rendered "without knowing its full value." And at this point he remembered that he couldn't swim, anyway.

Ah—*there* was a point which he had been overlooking from the start: it had to be a service which he had rendered "possibly without knowing the full value of it." Why, really, that ought to be an easy hunt—much easier than those others. And sure enough, by-and-by he found it. Goodson, years and years ago, came near marrying a very sweet and pretty girl, named Nancy Hewitt, but in some way or other the match had been broken off; the girl died, Goodson remained a bachelor, and by-and-by became a soured one and a frank despiser of the human species. Soon after the girl's death the village found out, or thought it had found out, that she carried a spoonful of negro blood in her veins. Richards worked at these details a good while, and in the end he thought he remembered things concerning them which must have gotten mislaid in his memory through long neglect. He seemed to dimly remember that it was *he* that found out about the negro blood; that it was he that told the village; that the village told Goodson where they got it; that he thus saved Goodson from marrying the tainted girl; that he had done him this great service "without knowing the full value of it," in fact without knowing that he *was* doing it; but that Goodson knew the value of it, and what a narrow escape he had had, and so went to his grave grateful to his benefactor and wishing he had a fortune to leave him. It was all clear and simple now, and the more he went over it the more luminous and certain it grew; and at last, when he nestled to sleep satisfied and happy, he remembered the whole thing just as if it had been yesterday. In fact, he dimly remembered Goodsons's *telling* him his gratitude once. Meantime Mary had spent six thousand dollars on a new house for herself and a pair of slippers for her pastor, and then had fallen peacefully to rest.

That same Saturday evening the postman had delivered a letter to each of the other principal citizens—nineteen letters in all. No two of the envelopes were alike, and no two of the superscriptions were in the same hand, but the letters inside were just like each other in every detail but one. They were exact copies of the letter received by Richards—handwriting and all—and were all signed by Stephenson, but in place of Richards's name each receiver's own name appeared.

All night long eighteen principal citizens did what their caste-brother Richards was doing at the same time—they put in their energies trying to remember what notable service it was that they had unconsciously done Barclay Goodson. In no case was it a holiday job; still they succeeded.

And while they were at this work, which was difficult, their wives put in the night spending the money, which was easy. During that one night the nineteen wives spent an average of seven thousand dollars each out of the forty thousand in the sack—a hundred and thirty-three thousand altogether.

Next day there was a surprise for Jack Halliday. He noticed that the faces of the nineteen chief citizens and their wives bore that expression of peaceful and holy happiness again. He could not understand it, neither was he able to invent any remarks about it that could damage it or disturb it. And so it was his turn to be dissatisfied with life. His private guesses at the reasons for the happiness failed in all instances, upon examination. When he met Mrs. Wilcox and noticed the placid ecstasy in her face, he said to himself, "Her cat has had kittens"—and went and asked the cook; it was not so; the cook had detected the happiness, but did not know the cause. When Halliday found the duplicate ecstasy in the face of "Shadbelly" Billson (village nickname), he was sure some neighbor of Billson's had broken his leg, but inquiry showed that this had not happened. The subdued ecstasy in Gregory Yates's face could mean but one thing—he was a mother-in-law short; it was another mistake. "And Pinkerton—Pinkerton—he has collected ten cents that he thought he was going to lose." And so on, and so on. In some cases the guesses had to remain in doubt, in the others they proved distinct errors. In the end Halliday said to himself, "Anyway, it foots up that there's nineteen Hadleyburg families temporarily in heaven: I don't know how it happened; I only know Providence is off duty today."

An architect and builder from the next State had lately ventured to set up a small business in this unpromising village, and his sign had now been hanging out a week. Not a customer yet; he was a discouraged man, and sorry he had come. But his weather changed suddenly now. First one and then another chief citizen's wife said to him privately:

"Come to my house Monday week—but say nothing about it for the present. We think of building."

He got eleven invitations that day. That night he wrote his daughter and broke off her match with her student. He said she could marry a mile higher than that.

Pinkerton the banker and two or three other well-to-do men planned country-seats—but waited. That kind don't count their chickens until they are hatched.

The Wilsons devised a grand new thing—a fancy-dress ball. They made no actual promises, but told all their acquaintanceship in confidence that they were thinking the matter over and thought they should give it—"and if we do, you will be invited, of course." People were surprised, and said, one to another, "Why, they are crazy, those poor Wilsons, they can't afford it." Several among the nineteen said privately to their husbands, "It is a good idea, we will keep still till their cheap thing is over, then *we* will give one that will make it sick."

The days drifted along, and the bill of future squanderings rose higher and higher, wilder and wilder, more and more foolish and reckless. It began to look as if every member of the nineteen would not only spend his whole forty thousand dollars before receiving-day, but be actually in debt by the time he got the money. In some cases light-headed people did not stop with planning to spend, they really spent—on credit. They bought land, mortgages, farms, speculative stocks, fine clothes, horses, and various other things, paid down the bonus, and made themselves liable for the rest—at ten days. Presently the sober second thought came, and Halliday noticed that a ghastly anxiety was beginning to show up in a good many faces. Again he was puzzled, and didn't know what to make of it. "The Wilcox kittens aren't dead, for they weren't born; nobody's broken a leg; there's no shrinkage in mother-in-laws; *nothing* has happened—it is an insolvable mystery."

There was another puzzled man, too—the Rev. Mr. Burgess. For days, wherever he went, people seemed to follow him or to be watching out for him; and if he ever found himself in a retired spot, a member of the nineteen would be sure to appear, thrust an envelope privately into his hand, whisper "To be opened at the town-hall Friday evening," then vanish away like a guilty thing. He was expecting that there might be one claimant for the sack—doubtful, however, Goodson being dead—but it never occurred to him that all this crowd might be claimants. When the great Friday came at last, he found that he had nineteen envelopes.

### III

The town hall had never looked finer. The platform at the end of it was backed by a showy draping of flags; at intervals along the walls were festoons of flags; the gallery fronts were clothed in flags; the supporting columns were swathed in flags; all this was to impress the stranger, for he would be there in considerable force, and in a large degree he would be connected with the press. The house was full. The 412 fixed seats were occupied; also the 68 extra chairs which had been packed into the aisles; the steps of the platform were occupied; some distinguished strangers were given seats on the platform; at the horsehoe of tables which fenced the front and sides of the platform sat a strong force of special correspondents who had come from everywhere. It was the best-dressed house the town had ever produced. There were some tolerably expensive toilets there, and in several cases the ladies who wore them had the look of being unfamiliar with that kind of clothes. At least the town thought they had that look, but the notion could have arisen from the town's knowledge of the fact that these ladies had never inhabited such clothes before.

The gold-sack stood on a little table at the front of the platform where all the house could see it. The bulk of the house gazed at it with a burning interest, a mouth-watering interest, a wistful and pathetic interest; a minority of nineteen couples gazed at it tenderly, lovingly, proprietarily, and the male half of this minority kept saying over to themselves the moving little impromptu speeches of thankfulness for the audience's applause and congratulations which they were presently going to get up and deliver. Every now and then one of these got a piece of paper out of his vest pocket and privately glanced at it to refresh his memory.

Of course there was a buzz of conversation going on—there always is; but at last when the Rev. Mr. Burgess rose and laid his hand on the sack he could hear his microbes gnaw, the place was so still. He related the curious history of the sack, then went on to speak in warm terms of Hadleyburg's old and well-earned reputation for spotless honesty, and of the town's just pride in this reputation. He said that this reputation was a treasure of priceless value; that under Providence its value had now become inestimably enhanced, for the recent episode had spread this fame far and wide, and thus had focussed the eyes of the American world upon this village, and made its name for all time, as he hoped and believed, a synonym for commercial incorruptibility. [*Applause.*] "And who is to be the guardian of this noble treasure—the community as a whole? No! The responsibility is individual, not communal. From this day forth each and every one of you is in his own person its special guardian and individually responsible that no harm shall come to it. Do you—does each of you—accept this great trust? [*Tumultuous assent.*] Then all is well. Transmit it to your children and to your children's children. Today your purity is beyond reproach—see to it that it shall remain so. Today there is not a person in your community who could be beguiled to touch a penny not his own—see to it that you abide in this grace. [*"We will! we will!"*] This is not the place to make comparisons between ourselves and other communities—some of them ungracious toward us; they have their ways, we have ours; let us be content. [*Applause.*] I am done. Under my hand, my friends, rests a stranger's eloquent recognition of what we are: through him the world will always henceforth know what we are. We do not know who he is, but in your name I utter your gratitude, and ask you to raise your voices in endorsement."

The house rose in a body and made the walls quake with the thunders of its thankfulness for the space of a long minute. Then it sat down, and Mr. Burgess took an envelope out of his pocket. The house held its breath while he slit the envelope open and took from it a slip of paper. He read its contents—slowly and impressively—the audience listening with tranced attention to this magic document, each of whose words stood for an ingot of gold:

" *'The remark which I made to the distressed stranger was this: "You are very far from being a bad man; go, and reform."* ' " Then he continued: "We shall know in a moment now whether the remark here quoted corresponds with the one concealed in the sack; and if that shall prove to be so—and it undoubtedly will—this sack of gold belongs to a fellow-citizen who will henceforth stand before the nation as the symbol of the special virtue which has made our town famous throughout the land—Mr. Billson!"

The house had gotten itself all ready to burst into a proper tornado of applause; but instead of doing it, it seemed stricken with a paralysis; there was a deep hush for a moment or two, then a wave of whispered murmurs swept the place—of about this tenor: *"Billson!* oh, come, this is *too* thin! Twenty dollars to a stranger—or *anybody—"Billson!* Tell it to the marines!" And now at this point the house caught its breath all of a sudden in a new access of astonishment, for it discovered that whereas in one part of the hall Deacon Billson was standing up with his head meekly bowed, in another part of it Lawyer Wilson was doing the same. There was a wondering silence now for a while. Everybody was puzzled, and nineteen couples were surprised and indignant.

Billson and Wilson turned and stared at each other. Billson asked, bitingly,

"Why do *you* rise Mr. Wilson?"

"Because I have a right to. Perhaps you will be good enough to explain to the house why *you* rise?"

"With great pleasure. Because I wrote that paper."

It was Burgess's turn to be paralyzed. He stood looking vacantly at first one of the men and then the other, and did not seem to know what to do. The house was stupefied. Lawyer Wilson spoke up, now, and said.

"I ask the Chair to read the name signed to that paper."

That brought the Chair to itself, and it read out the name, " 'John Wharton *Billson.*' "

"There!" shouted Billson, "what have you got to say for yourself, now? And what kind of apology are you going to make to me and to this insulted house for the imposture which you have attempted to pay here?"

"No apologies are due, sir; and as for the rest of it, I publicly charge you with pilfering my note from Mr. Burgess and substituting a copy of it signed with your own name. There is no other way by which you could have gotten hold of the test-remark; I alone, of living men, possessed the secret of its wording."

There was likely to be a scandalous state of things if this went on; everybody noticed with distress that the short-hand scribes were scribbling like mad; many people were crying "Chair, Chair! Order! order!" Burgess rapped with his gavel, and said:

"Let us not forget the proprieties due. There has evidently been a mistake somewhere, but surely that is all. If Mr. Wilson gave me an envelope—and I remembered now that he did—I still have it."

He took one out of his pocket, opened it, glanced at it, looked surprised and worried, and stood silent a few moments. Then he waved his hand in a wandering and mechanical way, and made an effort or two to say something, then gave it up, despondently. Several voices cried out:

"Read it! read it! What is it?"

So he began in a dazed and sleep-walker fashion:

" 'The remark which I made to the unhappy stranger was this: *You are far from being a bad man.* [The house gazed at him marvelling.] *Go, and reform.*" '[*Murmurs:* "Amazing! what can this mean?"] "This one," said the Chair, "is signed Thurlow G. Wilson."

"There!" cried Wilson, "I reckon that settles it! I knew perfectly well my note was purloined."

"Purloined!" retorted Billson. "I'll let you know that neither you nor any man of your kidney must venture to—"

*The Chair.* "Order, gentlemen, order! Take your seats, both of you, please."

They obeyed, shaking their heads and grumbling angrily. The house was profoundly puzzled; it did not know what to do with this curious emergency. Presently Thompson got up. Thompson was the hatter. He would have liked to be a Nineteener; but such was not for him; his stock of hats was not considerable enough for the position. He said:

"Mr. Chairman, if I may be permitted to make a suggestion, can both of these gentlemen be right? I put it to you, sir, can both have happened to say the very same words to the stranger? It seems to me—"

The tanner got up and interrupted him. The tanner was a disgruntled man; he believed himself entitled to be a Nineteener, but he couldn't get recognition. It made him a little unpleasant in his ways and speech. Said he:

"Sho, *that's* not the point! *That* could happen—twice in a hundred years—but the other thing. *Neither* of them gave the twenty dollars!" [*A ripple of applause.*]

*Billson.* "I did!"

*Wilson.* "I did!"

Then each accused the other of pilfering.

*The Chair.* "Order! Sit down, if you please—both of you. Neither of the notes has been out of my possession at any moment."

*A Voice.* "Good—that settles *that!*"

*The Tanner.* "Mr. Chairman, one thing is now plain: one of these men has been eavesdropping under the other one's bed, and filching family secrets. If it is not unparliamentary to suggest it, I will remark that both are equal to it. [*The Chair.* "Order! order!"] I withdraw the remark, sir, and will confine myself to suggesting that *if* one of them has overheard the other reveal the test-remark to his wife, we shall catch him now."

*A Voice.* "How?"

*The Tanner*. "Easily. The two have not quoted the remark in exactly the same words. You would have noticed that, if there hadn't been a considerable stretch of time and an exciting quarrel inserted between the two readings."

*A Voice*. "Name the difference."

*The Tanner*. "The word *very* is in Billson's note, and not in the other."

*Many Voices*. "That's so—he's right."

*The Tanner*. "And so, if the Chair will examine the test-remark in the sack, we shall know which of these two frauds—[*The Chair*. "Order!"]—which of these two adventurers—[*The Chair*. "Order! order!"]—which of these two gentlemen—[*laughter and applause*]—is entitled to wear the belt as being the first dishonest blatherskite ever bred in this town—which he has dishonored, and which will be a sultry place for him from now out!" [*Vigorous applause.*]

*Many Voices*. "Open it!—open the sack!"

Mr. Burgess made a slit in the sack, slid his hand in and brought out an envelope. In it were a couple of folded notes. He said:

"One of these is marked, 'Not to be examined until all written communications which have been addressed to the Chair—if any—shall have been read.' The other is marked *'The Test.'* Allow me. It is worded—to wit:

" 'I do not reguire that the first half of the remark which was made to me by my benefactor shall be quoted with exactness, for it was not striking, and could be forgotten; but its closing fifteen words are quite striking, and I think easily remembrable; unless *these* shall be accurately reproduced, let the applicant be regarded as an imposter. My benefactor began by saying he seldom gave advice to any one, but that it always bore the hall-mark of high value when he did give it. Then he said this—and it has never faded from my memory: *"You are far from being a bad man—"* ' "

*Fifty Voices*. "That settles it—the money's Wilson's! Wilson! Wilson! Speech! Speech!"

People jumped up and crowded around Wilson, wringing his hand and congratulating fervently—meantime the Chair was hammering with the gavel and shouting:

"Order, gentlemen! Order! Order! Let me finish reading, please." When quiet was restored, the reading was resumed—as follows:

" ' *"Go, and reform—or, mark my words —some day, for your sins, you will die and go to hell or Hadleyburg—*TRY AND MAKE IT THE FORMER." ' "

A ghastly silence followed. First an angry cloud began to settle darkly upon the faces of the citizenship; after a pause the cloud began to rise, and a tickled expression tried to take its place; tried so hard that it was only kept under with great and painful difficulty; the reporters, the Brixtonites, and other strangers bent their heads down and shielded their faces with their hands, and managed to hold in by main strength and heroic courtesy. As this most inopportune time burst upon the stillness the roar of a solitary voice— Jack Halliday's:

*"That's* got the hall-mark on it!"

Then the house let go, strangers and all. Even Mr. Burgess's gravity broke down presently, then the audience considered itself officially absolved from all restraint, and it made the most of its privilege. It was a good long laugh, and a tempestuously wholehearted one, but it ceased at last—long enough for Mr. Burgess to try to resume, and for the people to get their eyes partially wiped; then it broke out again; and afterward yet again; then at last Burgess was able to get out these serious words:

"It is useless to try to disguise the fact—we find ourselves in the presence of a matter of grave import. It involves the honor of your town, it strikes at the town's good name. The difference of a single word between the test-remarks offered by Mr. Wilson and Mr. Billson was itself a serious thing, since it indicated that one or the other of these gentlemen had committed a theft—"

The two men were sitting limp, nerveless, crushed; but at these words both were electrified into movement, and started to get up—

"Sit down!" said the Chair, sharply, and they obeyed. "That, as I have said, was a serious thing. And it was—but for only one of them. But the matter has become graver; for the honor of *both* is now in formidable peril. Shall I go even further, and say in inextricable peril? *Both* left out the crucial fifteen words." He paused. During several moments he allowed the pervading stillness to gather and deepen its impressive effects, then added: "There would seem to be but one way whereby this could happen. I ask these gentlemen—Was there *collusion?—agreement?*"

A low murmur sifted through the house; its import was, "He's got them both."

Billson was not used to emergencies; he sat in a helpless collapse. But Wilson was a lawyer. He struggled to his feet, pale and worried, and said:

"I ask the indulgence of the house while I explain this most painful matter. I am sorry to say what I am about to say, since it must inflict irreparable injury upon Mr. Billson, whom I have always esteemed and respected until now, and in whose invulnerability to temptation I entirely believed—as did you all. But for the preservation of my own honor I must speak—and with frankness. I confess with shame—and I now beseech your pardon for it—that I said to the ruined stranger all of the words contained in the test-remark, including the disparaging fifteen. [*Sensation.*] When the late publication was made I recalled them, and I resolved to claim the sack of coin, for by every right I was entitled to it. Now I will ask you to consider this point, and weigh it well: that stranger's gratitude to me that night knew no bounds; he said himself that he could find no words for it that were adequate, and that if he should ever be able he would repay me a thousand-fold. Now, then, I ask you this: could I expect—could I believe—could I even remotely imagine—that, feeling as he did, he would do so ungrateful a thing as to add those quite unnecessary fifteen words to his test?—set a trap for me?—expose me as a slanderer of my own town before my own people assembled in a public hall? It was preposterous; it was impossible. His test would contain only the kindly opening clause of my remark. Of that I had no shadow of doubt. You would have thought as I did. You would not have expected a base betrayal from one whom you had befriended and against whom you had committed no offense. And so, with perfect confidence, perfect trust, I wrote on a piece of paper the opening words—ending with

'Go, and reform,'—and signed it. When I was about to put it in an envelope I was called into my back office, and without thinking I left the paper lying open on my desk." He stopped, turned his head slowly toward Billson, waited a moment, then added: "I ask you to note this: when I returned, a little later, Mr. Billson was retiring by my street door." (*Sensation.*)

In a moment Billson was on his feet and shouting:

"It's a lie! It's an infamous lie!"

*The Chair.* "Be seated, sir! Mr. Wilson has the floor."

Billson's friends pulled him into his seat and quieted him, and Wilson went on:

"Those are the simple facts. My note was now lying in a different place on the table from where I had left it. I noticed that, but attached no importance to it, thinking a draught had blown it there. That Mr. Billson would read a private paper was a thing which could not occur to me; he was an honorable man, and he would be above that. If you will allow me to say it, I think his extra word '*very*' stands explained; it is attributable to a defect of memory. I was the only man in the world who could furnish here any detail of the test-mark—by *honorable* means. I have finished."

There is nothing in the world like a persuasive speech to fuddle the mental apparatus and upset the convictions and debauch the emotions of an audience not practiced in the tricks and delusions of oratory. Wilson sat down victorious. The house submerged him in tides of approving applause; friends swarmed to him and shook him by the hand and congratulated him, and Billson was shouted down and not allowed to say a word. The Chair hammered and hammered with its gavel, and kept shouting:

"But let us proceed, gentlemen, let us proceed!"

At last there was a measurable degree of quiet, and the hatter said:

"But what is there to proceed with, sir, but to deliver the money?"

*Voices.* "That's it! That's it! Come forward, Wilson!"

*The Hatter.* "I move three cheers for Mr. Wilson, Symbol of the special virtue which—"

The cheers burst forth before he could finish; and in the midst of them—and in the midst of the clamor of the gavel also—some enthusiasts mounted Wilson on a big friend's shoulder and were going to fetch him in triumph to the platform. The Chair's voice now rose above the noise—

"Order! To your places! You forget that there is still a document to be read." When quiet had been restored he took up the document, and was going to read it, but laid it down again, saying, "I forgot; this is not to be read until all written communications received by me have first been read." He took an envelope out of his pocket, removed its enclosure, glanced at it—seemed astonished—held it out and gazed at it—stared at it.

Twenty or thirty voices cried out:

"What is it? Read it! read it!"

And he did—slowly, and wondering:

" 'The remark which I made to the stranger—[*Voices.* "Hello! how's this?"]—was this: "You are far from being a bad man. [*Voices.* "Great Scott!"] Go, and reform." ' [*Voice.* "Oh, saw my leg off!"] Signed by Mr. Pinkerton the banker."

The pandemonium of delight which turned itself loose now was a sort to make the judicious weep. Those whose withers were unwrung laughed till the tears ran down; the reporters, in throes of laughter, set down disordered pothooks which would never in the world be decipherable; and a sleeping dog jumped up, scared out of its wits, and barked itself crazy at the turmoil. All manner of cries were scattered through the din: "We're getting rich — *two* Symbols of Incorruptibility! —without counting Billson!" *"Three!* — count Shadbelly in—we can't have too many!" "All right—Billson's elected!" Alas, poor Wilson—victim of *two* thieves!"

*A Powerful Voice.* "Silence! The Chair's fished up something more out of its pocket."

*Voices.* "Hurrah! Is it something fresh; Read it! read! read!"

*The Chair* [reading]. " 'The remark which I made,' etc. 'You are far from being a bad man. Go,' etc. Signed, 'Gregory Yates.' "

*Tornado of Voices.* "Four Symbols!" " 'Rah for Yates!" "Fish again!"

The house was in a roaring humor now, and ready to get all the fun out of the occasion that might be in it. Several Nineteeners, looking pale and distressed, got up and began to work their way toward the aisles, but a score of shouts went up:

"The doors, the doors—close the doors; no Incorruptible shall leave this place! Sit down, everybody!"

The mandate was obeyed.

"Fish again! Read! read!"

The Chair fished again, and once more the familiar words began to fall from its lips— " 'You are far from being a bad man —' "

"Name! name! What's his name?"

" 'L. Ingoldsby Sargent.' "

"Five elected! Pile up the Symbols! Go on, go on!"

" 'You are far from being a bad —' "

"Name! name!"

" 'Nicholas Whitworth.' "

"Hooray! hooray! it's a symbolical day!"

Somebody wailed in, and began to sing this rhyme (leaving out "it's") to the lovely "Mikado" tune of "When a man's afraid, a beautiful maid—"; the audience joined in, with joy; then, just in time, somebody contributed another line—

"And don't you this forget————"

The house roared it out. A third line was at once furnished—

"Corruptibles far from Hadleyburg are————"

The house roared that one too. As the last note died, Jack Halliday's voice rose high and clear, freighted with a final line—

"But the Symbols are here, you bet!"

That was sung, with booming enthusiasm. Then the happy house started in at the beginning and sang the four lines through twice, with immense swing and dash, and finished up with a crashing three-times-three and a tiger for "Hadleyburg the Incorruptible and all Symbols of it which we shall find worthy to receive the hall-mark tonight."

Then the shoutings at the Chair began again, all over the place:

"Go on! go on! Read! read some more! Read all you've got!"

"That's it—go on! We are winning eternal celebrity!"

A dozen men got up now and began to protest. They said that this farce was the work of some abandoned joker, and was an insult to the whole community. Without a doubt these signatures were all forgeries—

"Sit down! sit down! Shut up! You are confessing. We'll find *your* names in the lot."

"Mr. Chairman, how many of those envelopes have you got?"

The Chair counted.

"Together with those that have been already examined, there are nineteen."

A storm of derisive applause broke out.

"Perhaps they all contain the secret. I move that you open them all and read every signature that is attached to a note of that sort—and read also the first eight words of the note."

"Second the motion!"

It was put and carried—uproariously. Then poor old Richards got up, and his wife rose and stood at his side. Her head was bent down, so that none might see that she was crying. Her husband gave her his arm, and so supporting her, he began to speak in a quavering voice:

"My friends, you have known us two—Mary and me—all our lives, and I think you have liked us and respected us—"

The Chair interrupted him:

"Allow me. It is quite true—that which you are saying, Mr. Richards; this town *does* know you two; it *does* like you; it *does* respect you; more—it honors you and *loves* you—"

Halliday's voice rang out:

"That's the hall-marked truth, too! If the Chair is right, let the house speak up and say it. Rise! Now, then—hip! hip! hip!—all together!"

The house rose in mass, faced toward the old couple eagerly, filled the air with a snowstorm of waving handkerchiefs, and delivered the cheers with all its affectionate heart.

The Chair then continued:

"What I was going to say is this: We know your good heart, Mr. Richards, but this is not a time for the exercise of charity toward offenders. [Shouts of "Right! right!"] I see your generous purpose in your face, but I cannot allow you to plead for these men—"

"But I was going to—"

"Please take your seat, Mr. Richards. We must examine the rest of these notes—simple fairness to the men who have already been exposed requires this. As soon as that has been done—I give you my word for this—you shall be heard."

*Many Voices.* "Right!—the Chair is right—no interruption can be permitted at this state! Go on!—the names! the names!—according to the terms of the motion!"

The old couple sat reluctantly down, and the husband whispered to the wife, "It is pitifully hard to have to wait; the shame will be greater than ever when they find we were only going to plead for *ourselves.*"

Straightway the jollity broke loose again with the reading of the names.

" 'You are far from being a bad man—' Signature, 'Robert J. Titmarsh.'

" 'You are far from being a bad man—' Signature, 'Eliphalet Weeks.'

" 'You are far from being a bad man—' Signature, 'Oscar B. Wilder.' "

At this point the house lit upon the idea of taking the eight words out of the Chairman's hands. He was not unthankful for that. Thenceforward he held up each note in its turn, and waited. The house droned out the eight words in a massed and measured and musical deep volume of sound (with a daringly close resemblance to a well-known church chant)—" 'You are f-a-r from being a b-a-a-a-d man.' " Then the Chair said, "Signature, 'Archibald Wilcox.' " And so on, and so on, name after name, and everybody had an increasingly and gloriously good time except the wretched Nineteen. Now and then, when a particularly shining name was called, the house made the Chair wait while it chanted the whole of the test-remark from the beginning to the closing words, "And go to hell or Hadleyburg—try and make it the for-or-m-e-r!" And in these special cases they added a grand and agonized and imposing "A-a-a-a-*men!*"

The list dwindled, dwindled, dwindled, poor old Richards keeping tally of the count, wincing when a name resembling his own was pronounced, and waiting in miserable suspense for the time to come when it would be his humiliating privilege to rise with Mary and finish his plea, which he was intending to word thus: "...for until now we have never done any wrong thing, but have gone our humble way unreproached. We are very poor, we are old, and have no chick nor child to help us; we were sorely tempted, and we fell. It was my purpose when I got up before to make confession and beg that my name might not be read out in this public place, for it seemed to us that we could not bear it; but I was prevented. It was just; it was our place to suffer with the rest. It has been hard for us. It is the first time we have ever heard our name fall from any one's lips—sullied. Be merciful—for the sake of the better days; make our shame as light to bear as in your charity you can." At this point in his revery Mary nudged him, perceiving that his mind was absent. The house was chanting. "You are f-a-r," etc.

"Be ready," Mary whispered. "Your name comes now; he has read eighteen."

The chant ended.

"Next! next! next!" came volleying from all over the house.

Burgess put his hand into his pocket. The old couple, trembling, began to rise, Burgess fumbled a moment, then said,

"I find I have read them all."

Faint with joy and surprise, the couple sank into their seats, and Mary whispered:

"Oh, bless God, we are saved!—he has lost ours—I wouldn't give this for a hundred of those sacks!"

The house burst out with its "Mikado" travesty, and sang it three times with ever-increasing enthusiasm, rising to its feet when it reached for the third time the closing line—

"But the Symbols are here, you bet!"

and finishing up with cheers and a tiger for "Hadleyburg purity and our eighteen immortal representatives of it."

Then Wingate, the saddler, got up and proposed cheers "for the cleanest man in town, the one solitary important citizen in it who didn't try to steal that money—Edward Richards."

They were given with great and moving heartiness; then somebody proposed that Richards be elected sole Guardian and Symbol of the now Sacred Hadleyburg Tradition, with power and right to stand up and look the whole sarcastic world in the face.

Passed, by acclamation; then they sang the "Mikado" again, and ended it with,

"And there's *one* Symbol left, you bet!"

There was a pause; then—

*A Voice.* "Now, then, who's to get the sack?"

*The Tanner* (*with bitter sarcasm*). "That's easy. The money has to be divided among the eighteen Incorruptibles. They gave the suffering stranger twenty dollars apiece—and that remark—each in his turn—it took twenty-two minutes for the procession to move past. Staked the stranger—total contribution, $360. All they want is just the loan back—and interest—forty thousand dollars altogether."

*Many voices* [*derisively*]. "That's it! Divvy! divvy! Be kind to the poor—don't keep them waiting!"

*The Chair.* "Order! I now offer the stranger's remaining document. It says: 'If no claimant shall appear [*grand chorus of groans*], I desire that you open the sack and count out the money to the principal citizens of your town, they to take it in trust [*Cries of "Oh! Oh! Oh!"*], and use it in such ways as to them shall seem best for the propagation and preservation of your community's noble reputation for incorruptible honesty [*more cries*]—a reputation to which their names and their efforts will add a new and far-reaching lustre.' [*Enthusiastic outburst of sarcastic applause.*] That seems to be all. No—here is a postscript:

" 'P. S.—CITIZENS OF HADLEYBURG: There *is* no test-remark—nobody made one. [*Great sensation.*] There wasn't any pauper stranger, nor any twenty-dollar contribution, nor any accompanying benediction and compliment—these are all inventions. [*General buzz and hum of astonishment and delight.*] Allow me to tell my story—it will take but a word or two. I passed through your town at a certain time, and received a deep offense which I had not earned. Any other man would have been content to kill one or two of you and call it square, but to me that would have been a trivial revenge, and inadequate; for the dead do not *suffer*. Besides, I could not kill you all—and, anyway, made as I am, even that would not have satisfied me. I wanted to damage every man in the place, and every woman—and not in their bodies or in their estate, but in their vanity—the place where feeble and foolish people are most vulnerable. So I disguised myself and came back and studied you. You were easy game. You had an old and lofty reputation for honesty, and naturally you were proud of it—it was your treasure of treasures, the very apple of your eye. As soon as I found out that you carefully and vigilantly kept yourselves and your children *out of temptation,* I knew how to proceed. Why, you simple creatures, the weakest of all weak things is a virtue which has not been tested in the fire. I laid a plan, and gathered a list of names. My project was to corrupt Hadleyburg the incorruptible. My idea was to make liars and thieves of nearly half a hundred smirchless men and women who had never in their lives uttered a lie or stolen a penny. I was afraid of Goodson. He was neither born nor reared in Hadleyburg. I was afraid that if I started to operate my scheme by getting my letter laid before you, you would say to yourselves, "Goodson is the only man among us who would give away twenty dollars to a poor devil"—and then you might not bite at my bait. But Heaven took Goodson; then I knew I was safe, and I set my trap and baited it. It may be that I shall not catch all the men to whom I mailed the pretended test secret, but I shall catch the most of them, if I know Hadleyburg nature. [*Voices.* "Right—he got every last one of them."] I believe they will even steal ostensible *gamble*-money, rather than miss, poor, tempted, and mistrained fellows. I am hoping to eternally and everlastingly squelch your vanity and give Hadleyburg a new renown—one that will *stick*—and spread far. If I have succeeded, open the sack and summon the Committee on Propagation and Preservation of the Hadleyburg Reputation.' "

*A Cyclone of Voices.* "Open it! Open it! The Eighteen to the front! Committee on Propagation of the Tradition! Forward—the Incorruptibles!"

The Chair ripped the sack wide, and gathered up a handful of bright, broad, yellow coins, shook them together, then examined them—

"Friends, they are only gilded disks of lead!"

There was a crashing outbreak of delight over this news, and when the noise had subsided, the tanner called out:

"By right of apparent seniority in this business, Mr. Wilson is Chairman of the Committee on Propagation of the Tradition. I suggest that he step forward on behalf of his pals, and receive in trust the money."

*A Hundred Voices.* "Wilson! Wilson! Wilson! Speech! Speech!"

*Wilson* [*in a voice trembling with anger*]. "You will allow me to say, without apologies for my language, *damn* the money!"

*A Voice.* "Oh, and him a Baptist!"

*A Voice.* "Seventeen Symbols left! Step up, gentlemen, and assume your trust!"

There was a pause—no response.

*The Saddler.* "Mr. Chairman, we've got *one* clean man left, anyway, out of the late aristocracy; and he needs money, and deserves it. I move that you appoint Jack Halliday to get up there and auction off that sack of gilt twenty dollar pieces, and give the result to the right man—the man whom Hadleyburg delights to honor—Edward Richards."

This was received with great enthusiasm, the dog taking a hand again; the saddler started the bids at a dollar, the Brixton folk and Barnum's representative fought hard for it, the people cheered every jump that the bids made, the excitement climbed moment by moment higher and higher, the bidders got on their mettle and grew steadily more and more daring, more and more determined, the jumps went from a dollar up to five, then to ten, then to twenty, then fifty, then to a hundred, then—

At the beginning of the auction Richards whispered in distress to his wife: "Oh, Mary, can we allow it? It—it—you see, it is an honor-reward, a testimonial to purity of character, and—and—can we allow it? Hadn't I better get up and—Oh, Mary, what ought we to do?—what do you think we—" [*Halliday's voice. "Fifteen I'm bid!—fifteen for the sack!—twenty!—ah, thanks!—thirty—thanks again! Thirty, thirty, thirty! do I hear forty?—forty it is! Keep the ball rolling, gentlemen, keep it rolling!—fifty!—thanks, noble Roman!—going at fifty, fifty, fifty!—seventy! ninety!—splendid!—a hundred!—pile it up, pile it up!—hundred and twenty—forty!—just in time! —hundred and fifty!—*TWO *hundred!—superb! Do I hear two h— thanks!— two hundred and fifty!——"*]

"It is another temptation, Edward—I'm all in a tremble—but, oh, we've escaped *one* temptation, and that ought to warn us, to—[*"Six did I hear?— thanks!—six fifty, six f—*SEVEN *hundred!"*] And yet, Edward, when you think—nobody susp— [*"Eight hundred dollars!—hurrah!—make it nine!— Mr. Parsons, did I hear you say — thanks!— nine—this noble sack of virgin lead going at only nine hundred dollars, gilding and all—come! do I hear—a thousand!— gratefully yours!—did some one say eleven? —a sack which is going to be the most celebrated in the whole Uni——"*] "Oh, Edward" (*beginning to sob*), "we are *so* poor!—but—but— do as you think best—do as you think best."

Edward fell—that is, he sat still; sat with a conscience which was not satisfied, but which was overpowered by circumstances.

Meanwhile a stranger, who looked like an amateur detective gotten up as an impossible English earl, had been watching the evening's proceedings with manifest interest, and with a contented expression in his face; and he had been privately commenting to himself. He was now soliloquizing somewhat like this: "None of the Eighteen are bidding; that is not satisfactory; I must change that—the dramatic unities require it; they must buy the sack they tried to steal; they must pay a heavy price, too—some of them are rich. And other thing, when I make a mistake in Hadleyburg nature the man that puts that error upon me is entitled to a high honorarium, and some one must pay it. This poor old Richards has brought my judgment to shame; he is an honest man;—I don't understand it, but I acknowledge it. Yes, he saw my deuces—*and* with a straight flush, and by rights the pot is his. And it shall be a jackpot, too, if I can manage it. He disappointed me, but let that pass."

He was watching the bidding. At a thousand, the market broke; the prices tumbled swiftly. He waited—and still watched. One competitor dropped out; then another, and another. He put in a bid or two, now. When the bids had sunk to ten dollars, he added a five; some one raised him a three; he waited a moment, then flung in a fifty-dollar jump, and the sack was his—at $1,282. The house broke out in cheers—then stopped; for he was on his feet and had lifted his hand. He began to speak.

"I desire to say a word, and ask a favor. I am a speculator in rarities, and I have dealings with persons interested in numismatics all over the world. I can make a profit on this purchase, just as it stands; but there is a way, if I can get your approval, whereby I can make every one of these leaden twenty dollar pieces worth its face in gold, and perhaps more. Grant me that approval, and I will give part of my gains to your Mr. Richards, who invulnerable probity you have so justly and so cordially recognized tonight; his share shall be ten thousand dollars, and I will hand him the money tomorrow. [*Great applause from the house.* But the "invulnerable probity" made the Richardses blush prettily; however, it went for modesty, and did no harm.] If you will pass my proposition by a good majority—I would like a two-thirds vote—I will regard that as the town's consent, and that is all I ask. Rarities are always helped by any device which will rouse curiosity and compel remark. Now if I may have your permission to stamp upon the faces of each of these ostensible coins the names of the eighteen gentlemen who—"

Nine-tenths of the audience were on their feet in a moment—dog and all—and the proposition was carried with a whirlwind of approving applause and laughter.

They sat down, and all the Symbols except "Dr." Clay Harkness got up, violently protesting against the proposed outrage, and threatening to—

"I beg you not to threaten me," said the stranger, calmly. "I know my legal rights, and am not accustomed to being frightened at bluster." [*Applause.*] He sat down. "Dr." Harkness saw an opportunity here. He was one of the two very rich men of the place, and Pinkerton was the other. Harkness was proprietor of a mint; that is to say, a popular patent medicine. He was running for the Legislature on one ticket, and Pinkerton on the other. It was a close race and a hot one, and getting hotter every day. Both had strong appetites for money; each had bought a great tract of land, with a purpose; there was going to be a new railway, and each wanted to be in the Legislature and help locate the route to his own advantage; a single vote might make the decision, and with it two or three fortunes. The stake was large, and Harkness was a daring speculator. He was sitting close to the stranger. He leaned over while one or another of the other Symbols was entertaining the house with protests and appeals, and asked in a whisper,

"What is your price for the sack?"

"Forty thousand dollars."

"I'll give you twenty."

"No."

"Twenty-five."

"No."

"Say thirty."

"The price is forty thousand dollars; not a penny less."

"All right, I'll give it. I will come to the hotel at ten in the morning. I don't want it known; will see you privately."

"Very good." Then the stranger got up and said to the house:

"I find it late. The speeches of these gentlemen are not without merit, not without interest, not without grace; yet if I may be excused I will take my leave. I thank you for the great favor which you have shown me in granting my petition. I ask the Chair to keep the sack for me until tomorrow, and to hand these three five-hundred-dollar notes to Mr. Richards." They were passed up to the Chair. "At nine I will call for the sack, and at eleven will deliver the rest of the ten thousand to Mr. Richards in person, at his home. Good night."

Then he slipped out, and left the audience making a vast noise, which was composed of a mixture of cheers, the "Mikado" song, dog-disapproval, and the chant, "you are f-a-r from being a b-a-a-d man—a-a-a-a-men!"

## IV

At home the Richardses had to endure congratulations and compliments until midnight. Then they were left to themselves. They looked a little sad, and they sat silent and thinking. Finally Mary sighed and said,

"Do you think we are to blame, Edward—*much* to blame?" and her eyes wandered to the accusing triplet of big bank-notes lying on the table, where the congratulators had been gloating over them and reverently fingering them. Edward did not answer at once; then he brought out a sigh and said, hesitatingly:

"We—we couldn't help it, Mary. It—well, it was ordered. *All* things are."

Mary glanced up and looked at him steadily, but he didn't return the look. Presently she said:

"I thought congratulations and praises always tasted good. But—it seems to me, now—Edward?"

"Well?"

"Are you going to stay in the bank?"

"N-no."

"Resign?"

"In the morning—by note."

"It does seem best."

Richards bowed his head in his hands and muttered:

"Before, I was not afraid to let oceans of people's money pour through my hands, but—Mary, I am so tired, so tired—"

"We will go to bed."

At nine in the morning the stranger called for the sack and took it to the hotel in a cab. At ten Harkness had a talk with him privately. The stranger asked for and got five checks on a metropolitan bank—drawn to "Bearer,"—four for $1,500 each, and one for $34,000. He put one of the former in his pocket-book, and the remainder, representing $38,500, he put in an envelope, and with these he added a note, which he wrote after Harkness was gone. At eleven he called at the Richards house and knocked. Mrs. Richards peeped through the shutters, then went and received the envelope, and the stranger disappeared without a word. She came back flushed and a little unsteady on her legs, and gasped out:

"I am sure I recognized him! Last night it seemed to me that maybe I had seen him somewhere before."

"He is the man that brought the sack here?"

"I am almost sure of it."

"Then he is the ostensible Stephenson too, and sold every important citizen in this town with his bogus secret. Now if he has sent checks instead of money, we are sold too, after we thought we had escaped. I was beginning to feel fairly comfortable once more, after my night's rest, but the look of that envelope makes me sick. It isn't fat enough; $8,500 in even the largest bank-notes makes more bulk than that."

"Edward, why do you object to checks?"

"Checks signed by Stephenson! I am resigned to take the $8,500 if it could come in bank-notes—for it does seem that it was so ordered, Mary—but I have never had much courage, and I have not the pluck to try to market a check signed with that disastrous name. It would be a trap. That man tried to catch me; we escaped somehow or other; and now he is trying a new way. If it is checks——"

"Oh, Edward, it is *too* bad!" and she held up the checks and began to cry.

"Put them in the fire! quick! we mustn't be tempted. It is a trick to make the world laugh at *us,* along with the rest, and—Give them to *me,* since you can't do it!" He snatched them and tried to hold his grip till he could get to the stove; but he was human, he was a cashier, and he stopped a moment to make sure of the signature. Then he came near to fainting.

"Fan me, Mary, fan me! They are the same as gold!"

"Oh, how lovely, Edward! Why?"

"Signed by Harkness. What can the mystery of that be, Mary?"

"Edward, do you think——"

"Look here—look at this! Fifteen—fifteen—fifteen—thirty-four. Thirty-eight thousand five hundred! Mary, the sack isn't worth twelve dollars, and Harkness—apparently—has paid about par for it."

"And does it all come to us, do you think—instead of the ten thousand?"

"Why, it looks like it. And the checks are made to 'Bearer,' too."

"Is that good, Edward? What is it for?"

"A hint to collect them at some distant bank, I reckon. Perhaps Harkness doesn't want the matter known. What is that—a note?

"Yes, It was with the checks."

It was in the "Stephenson" handwriting, but there was no signature. It said:

*"I am a disappointed man. Your honesty is beyond the reach of temptation. I had a different idea about it, but I wronged you in that, and I beg pardon, and do it sincerely. I honor you—and that is sincere, too. This town is not worthy to kiss the hem of your garment. Dear sir, I made a square bet with myself that there were nineteen debauchable men in your self-righteous community. I have lost. Take the whole pot, you are entitled to it."*

Richards drew a deep sigh, and said:

"It seems written with fire—it burns so. Mary—I am miserable again."

"I, too. Ah, dear, I wish——"

"To think, Mary——he *believes* in me."

"Oh, don't, Edward——I can't bear it."

"If those beautiful words were deserved, Mary—and God knows I believed

I deserved them once—I think I could give the forty thousand dollars for them. And I would put that paper away, as representing more than gold and jewels, and keep it always. But now—We could not live in the shadow of its accusing presence, Mary."

He put it in the fire.

A messenger arrived and delivered an envelope. Richards took from it a note and read it; it was from Burgess:

*"You saved me, in a difficult time. I saved you last night. It was at cost of a lie, but I made the sacrifice freely, and out of grateful heart. None in this village knows so well as I know how brave and good and noble you are. At bottom you cannot respect me, knowing as you do of that matter of which I am accused, and by the general voice condemned; but I beg that you will at least believe that I am a grateful man; it will help me to bear my burden.* [*Signed*] "BURGESS."

"Saved, once more. And on such terms!" He put the note in the fire. "I—I wish I were dead, Mary, I wish I were out of it all."

"Oh, these are bitter, bitter days, Edward. The stabs, through their very generosity, are so deep—and they come so fast!"

Three days before the election each of two thousand voters suddenly found himself in possession of a prized memento—one of the renowned bogus double-eagles. Around one of its faces was stamped these words "THE REMARK I MADE TO THE POOR STRANGER WAS—" Around the other face was stamped these: "GO, AND REFORM. [SIGNED] PINKERTON." Thus the entire remaining refuse of the renowned joke was emptied upon a single head, and with calamitous effect. It revived the recent vast laugh and concentrated it upon Pinkerton; and Harkness's election was a walk-over.

Within twenty-four hours after the Richardses had received their checks their consciences were quieting down, discouraged; the old couple were learning to reconcile themselves to the sin which they had committed. But they were to learn, now, that a sin takes on new and real terrors when there seems a chance that it is going to be found out. This gives it a fresh and most substantial and important aspect. At church the morning sermon was of the usual pattern; it was the same old things said in the same old way; they had heard them a thousand times and found them innocuous, next to meaning-less, and easy to sleep under; but now it was different: the sermon seemed to bristle with accusations; it seemed aimed straight and specially at people who were concealing deadly sins. After church they got away from the mob of congratulators as soon as they could, and hurried homeward, chilled to the bone at they did not know what—vague, shadowy, indefinite fears. And by chance they caught a glimpse of Mr. Burgess as he turned a corner. He paid no attention to their nod of recognition! He hadn't seen it; but they did not know that. What could his conduct mean? It might mean—it might mean—oh, a dozen dreadful things. Was it possible that he knew that Richards could have cleared him of guilt in that bygone time, and had been silently waiting for a chance to even up accounts? At home, in their distress they got to imagining that their servant might have been in the next room listening when Richards revealed the secret to his wife that he knew of Burgess's innocence; next, Richards began to imagine that he had heard the swish of a gown in there at that time; next, he was sure he *had* heard it. They would call Sarah in, on a pretext, and watch her face: if she had been betraying them to Mr. Burgess, it would show in her manner. They asked her some questions—questions which were so random and incoherent and seemingly purposeless that the girl felt sure that the old people's mind had been affected by their sudden good fortune; the sharp and watchful gaze which they bent upon her frightened her, and that completed the business. She blushed, she became nervous and confused, and to the old people these were plain signs of guilt—guilt of some fearful sort or other—without doubt she was a spy and a traitor. When they were alone again they began to piece many unrelated things together and get horrible results out of the combination. When things had got about to the worst, Richards was delivered of a sudden gasp, and his wife asked:

"Oh, what is it?—what is it?"

"The note—Burgess's note! Its language was sarcastic, I see it now." He quoted: " 'At bottom you cannot respect me, *knowing*, as you do, of *that matter* of which I am accused'—oh, it is perfectly plain, now, God help me! He knows that I know! You see the ingenuity of the phrasing. It was a trap—and like a fool, I walked into it. And Mary—?"

"Oh, it is dreadful—I know what you are going to say—he didn't return your transcript of the pretended test-remark."

"No—kept it to destroy us with. Mary, he has exposed us to some already. I know it—I know it well. I saw it in a dozen faces after church. Ah, he wouldn't answer our nod of recognition—*he* knew what he had been doing!"

In the night the doctor was called. The news went around in the morning that the old couple were rather seriously ill—prostrated by the exhausting excitement growing out of their great windfall, the congratulations, and the late hours, the doctor said. The town was sincerely distressed; for these old people were about all it had left to be proud of, now.

Two days later the news was worse. The old couple were delirious, and were doing strange things. By witness of the nurses, Richards had exhibited checks—for $8,500? No—for an amazing sum—$38,500! What could be the explanation of this gigantic piece of luck?

The following day the nurses had more news—and wonderful. They had concluded to hide the checks, lest harm come to them; but when they searched they were gone from under the patient's pillow—vanished away. The patient said:

"Let the pillow alone; what do you want?"

"We thought it best that the checks——"

"You will never see them again—they are destroyed. They came from Satan. I saw the hell-brand on them, and I knew they were sent to betray me to sin." Then he fell to gabbling strange and dreadful things which were not clearly understandable, and which the doctor admonished them to keep to themselves.

Richards was right; the checks were never seen again.

A nurse must have talked in her sleep, for within two days the forbidden gabblings were the property of the town; and they were of a surprising sort. They seemed to indicate that Richards had been a claimant for the sack himself, and that Burgess had concealed that fact and then maliciously betrayed it.

Burgess was taxed with this and stoutly denied it. And he said it was not fair to attach weight to the chatter of a sick old man who was out of his mind. Still, suspicion was in the air, and there was much talk.

After a day or two it was reported that Mrs. Richards's delirious deliveries were getting to be duplicates of her husband's. Suspicion flamed up into conviction, now, and the town's pride in the purity of its one undiscredited important citizen began to dim down and flicker toward extinction.

Six days passed, then came more news. The old couple were dying. Richards's mind cleared in his latest hour, and he sent for Burgess. Burgess said:

"Let the room be cleared. I think he wishes to say something in privacy."

"No!" said Richards; "I want witnesses. I want you all to hear my confession, so that I may die a man, and not a dog. I was clean—artificially—like the rest; and like the rest I fell when temptation came. I signed a lie, and claimed the miserable sack. Mr. Burgess remembered that I had done him a service, and in gratitude (and ignorance) he suppressed my claim and saved me. You know the thing that was charged against Burgess years ago. My testimony, and mine alone, could have cleared him, and I was a coward, and left him to suffer disgrace—"

"No—no—Mr. Richards, you—"

"My servant betrayed my secret to him—"

"No one has betrayed anything to me—"

—"and then he did a natural and justifiable thing, he repented of the saving kindness which he had done me, and he *exposed* me—as I deserved—"

"Never!—I make oath—"

"Out of my heart I forgive him."

Burgess's impassioned protestations fell upon deaf ears; the dying man passed away without knowing that once more he had done poor Burgess a wrong. The old wife died that night.

That last of the sacred Nineteen had fallen a prey to the fiendish sack; the town was stripped of the last rag of its ancient glory. Its mourning was not showy, but it was deep.

By act of the Legislature—upon prayer and petition—Hadleyburg was allowed to change its name to (never mind what—I will not give it away), and leave one word out of the motto that for many generations had graced the town's official seal.

It is an honest town once more, and the man will have to rise early that catches it napping again.

# Unit 13

## The Man That Corrupted Hadleyburg

- Comprehension Questions
- Satire
- Discussion Guides
- Writing Exercise

# COMPREHENSION QUESTIONS

For each of the following statements and questions, select the option containing the most complete or most accurate answer.

1. The town of Hadleyburg had a reputation for its
(b) ☐ a. hospitality.     ☐ c. honesty.
    ☐ b. bad luck.     ☐ d. piety.

2. A good word to describe the citizens of Hadleyburg before their down-
(c) fall might be
    ☐ a. pessimistic.     ☐ c. modest.
    ☐ b. generous.     ☐ d. smug.

3. All their lives, the citizens of Hadleyburg had been
(c) ☐ a. shielded from temptation.
    ☐ b. distrusted by neighboring towns.
    ☐ c. testing and reaffirming their honesty.
    ☐ d. secretly cheating one another.

4. Hadleyburg's troubles began when
(d) ☐ a. one of its prominent citizens inherited a fortune.
    ☐ b. the town unknowingly offended a stranger passing through.
    ☐ c. Mr. and Mrs. Richards were presented with a sack of gold.
    ☐ d. the townspeople became greedy.

5. The stranger concocts an elaborate plan involving a sack of gold in
(e) order to
    ☐ a. blacken the town's reputation.
    ☐ b. corrupt Mr. and Mrs. Richards.
    ☐ c. get rich quick.
    ☐ d. get even with Barclay Goodson.

6. According to the letter attached to the sack of gold, the $40,000 came
(a) from unexpected inheritance
    ☐ a. an unexpected inheritance.
    ☐ b. a lucky business investment.
    ☐ c. a lifetime of savings.
    ☐ d. gambling winnings.

7. From the remarks made by Mr. and Mrs. Richards, the reader might
(h) infer that Barclay Goodson was
    ☐ a. crook.           ☐ c. rich and stingy.
    ☐ b. a generous man.    ☐ d. very religious.

8. The townspeople of Hadleyburg disliked Barclay Goodson because
(c) ☐ a. he was rich.
    ☐ b. he wasn't born in Hadleyburg.
    ☐ c. he poked fun at their virtue.
    ☐ d. he was dishonest.

9. Which of the following choices best defines the word *vexation* as used
(l) in the following sentence: "He sat long, gazing vacantly at the floor,
    and by and by he began to punctuate his thoughts with little nervous
    movements of his hands that seemed to indicate *vexation*"?
    ☐ a. Emotional distress
    ☐ b. Deep regret
    ☐ c. A sudden inspiration
    ☐ d. A feeling of peacefulness

10. A good word to describe the Richardses toward the end of the story is
 (j)  ☐ a. noble.         ☐ c. stupid.
    ☐ b. pathetic.      ☐ d. ambitious.

11. Mrs. Richards says about Hadleyburg that, ". . . if ever the day comes
(k) that its honesty falls under great temptation, its grand reputation will go
    to ruin *like a house of cards.*"   The phrase *like a house of cards* is a
    simile used to express the town's
    ☐ a. delight in gambling.
    ☐ b. strength and moral fortitude.
    ☐ c. vulnerability.
    ☐ d. enjoyment of card games.

12. What does Mrs. Richards learn about herself in the course of the story?
 (j)  ☐ a. She does not love her husband.
    ☐ b. She is getting old.
    ☐ c. Money means nothing to her.
    ☐ d. She is no more honest than the next person.

13. Mr. Richards finally decides that the "great service" he had performed
(b) for Barclay Goodson was to
    ☐ a. save him from drowning.
    ☐ b. save his soul.
    ☐ c. prevent his marriage to Nancy Hewitt.
    ☐ d. warn him to leave town.

14. The architect who had recently opened a new office in Hadleyburg
(d) enjoyed a flurry of business at about the time
    ☐ a. the stranger first left the sack with Mrs. Richards.
    ☐ b. the nineteen received the letters containing the test remark.
    ☐ c. Mr. and Mrs. Richards received the checks for $40,000.
    ☐ d. the town changed its name.

15. The attitude toward money expressed in this story is
(e) ☐ a. money corrupts.
    ☐ b. money can buy happiness.
    ☐ c. money can be used for good as well as evil.
    ☐ d. money and politics don't mix.

16. A good word to describe the citizens of Hadleyburg might be
(g) ☐ a. saints.     ☐ c. knaves.
    ☐ b. charlatans.     ☐ d. hypocrites.

17. Social classes in the town of Hadleyburg were
(h) ☐ a. flexible.     ☐ c. rigidly defined.
    ☐ b. nonexistant.     ☐ d. ignored.

18. The mood of the spectators in the Town Hall as one after another of
(i) the test remarks are read aloud is one of
    ☐ a. pandemonium and delight.
    ☐ b. shock and disappointment.
    ☐ c. polite interest.
    ☐ d. puzzlement.

19. Mr. and Mrs. Richards's test remark was never read aloud at the town
(b) meeting because
    ☐ a. they never submitted one.
    ☐ b. Reverend Burgess lost it.
    ☐ c. Reverend Burgess pretended not to have it.
    ☐ d. Mr. Richards took it back before the meeting began.

20. In the following statement, the stranger likens the scene at the town
(k) hall to a poker game: "Yes, he saw my deuces —*and* with a straight
flush, and by rights the pot is his." This is an example of a literary
device called
- ☐ a. a metaphor (an implied comparison).
- ☐ b. a simile (a comparison using "like" or "as").
- ☐ c. meiosis (understatement).
- ☐ d. oxymoron (seems to contradict itself).

21. From his portrayal of Harkness and Pinkerton, the two candidates
(f) running for Legislature, the reader might conclude that the author
- ☐ a. was once a politician.
- ☐ b. thinks politicans are stupid.
- ☐ c. is suspicious of politicans' motives.
- ☐ d. thinks politicians should be better paid.

22. Harkness bought the bogus coins from the stranger and
(a) ☐ a. sold them as souvenirs.
- ☐ b. kept them as a reminder of his greed.
- ☐ c. destroyed them.
- ☐ d. used them to embarrass Pinkerton.

23. After accepting the $40,000, Mr. and Mrs. Richards are
(b) ☐ a. blackmailed by the Reverend Burgess.
- ☐ b. robbed on their way to the bank.
- ☐ c. visited by the tax collector.
- ☐ d. afflicted with a guilty concience.

24. In the end, the citizens of Hadleyburg
(g) ☐ a. had learned their lesson.
- ☐ b. were as vain as ever.
- ☐ c. were angry with the Richardses.
- ☐ d. were bent on revenge.

25. The author's attitude toward the self-righteous citizens of Hadleyburg
(i) is
- ☐ a. admiring.          ☐ c. sympathetic.
- ☐ b. contemptuous.   ☐ d. neutral.

---

Comprehension Skills: a — isolating details; b — recalling specific facts; c — retaining
concepts; d — organizing facts; e — understanding the main idea; f — drawing a
conclusion; g — making a judgment; h — making an inference; i — recognizing tone;
j — understanding characters; k — appreciation of literary forms; l — understanding
vocabulary.

# SATIRE

**Practice Exercise A**

Hadleyburg village woke up world-celebrated—astonished—happy—vain. Vain beyond imagination. Its nineteen principal citizens and their wives went about shaking hands with each other, and beaming, and smiling, and congratulating, and saying *this* thing adds a new word to the dictionary— *Hadleyburg*, synonym for *incorruptible*—destined to live in dictionaries forever!

1. The satiric irony of this passage lies in the fact that
   - ☐ a. its citizens aren't really vain; they only seem to be vain.
   - ☐ b. Hadleyburg is destined to live on as a synonym for "corruptible," not "incorruptible."
   - ☐ c. no one in the outside world cares one way or the other about Hadleyburg.
   - ☐ d. the nineteen principal citizens never liked living in Hadleyburg in the first place.

2. Underline the brief sentence in this passage that reveals a moral weakness in the citizens of Hadleyburg.

**Practice Exercise B**

The gold sack stood on a little table at the front of the platform where all the house could see it. The bulk of the house gazed at it with a burning interest, a mouth-watering interest, a wistful and pathetic interest; a minority of nineteen couples gazed at it tenderly, lovingly, proprietarily, and the male half of this minority kept saying over to themselves the moving little impromptu speeches of thankfulness for the audience's applause and congratulations which they were presently going to get up and deliver. Every now and then one of these got a piece of paper out of his vest pocket and privately glanced at it to refresh his memory.

1. The human frailty satirized in this passage is
   - ☐ a. hypocrisy.       ☐ c. greed.
   - ☐ b. ignorance.       ☐ d. deceit.

2. Circle the one adjective in the second sentence which is used sarcastically (sarcasm conveys the *opposite* of a word's literal meaning.)

## Practice Exercise C

Three days before the election each of two thousand voters suddenly found himself in possession of a prized memento — one of the renowned bogus double-eagles. Around one of its faces was stamped these words. "THE REMARK I MADE TO THE POOR STRANGER WAS—" Around the other face was stamped these: "GO, AND REFORM" [SIGNED] PINKERTON." Thus the entire remaining refuse of the renowned joke was emptied upon a single head, and with calamitous effect. It revived the recent vast laugh and concentrated it upon Pinkerton; and Harkness's election was a walk-over.

1. The satiric attack in the passage above is directed at
   - ☐ a. money.
   - ☐ b. apathy.
   - ☐ c. voters.
   - ☐ d. politicians.

2. Underline the sentence revealing the motivation behind the dirty political trick which Harkness played on Pinkerton.

## Practice Exercise D

"Let the room be cleared. I think he wishes to say something in privacy."

"No!" said Richards; "I want witnesses. I want you all to hear my confession, so that I may die like a man, and not a dog. I was clean—artifically—like the rest; and like the rest I fell when temptation came. I signed a lie, and claimed the miserable sack. Mr. Burgess remembered that I had done him a service, and in gratitude (and ignorance) he suppressed my claim and saved me. You know the thing that was charged against Burgess years ago. My testimony, and mine alone, could have cleared him, and I was a coward, and left him to suffer disgrace—"

"No—no—Mr. Richards, you—"

"My servant betrayed my secret to him—"

"No one has betrayed anything to me—"

—"and then he did a natural and justifiable thing, he repented of the saving kindness which he had done me, and he *exposed* me—as I deserved—"

"Never! —I make oath—"

"Out of my heart I forgive him."

Burgess's impassioned protestations fell upon deaf ears; the dying man passed away without knowing that once more he had done poor Burgess a wrong. The old wife died that night.

1. The fate of Mr. and Mrs. Richards as described in the passage above *is not* satiric because
   - ☐ a. it is no longer humorous.
   - ☐ b. it is not critical enough.
   - ☐ c. they never recognize their own vanity.
   - ☐ d. the Richards do not suffer enough.

2. Underline at least two phrases in the passage above showing that Mr. Richards is no longer vain.

# DISCUSSION GUIDES

## Analyzing Satire

1. As a rule, characters in satire are flat and one-dimensional. Does this rule hold true in "The Man That Corrupted Hadleyburg"? Give examples to support your opinion.

2. In what ways is the Town Hall scene in Part III of the story a parody, or mockery, of the traditional town meeting? How do you think the author feels about town meetings in general?

3. In the last sentence of the story, Hadleyburg has apparently learned its lesson — "It is an honest town once more, and the man will have to rise early that catches it napping again." How might it be argued that this ending departs from the spirit of satire?

4. Critics have divided satire into two categories—*Horatian* satire, which is gentle, smiling and broadly sympathetic; and *Juvenalian* satire, which is biting, bitter and angry. Into which category would you place "The Man That Corrupted Hadleyburg"?

5. What, if anything, does satire accomplish among readers? For instance, has the story you just read made you a more honest person? Or has it merely provided entertainment? Do people mend their ways as a result of reading satire?

## Interpreting the Story

6. When Richards receives the stranger's note praising his honesty, Richards asserts that, "If those beautiful words were deserved, . . . I think I could give the forty thousand dollars for them." Do you believe him? Or do you think Richards would give in to temptation the next time, too? Explain.

7. Why does Mr. Richards quit his bank job towards the end of the story?

8. The town of Hadleyburg changes its motto from "Lead us not into temptation" to "Lead us into temptation." What is the meaning of the new motto?

## Analyzing the Author's Technique

9. Why doesn't Twain identify either the crime which the Reverend Burgess was thought to have committed, or the offense done to the stranger?

10. Which character in the story do you think most nearly represents the author's own point of view? Explain your choice.

## WRITING EXERCISE

One of the most popular forms of satire is parody. A parody is a comic imitation of a familiar subject. For example, in "The Man That Corrupted Hadleyburg," Mark Twain parodies a popular song from *The Mikado* by substituting new words for the original verse. One of the funniest parodies of our own time is comedian Bill Cosby's interpretation of the story of Noah:

> Noah: "Build an ark? Why should I?"
> God: "I can't tell you."
> Noah: "Give me a hint."
> God: "How long can you tread water?"

*Mad* magazine regularly features thinly disguised take-offs on new movies, popular television shows, and oft-repeated commercials.

Take a look at some examples of parody (the *National Lampoon* is another good source). Then choose a topic (a popular song, TV show, movie, or commercial) and create your own parody by playfully distorting the original message.

Unit 14
**Folklore and
the Folk Tale**

# The Gentleman
from Cracow

Isaac B. Singer

# Introduction

Isaac Bashevis Singer is the only American member of the National Institute of Arts who does not write in English. He writes in Yiddish, as he has since he was a young man growing up in rural and urban Jewish communities of eastern Poland in the years before World War II. Although Singer has been an American citizen for forty years and has a scholar's expert command of English, he prefers to write in Yiddish. It is the idiom of the people he writes about—the Jews he knew in Poland and their American descendants. In an interview for the *New York Times* the author said: "I had to stay with my language and with the people whom I know best... A writer belongs to his people, to his clan... If you write about the things and the people you know best, you discover your roots."

When Singer won the Nobel Prize for literature in 1978, it was the first time that Yiddish was spoken before the Swedish Academy. The author said of his language, "In a figurative way, Yiddish is the wise and humble language of us all, the idiom of frightened and hopeful humanity." Because Yiddish is a wise and humble language, it is ideal for writing wise and humble stories—folk tales. Singer has written more than thirty books for adults, numerous short stories, and eleven books for children. All have a recognizable "folksy" sound that comes, in large part because they were written in Yiddish and then translated into English.

Because Singer is one of the leading folk writers of our time, his stories, especially "The Gentleman from Cracow," are excellent examples of the use that modern authors can make of the folk-tale style in their writing. His situations and themes are universal and you won't have any difficulty in recognizing them whether you come from eastern Poland or from middle America. The situation in "The Gentleman from Cracow" is traditional in folklore all over the world—an encounter with the forces of evil. The theme is equally well known, a temptation by the devil through the lure of great riches. You may find it helpful, however, to have a glossary of some of the less familiar terms that apply more specifically to Jewish customs and traditions. The following is a list of terms, arranged in the order in which they first appear in the story.

## Glossary of Words and Expressions

**peasants:** This refers to the non-Jewish farm workers in the countryside surrounding Frampol. In those days, Jews were often not permitted to own land.

**Wonder Rabbi:** an especially wise and pious rabbi who was believed to be a prophet

**groszy:** A small coin of very small value

**ritual slaughterer:** Among orthodox Jews, animals for food must be slaughtered in a particular way. According to Biblical laws, a blessing must be said for the slaughter to be *kosher.*

**matchmaker:** Marriages were arranged by parents with the help of a matchmaker. It was the custom to have a marriage contract and the woman was required to have a dowry of goods or money. This is a familiar (and still current) custom among many different groups of people.

**caftan:** A long, robe-like garment, sometimes tied at the waist with a sash. The caftan was common dress for everyone in the middle ages, and has been maintained as traditional dress afterwards among orthodox Jews, even into modern times.

**gulden:** A gold coin

**Feast of the Tabernacles:** A Jewish fall festival occurring in late September or early October. Also known as *Sukkoth* or *Succos.*

**Chanukah:** A joyful holiday celebration occurring in December. Also known as Hanukkah.

**destruction of the Temple:** The final destruction of the Temple at Jerusalem was accomplished by the Romans in 70 A.D., an occasion still mourned by Jews. The last remnant of this temple, known as the *wailing wall*, is considered a most holy place.

**Month of Heshvan:** Late October or early November

**ritual bath:** Married women were required to bathe and undergo a ritual cleansing once a month.

**Talmud:** An accumulation of wisdom and rabbinical laws

**east wall of the synagogue:** Older synagogues were constructed with the pulpit in the center and pews around it. Since worship was in the direction of Jerusalem (east), the east side of the synagogue was a prominent position.

**Pentecost:** A holiday in late spring

**Purim rattles and Torah flags:** Used by children in religious celebrations: Purim, the Feast of Esther, and Simchas Torah, a festival which gives thanks for the five books of Moses.

**yeshiva students:** A yeshiva is a school that emphasizes religious education.

**beadle:** A caretaker of the synagogue

**Osnath, Machlath and Lilith:** Evil characters out of Jewish folklore

**Korah and Ishmael:** Biblical characters. Korah led a revolt against Moses; Ishmael was a son of Abraham banished to the wilderness. Ishmael became the parent founder of the nations of the Arabian peninsula. Thus, both Jews and Arabs trace their ancestry to Abraham, and he is a patriarch of both people.

**Messiah:** The promised and expected heavenly deliverer of the Jewish people. Jesus Christ is recognized as the Messiah by Christians.

# Folklore and
# the Folk Tale

*Folk* are plain people, which includes most of us. *Lore* is a body of knowledge that is traditional in nature—handed down from one generation to the next for so long that its origins are lost in time. So *folklore* is any body of traditional knowledge with origins rooted among the people. In American folklore there are folk songs: cowboy ballads, spirituals, Appalachian Mountain music and war songs. There is folk medicine: rituals that cure warts, herbs that cure stomach aches and spring fever, charms that ward off colds, and plasters and poultices that cure those colds that the charms don't prevent. There are folk tales: legends about George Washington and Abraham Lincoln; tales of fabled strong men like John Henry, the steel-driving man, and Paul Bunyan, whose giant footsteps made the Great Lakes. There are Indian stories of the creation of the world and the origins of people and animals. Religious customs, superstitions, holiday traditions and the way we act on the occasions of births, marriages and deaths are all part of our folklore.

Because these things are so much a part of our living patterns, you would expect them to turn up in our literature and they do—more often than many people are aware. Nathaniel Hawthorne's novel *The Scarlet Letter* and his story "Young Goodman Brown" are based on the beliefs and customs of the early New England settlers. Herman Melville's *Moby Dick* describes the lore of our seafaring ancestors, and authors like Mark Twain, Bret Harte and Jack London have drawn heavily on the folklore of the American frontier in writing their stories.

In modern American literature, Truman Capote, William Faulkner, Carson McCullers, John Steinbeck, Mario Puzo, Richard Wright, James Baldwin and countless others reach deep into the traditions, customs and life styles of plain people, in every culture and in every condition of life in America, for material for their stories.

When, in addition to using the folklore of a group of people, an author adds a dream-like quality or a touch of the supernatural to a story, it takes on the character of a true folk tale. This happens, as you saw, in "Young Goodman Brown." The difference is that our later stories are usually more complex than most folk literature. And of course we know the immediate authorship of a modern story whereas the origins of folk tales are usually lost in time.

Because the elements of folk literature appear so often in modern writing, it is useful to be able to spot some of these elements when you meet them in your reading. These are the most important:

- The language of a folk tale is usually simple and uncomplicated.
- The story deals with the customs, traditions and beliefs of a certain group of people. Usually, some conflict with tradition or belief arises.
- The story brings characters face to face with their identity—their culture, their origins and the beliefs of their people. Spiritual and moral values of the people are prominently displayed.
- There is an element of fantasy. There is an encounter with magic or with some supernatural force or being. Sometimes the tale has a dream-like quality, or a dream is closely connected with reality.

Isaac Singer is at his best when he is writing a folk tale and many of his stories appear to be pure folk literature, as is "The Gentleman from Cracow." The folk in this story, as you learned in the introduction to the lesson, are the Jews of Poland at some indefinite time in the past. The tale is filled with their lore, and it tells of the terrible things that can happen when people attempt to trade their beliefs for wealth.

**1. Plain Language.** Folk tales almost always involve plain people, often poor people. Even when the principal characters are knights and princes, there must be a quota of poor but honest villagers who help the hero on his quest. Because folk tales come out of an oral tradition—being passed along by word of mouth—they are simple in language and structure. The original audiences for folk stories were unschooled and illiterate for the most part. They would not listen for very long to complicated stories they could not understand.

"The Gentleman from Cracow," like all of Singer's stories, was written in Yiddish, the principal language of provincial eastern European Jews until fifty or sixty years ago. Although the Jews, even in direst poverty, were always a remarkably literate people, Yiddish still developed with a distinctly folk character. This is because it was the *mama-loshen*, mother's language, of the people as opposed to the language of learning, which was Hebrew.

(Hebrew and Yiddish are quite different languages. Boys were educated in Hebrew so that they could read The Law—the five books of Moses that are the first books of the Bible—and other sacred writings. It was not thought either necessary or advisable to teach girls. Yiddish developed in an oral tradition with heavy borrowings from German and a smattering of Hebrew, Slavic and other languages. This language children learned from their mothers—hence *mama-loshen*—and it was the language of everyday business, household and social conversation. Yiddish is still a "live" language, as we can see from Singer's writing, but it does not enjoy the universality of use among Jews that it did before the holocaust of World War II.)

Yiddish, then, has a plainness and directness built into it that is ideal for writing a folk tale. Notice the folk sound that comes through, even in the English translation, in "The Gentleman from Cracow." Notice also how Singer suggests in his opening paragraph that the story will be a folk tale.

> Amid thick forests and deep swamps, on the slope of a hill, level at the summit, lay the village of Frampol. Nobody knew who had founded it, or why just there. Goats grazed among the tombstones which were already sunk in the ground of the cemetery. In the community house there was a parchment with a chronicle on it, but the first page was missing and the writing had faded. Legends were current among the people, tales of wicked intrigue concerning a mad nobleman, a lascivious lady, a Jewish scholar, and a wild dog. But their true origin was lost in the past.

The story might almost begin, "Once upon a time...." The setting sounds very long ago and far away—someplace quite foreign to our own experience. The sentences are short, compared to the writing in most stories, and the only elaborate words are *intrigue* and *lascivious*, which would be much more direct and down-to-earth in the original Yiddish.

Singer speaks of parchment chronicles and about legends whose origins are lost in time, like the origins of Frampol itself. He virtually tells you straight out: "Just so you don't miss the point, reader, this is a folk tale I'm writing."

**2. Customs, Traditions and Beliefs.** One definition of folklore is that it is the collective, unrecorded traditions of a people. To understand the power of tale-telling in preserving our beliefs and traditions, we need only consider the 5,000-year history of the stories of the Bible. The wealth of lore found in the Old Testament only began to be assembled in book form after 2,000 years of oral telling from one generation to the next. It took more thousands of years to assemble what we consider a complete Bible. And it has been a mere 500 years that printed Bibles have been available to the general population. But with all the oral telling and retelling and the copying and recopying, over all those years, the Bible has come down to us in a remarkably pure form. And it is probably the single most important influence in shaping the western culture and way of life.

On a less grand scale, in American folklore, any small child can tell how George Washington cut down his father's cherry tree and how he bravely admitted the deed saying, "I cannot tell a lie," even though they, and most adults, know little else of importance about the great general and President. What children learn from this bit of folklore, however, and what they pass on to *their* children, is that "moral heroism" is a traditional American ideal.

Up to now, you may not have known much about the traditions, beliefs, and customs of Jews of a bygone era in Poland. But see how much you learn just from this one passage in Singer's mythical tale. The gentleman from Cracow has just proposed that a ball be held so he can choose a wife.

The elders were incredulous when they heard what had been proposed. But the young girls were excited. The young men approved also. The mothers pretended to hesitate, but finally gave their consent. When a delegation of the older men sought out Rabbi Ozer for his approval, he was outraged.

"What kind of charlatan is this?" he shouted. "Frampol is not Cracow. All we need is a ball! Heaven forbid that we bring down a plague, and innocent infants be made to pay for our frivolity!"

But the more practical of the men reasoned with the rabbi, saying, "Our daughters walk around barefoot and in tatters now. He will provide them with shoes and clothing. If one of them should please him he would marry her and settle here. Certainly that is to our advantage. The synagogue needs a new roof. The windowpanes of the house of study are broken, the bathhouse is badly in need of repairs. In the poorhouse the sick lie on bundles of rotting straw."

These Jews are obviously a serious people, and frivolity, except on very special occasions, is frowned upon. (They remind us a bit of the Pilgrim Fathers whose Puritan ways, incidentally, also were based on the Bible.) The town elders didn't go to a mayor for permission to hold a ball, but to the rabbi. So we assume that the management of village affairs is in religious hands.

The rabbi speaks of a plague that may descend on their heads, which leads us to believe that the people were somewhat superstitious. We also see something of the structure of the community. As dirt poor as the village is, there are a synagogue, a house of study, a bathhouse and a poorhouse. Prayer, study, cleanliness and taking care of the needy are important values of these people. Because of Jewish teaching, reflected in stories like Singer's and hundreds of other stories before his, these values have always been top priorities among Jews, regardless of their circumstances.

**3. Fantasy and the Supernatural.** No traditional tale is without a touch of magic, fantasy, or a visit by something supernatural. "Cinderella," "Snow White," *The Arabian Nights*, and Homer's *Odyssey*, all have their magicians, witches, wizards, fairies, genies and gods. In all of these we are asked to believe the unbelievable for the sake of the story. And we are always happy to oblige, mostly because it is fun. But fantasy can also be instructive for the reader and useful for an author in making whatever use is to be made of the story.

In Poe's "The Black Cat," supernatural events emphasize the tortures of a sick mind. In Isaac Asimov's "Nightfall," fantasy enables us to look at our world from a new point of view. In Woody Allen's "The Kugelmass Episode," fantasy and magic are used to poke fun at people who would indulge in shady romance.

In folk tales, fantasy and contact with the supernatural are often used to explain the unexplainable: the origin of the world, the power of God, punishment of sin, the lure of evil, rewards for goodness, and so on. Singer uses fantasy and the supernatural in "The Gentleman from Cracow" to show that when people abandon their traditional values in pursuit of gold, they become utterly corrupt and give themselves over to the devil. (Encounters with the devil are among the most frequent occurrences in folk literature.)

In the midst of frenzied celebration, and with their village in flames, the people of Frampol finally realize the true nature of the wealthy gentleman.

> Now at last the deluded people realized that there was no natural origin to these occurrences. Although the rain continued to fall and even increased in intensity, the fire was not extinguished. An eerie light glowed in the market place. Those few prudent individuals who tried to disengage themselves from the demented crowd were crushed to earth and trampled.
>
> And then the gentleman from Cracow revealed his true identity. He was no longer the young man the villagers had welcomed, but a creature covered with scales, with an eye in his chest, and on his forehead a horn that rotated at great speed. His arms were covered with hair, thorns, and elflocks, and his tail was a mass of live serpents, for he was none other than Ketev Mriri, Chief of the Devils.

**4. Ethnic Identity and Moral Values.** Everyone wants to know who they are, their roots, what their people believe and what is important to them. This is all part and parcel of a person's identity. Folk tales, or elements of folk tales in modern literature, often attempt to answer these very important questions.

Authors like William Faulkner and James Baldwin often set their stories among the people where their own roots lie, and they seem to say to us, "By showing you who these people are, how they act and what they believe, you will understand who I am and perhaps who you are yourself." In the following passage the rabbi of Frampol finds his people so degraded that they are hardly recognizable as humans and much less as keepers of God's laws. Singer uses the situation to go to the center of Judeo-Christian tradition in having Rabbi Ozer restore the group's identity. The author also shows the moral options that their heritage provides.

> "We are doomed, my sisters," lamented a woman.
>
> "Let us drown ourselves in the river," a girl shrieked. "Why go on living?"
>
> One of the yeshiva boys said, "Let us strangle ourselves with our sashes."
>
> "Brothers, we are lost. Let us blaspheme God," said a horse dealer.
>
> "Have you lost your minds, Jews?" cried Rabbi Ozer, "Repent, before it is too late. You have fallen into Satan's snare, but it is my fault, I take the sin upon myself. I am the guilty one. I will be your scapegoat, and you shall remain clean."
>
> "This is madness!" one of the scholars protested, "God forbid that there be so many sins on your holy Head!"

"Do not worry about that. My shoulders are broad. I should have had more foresight. I was blind not to realize that the Cracow doctor was the Evil One. And when the shepherd is blind, the flock goes astray. It is I who deserve the punishment, the curses."

Rabbi Ozer could have simply explained, "Have you lost your minds?" —a more natural way of speaking. But he appeals to his people by their collective ethnic name: "Have you lost your mind's, *Jews*?—reminding them who they are. As God's people they still have the option to repent, a central belief of both Judaism and Christianity.

The idea of a scapegoat who assumes the sins of the people first appears in Hebrew literature in the Book of Leviticus in the Bible. The idea culminates in Christian belief in the sacrifice of Jesus for the sins of the world. Rabbi Ozer, the only one who has not sinned, assumes the awful responsibility of what has happened in order to save his people. In both Jewish and Christian lore there is no greater way that a person can demonstrate love for humanity than by assuming responsibility for the salvation of others. This is the quality of a saint.

In your general reading you won't always find the elements of folklore and the folk tale used as obviously as they are in Singer's work. But they are important elements of literature and the principal source of interest in much of what you read. Now that you are more aware of folklore and the folk tale, you may find it is difficult *not* to discover some of their characteristics in whatever you read from now on.

As you read the story:

- See how, early in the story, Singer presents the gentleman from Cracow like a character out of a fairy tale.

- Watch how a wealth of information is brought out in the story about marriage customs and traditions among the Jews of Eastern Poland.

- Notice the supernatural elements present as the ball begins.

- Think about how the people of Frampol are ultimately saved by being forced back to their traditional beliefs.

# The Gentleman
# from Cracow
## Isaac B. Singer

Amid thick forests and deep swamps, on the slope of a hill, level at the summit, lay the village of Frampol. Nobody knew who had founded it, or why just there. Goats grazed among the tombstones which were already sunk in the ground of the cemetery. In the community house there was a parchment with a chronicle on it, but the first page was missing and the writing had faded. Legends were current among the people, tales of wicked intrigue concerning a mad nobleman, a lascivious lady, a Jewish scholar, and a wild dog. But their true origin was lost in the past.

Peasants who tilled the surrounding countryside were poor; the land was stubborn. In the village, the Jews were impoverished; their roofs were straw, their floors dirt. In summer many of them wore no shoes, and in cold weather they wrapped their feet in rags or wore sandals made of straw.

Rabbi Ozer, although renowned for his erudition, received a salary of only eighteen *groszy* a week. The assistant rabbi, besides being ritual slaughterer, was teacher, matchmaker, bath attendant, and poorhouse nurse as well. Even those villagers who were considered wealthy knew little of luxury. They wore cotton gabardines, tied about their waists with string, and tasted meat only on the Sabbath. Gold coin was rarely seen in Frampol.

But the inhabitants of Franpol had been blessed with fine children. The boys grew tall and strong, the girls handsome. It was a mixed blessing, however, for the young men left to marry girls from other towns, while their sisters, who had no dowries, remained unwed. Yet despite everything, inexplicably, though the food was scarce and the water foul, the children continued to thrive.

Then, one summer, there was a drought. Even the oldest peasants could not recall a calamity such as this one. No rain fell. The corn was parched and stunted. There was scarcely anything worth harvesting. Not until the few sheaves of wheat had been cut and gathered did the rain come, and with it hail which destroyed whatever grain the drought had spared. Locusts huge as birds came in the wake of the storm; human voices were said to issue from their throats. They flew at the eyes of the peasants who tried to drive them away. That year there was no fair, for everything had been lost. Neither the peasants nor the Jews of Frampol had food. Although there was grain in the large towns, no one could buy it.

Just when all hope had been abandoned and the entire town was about to go begging, a miracle occurred. A carriage drawn by eight spirited horses, came into Frampol. The villagers expected its occupant to be a Christian gentleman, but it was a Jew, a young man between the ages of twenty and thirty, who alighted. Tall and pale, with a round black beard and fiery dark eyes, he wore a sable hat, silver-buckled shoes, and a beaver-trimmed caftan. Around his waist was a green silk sash. Aroused, the entire town rushed to get a glimpse of the stranger. This is the story he told: He was a doctor, a widower from Cracow. His wife, the daughter of a wealthy merchant, had died with their baby in childbirth.

Overwhelmed, the villagers asked why he had come to Frampol. It was on the advice of a Wonder Rabbi, he told them. The melancholy he had known after his wife's death would, the rabbi assured him, disappear in Frampol. From the poorhouse the beggars came, crowding about him as he distributed alms—three groszy, six groszy, half-gulden pieces. The stranger was clearly a gift from Heaven, and Frampol was not destined to vanish. The beggars hurried to the baker for bread, and the baker sent to Zamosc for a sack of flour.

"One sack?" the young doctor asked. "Why that won't last a single day. I will order a wagonload, and not only flour, but cornmeal also."

"But we have no money," the village elders explained.

"God willing, you will repay me when times are good," and saying this, the stranger produced a purse crammed with golden ducats. Frampol rejoiced as he counted out the coins.

The next day, wagons filled with flour, buckwheat, barley, millet, and beans, drove into Frampol. News of the village's good fortune reached the ears of the peasants, and they came to the Jews, to buy goods, as the Egyptians had once come to Joseph. Being without money, they paid in kind; as a result, there was meat in town. Now the ovens burned once more; the pots were full. Smoke rose from the chimneys, sending the odors of roast chicken and goose, onion and garlic, fresh bread and pastry, into the evening air. The villagers returned to their occupations; shoemakers mended shoes; tailors picked up their rusted shears and irons.

The evenings were warm and the sky clear, though the Feast of the Tabernacles had already passed. The stars seemed unusually large. Even the birds were awake, and they chirped and warbled as though in midsummer. The stranger from Cracow had taken the best room at the inn, and his dinner consisted of broiled duck, marchpane, and twisted bread. Apricots and Hungarian wine were his dessert. Six candles adorned the table. One evening after dinner, the doctor from Cracow entered the large public room where some of the more inquisitive townspeople had gathered and asked:

"Would anyone care for a game of cards?"

"But it isn't Chanukah yet," they answered in surprise.

"Why wait for Chanukah? I'll put up a gulden for every groszy."

A few of the more frivolous men were willing to try their luck, and it turned out to be good. A groszy meant a gulden, and one gulden became thirty. Anyone played who wished to do so. Everybody won. But the stranger did not seem distressed. Bank notes and coins of silver and gold covered the table. Women and girls crowded into the room, and it seemed as though the gleam of the gold before them was reflected in their eyes. They gasped in wonderment. Never before in Frampol had such things happened. Mothers cautioned their daughters to take pains with their hair, and allowed them to dress in holiday clothes. The girl who found favor in the eyes of the young doctor would be fortunate; he was not one to require a dowry.

## II

The next morning, matchmakers called on him, each extolling the virtues of the girl he represented. The doctor invited them to be seated, served them honey cake, macaroons, nuts, and mead, and announced:

"From each of you I get exactly the same story: Your client is beautiful and clever and possesses every possible distinction. But how can I know which of you is telling the truth? I want the finest of them all as my wife. Here is what I suggest: Let there be a ball to which all the eligible young women are invited. By observing their appearance and behavior, I shall be able to choose among them. Then the marriage contract will be drawn and the wedding arranged."

The matchmakers were astounded. Old Mendel was the first to find words. "A ball? That sort of thing is all right for rich Gentiles, but we Jews have not indulged in such festivities since the destruction of the Temple— except when the Law prescribes it for certain holidays."

"Isn't every Jew obliged to marry off his daughters?" asked the doctor.

"But the girls have no appropriate clothes," another matchmaker protested. "Because of the drought they would have to go in rags."

"I will see that they all have clothes. I'll order enough silk, wool, velvet, and linen from Zamosc to outfit every girl. Let the ball take place. Let it be one that Frampol will never forget."

"But where can we hold it?" another matchmaker interjected. "The hall where we used to hold weddings has burned down, and our cottages are too small."

"There's the market place," the gentleman from Cracow suggested.

"But it is already the month of Heshvan. Any day now, it will turn cold."

"We'll choose a warm night when the moon is out. Don't worry about it."

To all the numerous objections of the matchmakers, the stranger had an answer ready. Finally they agreed to consult the elders. The doctor said he was in no hurry, he would await their decision. During the entire discussion, he had been carrying on a game of chess with one of the town's cleverest young men, while munching raisins.

The elders were incredulous when they heard what had been proposed. But the young girls were excited. The young men approved also. The mothers pretended to hesitate, but finally gave their consent. When a delegation of the older men sought out Rabbi Ozer for his approval he was outraged.

"What kind of charlatan is this?" he shouted. "Frampol is not Cracow. All we need is a ball! Heaven forbid that we bring down a plague, and innocent infants be made to pay for our frivolity!"

But the more practical of the men reasoned with the rabbi, saying, "Our daughters walk around barefoot and in tatters now. He will provide them with shoes and clothing. If one of them should please him he would marry her and settle here. Certainly that is to our advantage. The synagogue needs a new roof. The windowpanes of the house of study are broken, the bathhouse is badly in need of repairs. In the poorhouse the sick lie on bundles of rotting straw."

"All this is true. But suppose we sin?"

"Everything will be done according to the Law, Rabbi. You can trust us."

Taking down the book of the Law, Rabbi Ozer leafed through it. Occasionally he stopped to study a page, and then, finally, after sighing and hesitating, he consented. Was there any choice? He himself had received no salary for six months.

As soon as the rabbi had given his consent there was a great display of activity. The dry goods merchants traveled immediately to Zamosc and Yanev, returning with cloth and leather paid for by the gentleman from Cracow. The tailors and seamstresses worked day and night; the cobblers left their benches only to pray. The young women, all anticipation, were in a feverish state. Vaguely remembered dance steps were tried out. They baked cakes and other pastries, and used up their stores of jams and preserves which they had been keeping in readiness for illness. The Frampol musicians were equally active. Cymbals, fiddles, and bagpipes, long forgotten and neglected, had to be dusted off and tuned. Gaiety infected even the very old, for it was rumored that the elegant doctor planned a banquet for the poor where alms would be distributed.

The eligible girls were wholly concerned with self-improvement. They scrubbed their skin and arranged their hair, a few even visited the ritual bath to bathe among the married women. In the evenings, faces flushed, eyes sparkling, they met at each other's houses, to tell stories and ask riddles. It was difficult for them, and for their mothers as well, to sleep at night. Fathers sighed as they slept. And suddenly the young girls of Frampol seemed so attractive that the young men who had contemplated marrying outside of town fell in love with them. Although the young men still sat in the study-house poring over the Talmud, its wisdom no longer penetrated to them. It was the ball alone that they spoke of now, only the ball that occupied their thoughts.

The doctor from Cracow also enjoyed himself. He changed his clothes several times daily. First it was a silk coat worn with pom-pommed slippers, then a woolen caftan with high boots. At one meal he wore a pelerine trimmed with beaver tails, and at the next a cape embroidered with flowers and leaves. He breakfasted on roast pigeon which he washed down with dry wine. For lunch he ordered egg noodles and blintzes, and he was audacious enough to eat Sabbath pudding on weekdays. He never attended prayer, but instead played all sorts of games: cards, goats and wolves, coin-pitching. Having finished lunch, he would drive through the neighborhood with his coachman. The peasants would lift their hats as he passed, and bow almost to the ground. One day he strolled through Frampol with a gold-headed cane. Women crowded to the windows to observe him, and boys, following after him, picked up the rock candy he tossed them. In the evenings he and his companions, gay young men, drank wine until all hours. Rabbi Ozer constantly warned his flock that they walked a downhill path led by the Evil One, but they paid no attention to him. Their minds and hearts were completely possessed by the ball, which would be held at the market place in the middle of that month, at the time of the full moon.

III

At the edge of town, in a small valley close to a swamp, stood a hut no larger than a chicken coop. Its floor was dirt, its window was boarded; and the roof, because it was covered with green and yellow moss, made one think of a bird's nest that had been forsaken. Heaps of garbage were strewn before the hut, and lime ditches furrowed the soggy earth. Amidst the refuse there was an occasional chair without a seat, a jug missing an ear, a table without legs. Every type of broom, bone, and rag seemed to be rotting there. This was where Lipa the Rag-picker lived with his daughter, Hodle. While his first wife was alive, Lipa had been a respected merchant in Frampol where he occupied a pew at the east wall of the synagogue. But after his wife had drowned herself in the river, his condition declined rapidly. He took to drink, associated with the town's worst element, and soon ended up bankrupt.

His second wife, a beggar woman from Yanev, bore him a daughter whom she left behind when she deserted him for nonsupport. Unconcerned about his wife's departure, Lipa allowed the child to shift for herself. Each week he spent a few days collecting rags from the garbage. The rest of the time he was in the tavern. Although the innkeeper's wife scolded him, she received only abusive answers in reply. Lipa had his success among the men as a talespinner. He attracted business to the place with his fantastic yarns about witches and windmills and devils and goblins. He could also recite Polish and Ukrainian rhymes and had a knack for telling jokes. The innkeeper allowed him to occupy a place near the stove, and from time to time he was given a bowl of soup and a piece of bread. Old friends, remembering Lipa's former affluence, occasionally presented him with a pair of pants, a threadbare coat, or a shirt. He accepted everything ungraciously. He even stuck out his tongue at his benefactors as they turned away from him.

As in the saying, "Like father, like son," Hodle inherited the vices of both parents—her drunken father, her begging mother. By the time she was six, she had won a reputation as a glutton and thief. Barefoot and half naked, she roamed the town, entering houses and raiding the larders of those who were not home. She preyed on chickens and ducks, cut their throats with glass, and ate them. Although the inhabitants of Frampol had often warned her father that he was rearing a wanton, the information did not seem to bother him. He seldom spoke to her and she did not even call him father. When she was twelve, her lasciviousness became a matter for discussion among the women. Gypsies visited her shack, and it was rumored that she devoured the meat of cats and dogs, in fact, every kind of carcass. Tall and lean, with red hair and green eyes, she went barefoot summer and winter, and her skirts were made of colored scraps discarded by the seamstresses. She was feared by mothers who said she wove spells that blighted the young. The village elders who admonished her received brazen answers. She had the shrewdness of a bastard, the quick tongue of an adder, and when attacked by street urchins, did not hesitate to strike back. Particularly skilled in swearing, she had an unlimited repertoire. It was like her to call out, "Pox on your tongue and gangrene in your eyes," or, possibly, "May you rot till the skunks run from your smell.'

Occasionally her curses were effective, and the town grew wary of incurring her anger. But as she matured she tended to avoid the town proper, and the time came when she was almost forgotten. But on the day that the Frampol merchants, in preparation for the ball, distributed cloth and leather among the town's young women, Hodle reappeared. She was now about seventeen, fully grown, though still in short skirts; her face was freckled, and her hair disheveled. Beads, such as those worn by gypsies, encircled her throat, and on her wrists were bracelets made from wolves' teeth. Pushing her way through the crowd, she demanded her share. There was nothing left but a few odds and ends, which were given to her. Furious with her allotment, she hastened home with it. Those who had seen what had happened laughed, "Look who's going to the ball! What a pretty picture she'll make!"

At last the shoemakers and tailors were done; every dress fit, every shoe was right. The days were miraculously warm, and the nights as luminous as the evenings of Pentecost. It was the morning star that, on the day of the ball, woke the entire town. Tables and benches lined one side of the market. The cooks had already roasted calves, sheep, goats, geese, ducks, and chicken, and had baked sponge and raisin cakes, braided bread and rolls, onion biscuits and ginger bread. There were mead and beer and a barrel of Hungarian wine that had been brought by the wine dealer. When the children arrived they brought the bows and arrows with which they were accustomed to play at the Omer feast, as well as their Purim rattles and Torah flags. Even the doctor's horses were decorated with willow branches and autumn flowers, and the coachman paraded them through the town. Apprentices left their work, and yeshiva students their volumes of the Talmud. And despite Rabbi Ozer's injunction against the young matrons' attending the ball, they dressed in their wedding gowns and went, arriving with the young girls, who also came in white, each bearing a candle in her hand as though she were a bridesmaid. The band had already begun to play, and the music was lively. Rabbi Ozer alone was not present, having locked himself in his study. His maidservant had gone to the ball, leaving him to himself. He knew no good could come of such behavior, but there was nothing he could do to prevent it.

By late afternoon all the girls had gathered in the market place, surrounded by the townspeople. Drums were beaten. Jesters performed. The girls danced; first a quadrille, then a scissor dance. Next it was Kozack, and finally the Dance of Anger. Now the moon appeared, although the sun had not yet set. It was time for the gentleman from Cracow. He entered on a white mare, flanked by bodyguards and his best man. He wore a large-plumed hat, and silver buttons flashed on his green coat. A sword hung at his side, and his shiny boots rested in the stirrups. He resembled a gentleman off to war with his entourage. Silently he sat in his saddle, watching the girls as they danced. How graceful they were, how charmingly they moved! But one who did not dance was the daughter of Lipa the Ragpicker. She stood to one side, ignored by them all.

## IV

The setting sun, remarkably large, stared down angrily like a heavenly eye upon the Frampol market place. Never before had Frampol seen such a sunset. Like rivers of burning sulphur, fiery clouds streamed across the heavens, assuming the shapes of elephants, lions, snakes, and monsters. They seemed to be waging a battle in the sky, devouring one another, spitting, breathing fire. It almost seemed to be the River of Fire they watched, where demons tortured the evil-doers amidst glowing coals and heaps of ashes. The moon swelled, became vast, blood-red, spotted, scarred, and gave off little light. The evening grew very dark, dissolving even the stars. The young men fetched torches, and a barrel of burning pitch was prepared. Shadows danced back and forth as though attending a ball of their own. Around the market place the houses seemed to vibrate; roofs quivered, chimneys shook. Such gaiety and intoxication had never before been known in Frampol. Everyone, for the first time in months, had eaten and drunk sufficiently. Even the animals participated in the merrymaking. Horses neighed, cows mooed, and the few roosters that had survived the slaughter of the fowl crowed. Flocks of crows and strange birds flew in to pick at the leavings. Fireflies illumined the darkness, and lightning flashed on the horizon. But there was no thunder. A weird circular light glowed in the sky for a few moments and then suddenly plummeted toward the horizon, a crimson tail behind it, resembling a burning rod. Then, as everyone stared in wonder at the sky, the gentleman from Cracow spoke:

"Listen to me. I have wonderful things to tell you, but let no one be overcome by joy. Men, take hold of your wives. Young men, look to your girls. You see in me the wealthiest man in the entire world. Money is sand to me, and diamonds are pebbles. I come from the land of Ophir, where King Solomon found the gold for his temple. I dwell in the palace of the Queen of Sheba. My coach is solid gold, its wheels inlaid with sapphires, with axles of ivory, its lamps studded with rubies and emeralds, opals and amethysts. The ruler of the Ten Lost Tribes of Israel knows of your miseries, and he has sent me to be your benefactor. But there is one condition. Tonight, every virgin must marry. I will provide a dowry of ten thousand ducats for each maiden, as well as a string of pearls that will hang to her knees. But make haste. Every girl must have a husband before the clocks strike twelve."

The crowd was hushed. It was as quiet as New Year's Day before the blowing of the ram's horn. One could hear the buzzing of a fly.

Then one old man called out, "But that's impossible. The girls are not even engaged!"

"Let them become engaged."

"To whom?"

"We can draw lots," the gentleman from Cracow replied. "Whoever is to be married will have his or her name written on a card. Mine also. And then we shall draw to see who is meant for whom."

"But a girl must wait seven days. She must have the prescribed ablutions."

"Let the sin be on me. She needn't wait."

Despite the protestations of the old men and their wives, a sheet of paper was torn into pieces, and on each piece the name of a young man or young woman was written by a scribe. The town's beadle, now in the service of the gentleman from Cracow, drew from one skullcap the names of the young men, and from another those of the young women, chanting their names to the same tune with which he called up members of the congregation for the reading of the Torah.

"Nahum, son of Katriel, betrothed to Yentel, daughter of Nathan. Solomon, son of Cov Baer, betrothed to Tryna, daughter of Jonah Lieb." The assortment was a strange one, but since in the night all sheep are black, the matches seemed reasonable enough. After each drawing, the newly engaged couple hand in hand, approached the doctor to collect the dowry and wedding gift. As he had promised, the gentleman from Cracow gave each the stipulated sum of ducats, and on the neck of each bride he hung a strand of pearls. Now the mothers, unable to restrain their joy, began to dance and shout. The fathers stood by, bewildered. When the girls lifted their dresses to catch the gold coins given by the doctor, their legs and underclothing were exposed, which sent the men into paroxysms of lust. Fiddles screeched, drums pounded, trumpets blared. The uproar was deafening. Twelve-year-old boys were mated with "spinsters" of nineteen. The sons of substantial citizens took the daughters of paupers as brides; midgets were coupled with giants, beauties with cripples. On the last two slips appeared the names of the gentleman from Cracow and Hodle, the daughter of Lipa the Ragpicker.

The same old man who had called out previously said, "Woe unto us, the girl is a harlot."

"Come to me, Hodle, come to your bridegroom," the doctor bade.

Hodle, her hair in two long braids, dressed in a calico skirt, and with sandals on her feet, did not wait to be asked twice. As soon as she had been called she walked to where the gentleman from Cracow sat on his mare, and fell to her knees. She prostrated herself seven times before him.

"Is is true, what that old fool says?" her prospective husband asked her.

"Yes, my lord, it is so."

"Have you sinned only with Jews or with Gentiles as well?"

"With both."

"Was it for bread?"

"No. For the sheer pleasure."

"How old were you when you started?"

"Not quite ten."

"Are you sorry for what you have done?"

"No."

"Why not?"

"Why should I be?" she answered shamelessly.

"You don't fear the tortures of hell?"

"I fear nothing—not even God. There is no God."

Once more the old man began to scream, "Woe to us, woe to us, Jews! A fire is upon us, burning, Jews, Satan's fire. Save your souls, Jews. Flee, before it is too late!"

"Gag him," the gentleman from Cracow commanded.

The guards seized the old man and gagged him. The doctor, leading Hodle by the hand, began to dance. Now, as though the powers of darkness had been summoned, the rain and hail began to fall; flashes of lightning were accompanied by mighty thunderclaps. But, heedless of the storm, pious men and women embraced without shame, dancing and shouting as though possessed. Even the old were affected. In the furor, dresses were ripped, shoes shaken off, hats, wigs and skullcaps trampled in the mud. Sashes, slipping to the ground, twisted there like snakes. Suddenly there was a terrific crash. A huge bolt of lightning had simultaneously struck the synagogue, the study house, and the ritual bath. The whole town was on fire.

Now at last the deluded people realized that there was no natural origin to these occurrences. Although the rain continued to fall and even increased in intensity, the fire was not extinguished. An eerie light glowed in the market place. Those few prudent individuals who tried to disengage themselves from the demented crowd were crushed to earth and trampled.

And then the gentleman from Cracow revealed his true identity. He was no longer the young man the villagers had welcomed, but a creature covered with scales, with an eye in his chest, and on his forehead a horn that rotated at great speed. His arms were covered with hair, thorns, and elflocks, and his tail was a mass of live serpents, for he was none other than Ketev Mriri, Chief of the Devils.

Witches, werewolves, imps, demons, and hobgoblins plummeted from the sky, some on brooms, others on hoops, still others on spiders. Osnath, the daughter of Machlath, her fiery hair loosened in the wind, her breasts bare and thighs exposed, leaped from chimney to chimney, and skated along the eaves. Namah, Hurmizah the daughter of Aff, and many other she-devils did all sorts of somersaults. Satan himself gave away the bridegroom, while four evil spirits held the poles of the canopy, which had turned into writhing pythons. Four dogs escorted the groom. Hodle's dress fell from her and she stood naked. Her breasts hung down to her navel and her feet were webbed. Her hair was a wilderness of worms and caterpillars. The groom held out a triangular ring and, instead of saying, "With this ring be thou consecrated to me according to the laws of Moses and Israel," he said, "With this ring, be thou desecrated to me according to the blasphemy of Korah and Ishmael." And instead of wishing the pair good luck, the evil spirits called out, "Bad luck," and they began to chant:

> *"The curse of Eve, the Mark of Cain,*
> *The cunning of the snake, unite the twain."*

Screaming for the last time, the old man clutched at his head and died. Ketev Mriri began his eulogy:

> *"Devil's dung and Satan's spell*
> *Bring his ghost to roast in hell."*


## V

In the middle of the night, old Rabbi Ozer awoke. Since he was a holy man, the fire which was consuming the town had no power over his house. Sitting up in bed he looked about, wondering if dawn were already breaking. But it was neither day nor night without. The sky was a fiery red, and from the distance came a clamor of shouts and songs that resembled the howling of wild beasts. At first, recalling nothing, the old man wondered what was going on. "Has the world come to an end? Or have I failed to hear the ram's horn heralding the Messiah? Has He arrived?" Washing his hands, he put on his slippers and overcoat and went out.

The town was unrecognizable. Where houses had been, only chimneys stood. Mounds of coal smoldered here and there. He called the beadle, but there was no answer. With his cane, the rabbi went searching for his flock.

"Where are you, Jews, where are you?" he called piteously.

The earth scorched his feet, but he did not slacken his pace. Mad dogs and strange beings attacked him, but he wielded his cane against them. His sorrow was so great that he felt no fear. Where the market place used to be, a terrible sight met him. There was nothing but one great swamp, full of mud, slime, and ashes. Floundering in mud up to their waists, a crowd of naked people went through the movements of dance. At first, the rabbi mistook the weirdly moving figures for devils, and was about to recite the chapter, "Let there be contentment," and other passages dealing with exorcism, when he recognized the men of his town. Only then did he remember the doctor from Cracow, and the rabbi cried out bitterly, "Jews, for the sake of God, save your souls! You are in the hands of Satan!"

But the townspeople, too entranced to heed his cries, continued their frenzied movements for a long time, jumping like frogs, shaking as though with fever. With hair uncovered and breasts bare, the women laughed, cried, and swayed. Catching a yeshiva boy by his side-locks, a girl pulled him to her lap. A woman tugged at the beard of a strange man. Old men and women were immersed in slime up to their loins. They scarcely looked alive.

Relentlessly, the rabbi urged the people to resist evil. Reciting the Torah and other holy books, as well as incantations and the several names of God, he succeeded in rousing some of them. Soon others responded. The rabbi had helped the first man from the mire, then that one assisted the next, and so on. Most of them had recovered by the time the morning star appeared. Perhaps the spirits of their forebears had interceded, for although many had sinned, only one man had died this night in the market place square.

Now the men were appalled, realizing that the devil had bewitched them, had dragged them through muck; and they wept.

"Where is our money?" the girls wailed. "And our gold and our jewelry? Where is our clothing? What happened to the wine, the mead, the wedding gifts?"

But everything had turned to mud; the town of Frampol, stripped and ruined, had become a swamp. Its inhabitants were mud-splashed, denuded, monstrous. For a moment, forgetting their grief, they laughed at each other. The hair of the girls had turned into elflocks, and bats were entangled there. The young men had grown gray and wrinkled; the old were yellow as corpses. In their midst lay the old man who had died. Crimson with shame, the sun rose.

"Let us rend our clothes in mourning," one man called, but his words evoked laughter, for all were naked.

"We are doomed, my sisters," lamented a woman.

"Let us drown ourselves in the river," a girl shrieked. "Why go on living.?"

One of the yeshiva boys said, "Let us strangle ourselves with our sashes."

"Brothers, we are lost. Let us blaspheme God," said a horse dealer.

"Have you lost your minds, Jews?" cried Rabbi Ozer. "Repent, before it is too late. You have fallen into Satan's snare, but it is my fault, I take the sin upon myself. I am the guilty one. I will be your scapegoat, and you shall remain clean.'

"This is madness!" one of the scholars protested, "God forbid that there be so many sins on your holy head!"

"Do not worry about that. My shoulders are broad. I should have had more foresight. I was blind not to realize that the Cracow doctor was the Evil One. And when the shepherd is blind, the flock goes astray. It is I who deserve the punishment, the curses."

"Rabbi, what shall we do? We have no homes, no bed clothes, nothing. Woe to us, to our bodies and to our souls.'

"Our babies!" cried the young matrons. "Let us hurry to them!"

But it was the infants who had been the real victims of the passion for gold that had caused the inhabitants of Frampol to transgress. The infants' cribs were burned, their little bones were charred. The mothers stooped to pick up little hands, feet, skulls. The wailing and crying lasted long, but how long can a whole town weep? The gravedigger gathered the bones and carried them to the cemetery. Half the town began the prescribed seven days of mourning. But all fasted, for there was no food anywhere.

But the compassion of the Jews is well known, and when the neighboring town of Yanev learned what had happened, clothing, bed linen, bread, cheese, and dishes were collected and sent to Frampol. Timber merchants brought logs for building. A rich man offered credit. The next day the reconstruction of the town was begun. Although work is forbidden to those in mourning, Rabbi Ozer issued a verdict that this was an exceptional case: the lives of the people were in danger. Miraculously, the weather remained mild; no snow fell. Never before had there been such diligence in Frampol. The inhabitants built and prayed, mixed lime with sand, and recited psalms. The women worked with the men while girls, forgetting their fastidiousness, helped also. Scholars and men of high position assisted. Peasants from the surrounding villages, hearing of the catastrophe, took the old and infirm into their homes. They also brought wood, potatoes, cabbages, onions and other food. Priests and bishops from Lublin, hearing of events suggested witchcraft, came to examine witnesses. As the scribe recorded the names of those living in Frampol, Hodle, the daughter of Lipa the Ragpicker, was suddenly remembered. But when the townspeople went to where her hut had been, they found the hill covered with weeds and bramble, silent save for the cries of crows and cats; there was no indication that human beings had ever dwelt there.

Then it was understood that Hodle was in truth Lilith, and that the host of the netherworld had come to Frampol because of her. After their investigations, the clergymen from Lublin, greatly astonished at what they had seen and heard, returned home. A few days later, the day before the Sabbath, Rabbi Ozer died. The entire town attended his funeral, and the town preacher said a eulogy for him.

In time, a new rabbi came to the community, and a new town arose. The old people died, the mounds in the cemetery sifted down, and the monuments slowly sank. But the story, signed by trustworthy witnesses, can still be read in the parchment chronicle.

And the events in the story brought their epilogue: the lust for gold had been stifled in Frampol; it was never rekindled. From generation to generation the people remained paupers. A gold coin became an abomination in Frampol, and even silver was looked at askance. Whenever a shoemaker or tailor asked too high a price for his work he was told, "Go to the gentleman from Cracow and he will give you buckets of gold."

And on the grave of Rabbi Ozer, in the memorial chapel, there burns an eternal light. A white pigeon is often seen on the roof: the sainted spirit of Rabbi Ozer.

*—Translated by*
Martha Glicklich and Elaine Gottlieb.

# Unit 14

## The Gentleman from Cracow

- Comprehension Questions
- Folklore and the Folk Tale
- Discussion Guides
- Writing Exercise

## COMPREHENSION QUESTIONS

For each of the following statements and questions, select the option containing the most complete or most accurate answer.

1. The village of Frampol was located
(a) ☐ a. on an open plain.
     ☐ b. in an area of swamp and forest.
     ☐ c. in the mountains.
     ☐ d. beside a lake.

2. The children of Frampol were
(b) ☐ a. pale and sickly.
     ☐ b. discontented and rebellious.
     ☐ c. ugly and surly.
     ☐ d. tall and strong.

3. Which of the following sayings best expresses the main idea of the story?
(e) ☐ a. Evil comes in attractive dress.
     ☐ b. We will know the devil when we see him.
     ☐ c. Poverty is better than riches.
     ☐ d. Tradition guards against evil.

4. Under similar circumstances most people would
(g) ☐ a. be more suspicious of the doctor than the Frampol villagers were.
     ☐ b. check carefully on the doctor's background before they believed him.
     ☐ c. reject gold that came from an uncertain source.
     ☐ d. react to the generous doctor in the same way as the people of Frampol.

5. The town's attitude toward the doctor from Cracow may best be
(c) described as
     ☐ a. envious but trusting.
     ☐ b. wait and see.
     ☐ c. awed and admiring.
     ☐ d. suspicious and fearful.

6. Over the course of the story, Rabbi Ozer is
(g) ☐ a. weak and indecisive at first but finally strong.
☐ b. generally a poor leader of his people.
☐ c. more under the influence of evil than anyone.
☐ d. a foolish old man until the very end when he proves himself a saint.

7. The condition of children is referred to at the beginning and at the end
(h) of the story. As you think of the beginning and the end of the story, you may infer that the people of Frampol believed that
☐ a. children bring nothing but worry to the parents.
☐ b. the devil is envious of handsome children.
☐ c. the blessings and sins of parents are visited on the children.
☐ d. children are better off brought up in poverty than in riches.

8. If this story were presented as a play on television, it would be
(i) ☐ a. much like a Shakesperian drama.
☐ b. dignified like a story from the Bible.
☐ c. generally low key except for the dance scene.
☐ d. lively until the end, which would be somber.

9. The characters in the story are
(j) ☐ a. highly developed in great detail.
☐ b. hardly developed at all.
☐ c. used to develop themes.
☐ d. examined for good and bad points.

10. When the Jews of Frampol first saw the doctor arriving in his carriage,
(a) they thought he was
☐ a. a Christian gentleman.
☐ b. an officer of the Czar.
☐ c. a clergyman from Cracow.
☐ d. a wealthy Jewish doctor.

11. The people of Frampol viewed the ball as a
(c) ☐ a. chance for improvement.
☐ b. rebellion against religion.
☐ c. last fling.
☐ d. wanton orgy.

12. Rabbi Ozer may seem at times like a
(j) ☐ a. country preacher.          ☐ c. scientist
☐ b. dictator.                         ☐ d. prophet.

13. The elders were *incredulous* when they heard the doctor had proposed
(l)  a ball be held. The word *incredulous* means
- □ a. shocked.
- □ b. unnerved.
- □ c. angry beyond belief.
- □ d. unbelieving.

14. The true nature of the doctor from Cracow
(d) □ a. is obvious from the beginning.
- □ b. becomes known gradually.
- □ c. isn't known until the end of the story.
- □ d. is revealed suddenly.

15. The rabbi finally gave permission for the ball because
(f) □ a. he found the law permitted it.
- □ b. it would have been sinful not to.
- □ c. the town was so much in need.
- □ d. he was under the influence of the devil.

16. From what you saw of the people of Frampol, you may infer that they
(h) were
- □ a. too well educated to be superstitious.
- □ b. superstitious as well as religious.
- □ c. secretly superstitious.
- □ d. too firmly religious to be superstitious.

17. Whenever the weather, the stars, the sun, the crops or any natural events
(i) are mentioned, the tone of the story seems to become
- □ a. ominous and threatening.
- □ b. light and airy.
- □ c. spiritual and uplifting.
- □ d. awesome and wonderful.

18. Hodle was the daughter of the
(b) □ a. innkeeper.
- □ b. ragpicker.
- □ c. beadle.
- □ d. horse dealer.

19. The reader can conclude that Hodle was
(f) □ a. just a victim of circumstance.
- □ b. a force for evil in the community.
- □ c. an example of misdirected energy.
- □ d. the conscience of Frampol.

20. The villagers said that Hodle was a *wanton*. A *wanton* is
(l)  ☐ a. a beggar.
    ☐ b. a person lacking morals.
    ☐ c. someone who lacks education.
    ☐ d. a glutton.

21. Personification gives human qualities to objects and animals. Which
(k) of the following expressions from the story is an example of person-
    ification?
    ☐ a. "The setting sun. . . stared down angrily. . . . "
    ☐ b. "Goats grazed among the tombstones. . . . "
    ☐ c. "The stranger was clearly a gift from heaven. . . ."
    ☐ d. "What a pretty picture she'll make!"

22. The style of the story makes it seem as if it is being told by
(k)  ☐ a. an eyewitness.        ☐ c. a storyteller.
    ☐ b. a schoolteacher.     ☐ d. a historian.

23. The gentleman from Cracow arrived at the ball "on a white mare"
(l) flanked by bodyguards and his best man. . . .He resembled a gentle-
    man off to war with his *entourage.* "An *entourage* is
    ☐ a. a flourish of drums and trumpets.
    ☐ b. an assortment of weapons.
    ☐ c. a variety of gifts.
    ☐ d. a body of followers and servants.

24. The doctor from Cracow
(d)  ☐ a. promised riches to all when he arrived at Frampol.
    ☐ b. made everyone wealthy by gambling with them.
    ☐ c. made a money deal with the matchmakers.
    ☐ d. showered riches on the people during the ball.

25. Near the end of the story the author asks, "But how long can a whole
(e) town weep?" This is much the same as saying
    ☐ a. you are better off dead.
    ☐ b. life must go on.
    ☐ c. there is no reprieve from sin.
    ☐ d. tears serve no purpose.

---

Comprehension Skills: a — isolating details; b — recalling specific facts; c — retaining
concepts; d — organizing facts; e — understanding the main idea; f — drawing a
conclusion; g — making a judgment; h — making an inference; i — recognizing tone;
j — understanding characters; k — appreciation of literary forms; l — understanding
vocabulary.

# FOLKLORE AND THE FOLK TALE

**Practice Exercise A**

Just when all hope had been abandoned and the entire town was about to go begging, a miracle occurred. A carriage drawn by eight spirited horses came into Frampol. The villagers expected its occupant to be a Christian gentleman, but it was a Jew, a young man between the ages of twenty and thirty, who alighted. Tall and pale, with a round black beard and fiery dark eyes, he wore a sable hat, silver-buckled shoes, and a beaver-trimmed caftan. Around his waist was a green silk sash. Aroused, the entire town rushed to get a glimpse of the stranger. This is the story he told: He was a doctor, a widower from Cracow. His wife, the daughter of a wealthy merchant, had died with their baby in childbirth.

1. The gentleman from Cracow is made to sound like a character you have met many times before in fairy tales. Who does he most resemble?
   - ☐ a. The evil duke
   - ☐ b. The good and clever genie
   - ☐ c. The handsome young prince
   - ☐ d. The kindly doctor with magic potions

2. Often, in folk tales, there is a sudden shift in the fortunes of the characters. Underline the sentence in this passage which indicates just such a change.


**Practice Exercise B**

"I want the finest of them all as my wife. Here is what I suggest: Let there be a ball to which all the eligible young women are invited. By observing their appearance and behavior, I shall be able to choose among them. Then the marriage contract will be drawn and the wedding arranged."

The matchmakers were astounded. Old Mendel was the first to find words. "A ball? That sort of thing is all right for rich Gentiles, but we Jews have not indulged in such festivities since the destruction of the Temple—except when the Law prescribes it for certain holidays."

"Isn't every Jew obliged to marry off his daughters?" asked the doctor.

1. The gentleman from Cracow is obviously pitting one tradition against another to make trouble. He is using a tactic that is typical of devils and other evil characters throughout folklore. Which of the following statements describes his strategy best?
   - ☐ a. He is denouncing custom and tradition.
   - ☐ b. He is being reasonable as well as tempting.
   - ☐ c. He is obviously bidding for a role as leader in the community.
   - ☐ d. He proposes to rewrite Jewish law.

2. Several customs and traditions of these Jews of rural Poland are suggested in the passage. Circle the sentence in the first paragraph that mentions two marriage customs.

Practice Exercise C

The setting sun, remarkably large, stared down angrily like a heavenly eye upon the Frampol market place. Never before had Frampol seen such a sunset. Like rivers of burning sulphur, fiery clouds streamed across the heavens, assuming the shapes of elephants, lions, snakes and monsters. They seemed to be waging a battle in the sky, devouring one another, spitting, breathing fire. It almost seemed to be the River of Fire they watched, where demons tortured the evil-doers amidst glowing coals and heaps of ashes. The moon swelled, became vast, blood-red, spotted, scarred, and gave off little light. The evening grew very dark, dissolving even the stars. The young men fetched torches, and a barrel of burning pitch was prepared. Shadows danced back and forth as though attending a ball of their own.

1. The passage has a dream-like quality. What is the dominant dream image here?
   ☐ a. Sun and moon
   ☐ b. Clouds
   ☐ c. Monsters
   ☐ d. Fire

2. On the lines provided, write one sentence that suggests an angry God is watching. Write another sentence that suggests traditional punishment for sinners.

_____

_____

_____

_____

_____

_____

_____

_____

## Practice Exercise D

Only then did he [Rabbi Ozer] remember the doctor from Cracow, and the rabbi cried out bitterly, "Jews, for the sake of God, save your souls! You are in the hands of Satan!"

But the townspeople, too entranced to heed his cries, continued their frenzied movements for a long time, jumping like frogs, shaking as though with fever . . . .

Relentlessly, the rabbi urged the people to resist evil. Reciting the Torah and other holy books, as well as incantations and the several names of God, he succeeded in rousing some of them. Soon others responded. The rabbi had helped the first man from the mire, then that one assisted the next, and so on. Most of them had recovered by the time the morning star appeared. Perhaps the spirits of their forebears had interceded, for although many had sinned, only one man had died this night in the market place square.

1. Which of the following quotations from the Old Testament seems to apply best to the situation described in the passage?
   - ☐ a. He brought me up out of a horrible pit, out of the miry clay and set my feet upon a rock.
   - ☐ b. But the miry places thereof and the marshes thereof shall not be healed.
   - ☐ c. He sent flies among them and frogs which destroyed them.
   - ☐ d. Their land brought forth frogs in abundance.

2. The Jews are brought face to face with many aspects of their beliefs and traditions. One belief is that salvation is achieved by one person helping another. On the lines provided, write one sentence that expresses this idea. A second idea is that ancestral traditions may help protect the people. Also write one sentence that expresses this idea.

_____

_____

_____

_____

_____

_____

# DISCUSSION GUIDES

## Analyzing Folklore and the Folk Tale

1. Many folk tales have these kinds of characters: a good and wise person, a clever and evil person, fools, innocent victims, supernatural beings, a witch. Which characters correspond roughly to these descriptions in "The Gentleman from Cracow"?

2. What story elements can you find that are similar in "The Gentleman from Cracow" and the stories "Cinderella" and "Snow White"? What story elements are different?

3. Compare Nathaniel Hawthorne's "Young Goodman Brown" with "The Gentleman from Cracow". How are they the same, and how do they differ?

## Interpreting the Story

4. According to the story, the people of Frampol felt obliged to "marry off" their daughters. What do you think was behind this feeling of obligation? Was it male chauvinism, a religious requirement or something else?

5. When we speak of making someone a scapegoat today, we mean something different from what the people of Frampol meant. How has the meaning changed?

6. Rabbi Ozer considers the first five books of the Bible as the Law—that is, the Law of God. To what extent is the Bible still the Law in our society today?

7. The author explains Hodle's wickedness saying, "Hodle inherited the vices of both parents — her drunken father, her begging mother." According to the way we think of children who get in trouble today, Hodle might be a victim of her impoverished circumstances. What do you think?

## Analyzing the Author's Technique

8. The cemetery appears in the first and last paragraphs of the story. What does this contribute to the tale?

9. Isaac Singer has said that two important drives in a person's life are sex and striving for power. How are these drives reflected in the story?

10. The author spends a good deal of time describing the depths to which people sink and how they lose everything. That would seem enough punishment for anyone. But he adds to this the horrible deaths of the infants. How does this add to or detract from the story?

## WRITING EXERCISE

In a short paragraph, describe a bit of folklore that is followed in your family. Use the following guidelines in making your selection and telling about it.

1. Choose something that occurs rather frequently in the family at the present time.

2. Try to trace the folklore to a particular place or a special group of people.

3. Discuss the folklore with other members of your family to see what they know about it.

4. You may want to do a bit of library research into the source of the folklore. Some suggestions are Halloween or Thanksgiving customs, religious festivals, the tooth fairy, cures and remedies, favorite foods, weddings and other celebrations. Or describe any other folklore your family follows.

Unit 15
**Finding the Meaning
of a Short Story**

# The Lottery

Shirley Jackson

# Introduction

Shirley Jackson wrote "The Lottery" in one day, a most unusual feat even for an expert writer, and her agent sold it at once to *New Yorker* magazine where it was published in June 1948. An editor at *New Yorker* called Miss Jackson to say that although they planned to use the story, there was one small problem—they were not sure they understood it. Did Miss Jackson care to enlarge on the meaning? "No," she replied.

But what if people wrote to the magazine asking about the story? Was there anything Miss Jackson wanted them to say? "No," she said, "nothing in particular; it's just a story I wrote."

"The Lottery" is a very simple, straightforward story, but it has an ending that throws everything out of kilter and defies explanation. It is an unforgettable story. It is remembered for its strange and horrifying end and for the uncomfortable feeling it leaves with readers that there is something here that must be grappled with. It cannot be left with Miss Jackson's simple explanation that "It's just a story I wrote."

When the story first appeared in *New Yorker*, reader response was immediate, and most of it was negative. Even Miss Jackson's mother objected to the story. The magazine received more mail because of it than for any other story they had ever published. Subscriptions were cancelled by the hundreds by irate readers. A London psychologist wrote:

"I have received requests... from English friends and patients. They would like to know if the barbarity of stoning still exists in the U.S.A. and in general what the tale is all about...."

Others wrote:

"Is it just a story? Why was it published?"

"Is it a parable?"

"Is it an allegory?"

"Please tell us it was all in fun."

"There is the uncomfortable feeling that maybe the story wasn't supposed to make sense."

"I will never buy *New Yorker* again. I resent being tricked into reading perverted stories like 'The Lottery.' "

"My only comment is what the hell."

And from Canada a letter said: "Tell Miss Jackson to stay out of Canada."

Since then, the story has become more respectable. It has been included in countless short story collections, it is a favorite for teaching in literature courses, and it has been dramatized on the stage, shown on television and even done as a ballet. But the challenge of its meaning remains.

In recent years, there have been almost as many explanations of the story as there have been readers. We are adding one more explanation here to those already in existence for the sole purpose of showing students how to search for meaning in a story where meanings are elusive. We don't claim it is the only explanation or even a correct explanation; it is one possible explanation from among many others. Students should regard it as a challenge to form their own thoughts about the story and should initiate their own discussions of its meanings with the help of the discussion guides that follow the story in the exercise section.

Shirley Jackson was known during her lifetime for her gothic romances, mysteries, and stories in the horrific vein, but she also had a marvelous sense of humor and wrote two exceptionally funny books about life in Vermont with her husband and four children. She took pride in being—in the language of the fifties and sixties—"just an ordinary housewife," and she did her writing quickly and easily between household chores. She was interested in social anthropology, abnormal psychology and even witchcraft (she was accused of writing with a broomstick) and these interests showed themselves in her stories. She died an untimely death in 1965 at age forty-five.

# Finding the Meaning
# of a Short Story

The best stories provide enjoyment in two ways: they play upon your emotions, and they provide ideas for you to think about. Ultimately, the extent to which a story provides this dual experience determines the extent to which a story is successful. Good writers know this, and they work very hard to produce tales that read well—that arouse interest simply in the telling—and that provide ideas worth thinking about. The reader, on the other hand, needs to approach a story with a disposition to be interested and a mind ready to receive the ideas the author is presenting. For a story to have both meaning and effect, then, there must be an active partnership between the author and the reader.

Not all stories are easy to deal with in terms of meaning, however. Some are more complicated than others, just as some life situations are more complicated than others. And some stories may have the additional problem of a challenge from the author's imagination. Added to an account of a lifelike happening is the author's "what if?" "What if events become skewed just a bit? What if we add just a touch of fantasy? How much closer may we get to the truth of a situation then?" But if a piece of fiction comes well recommended, or if it reads well and arouses your interest, it will probably be worth your while to stop and give serious thought to meanings suggested in the story. And you will find it interesting to search for parallel meanings and applications of the author's ideas in the real world around you.

Meanings are extracted from fictional situations using the same thought processes you use to deal with situations in real life. First, you observe what is evident or obvious in the situation. Next, you observe as many facts and details as you can; you listen to what people are saying. You will give special attention to the story's conclusion, its outcome, in the light of what has gone before. Observations then give rise to questions. Answers to your questions come in the form of inferences and judgments that you make. Inferences and judgments are made by mentally organizing the facts and details you have observed. Finally, putting everything together in your mind, you arrive at conclusions which lead to opinions about the ideas and meanings suggested in the story. We will see how all this works in a moment.

Shirley Jackson's "The Lottery" is rather famous for the challenge it presents to penetrate its meaning and understand the author's ideas. It is not obscure in any way, nor is it difficult to read—it is quite simple and straightforward, in fact. But the ending of the story is so unusual and unexpected that when you encounter it you feel obliged to go back to the beginning and read the story again to see what it was you missed. In this particular story, that's when the real search for meaning begins.

Because the ending of "The Lottery" is so crucial to a discussion of the ideas and meanings implied in the story, it is strongly suggested that you stop at this point in the lesson and read the story. Then, having read it, see if you agree with the reasoning process outlined below. Following the lesson, read the story again.

**1. Questions Raised by the Situation.** When something is happening and you want to find out what it's all about, like a policeman wading into an argument, the first question you ask is, "What's going on here?" In a story, you survey the situation described and draw first impressions from it. This is easily done in "The Lottery" because, true to short story form, the author tells you a great deal about what's going on in the opening paragraph.

> The morning of June 27th was clear and sunny with the fresh warmth of a full-summer day; the flowers were blossoming profusely and the grass was richly green. The people of the village began to gather in the square, between the post office and the bank around ten o'clock; in some towns there were so many people that the lottery took two days and had to be started on June 26th, but in this village, where there were only about three hundred people, the whole lottery took less than two hours, so it could begin at ten o'clock in the morning and still be through in time to allow the villagers to get home for noon dinner.

It is a fine day in late June and everything is just as it should be for this time of year. We are in the square of a small village of three hundred people. The fact that there is a square to gather in suggests New England or somewhere else in the northeastern United States, but it could be many other places as well. What's going on is a lottery which is expected to take two hours.

The first question that will arise in your mind is likely to be, "What is the lottery for?" We tend to think of a lottery in terms of winning a prize or selecting a leader; winning a turkey or a car for the good purpose of supporting a church or buying band uniforms. By no stretch of the imagination do you consider that someone will be selected to be stoned to death. Then why the bright, cheerful atmosphere? Neither the tone nor the mood of the setting seems to allow for the grim tale that follows. What is the author up to? Why is everything made to seem so normal and routine?

Any questions like these that you can ask yourself may be important later as you pull all the facts of the story together in your search for meaning.

**2. Questions That Arise from Facts and Details.** Surface meanings arise quickly when we observe isolated facts and details in a situation, and we tend to jump to conclusions about what is going on. On a first reading of "The Lottery" the opening paragraphs lead you to the conclusion that a pleasant community gathering is in progress. But soon, other little details creep into the story that make you wonder if there isn't something more here than meets the eye. People are just a trifle nervous, "they smiled rather than laughed," and they quickly gather in tight family groups.

When we begin to assemble a *set* of facts and details, and mentally organize them, questions often arise that put a situation in an entirely different light. Answers to the questions raised will generally form a more complete picture of what is going on and will provide deeper insight than what was gained from first impressions.

What questions might be raised about the black box and the ritual of the lottery, in this passage, in the light of other things that happen in the story?

> The rest of the year, the box was put away, sometimes in one place, sometimes another; it had spent one year in Mr. Graves's barn and another year under foot in the post office, and sometimes it was set on a shelf in the Martin grocery and left there.
>
> There was a great deal of fussing to be done before Mr. Summers declared the lottery open. There were the lists to make up—of heads of families, heads of households in each family, members of each household in each family. There was the proper swearing-in of Mr. Summers by the postmaster, as the official of the lottery; at one time, some people remembered, there had been a recital of some sort, performed by the official of the lottery, a perfunctory, tuneless chant that had been rattled off duly each year; some people believed that the official of the lottery used to stand just so when he said or sang it, others believed that he was supposed to walk among the people, but years and years ago this part of the ritual had been allowed to lapse.

We have a black box for the lottery which, on the surface, is not remarkable because something is needed to put the lottery slips in, and it may as well be a box as a hat or some other container. What an observant reader will ask, however, is "Isn't it strange how they treat this box?" A little earlier in the story we are given the impression that this box is somehow important and wrapped up in tradition. Now we are told that, except for this one day, the box is cast aside in a barn or left under foot or just discarded on a shelf somewhere. What is behind this contradiction?

Further, there had been a recital or ritual attached to the lottery which had been allowed to lapse and is now forgotten. This will become more important later when the author points out at the end that the one part of the ritual that has not been forgotten is that stones are used in the execution. Why, you might ask, does the author make such a point of telling us these things?

In the following passage, Mrs. Hutchinson arrives late but just in time for the beginning of the lottery. What is it about the attitude of the crowd that only becomes important later in light of what the crowd does to Mrs. Hutchinson?

> Just as Mr. Summers finally left off talking and turned to the assembled villagers, Mrs. Hutchinson came hurriedly along the path to the square, her sweater thrown over her shoulders, and slid into place in the back of the crowd. "Clean forgot what day it was," she said to Mrs. Delacroix, who stood next to her, and they both laughed softly....
>
> Mrs. Hutchinson craned her neck to see through the crowd and found her husband and children standing near the front. She tapped Mrs. Delacroix on the arm as a farewell and began to make her way through the crowd. The people separated good-humoredly to let her through; two or three people said, in voices just loud enough to be heard across the crowd, "Here comes your Missus, Hutchinson," and "Bill, she made it after all." Mrs. Hutchinson reached her husband, and Mr. Summers, who had been waiting, said cheerfully, "Thought we were going to have to get on without you, Tessie." Mrs. Hutchinson said, grinning, "Wouldn't have me leave m'dishes in the sink, now, would you, Joe?," and soft laughter ran through the crowd as the people stirred back into position after Mrs. Hutchinson's arrival.

This is a friendly crowd. Everyone knows everyone else and they are neighborly toward one another. Tessie Hutchinson had "clean forgot what day it was." The lottery, it seems, was not very much on her mind. These people forget a good deal about the lottery. Tessie and Mrs. Delacroix are familiar enough to communicate silently with a touch on the arm, as people do. The crowd kids Mrs. Hutchinson and her husband good naturedly and she answers in kind.

All of this is very trivial. It is the way any group of familiar people would act at a friendly community affair. The little details of the passage only become important in retrospect, or upon rereading the story. This is no friendly community affair, it turns out; these people have gathered for a very grim purpose.

The author could have chosen to make the crowd angry, hostile or frightened, but she didn't. She has made a particular point throughout the story of a friendly crowd of neighbors. What idea is the author trying to communicate this way?

**3. Questions Raised by the Story's Climax and Conclusion.** Since authors usually use the story's climax and its conclusion to bring together various ideas and strands of plot, this is a good place to look for clues to the story's meaning. Just so, several points in the following passage from the end of "The Lottery" are likely to be important in penetrating its meaning. See if you can spot some of them.

"All right, folks," Mr. Summers said. "Let's finish quickly."

Although the villagers had forgotten the ritual and lost the original black box, they still remembered to use stones. The pile of stones the boys had made earlier was ready; there were stones on the ground with the blowing scraps of paper that had come out of the box. Mrs. Delacroix selected a stone so large she had to pick it up with both hands and turned to Mrs. Dunbar. "Come on," she said. "Hurry up...."

The children had stones already, and someone gave little Davy Hutchinson a few pebbles.

Tessie Hutchinson was in the center of a cleared space by now, and she held her hands out desperately as the villagers moved in on her. "It isn't fair," she said. A stone hit her on the side of the head.

Those who know the Bible immediately think of the ancient punishment for sinners—death by stoning. And Jesus' admonition to townspeople who are about to stone a woman to death also comes to mind: "He that is without sin among you, let him first cast a stone at her." There is no one without sin, of course, and shamed by the admonition, the people in the Bible let the woman go unharmed. Not so here.

Mrs. Delacroix, Tessie's friend, picks a stone so large she can hardly carry it. The children are eager for action. Copying their elders, they are sure to carry on the tradition. What you may find most chilling is that even little Davy, Mrs. Hutchinson's baby, is given a few pebbles to attack his mother. Notice that the author sets this horror in a paragraph all by itself.

Many questions must occur to you as you read this most puzzling ending. Why does the author reintroduce these particular characters at the stoning? How can Tessie keep complaining "It isn't fair, it isn't right," when we all know the lottery was conducted as fairly as possible: Is it fair or isn't it? And the big question is, of course, why are they doing this thing anyway?

**4. The Search for Meaning.** The situation seems so far-fetched, so foreign to anything we have experienced (at first glance, at least), that it hardly seems worthwhile to take time to look for meaning in such a fantastic tale. But the story does come highly recommended, it is certainly an interesting yarn in its way, and Shirley Jackson is a highly respected writer. We must assume, therefore, that she and her story have ideas for us that are worth thinking about.

We have already made a good start in the search for meaning. Like a detective looking for a solution to a puzzling case, we have made observations and we have asked questions. Here are some of the major questions in summary:

- Why is there a light, neighborly atmosphere throughout the story?
- Why is everything made to seem normal and routine?
- What is significant in the accounts of the black box and the ritual?
- What point is made by having the crowd treat Tessie Hutchinson so cordially?

- What is the importance of the story's climax?
- What point is the author making by having Tessie repeat "It isn't fair?"

At this point, the reader must make some inferences and judgments about the meaning of the story. Making an inference is something like making a good guess except that there is less chance involved and more reasoning. Inferences are made from the observations you have made, the facts you have assembled and the questions you have asked.

We must infer that the box, the ritual, the whole affair is bound with tradition. Everything is lost and forgotten, however, except the need to select a victim and perform the stoning. Even that is forgotten, ignored, except for one day of the year. Tessie almost forgot the event, it was so far from her mind.

This seems to answer another question. Things are made to seem normal and routine because that is how it is with traditions. We don't think about them, they don't bother us; whatever they are, for better or worse, they are a natural part of our lives.

We may judge that the atmosphere is neighborly because that's how people are, most of the time, especially under familiar circumstances. We may also judge that the author makes a special point of Mrs. Hutchinson's cordial reception at mid-story in order to emphasize what happens to her later.

We may judge from the actions described in the climax of the story that not friendship, nor sympathy, nor family ties will interfere with the performance of a rite that is ordered by habit and tradition. And traditions are perpetuated through the participation of the children.

Finally, what is it that isn't fair? The lottery was conducted in all fairness; we saw that. So we must infer that perhaps the whole business isn't right, as Tessie Hutchinson screams at us. This is a judgment, however, that only the victim can make—and, of course, we can now make the same judgment as interested observers of the story.

Mulling over all this, we have to conclude that the author is saying something negative about a mindless pursuit of tradition. The tradition, in this case, is selecting an innocent person to be stoned to death. There seems to be the idea of a scapegoat here—a person made to bear the blame or sin of others, and who is made to suffer for the general good.

Shirley Jackson has taken great pains to make the setting history-book or storybook American. Is she saying, then, that in America we regularly select people at random to be stoned to death? Is she saying that we behave this way for reasons that we don't understand, that we have forgotten, but which are somehow bound up in our traditions? The evidence we have accumulated certainly points us in this direction.

But that is a lot to ask a reader to swallow, so we have to carry the reasoning process one step further and see if we can actually apply these ideas to the real world. Do the ideas presented in the story have any application in society, or is the author simply fantasizing for the sake of writing an obscure and shocking tale? Do we, in modern times, pick on innocent people for stoning? Do we regularly select scapegoats to be put to death for reasons we don't understand, motivated by traditions we have forgotten?

We don't do it just the way it happened in the story, but we do, from time to time, stone school buses and bring children along to help. We burn crosses in front of people's houses and drive them out of neighborhoods. We accuse people of vague crimes if they are active in unpopular causes, we vilify others with poisonous publicity and perform other "rites" that are equally deadly. And those of us who are unaffected by these social "stonings"—do we really care about the fairness of it all, as long as we are not victims ourselves?

Shirley Jackson could have presented her ideas in a more straightforward manner in an essay titled "Scapegoating in American Society." But having made us wrestle with an intriguing story, she has succeeded in impressing us with her ideas in a much more striking and memorable way.

As you read the story:

- Try to decide how the character of Mr. Summers fits into the circumstances of the story.

- See what you may infer from the facts given about the black box which is used for the lottery.

- Consider the role that Old Man Warner plays in adding meaning to the story.

- Ask yourself what inferences and judgments can be made from the actions of the villagers and the Hutchinson children as the lottery is completed.

# The Lottery
## Shirley Jackson

The morning of June 27th was clear and sunny, with the fresh warmth of a full-summer day; the flowers were blossoming profusely and the grass was richly green. The people of the village began to gather in the square, between the post office and the bank, around ten o'clock; in some towns there were so many people that the lottery took two days and had to be started on June 26th, but in this village, where there were only about three hundred people, the whole lottery took less than two hours, so it could begin at ten o'clock in the morning and still be through in time to allow the villagers to get home for noon dinner.

The children assembled first, of course. School was recently over for the summer, and the feeling of liberty sat uneasily on most of them; they tended to gather together quietly for a while before they broke into boisterous play, and their talk was still of the classroom and the teacher, of books and reprimands. Bobby Martin had already stuffed his pockets full of stones, and the other boys soon followed his example, selecting the smoothest and roundest stones; Bobby and Harry Jones and Dickie Delacroix—the villagers pronounced this name "Dellacroy"—eventually made a great pile of stones in one corner of the square and guarded it against the raids of the other boys. The girls stood aside, talking among themselves, looking over their shoulders at the boys, and the very small children rolled in the dust or clung to the hands of their older brothers or sisters.

Soon the men began to gather, surveying their own children, speaking of planting and rain, tractors and taxes. They stood together, away from the pile of stones in the corner, and their jokes were quiet and they smiled rather than laughed. The women, wearing faded house dresses and sweaters, came shortly after their menfolk. They greeted one another and exchanged bits of gossip as they went to join their husbands. Soon the women, standing by their husbands, began to call to their children, and the children came reluctantly, having to be called four or five times. Bobby Martin ducked under his mother's grasping hand and ran, laughing, back to the pile of stones. His father spoke up sharply, and Bobby came quickly and took his place between his father and his oldest brother.

The lottery was conducted—as were the square dances, the teen-age club, the Halloween program—by Mr. Summers, who had time and energy to devote to civic activities. He was a round-faced, jovial man and he ran the coal business, and people were sorry for him, because he had no children and his wife was a scold. When he arrived in the square, carrying the black wooden box, there was a murmur of conversation among the villagers, and he waved and called, "Little late today, folks." The postmaster, Mr. Graves, followed him, carrying a three-legged stool, and the stool was put in the center of the square and Mr. Summers set the black box down on it. The villagers kept their distance, leaving a space between themselves and the stool, and when Mr. Summers said, "Some of you fellows want to give me a hand?" there was a hesitation before two men, Mr. Martin and his oldest son, Baxter, came forward to hold the box steady on the stool while Mr. Summers stirred up the papers inside it.

The original paraphernalia for the lottery had been lost long ago, and the black box now resting on the stool had been put into use even before Old Man Warner, the oldest man in town, was born. Mr. Summers spoke frequently to the villagers about making a new box, but no one liked to upset even as much tradition as was represented by the black box. There was a story that the present box had been made with some pieces of the box that had preceded it, the one that had been constructed when the first people settled down to make a village here. Every year, after the lottery, Mr. Summers began talking again about a new box, but every year the subject was allowed to fade off without anything's being done. The black box grew shabbier each year; by now it was no longer completely black but splintered badly along one side to show the original wood color, and in some places faded or stained.

Mr. Martin and his oldest son, Baxter, held the black box securely on the stool until Mr. Summers had stirred the papers thoroughly with his hand. Because so much of the ritual had been forgotten or discarded, Mr. Summers had been successful in having slips of paper substituted for the chips of wood that had been used for generations. Chips of wood, Mr. Summers had argued, had been all very well when the village was tiny, but now that the population was more than three hundred and likely to keep on growing, it was necessary to use something that would fit more easily into the black box. The night before the lottery, Mr. Summers and Mr. Graves made up the slips of paper and put them in the box, and it was then taken to the safe of Mr. Summers's coal company and locked up until Mr. Summers was ready to take it to the square next morning. The rest of the year, the box was put away, sometimes one place, sometimes another; it had spent one year in Mr. Graves's barn and another year under foot in the post office, and sometimes it was set on a shelf in the Martin grocery and left there.

There was a great deal of fussing to be done before Mr. Summers declared the lottery open. There were the lists to make up—of heads of families, heads of households in each family, members of each household in each family. There was the proper swearing-in of Mr. Summers by the postmaster, as the official of the lottery; at one time, some people remembered, there had been a recital of some sort, performed by the official of the lottery, a perfunctory, tuneless chant that had been rattled off duly each year; some people believed that the official of the lottery used to stand just so when he said or sang it, others believed that he was supposed to walk among the people, but years and years ago this part of the ritual had been allowed to lapse. There had been, also, a ritual salute, which the official of the lottery had had to use in addressing each person who came up to draw from the box, but this also had changed with time, until now it was felt necessary only for the official to speak to each person approaching. Mr. Summers was very good at all this; in his clean white shirt and blue jeans, with one hand resting carelessly on the black box, he seemed very proper and important as he talked interminably to Mr. Graves and the Martins.

Just as Mr. Summers finally left off talking and turned to the assembled villagers, Mrs. Hutchinson came hurriedly along the path to the square, her sweater thrown over her shoulders, and slid into place in the back of the crowd. "Clean forgot what day it was," she said to Mrs. Delacroix, who stood next to her, and they both laughed softly. "Thought my old man was out back stacking wood," Mrs. Hutchinson went on, "and then I looked out the window and the kids was gone, and then I remembered it was the twenty-seventh and came a-running." She dried her hands on her apron, and Mrs. Delacroix said, "You're in time, though. They're still talking away up there."

Mrs. Hutchinson craned her neck to see through the crowd and found her husband and children standing near the front. She tapped Mrs. Delacroix on the arm as a farewell and began to make her way through the crowd. The people separated good-humoredly to let her through; two or three people said, in voices just loud enough to be heard across the crowd, "Here comes your Missus, Hutchinson," and "Bill, she made it after all." Mrs. Hutchinson reached her husband, and Mr. Summers, who had been waiting, said cheerfully, "Thought we were going to have to get on without you, Tessie." Mrs. Hutchinson said, grinning, "Wouldn't have me leave m'dishes in the sink, now, would you, Joe?," and soft laughter ran through the crowd as the people stirred back into position after Mrs. Hutchinson's arrival.

"Well, now," Mr. Summers said soberly, "guess we better get started, get this over with, so's we can go back to work. Anybody ain't here?"

"Dunbar," several people said. "Dunbar, Dunbar."

Mr. Summers consulted his list. "Clyde Dunbar," he said. "That's right. He's broke his leg, hasn't he? Who's drawing for him?"

"Me, I guess," a woman said, and Mr. Summers said. "Don't you have a grown boy to do it for you, Janey?" Although Mr. Summers and everyone else in the village knew the answer perfectly well, it was the business of the official of the lottery to ask such questions formally. Mr. Summers waited with an expression of polite interest while Mrs. Dunbar answered.

"Horace's not but sixteen yet," Mrs. Dunbar said regretfully. "Guess I gotta fill in for the old man this year."

"Right," Mr. Summers said. He made a note on the list he was holding. Then he asked, "Watson boy drawing this year?"

A tall boy in the crowd raised his hand. "Here," he said. "I'm drawing for m'mother and me." He blinked his eyes nervously and ducked his head as several voices in the crowd said things like "Good fellow, Jack," and "Glad to see your mother's got a man to do it."

"Well," Mr. Summers said, "guess that's everyone. Old Man Warner make it?"

"Here," a voice said, and Mr. Summers nodded.

A sudden hush fell on the crowd as Mr. Summers cleared his throat and looked at the list. "All ready?" he called. "Now, I'll read the names—heads of families first—and the men come up and take a paper out of the box. Keep the paper folded in your hand without looking at it until everyone has had a turn. Everything clear?"

The people had done it so many times that they only half listened to the directions; most of them were quiet, wetting their lips, not looking around. Then Mr. Summers raised one hand high and said, "Adams." A man disengaged himself from the crowd and came forward. "Hi, Steve," Mr. Summers said, and Mr. Adams said, "Hi, Joe." They grinned at one another humorlessly and nervously. Then Mr. Adams reached into the black box and took out a folded paper. He held it firmly by one corner as he turned and went hastily back to his place in the crowd, where he stood a little apart from his family, not looking down at his hand.

"Allen," Mr. Summers said. "Anderson.... Bentham."

"Seems like there's no time at all between lotteries any more," Mrs. Delacroix said to Mrs. Graves in the back row. "Seems like we got through with the last one only last week."

"Time sure goes fast," Mrs. Graves said.

"Clark.... Delacroix."

"There goes my old man," Mrs. Delacroix said. She held her breath while her husband went forward.

"Dunbar," Mr. Summers said, and Mrs. Dunbar went steadily to the box while one of the women said, "Go on, Janey," and another said, "There she goes."

"We're next," Mrs. Graves said. She watched while Mr. Graves came around from the side of the box, greeted Mr. Summers gravely, and selected a slip of paper from the box. By now, all through the crowd there were men holding the small folded papers in their large hands, turning them over and over nervously. Mrs. Dunbar and her two sons stood together, Mrs. Dunbar holding the slip of paper.

"Harburt.... Hutchinson."

"Get up there, Bill," Mrs. Hutchinson said, and the people near her laughed.

"Jones."

"They do say," Mr. Adams said to Old Man Warner, who stood next to him, "that over in the north village they're talking of giving up the lottery."

Old Man Warner snorted. "Pack of crazy fools," he said. "Listening to the young folks, nothing's good enough for *them*. Next thing you know, they'll be wanting to go back to living in caves, nobody work any more, live *that* way for a while. Used to be a saying about 'Lottery in June, corn be heavy soon.' First thing you know, we'd all be eating stewed chickweed and acorns. There's *always* been a lottery," he added petulantly. "Bad enough to see young Joe Summers up there joking with everybody."

"Some places have already quit lotteries," Mrs. Adams said.

"Nothing but trouble in *that*," Old Man Warner said stoutly. "Pack of young fools."

"Martin." And Bobby Martin watched his father go forward. "Overdyke.... Percy."

"I wish they'd hurry," Mrs. Dunbar said to her older son. "I wished they'd hurry."

"They're almost through," her son said.

"You get ready to run tell Dad," Mrs. Dunbar said.

Mr. Summers called his own name and then stepped forward precisely and selected a slip from the box. Then he called, "Warner."

"Seventy-seventh year I been in the lottery," Old Man Warner said as he went through the crowd. "Seventy-seventh time."

"Watson." The tall boy came awkwardly through the crowd. Someone said, "Don't be nervous, Jack," and Mr. Summers said, "Take your time, son."

"Zanini."

After that, there was a long pause, a breathless pause, until Mr. Summers, holding his slip of paper in the air, said, "All right, fellows." For a minute, no one moved, and then all the slips of paper were opened. Suddenly, all the women began to speak at once, saying, "Who is it?," "Who's got it?," "Is it the Dunbars?," "Is it the Watsons?" Then the voices began to say, "It's Hutchinson. It's Bill." "Bill Hutchinson's got it."

"Go tell your father," Mrs. Dunbar said to her older son.

People began to look around to see the Hutchinsons. Bill Hutchinson was standing quiet, staring down at the paper in his hand. Suddenly, Tessie Hutchinson shouted to Mr. Summers, "You didn't give him time enough to take any paper he wanted. I saw you. It wasn't fair!"

"Be a good sport, Tessie," Mrs. Delacroix called, and Mrs. Graves said, "All of us took the same chance."

"Shut up, Tessie," Bill Hutchinson said.

"Well, everyone," Mr. Summers said, "that was done pretty fast, and now we've got to be hurrying a little more to get done in time." He consulted his next list. "Bill," he said, "you draw for the Hutchinson family. You got any other households in the Hutchinsons?"

"There's Don and Eva," Mrs. Hutchinson yelled. "Make *them* take their chance!"

"Daughters draw with their husbands' families, Tessie," Mr. Summers said gently. "You know that as well as anyone else."

"It wasn't *fair*," Tessie said.

"I guess not, Joe," Bill Hutchinson said regretfully. "My daughter draws with her husband's family, that's only fair. And I've got no other family except the kids."

"Then, as far as drawing for families is concerned, it's you," Mr. Summers said in explanation, "and as far as drawing for households is concerned, that's you, too. Right?"

"Right," Bill Hutchinson said.

"How many kids, Bill?" Mr. Summers asked formally.

"Three," Bill Hutchinson said. "There's Bill, Jr., and Nancy, and little Dave. And Tessie and me.'

"All right, then," Mr. Summers said. "Harry, you got their tickets back?"

Mr. Graves nodded and held up the slips of paper. "Put them in the box, then," Mr. Summers directed. "Take Bill's and put it in."

"I think we ought to start over," Mrs. Hutchinson said, as quietly as she could. "I tell you it wasn't *fair*. You didn't give him time enough to choose. *Every*body saw that."

Mr. Graves had selected the five slips and put them in the box, and he dropped all the papers but those onto the ground, where the breeze caught them and lifted them off.

"Listen, everybody," Mrs. Hutchinson was saying to the people around her.

"Ready, Bill?" Mr. Summers asked, and Bill Hutchinson, with one quick glance around at his wife and children, nodded.

"Remember," Mr. Summers said, "take the slips and keep them folded until each person has taken one. Harry, you help little Dave." Mr. Graves took the hand of the little boy, who came willingly with him up to the box. "Take a paper out of the box, Davy," Mr. Summers said. Davy put his hand into the box and laughed. "Take just *one* paper," Mr. Summers said. "Harry, you hold it for him." Mr. Graves took the child's hand and removed the folded paper from the tight fist and held it while little Dave stood next to him and looked up at him wonderingly.

"Nancy next," Mr. Summers said. Nancy was twelve, and her school friends breathed heavily as she went forward, switching her skirt, and took a slip daintily from the box. "Bill, Jr.," Mr. Summers said, and Billy, his face red and his feet over-large, nearly knocked the box over as he got a paper out. "Tessie," Mr. Summers said. She hesitated for a minute, looking around defiantly, and then set her lips and went up to the box. She snatched a paper out and held it behind her.

"Bill," Mr. Summers said, and Bill Hutchinson reached into the box and felt around, bringing his hand out at last with the slip of paper in it.

The crowd was quiet. A girl whispered, "I hope it's not Nancy," and the sound of the whisper reached the edges of the crowd.

"It's not the way it used to be," Old Man Warner said clearly. "People ain't the way they used to be."

"All right," Mr. Summers said. "Open the papers. Harry, you open little Dave's."

Mr. Graves opened the slip of paper and there was a general sigh through the crowd as he held it up and everyone could see that it was blank. Nancy and Bill, Jr., opened theirs at the same time, and both beamed and laughed, turning around to the crowd and holding their slips of paper above their heads.

"Tessie," Mr. Summers said. There was a pause, and then Mr. Summers looked at Bill Hutchinson, and Bill unfolded his paper and showed it. It was blank.

"It's Tessie," Mr. Summers said, and his voice was hushed. "Show us her paper, Bill."

Bill Hutchinson went over to his wife and forced the slip of paper out of her hand. It had a black spot on it, the black spot Mr. Summers had made the night before with the heavy pencil in the coal-company office. Bill Hutchinson held it up, and there was a stir in the crowd.

"All right, folks," Mr. Summers said. "Let's finish quickly."

Although the villagers had forgotten the ritual and lost the original black box, they still remembered to use stones. The pile of stones the boys had made earlier was ready; there were stones on the ground with the blowing scraps of paper that had come out of the box. Mrs. Delacroix selected a stone so large she had to pick it up with both hands and turned to Mrs. Dunbar. "Come on," she said. "Hurry up."

Mrs. Dunbar had small stones in both hands, and she said, gasping for breath, "I can't run at all. You'll have to go ahead and I'll catch up with you."

The children had stones already, and someone gave little Davy Hutchinson a few pebbles.

Tessie Hutchinson was in the center of a cleared space by now, and she held her hands out desperately as the villagers moved in on her. "It isn't fair," she said. A stone hit her on the side of the head.

Old Man Warner was saying, "Come on, come on, everyone." Steve Adams was in the front of the crowd of villagers, with Mrs. Graves beside him.

"It isn't fair, it isn't right," Mrs. Hutchinson screamed, and then they were upon her.

# Unit 15

## The Lottery

- Comprehension Questions

- Finding the Meaning of a Short Story

- Discussion Guides

- Writing Exercise

# COMPREHENSION QUESTIONS

For each of the following statements and questions, select the option containing the most complete or most accurate answer.

1. The lottery was conducted at the beginning of
(b) □ a. winter.          □ c. summer.
    □ b. spring.          □ d. fall.

2. The author provides a month and day for the story but no year. We
(h) must infer, however, that the story is set in
    □ a. the distant past.     □ c. the future.
    □ b. modern times.         □ d. any time you want.

3. How would you characterize the behavior of the children at the begin-
(g) ning of the story?
    □ a. Nervous          □ c. Serious
    □ b. Attentive        □ d. Normal

4. Evidence in the story suggests that this is a
(h) □ a. factory town.          □ c. suburb of a large city.
    □ b. farming community.     □ d. backwoods settlement.

5. The children gathered together quietly before they broke into *boisterous*
(l) play. *Boisterous* means
    □ a. active.          □ c. dangerous.
    □ b. annoying.        □ d. noisy.

6. The women came to the lottery dressed pretty much alike. The
(a) "uniform" was
    □ a. slacks and sweater.
    □ b. housedress and sweater.
    □ c. blue jeans and white blouse.
    □ d. shirt and sweater.

7. The crowd assembled
(d) □ a. helter-skelter.          □ c. according to age.
    □ b. in family groups.        □ d. in alphabetical order.

8. The people felt sorry for Mr. Summers because his wife was a scold.
(g) They must have had other feelings for him as well, such as
   ☐ a. respect and liking.   ☐ c. fear and suspicion.
   ☐ b. awe.                  ☐ d. jealousy.

9. The original *paraphernalia* for the lottery had been lost long ago.
(l) *Paraphernalia* is
   ☐ a. equipment.   ☐ c. a sort of box.
   ☐ b. a ritual.     ☐ d. a document.

10. All the fussing and talking among the officials of the lottery
(c) ☐ a. is typical behavior at city and town functions.
    ☐ b. occurs only under highly unusual circumstances.
    ☐ c. emphasizes the igorance of the villagers.
    ☐ d. satisfies the need for ritual.

11. The first settlers who conducted the lottery used
(a) ☐ a. straws.       ☐ c. wood chips.
    ☐ b. tree bark.    ☐ d. paper.

12. The black box was kept
(b) ☐ a. by the postmaster.        ☐ c. under lock and key.
    ☐ b. at Mr. Summers' house.    ☐ d. in various places.

13. The lottery narrowed its selection
(d) ☐ a. by sex first and then by individuals.
    ☐ b. alphabetically from Adams to Zanini.
    ☐ c. by town first and then by families.
    ☐ d. by choosing a family and then an individual.

14. To Old Man Warner's mind, discontinuing the lottery would be
(c) ☐ a. a dangerous step into the future.
    ☐ b. the beginning of socialism.
    ☐ c. a step backward to primitive life.
    ☐ d. the result of the foolishness of Mr. Summers.

15. As the lottery begins, the author says, "most of them were quiet, wetting
(i) their lips, not looking around." This suggests that the atmosphere is
  ☐ a. polite and friendly.
  ☐ b. calm and relaxed.
  ☐ c. a bit tense.
  ☐ d. suspicious.

16. Old Man Warner's opinions are best characterized as
(j) ☐ a. shallow.            ☐ c. spiteful.
    ☐ b. philosophic.         ☐ d. prophetic.

17. When Bill draws the black spot, Mrs. Hutchinson is best characterized as
(j) ☐ a. resigned.            ☐ c. vengeful.
    ☐ b. spiteful.            ☐ d. frightened.

18. The women tell Mrs. Hutchinson to *be a good sport.* In light of the
(k) story's ending, this provides
  ☐ a. irony by exaggeration.
  ☐ b. humor by comparison.
  ☐ c. shock through understatement.
  ☐ d. tension through attitude.

19. "It's not the way it used to be," Old Man Warner said clearly. "People
(e) ain't the way they used to be." One point of the story is that
  ☐ a. people are more violent today.
  ☐ b. people don't change much.
  ☐ c. traditions change drastically.
  ☐ d. past ways of living are best.

20. Tessie keeps saying "it wasn't fair." The author seems to be pointing
(f) out that
  ☐ a. "fairness" is meaningless.
  ☐ b. nothing is fair in life.
  ☐ c. fairness is most important to victims.
  ☐ d. victims are bad sports.

21. Which one of these sayings is appropriate for this story?
(e) ☐ a. There's no fool like an old fool.
    ☐ b. It takes two to make a quarrel.
    ☐ c. Peace in our time.
    ☐ d. Children learn by doing.

22. One way that the author creates an ordinary, down-home atmosphere
(i) in the story is by
    ☐ a. providing the characters with Southern accents.
    ☐ b. using simple language.
    ☐ c. long descriptions of the countryside.
    ☐ d. emphasizing the stoning ritual.

23. Tradition is represented symbolically by
(k) ☐ a. Mr. Summers.        ☐ c. the black box.
    ☐ b. the children.        ☐ d. the three-legged stool.

24. Tessie's behavior after Bill Hutchinson draws the black spot is
(f) ☐ a. shrewd.        ☐ c. cowardly.
    ☐ b. defensive.        ☐ d. unsportsmanlike.

25. Which of the following statements best describes how the author handles
(j) her characters in the story?
    ☐ a. They are only slightly developed.
    ☐ b. Readers are made to understand characters in depth.
    ☐ c. Physical descriptions are important to story development.
    ☐ d. There is no character development.

---

Comprehension Skills: a — isolating details; b — recalling specific facts; c — retaining concepts; d — organizing facts; e — understanding the main idea; f — drawing a conclusion; g — making a judgment; h — making an inference; i — recognizing tone; j — understanding characters; k — appreciation of literary forms; l — understanding vocabulary.

# FINDING THE MEANING OF A STORY

**Practice Exercise A**

The lottery was conducted — as were the square dances, the teen-age club, the Halloween program — by Mr. Summers, who had time and energy to devote to civic activities. He was a round-faced jovial man and he ran the coal business, and people were sorry for him, because he had no children and his wife was a scold. When he arrived in the square, carrying the black wooden box, there was a murmur of conversation among the villagers, and he waved and called, "Little late today, folks." The postmaster, Mr. Graves, followed him, carrying a three-legged stool, and the stool was put in the center of the square and Mr. Summers set the black box down on it.

1. The character of Mr. Summers falls into the general pattern of the story because he is
     ☐ a. rather sinister.        ☐ c. an important official.
     ☐ b. a very ordinary man.    ☐ d. a timid man.

2. In one sentence the lottery is compared to several other community events. Knowing what the lottery is for, the reader can appreciate the strangeness of the comparison. Underline the sentence.

**Practice Exercise B**

The original paraphernalia for the lottery had been lost long ago, and the black box now resting on the stool had been put into use even before Old Man Warner, the oldest man in town, was born. Mr. Summers spoke frequently to the villagers about making a new box, but no one liked to upset even as much tradition as was represented by the black box. There was a story that the present box had been made with some pieces of the box that had preceded it, the one that had been constructed when the first people settled down to make a village here. Every year, after the lottery, Mr. Summers began talking again about a new box, but every year the subject was allowed to fade off without anything's being done.

1. The implication here seems to be that when it comes to traditions, no one
     ☐ a. likes them.        ☐ c. can understand them.
     ☐ b. takes them seriously.    ☐ d. wants to disturb them.

2. Underline the sentence in the passage which suggests that the beginnings of the lottery tradition are unknown.

## Practice Exercise C

"They do say," Mr. Adams said to Old Man Warner, who stood next to him, "that over in the north village they're talking of giving up the lottery."

"Old Man Warner snorted. "Pack of crazy fools," he said. "Listening to the young folks, nothing's good enough for them. Next thing you know, they'll be wanting to go back to living in caves, nobody work any more, live that way for a while. Used to be a saying about 'Lottery in June, corn be heavy soon.' First thing you know, we'd all be eating stewed chickweed and acorns. There's *always* been a lottery," he added petulantly. "Bad enough to see young Joe Summers up there joking with everybody."

"Some places have already quit lotteries," Mrs. Adams said.

1. Mr. Warner is portrayed here as the town's
   - ☐ a. hard-nosed conservative.
   - ☐ b. fiery liberal.
   - ☐ c. worst grouch.
   - ☐ d. eccentric.

2. Most of what Mr. Warner says has no meaning. But one short phrase near the end of the passage sums up the reason the town continues to have a lottery. Find the phrase and circle it.

## Practice Exercise D

"All right," Mr. Summers said. "Open the papers. Harry, you open little Dave's."

Mr. Graves opened the slip of paper and there was a general sigh through the crowd as he held it up and everyone could see that it was blank. Nancy and Bill, Jr., opened theirs at the same time, and both beamed and laughed, turning around to the crowd and holding their slips of paper above their heads.

1. The crowd sighed when little Davey's paper was shown to be blank. We infer from this that if he had drawn the black spot they
   - ☐ a. would start the lottery over again.
   - ☐ b. would have killed him.
   - ☐ c. would discontinue lotteries.
   - ☐ d. would have liked him to draw the black spot.

2. Nancy and Bill, Jr., are the Hutchinson's children. By drawing blank slips, they know that one of their parents will be killed. Under the circumstances, you must judge that at least part of their conduct is not appropriate to the occasion. Circle the phrase that describes this conduct.

## Analyzing the Meaning of the Story

1. As they are preparing for the lottery, Mr. Summers asks: "Watson boy drawing this year?" Jack Watson replies, "I'm drawing for m'mother and me." The crowd seems pleased, saying, "Glad to see your mother's got a man to do it." Can you speculate about what may have happened to Jack Watson's father?

2. Old Man Warner has been in the lottery seventy-seven times. He is the one who seems most in favor of continuing the lottery. What connection can you make between these two facts?

3. After Bill Hutchinson draws the black spot for his family, Tessie Hutchinson yells out that her married daughter and son-in-law should be made to take a chance separately. What makes this interesting to think about?

## Interpreting the Story

4. At one time there had been a recital of some sort before the lottery which is now forgotten. What sorts of things do you think may have been included in the recital?

5. What is your attitude toward tradition in your life?

6. Mrs. Hutchinson arrived late for the lottery saying she had forgotten what day it was. Some readers think that she hadn't forgotten but was reluctant to come because she had a feeling what might happen. What do you think?

7. Men, as heads of households, drew for their families. The story was written in 1948. How might this detail be written into the story today?

8. Tell about people you know who are like Old Man Warner. Explain how or why they are like him.

## Analyzing the Author's Technique

9. Tension and suspense mount very gradually in the story. Find those places in the story where mounting tension and suspense become more apparent.

10. In the first paragraph of the story, the author makes a point of mentioning that the lottery would be over in time for the villagers to be home for noon dinner. This has a different effect on readers the first time through the story and the second time. What are the two different effects?

## WRITING EXERCISE

1. In a few sentences, tell of another way that the story might end that is different from the way Shirley Jackson ended it.

2. Tell how your new ending has changed the meaning of the story.

_____

_____

_____

_____

_____

_____

_____

_____

_____

_____

_____

_____

# Answer Key

## UNIT 1: THE GARDEN PARTY

### Comprehension Questions

| | | | | |
|---|---|---|---|---|
| 1. d | 6. b | 11. a | 16. d | 21. a |
| 2. b | 7. c | 12. c | 17. b | 22. b |
| 3. a | 8. a | 13. a | 18. c | 23. c |
| 4. c | 9. d | 14. b | 19. d | 24. b |
| 5. d | 10. a | 15. c | 20. d | 25. d |

### The Short Story

Practice Exercise A
1. b
2. Underline: When Laura saw that gesture she forgot all about the karakas in her wonder at him caring for things like that—caring for the smell of lavender.
Circle: caring

Practice Exercise B
1. d
2. The house was alive; a long, chuckling absurd sound; Little faint winds were playing chase; spots of sun . . . playing.

Practice Exercise C
1. c
2. gloomy (passage)
   low (kitchen)
   smoky (lamp)

Practice Exercise D
1. a
2. "Forgive my hat," she said.


## UNIT 2: TELL ME HOW LONG THE TRAIN'S BEEN GONE

### Comprehension Questions

| | | | | |
|---|---|---|---|---|
| 1. b | 6. c | 11. a | 16. d | 21. b |
| 2. c | 7. b | 12. c | 17. d | 22. a |
| 3. a | 8. c | 13. a | 18. c | 23. d |
| 4. c | 9. d | 14. a | 19. d | 24. c |
| 5. b | 10. c | 15. a | 20. b | 25. d |

### Setting

Practice Exercise A
1. a
2. joy

## UNIT 2: TELL ME HOW LONG THE TRAIN'S BEEN GONE
(Continued)

Practice Exercise B

1. c
2. The hall was dark, smelling of cooking, of stale wine, of rotting garbage.

Practice Exercise C

1. d
2. They looked exactly like the men and women who frightened me when I saw them standing on the corners, laughing and joking in front of the bars. But they did not seem frightening here.

Practice Exercise D

1. b
2. the voices and the music

## UNIT 3: MY OEDIPUS COMPLEX and
## THE JILTING OF GRANNY WEATHERALL

### Comprehension Questions

| | | | | |
|---|---|---|---|---|
| 1. d | 6. a | 11. c | 16. b | 21. d |
| 2. a | 7. d | 12. a | 17. b | 22. c |
| 3. d | 8. c | 13. b | 18. c | 23. b |
| 4. c | 9. c | 14. d | 19. a | 24. a |
| 5. b | 10. c | 15. d | 20. c | 25. c |

### Point of View

Practice Exercise A

1. c
2. I put my feet out from under the clothes—I called them Mrs. Left and Mrs. Right—and invented dramatic situations for them in which they discussed the problems of the day.

Practice Exercise B

1. a
2. Father gave a great guffaw out of him, but he didn't take me in.

## UNIT 3: MY OEDIPUS COMPLEX and
## THE JILTING OF GRANNY WEATHERALL (Continued)

Practice Exercise C
  1. d
  2. I want you to find George.
     Yes, she had changed her mind after sixty years and she would like to see George.
     Her breath crowded down under her ribs and grew into a monstrous frightening shape with cutting edges.

Practice Exercise D
  1. b
  2. Since the day the wedding cake was not cut, but thrown out and wasted.

## UNIT 4: THE WALL

### Comprehension Questions

| | | | | |
|---|---|---|---|---|
| 1. d | 6. b | 11. d | 16. a | 21. b |
| 2. b | 7. d | 12. a | 17. a | 22. b |
| 3. a | 8. c | 13. d | 18. c | 23. c |
| 4. b | 9. c | 14. c | 19. d | 24. d |
| 5. a | 10. a | 15. b | 20. c | 25. a |

### Analyzing Conflict

Practice Exercise A
  1. d
  2. "You want to think of something, you always have the impression that it's all right, that you're going to understand and then it slips, it escapes you and fades away." Or " I tell myself there will be nothing afterwards. But I don't understand what it means."

Practice Exercise B
  1. c
  2. There we were, three bloodless shadows; we watched him and we sucked his life like vampires.

Practice Exercise C
  1. b
  2. he wanted to dominate me

Practice Exercise D
  1. a
  2. I laughed so hard I cried.

## UNIT 5: THE CHRISTIAN ROOMMATES

### Comprehension Questions

| | | | | |
|---|---|---|---|---|
| 1. a | 6. b | 11. c | 16. a | 21. c |
| 2. d | 7. a | 12. b | 17. b | 22. a |
| 3. b | 8. b | 13. b | 18. a | 23. c |
| 4. d | 9. c | 14. d | 19. b | 24. b |
| 5. c | 10. d | 15. d | 20. b | 25. d |

### Characterization

Practice Exercise A
1. c
2. Orson's first impression; a white cap such as Orson had seen before only in photographs of Pandit Nehru.

Practice Exercise B
1. b
2. He had all the newsman's tricks: the side-of-the-mouth quip, the nip of whiskey, the hat on the back of the head, the habit of throwing still-burning cigarettes onto the floor.

Practice Exercise C
1. a
2. A keen quick pain cut through Orson's groin.
   This time, the pain went through Orson's chest.

Practice Exercise D
1. d
2. He never prays.


## UNIT 6: YOUNG GOODMAN BROWN

### Comprehension Questions

| | | | | |
|---|---|---|---|---|
| 1. d | 6. a | 11. b | 16. b | 21. d |
| 2. d | 7. b | 12. b | 17. a | 22. c |
| 3. a | 8. b | 13. a | 18. d | 23. a |
| 4. b | 9. d | 14. b | 19. b | 24. d |
| 5. b | 10. d | 15. c | 20. a | 25. a |

### Recognizing Themes

Practice Exercise A
1. d
2. Pray tarry with me this night, dear husband, of all nights in the year.

## UNIT 6: YOUNG GOODMAN BROWN (Continued)

Practice Exercise B
1. c
2. "My Faith is gone!"

Practice Exercise C
1. a
2. with the final peal of that dreadful anthem there came a sound, as if the roaring wind, the rushing streams, the howling beasts, and every other voice of the unconcerted wilderness were mingling and according with the voice of guilty man in homage to the prince of all.

Practice Exercise D
1. b
2. he shrank from the bosom of Faith

## UNIT 7: THE BLACK CAT

### Comprehension Questions

| | | | | |
|---|---|---|---|---|
| 1. b | 6. a | 11. d | 16. d | 21. b |
| 2. a | 7. c | 12. b | 17. a | 22. d |
| 3. d | 8. d | 13. a | 18. a | 23. b |
| 4. c | 9. d | 14. c | 19. c | 24. b |
| 5. c | 10. a | 15. b | 20. b | 25. c |

### Tone and Mood

Practice Exercise A
1. a
2. in a den of more than infamy

Practice Exercise B
1. d
2. oh, mournful and terrible engine of HORROR and of Crime—of Agony and of Death!

Practice Exercise C
1. b
2. In the rabid desire to say something easily, I scarcely knew what I uttered at all.
   through the mere frenzy of bravado

## UNIT 7: THE BLACK CAT  (Continued)

Practice Exercise D
1. c
2. the fangs of the Arch-Fiend!
   a voice from within the tomb!
   utterly anomalous and inhuman
   such as might have arisen only out of hell
   from the throats of the damned in their agony
   of the demons that exult in the damnation

## UNIT 8: A ROSE FOR EMILY

### Comprehension Questions

| | | | | |
|---|---|---|---|---|
| 1. d | 6. b | 11. c | 16. b | 21. a |
| 2. c | 7. c | 12. b | 17. a | 22. b |
| 3. a | 8. a | 13. d | 18. a | 23. d |
| 4. a | 9. c | 14. c | 19. c | 24. c |
| 5. c | 10. a | 15. a | 20. d | 25. a |

### Symbolism

Practice Exercise A
1. b
2. It smelled of dust and disuse—a close, dank smell.
   a faint dust rose sluggishly about their thighs, spinning with slow motes in the single sun-ray.

Practice Exercise B
1. b
2. she would have to cling to that which had robbed her

Practice Exercise C
1. a
2. in the same spirit that they were sent to church on Sunday with a twenty-five-cent piece for the collection plate.

Practice Exercise D
1. d
2. the town got free postal delivery; the negro grow grayer and more stooped; Each December we sent her a tax notice; she passed from generation to generation

## UNIT 9: A CHRISTMAS MEMORY

### Comprehension Questions

| | | | | |
|---|---|---|---|---|
| 1. d | 6. a | 11. a | 16. d | 21. b |
| 2. c | 7. b | 12. c | 17. b | 22. d |
| 3. c | 8. c | 13. b | 18. c | 23. b |
| 4. b | 9. b | 14. d | 19. d | 24. a |
| 5. d | 10. c | 15. d | 20. a | 25. a |

### Figurative Language

Practice Exercise A
  1. d
  2. like a lighted pumpkin

Practice Exercise B
  1. b
  2. something like a grin stretches her black lips

Practice Exercise C
  1. a
  2. round as an orange; orange as hot-weather moons
    balances on the horizon; burnishes the silvered winter woods

Practice Exercise D
  1. c
  2. we're up, wide-eyed and wandering while we wait for the others to waken

## UNIT 10: THE LEADER OF THE PEOPLE

### Comprehension Questions

| | | | | |
|---|---|---|---|---|
| 1. a | 6. c | 11. d | 16. b | 21. c |
| 2. b | 7. c | 12. d | 17. c | 22. a |
| 3. b | 8. d | 13. a | 18. b | 23. a |
| 4. c | 9. c | 14. c | 19. a | 24. a |
| 5. c | 10. a | 15. d | 20. b | 25. c |

*[handwritten note in left margin: This is an incorrect answer. Answer should be]*

### Dialogue *[handwritten: Letter arrived same day as grandfather]*

Practice Exercise A
  1. c
  2. Jody ran into the kitchen.
    he cried
    Mrs. Tiflin relented a little.

## UNIT 10: THE LEADER OF THE PEOPLE   (Continued)

Practice Exercise B
1. b
2. the dash in the second sentence. ("Why, sure I'll tell them, but only when—I'm sure people want to hear them.")

Practice Exercise C
1. a
2. westering

Practice Exercise D
1. d
2. "If you'd like a glass of lemonade, I could make it for you."

## UNIT 11: NIGHTFALL

### Comprehension Questions

| | | | | |
|---|---|---|---|---|
| 1. a | 6. a | 11. b | 16. c | 21. d |
| 2. d | 7. b | 12. b | 17. d | 22. a |
| 3. c | 8. b | 13. b | 18. c | 23. b |
| 4. b | 9. a | 14. c | 19. d | 24. a |
| 5. c | 10. c | 15. d | 20. c | 25. a |

### Science Fiction

Practice Exercise A
1. c
2. Aton; six suns; Beta; Its ruddy light flooding the landscape to an unusual orange; setting Gamma; Lagash's sky.

Practice Exercise B
1. a
2. claustrophobia (or claustrophobic fixation)

Practice Exercise C
1. a
2. a planet with only one sun; the planet would travel in a perfect ellipse; the exact nature of the gravitational force would be so evident it could be accepted as an axiom; Astronomers on such a world would start off with gravity probably before they even invent the telescope; if it rotated there would be total darkness half of each day.

Practice Exercise D
1. d
2. Two centuries might not have been enough.

# UNIT 12: THE KUGELMASS EPISODE

## Comprehension Questions

| | | | | |
|---|---|---|---|---|
| 1. c | 6. b | 11. b | 16. d | 21. d |
| 2. a | 7. c | 12. a | 17. b | 22. d |
| 3. d | 8. a | 13. c | 18. a | 23. d |
| 4. a | 9. b | 14. b | 19. c | 24. a |
| 5. b | 10. d | 15. c | 20. b | 25. b |

## Humor

Practice Exercise A
  1. c
  2. I'm not getting younger

Practice Exercise B
  1. a
  2. starved for excitement

Practice Exercise C
  1. d
  2. "Well, I guess the mark of a classic is that you can reread it a thousand times and always find something new."

Practice Exercise D
  1. a
  2. He had been projected into an old textbook, *Remedial Spanish,* and was running for his life over a barren, rocky terrain as the word *tener* ("to have")—a large and hairy irregular verb—raced after him on its spindly legs.

## Writing Exercise
  1. She hit him with it.
  2. He's bottling hot air from Congress.
  3. The alligator wasn't through wearing them.
  4. Next month I may try it with mayonaise or mustard.
  5. It tries to bite me back.
  6. I ate him.

# UNIT 13: THE MAN THAT CORRUPTED HADLEYBURG

## Comprehension Questions

| | | | | |
|---|---|---|---|---|
| 1. c | 6. d | 11. c | 16. d | 21. c |
| 2. d | 7. b | 12. d | 17. c | 22. d |
| 3. a | 8. c | 13. c | 18. a | 23. d |
| 4. b | 9. a | 14. b | 19. c | 24. a |
| 5. a | 10. b | 15. a | 20. a | 25. b |

# UNIT 13: THE MAN THAT CORRUPTED HADLEYBURG (Continued)

## Satire

Practice Exercise A
1. b
2. Vain beyond imagination.

Practice Exercise B
1. c
2. impromptu

Practice Exercise C
1. d
2. It revived the recent vast laugh and concentrated it upon Pinkerton; and Harkness's election was a walk-over.

Practice Exercise D
1. a
2. like the rest, I fell when temptation came; I was a coward; he exposed me—as I deserved

# UNIT 14: THE GENTLEMAN FROM CRACOW

## Comprehension Questions

| | | | | |
|---|---|---|---|---|
| 1. b | 6. a | 11. a | 16. b | 21. a |
| 2. d | 7. c | 12. d | 17. a | 22. c |
| 3. a | 8. d | 13. d | 18. b | 23. d |
| 4. d | 9. b | 14. d | 19. b | 24. d |
| 5. c | 10. a | 15. c | 20. b | 25. b |

## Folklore and the Folk Tale

Practice Exercise A
1. c
2. Just when all hope had been abandoned and the entire town was about to go begging, a miracle occurred.

Practice Exercise B
1. b
2. Then the marriage contract will be drawn and the wedding arranged.

Practice Exercise C

1. d

2. The setting sun, remarkably large, stared down angrily like a heavenly eye upon the Frampol market place.

It almost seemed to be the River of fire they watched, where demons tortured the evil-doers amidst glowing coals and heaps of ashes.

Practice Exercise D

1. a

2. The rabbi had helped the first man from the mire, then that one assisted the next, and so on.

Perhaps the spirits of their forebears had interceded, for although many had sinned, only one man had died this night in the market place square.

## UNIT 15: THE LOTTERY

### Comprehension Questions

| | | | | |
|---|---|---|---|---|
| 1. c | 6. b | 11. c | 16. a | 21. d |
| 2. b | 7. b | 12. d | 17. d | 22. b |
| 3. d | 8. a | 13. d | 18. c | 23. c |
| 4. b | 9. a | 14. c | 19. b | 24. b |
| 5. d | 10. a | 15. c | 20. c | 25. a |

### Finding the Meaning of a Story

Practice Exercise A

1. b

2. The lottery was conducted—as were the square dances, the teen-age club, the Halloween program—by Mr. Summers, who had time and energy to devote to civic activities.

Practice Exercise B

1. d

2. The original paraphernalia for the lottery had been lost long ago, and the black box now resting on the stool had been put into use even before Old Man Warner, the oldest man in town, was born.

Practice Exercise C

1. a

2. There's *always* been a lottery

Practice Exercise D

1. b

2. both beamed and laughed

# COMPREHENSION SKILLS

Use this graph to show the questions you get wrong. Starting at the bottom, put an *x* on the line above the appropriate letter every time you fail a question labeled with that letter. A line of *x*'s rising above the others indicates a specific comprehension weakness. The comprehension skills represented by the letters are given at the top of the graph. The numbers on the side show your total number of wrong answers for each comprehension skill. Consult your instructor if you fail ten questions in any one skill; this means you have discovered a comprehension weakness which must be corrected.

a—isolating details
b—recalling specific facts
c—retaining concepts
d—organizing facts
e—understanding the main idea
f—drawing a conclusion
g—making a judgment
h—making an inference
i—recognizing tone
j—understanding characters
k—appreciation of literary forms
l—knowledge of word meaning

# COMPREHENSION SCORES

Use this graph to plot your comprehension scores. The horizontal line represents the number of questions answered correctly. Put an *x* on the vertical line under each chapter title where it intersects the horizontal line. You should strive for scores of 80 percent or better (20 or more questions answered correctly). Connect the *x*'s to form a graph of your comprehension. See the left side of the graph for percentages (scores), the right side for number of questions answered correctly. Consult your instructor if you consistently score below 80 percent.

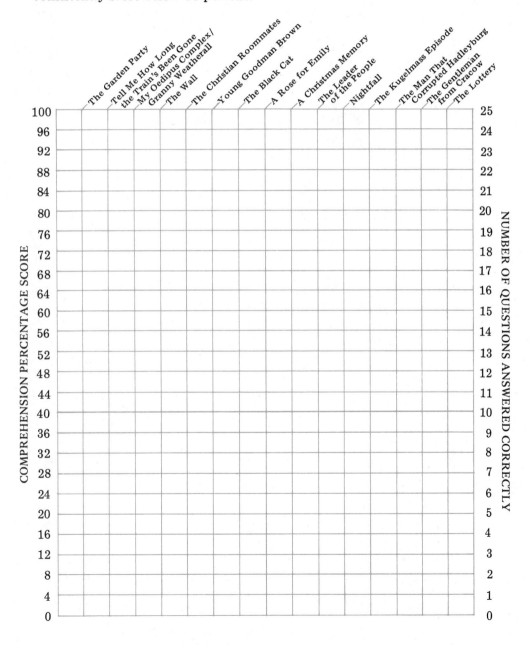